John Pritchard

A solicitor, John Pritchard is author of many
books on the law, including *The Penguin
Guide to the Law* (some quarter million
copies sold); *Personal Injury Litigation;*
and, of course, *The Legal 500.* He edits the
monthly *Busy Solicitors Digest* and is a
leading commentator on the law – and on
lawyers. John Pritchard is the managing
director (and founder) of Legalease.

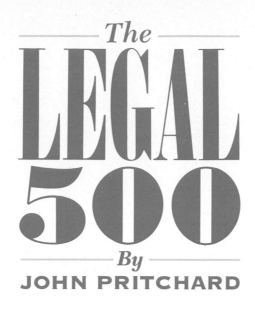

The
LEGAL
500

By
JOHN PRITCHARD

THE MAJOR LAW FIRMS
IN ENGLAND, WALES & SCOTLAND
AND FOREIGN LAW FIRMS IN LONDON

LEGALEASE

Published annually by Legalease, 3 Clifton Road,
London W9 1SZ

Editor: John Pritchard
Assistant Editor: Richard Davey
Managing Editor: Rosie McGechie
Editorial Staff: John Harris, Sarah Johnson, Annette
    Sheppard, Mark Stone, Noelle Ralph
Research: Marty Murrihy, Carol Barnes, Yvonne
    Murrihy, George Staines
Contibutors: Mary Trewby, Liz Davies, Justyn
    Trenner (foreign section)
Design: Jane Olswang, Roger Bradley Design
    (cover)
Software Adviser: Neal Wills
Printer: WS Cowell Limited, Ipswich

First published 1988
Second edition 1989

© Legalese Ltd and John Pritchard 1989

ISBN: hardback 1 870854 01 2
       paperback 1 870854 02 0

Contents

Introduction

The Legal 500 aims to be an introductory guide to the leading law firms.

In many ways The Legal 500 is a mixture of factual information and personal comment. The factual information about the firms (for instance, total numbers of staff and partners) has been supplied by the firms and is up to date as at January 1989. However, as an adjunct to this factual information, I have not been able to resist the temptation to express my own opinions! Thus the editorial section at the front of the book includes a general review of which firms, in which regions, do what types of work – and who is generally reckoned to have a 'good name' within the profession. In expressing these opinions I have been largely influenced by the many comments and suggestions made to me by solicitors throughout the country. I am grateful to all those who have taken the trouble to write to me, and especially to those who have provided me with confidential background information on the nature of their individual practices. I am also grateful to the many thousands of solicitors who replied to our editorial survey and expressed confidential opinions about the firms that they would recommend for particular types of work.

Since much of the material in the editorial is a matter of opinion (albeit largely based on comments made by other solicitors), it can happily be dismissed and rejected by those who do not agree with it (or who find that their firm's name does not appear!).

The Legal 500 does not claim to be one hundred per cent right. The aim of the book is to open up some of the secrecy and mystique that surrounds the legal profession. At the same time, I hope that it will stimulate discussion amongst all lawyers about the respective merits (and demerits!) of individual firms. In this way it will be part of the process of making information about the law – and lawyers – available to a wider audience. A vital part of that wider audience is those who pay the bills – the clients! Thus I hope that the book will be of use to lawyers and clients alike, and that it will help them to understand each other.

All comments, criticisms, suggestions (and rude letters!) are welcome. So if you think that I've got it wrong, tell me!

Finally, I should like to repeat my thanks to the many firms (and individual solicitors) that have taken the trouble to help verify the information in The Legal 500, and also – in confidence – recommended the expertise of rival firms!

John Pritchard
March 1989

REGIONAL SURVEY

Regional survey

In this section we look at some of the major provincial practices on a region by region basis. With the concentration of large law firms in London it is easy to forget about the provinces, and the importance of the medium sized firm to the local community. This section goes some way towards correcting that imbalance by looking at the various firms within a particular region – and commenting on the types of work that they do. In addition, we have given the names of certain firms that are generally associated with particular types of legal work.

In writing these regional commentaries we have been helped considerably by the confidential opinions of other solicitors. In particular, we are grateful to those solicitors who responded to our questionnaire in which we asked which other firm they would recommend for a particular category of work. We also asked for opinions on which firms would be likely to go from strength to strength in the next five to ten years. Their suggestions have been included in this section of the book. We do not pretend that our survey is comprehensive or statistically sound. However, we hope that our comments will provoke friendly discussion and give food for thought. (Please refer to the end of the book for details of how The Legal 500 is compiled.)

We look at twelve main categories of work: general company and commercial law; commercial property; town and country planning; commercial litigation; building and construction litigation; insolvency and debt collection; intellectual property; entertainment; tax; family and matrimonial; personal injury litigation; and crime. We have tried to recommend a broad range of firms – not just the largest. This is particularly true with the non-commercial categories of work, such as family and crime.

For the purposes of our regional survey we have divided England and Wales into nine regions. We have adopted the standard economic planning regions (as used by the government): the South East; the South West; the West Midlands; the East Midlands; East Anglia; the North West; the North; Yorkshire and Humberside; and Wales. Scotland and London (defined as the London postal area) are dealt with separately.

When we recommend certain firms for particular types of work, we are not necessarily claiming that those firms are better than other firms in the area. All we are doing is making suggestions as to which firms are regarded as having a 'good name' for particular categories of work. Our opinions are personal (although derived largely from confidential opinions expressed by practitioners). As such, they are obviously open to argument and dissension. Further, it should not be thought that, by implication, we are disparaging the reputations of those firms whose names we do not mention!

The South East

As one would expect, the South East is well served by law firms: indeed, there are some 100 firms in the region that have over 50 total staff.

Which are the largest firms? If you prefer to go by total staff size (which we do), then the largest firms are **Blake Lapthorn** *Portsmouth*, **Thomas Eggar Verrall Bowles**

Chichester, **Thomson Snell & Passmore** *Tunbridge Wells*, and **Donne Mileham & Haddock** *Brighton*. On the other hand, if you prefer to look at partnership size (which, although it is the conventional approach, does tend to be misleading) then the order is **Thomson Snell & Passmore**, **Thomas Eggar Verrall Bowles**, **Donne**

SOUTH EAST: Top firms by total number of staff

		Total staff	Partners	Assistant solicitors	Articled clerks
1	Blake Lapthorn *Portsmouth*	291	22	27	13
2	Thomas Eggar Verrall Bowles *Chichester*	290	35	20	12
3	Thomson Snell & Passmore *Tunbridge Wells*	260	48	14	4
4	Donne Mileham & Haddock *Brighton*	235	35	13	9
5	Durnford Ford *Hastings*	220	23	4	4
6	Argles & Court *Maidstone*	220	22	9	4
7	Coffin Mew & Clover *Portsmouth*	201	18	8	3
8	Leigh Williams *Bromley*	184	17	11	9
9	Penningtons *Newbury*	178	25	18	3
10	Cripps Harries Hall *Tunbridge Wells*	173	19	17	4
11	Pictons *St Albans*	171	20	17	9
12	Moore & Blatch *Lymington*	170	17	17	8
13	Linnells *Oxford*	161	21	25	5
14	Brutton & Co *Fareham*	160	18	10	1
15	Bates & Partners *Southend*	152	13	7	2
16	Cole and Cole *Oxford*	150	22	22	9
17	Stevens Drake & Pope *Crawley*	150	9	11	5
18	Girlings *Herne Bay*	148	18	4	4
19	Kidd Rapinet *Slough*	147	27	7	5
20	Winter-Taylors *High Wycombe*	137	15	17	5
21	Hawkins Russell Jones *Hitchin*	130	21	10	0
22	Warner Goodman & Streat *Fareham*	130	16	4	1
23	Breeze and Wyles *Enfield*	125	14	10	11
24	Hart Brown & Co *Guildford*	115	15	6	7
25	TG Baynes & Sons *Welling*	112	14	3	5

Mileham & Haddock, Kidd Rapinet *Slough*, Penningtons *Newbury*, Durnford Ford *Hastings*, and then Blake Lapthorn.

The other leading firms — by total staff — are Argles & Court *Maidstone*, Coffin Mew & Clover *Portsmouth* (both these firms have more than 200 staff), Leigh Williams *Bromley*, Penningtons *Newbury*, Cripps Harries Hall *Tunbridge Wells*, Pictons *St Albans*, Moore & Blatch *Lymington*, Linnells *Oxford*, Brutton & Co *Fareham*, Bates & Partners *Southend*, Cole & Cole *Oxford*, and Stevens Drake & Pope *Crawley* (all with at least 150 staff).

The accompanying table sets out a full listing, based on total staff sizes. It will be noticed that Stevens Drake & Pope *Crawley* has relatively few partners in relation to its total staff size and so, to a lesser extent, do Fennemores *Milton Keynes*, Leeds Smith *Sandy*, Willmett & Co *Windsor*, Bunker & Co *Hove*, and Wade Gery Farr *Bedford*.

Company and commercial: In a prosperous and commercially active area such as the South East there is no shortage of high-quality commercial lawyers. Indeed, the South East is spoiled for choice. Pride of

		Total staff	Partners	Assistant solicitors	Articled clerks
26	Bower & Bailey *Oxford*	110	14	18	6
27	Boys & Maughan *Margate*	110	13	1	4
28	Glanvilles *Portsmouth*	109	14	9	4
29	Charles Lucas & Marshall *Newbury*	108	18	14	2
30	Judge & Priestley *Bromley*	108	10	0	2
31	Wynne Baxter Godfree *Lewes*	107	17	8	4
32	Fennemores *Milton Keynes*	102	9	12	8
33	Leeds Smith *Sandy*	100	7	6	2
34	Stevens & Bolton *Farnham*	98	13	9	3
35	Burstows *Crawley*	95	15	7	5
36	Brain & Brain *Reading*	95	13	7	6
37	Buss Murton Partnership *Tunbridge Wells*	95	13	6	3
38	Lamb Brooks Wills Chandler *Basingstoke*	95	12	5	5
39	Robinson Jarvis & Rolf *Ryde*	95	10	3	2
40	Eric Robinson & Co *Southampton*	95	9	4	4
41	Tuck & Mann & Geffen *Leatherhead*	91	17	9	7
42	Smith Morton & Long *Colchester*	90	11	6	4
43	Rawlison and Butler *Crawley*	90	11	4	2
44	Martin Tolhurst Partnership *Gravesend*	90	11	3	2
45	Willmett & Co *Windsor*	90	7	10	2
46	Robinson & Allfree *Ramsgate*	88	10	2	0
47	Brachers *Maidstone*	87	12	11	1
48	Mayo & Perkins *Eastbourne*	86	11	3	3
49	Whitehead Monckton *Maidstone*	85	14	5	2
50	Furley Page Fielding & Barton *Canterbury*	85	12	4	1

Company
SOUTH EAST

Argles & Court *Maidstone*
Blake Lapthorn *Portsmouth*
Brain & Brain *Reading*
Burstows *Crawley*
Clarks *Reading*
Coffin Mew & Clover *Portsmouth*
Cole and Cole *Oxford*
Cripps Harries Hall *Tunbridge Wells*
Donne Mileham & Haddock *Brighton*
Ellison & Co *Colchester*
Fennemores *Milton Keynes*
Furley Page Fielding & Barton *Canterbury*
Kidd´Rapinet *Slough*
Kimbell & Co *Milton Keynes*
Machins *Luton*
Paris Smith & Randall *Southampton*
Pitmans *Reading*
Rawlison and Butler *Crawley*
Sherwin Oliver *Portsmouth*
Stevens & Bolton *Farnham*
Thomas Eggar Verrall Bowles *Chichester*
Thomson Snell & Passmore *Tunbridge Wells*
Turberville Woodbridge *Uxbridge*
Whitehead Monckton *Maidstone*
Wollastons *Chelmsford*

& Co *Colchester*, **Kidd Rapinet** *Slough*, **Wollastons** *Chelmsford*, and **Coffin Mew & Clover** *Portsmouth*. Smaller, but specialist, practices include the well-thought-of firms of **Kimbell & Co** *Milton Keynes*, **Wallis Prance** *Basingstoke*, **Miller Parris** *Worthing*, and **Waltons** *Luton*.

Other firms that should be mentioned include **Borneo Martell & Partners** *Bedford*, **Bolitho Way** *Portsmouth*, **Roach Pittis** *Newport*, **Mayo & Perkins** *Eastbourne*, **Field Seymour Parkes** *Reading*, **Brachers** *Maidstone*, **Herbert & Gowers** *Oxford*, **Linnells** *Oxford*, and **Turner & Debenhams** *St Albans*.

To complete the picture, we might also suggest **Dutton Gregory & Williams** *Winchester*, **Lamport Bassitt** *Southampton*, **Robbins Olivey** *Woking*, as well as **Lamb Brooks Wills Chandler** *Basingstoke*, **Marshalls** *Godalming*, **Sharman & Trethewy** *Bedford*, **Tuck & Mann & Geffen** *Leatherhead*, **Winter-Taylors** *High Wycombe*, plus the small firm of **H Montlake & Co** *Ilford*.

place, however, must surely go to **Thomson Snell & Passmore** *Tunbridge Wells* which has a particularly strong reputation. Our other lead firms are **Donne Mileham & Haddock** *Brighton*, **Cripps Harries Hall** *Tunbridge Wells*, and **Thomas Eggar Verrall Bowles** *Chichester*.

In addition, we might suggest firms such as **Blake Lapthorn** *Portsmouth*, **Stevens & Bolton** *Farnham*, **Paris Smith & Randall** *Southampton*, **Rawlison and Butler** *Horsham*, **Pitmans** *Reading*, and **Cole and Cole** *Oxford*. Not to be overlooked are **Burstows** *Crawley*, **Sherwins** *Fareham*, **Brain & Brain** *Reading*, **Whitehead Monckton & Co** *Maidstone*, **Clarks** *Reading*, **Machins** *Luton*, **Fennemores** *Milton Keynes*, **Turberville Woodbridge** *Uxbridge*, **Argles & Court** *Maidstone*, **Furley Page Fielding & Barton** *Canterbury*, **Ellison**

Employment: Our four lead firms for company and commercial practice are also strong on employment matters; of the four, **Donne Mileham & Haddock** *Brighton* deserves special mention. Other firms to be reckoned with include **Cole and Cole** *Oxford*, **Balderston Warren** *Letchworth*, **Horwood & James** *Aylesbury*, **Rapers** *Chichester*, **Kidd Rapinet** *Slough*, and **Winter-Taylors** *High Wycombe*.

Licensing: Most of the major commercial practices have licensing departments. Once again, however, **Donne Mileham & Haddock** *Brighton* is particularly strong in this area. More generally, there are firms such as **Rapers** *Chichester*, **Clarks** *Reading*, **Cole and Cole** *Oxford*, **Dale & Newbery** *Staines*, **Fitzhugh Gates** *Brighton*, **Girlings** *Herne Bay*, **Lamport Bassitt** *Southampton*,

Commercial property
SOUTH EAST

Argles & Court *Maidstone*
Blake Lapthorn *Portsmouth*
Borneo Martell & Partners *Bedford*
Brachers *Maidstone*
Burstows *Crawley*
Clarks *Reading*
Coffin Mew & Clover *Portsmouth*
Cole and Cole *Oxford*
Cripps Harries Hall *Tunbridge Wells*
Donne Mileham & Haddock *Brighton*
Ellison & Co *Colchester*
Linnells *Oxford*
Pitmans *Reading*
Sherwin Oliver *Portsmouth*
Taylor Walker *Harpenden*
Thomas Eggar Verrall Bowles *Chichester*
Thomson Snell & Passmore *Tunbridge Wells*

Leigh Williams *Bromley,* **Mullis & Peake** *Romford,* and **Winter-Taylors** *High Wycombe.* For a small firm in St Albans, one could try **Ottaways.**

Commercial property: Here, Thomson Snell & Passmore *Tunbridge Wells* dominates. It is firmly established as the property firm in the area. However, it has to be said that there are numerous other firms that are highly experienced in commercial property matters. A number of firms in the South East have done extremely well out of the property boom in recent years; apart from a desire to get into this lucrative market, there has also been a general concern to reduce dependence on domestic conveyancing. Thus many firms have moved into the area of commercial property (which, for this purpose, includes substantial residential developments).

Leading firms include **Blake Lapthorn** *Portsmouth,* **Sherwins** *Fareham,* **Pitmans** *Reading,* **Brachers** *Maidstone,* **Cole and Cole** *Oxford,* and **Cripps Harries Hall** *Tunbridge Wells.* Also strong are **Taylor Walker** *Harpenden,* **Linnells** *Oxford,*

Borneo Martell & Partners *Bedford,* Donne Mileham & Haddock *Brighton,* Clarks *Reading,* Argles & Court *Maidstone,* Coffin Mew & Clover *Portsmouth,* Thomas Eggar Verrall Bowles *Chichester,* and Burstows *Crawley.*

There are also several small firms that have strong reputations. For instance **Kimbell & Co** *Milton Keynes,* **Hart Reade & Co** *Eastbourne,* and **John Pearson** *New Malden.*

Other names that are recommended include **Rapers** *Chichester,* **Harold Benjamin & Collins** *Harrow,* **Boys & Maughan** *Margate,* **Bunkers** *Hove,* **Burt Brill & Cardens** *Brighton,* **Colemans** *Maidenhead,* **Curry Littlejohn** *Harrow,* **Hawkins Russell Jones** *Hitchin,* **Hepherd Winstanley & Pugh** *Southampton,* **Smith & Harrison** *Waltham Cross,* **Cripps & Shone** *Marlow,* and **Nicholas Bennett & Co** *Sandwich.* Finally, we should perhaps mention **Machins** *Luton,* **Marsland & Barber** *Margate,* **Mullis & Peake** *Romford,* **Rawlison and Butler** *Horsham,* **Henman Ballad & Co** *Oxford,* **Stanley Tee & Co** *Bishop's Stortford,* **Stevens Drake & Pope** *Crawley,* **White Brooks & Gilman** *Winchester,* and **Whitehead Monckton & Co** *Maidstone.*

Planning: The previous section shows how strong the South East is in terms of commercial property and development work. Largely this is a reflection of the recent property boom. Naturally, an expertise in town and country planning goes hand in hand with commercial property and residential development. Thus there are many firms in the South East that are strong on town & country planning matters. In particular, we would pick out **Pitmans** *Reading* and **Thomson Snell & Passmore** *Tunbridge Wells.* Other well-regarded firms include **Brachers** *Maidstone,* **Park Woodfine & Co** *Bedford,* **Argles & Court**

Planning
SOUTH EAST

Argles & Court *Maidstone*
Blake Lapthorn *Portsmouth*
Brachers *Maidstone*
Breeze and Wyles *Enfield*
Cole and Cole *Oxford*
Cripps Harries Hall *Tunbridge Wells*
Donne Mileham & Haddock *Brighton*
Downs *Dorking*
Park Woodfine & Co *Bedford*
Pitmans *Reading*
Thomas Eggar Verrall Bowles *Chichester*
Thomson Snell & Passmore *Tunbridge Wells*

Maidstone, **Cole and Cole** *Oxford*, **Blake Lapthorn** *Portsmouth*, **Breeze and Wyles** *Enfield*, **Thomas Eggar Verrall Bowles** *Chichester*, **Cripps Harries Hall** *Tunbridge Wells*, **Donne Mileham & Haddock** *Brighton*, and **Downs** *Dorking*.

In addition, we would name **Burstows** *Crawley*, **Fitzhugh Gates** *Brighton*, **Colemans** *Maidenhead*, **Harold Benjamin & Collins** *Harrow*, **Machins** *Luton*, **Stephen Rimmer and Co** *Eastbourne*, and — to complete the picture — the small firms of **Raymond C Tetlow** *Newport Pagnell* and **Kingsley Smith & Co** *Gillingham*.

Commercial litigation: The preferred choices would seem to be **Blake Lapthorn** *Portsmouth* and **Thomson Snell & Passmore** *Tunbridge Wells*. Other firms that feature strongly are **Brachers** *Maidstone*, **Cole and Cole** *Oxford*, **Donne Mileham & Haddock** *Brighton*, **Clarks** *Reading*, **Paris Smith & Randall** *Southampton*, **Furley Page Fielding & Barton** *Canterbury*, **Machins** *Luton*, **Whitehead Monckton & Co** *Maidstone*, and **Argles & Court** *Maidstone*.

Also recommended are **Mayo & Perkins** *Eastbourne*, **Sherwins** *Fareham*, **Buss Murton Partnership** *Tunbridge Wells*, **Burstows** *Crawley*, **Coffin Mew & Clover** *Portsmouth*, as well as **Glanvilles**

Portsmouth, **Hawkins Russell Jones** *Hitchin*, **Linnells** *Oxford*, and finally **Boys & Maughan** *Margate*.

For building and construction litigation the names are — as one would expect — largely the same. In particular, **Thomson Snell & Passmore** *Tunbridge Wells*, **Blake Lapthorn** *Portsmouth*, and **Clarks** *Reading* are strongly recommended. Names not previously mentioned in the context of commercial litigation are **Ellison & Co** *Colchester* and **Roach Pittis** *Newport*.

Insolvency and debt collection: Perhaps because of its relative prosperity the South East has few firms that are particularly experienced in insolvency matters. **Whitehead Monckton & Co** *Maidstone* is one firm that deserves special mention; otherwise, the field is fairly open. Suggestions include **Thomson Snell & Passmore** *Tunbridge Wells*, **Thomas Eggar Verrall Bowles** *Chichester*, **Paris Smith & Randall** *Southampton*, **Brachers** *Maidstone*, and **Blake Lapthorn** *Portsmouth*.

For general debt collection there is a much wider choice. All the firms mentioned for insolvency are strong in this regard, although we would particularly mention **Thomson Snell & Passmore** *Tunbridge Wells* and **Blake Lapthorn** *Portsmouth*. Other strong firms include **Balderston**

Commercial litigation
SOUTH EAST

Argles & Court *Maidstone*
Blake Lapthorn *Portsmouth*
Brachers *Maidstone*
Clarks *Reading*
Cole and Cole *Oxford*
Donne Mileham & Haddock *Brighton*
Furley Page Fielding & Barton *Canterbury*
Machins *Luton*
Paris Smith & Randall *Southampton*
Thomson Snell & Passmore *Tunbridge Wells*
Whitehead Monckton *Maidstone*

Insolvency
SOUTH EAST

Blake Lapthorn *Portsmouth*
Brachers *Maidstone*
Paris Smith & Randall *Southampton*
Thomas Eggar Verrall Bowles *Chichester*
Thomson Snell & Passmore *Tunbridge Wells*
Whitehead Monckton *Maidstone*

Warren *Letchworth*, Blaser Mills *Chesham*, Brachers *Maidstone*, Donne Mileham & Haddock *Brighton*, Fennemores *Milton Keynes*, Peard Webster Pringle & John *Croydon*, Redfern & Stigant *Gillingham* and Stevens Drake & Pope *Crawley*, as well as Boyes Turner & Burrows *Reading* and Parrott & Coales *Aylesbury*. Other suggestions include Buss Murton Partnership *Tunbridge Wells*, Crellins *Weybridge*, Furley Page Fielding & Barton *Canterbury*, Lee Davies and Co *Harlow* (especially for mortgage repossessions), and Linnells *Oxford*. Finally, there are firms such as Leftley & Co *Harrow*, Pictons *St Albans*, Turberville Woodbridge *Uxbridge*, and Wynne Baxter Godfree *Lewes*.

Intellectual property: Not surprisingly, it is the large commercial firms that dominate in intellectual property. In particular, Thomson Snell & Passmore *Tunbridge Wells*. Perhaps more surprising is the fact that the small Oxford firm of Dallas Brett has been highly recommended to us by many practitioners. Otherwise, our suggestions are Thomas Eggar Verrall Bowles *Chichester*, Donne Mileham & Haddock *Brighton*, Ellison & Co *Colchester*, and Blake Lapthorn *Portsmouth*.

Tax: Once again it is Thomson Snell & Passmore *Tunbridge Wells* that seems to be the lead firm. Other tax practices include Cole and Cole *Oxford*, Blake Lapthorn *Portsmouth*, Thomas Eggar Verrall Bowles *Chichester*, **Cripps Harries Hall** *Tunbridge Wells*, and **Paris Smith & Randall** *Southampton*. Also mentioned is **Marsh & Ferriman** *Worthing*. Other suggestions are **Blaser Mills** *Chesham*, **Moore & Blatch** *Lymington*, and **Wollastons** *Chelmsford*.

Family: There is a wide variety of firms doing family and matrimonial law. Generally it is the province of the medium sized and smaller firms; whilst nearly all the large firms do matrimonial work, they are not so dominant.

Firms that deserve special mention are Cole and Cole *Oxford*, Paris Smith & Randall *Southampton*, Warner Goodman & Streat *Fareham*, and Coffin Mew & Clover *Portsmouth*. Other firms that are strong in family matters are Neves *Luton*, Brachers *Maidstone*, Hart Reade & Co *Eastbourne*, Borneo Martell & Partners *Bedford*, Berry & Berry *Tunbridge Wells*, Thomson Snell & Passmore *Tunbridge Wells*, Blake Lapthorn *Portsmouth*, Baldocks *Guildford*, Darby & Son *Oxford*, Brain & Brain *Reading*,

Intellectual property
SOUTH EAST

Blake Lapthorn *Portsmouth*
Dallas Brett *Oxford*
Donne Mileham & Haddock *Brighton*
Ellison & Co *Colchester*
Thomas Eggar Verrall Bowles *Chichester*
Thomson Snell & Passmore *Tunbridge Wells*

Tax
SOUTH EAST

Blake Lapthorn *Portsmouth*
Cole and Cole *Oxford*
Cripps Harries Hall *Tunbridge Wells*
Marsh & Ferriman *Worthing*
Paris Smith & Randall *Southampton*
Thomas Eggar Verrall Bowles *Chichester*
Thomson Snell & Passmore *Tunbridge Wells*

Family
SOUTH EAST

Baldocks *Guildford*
Berry & Berry *Tunbridge Wells*
Blake Lapthorn *Portsmouth*
Borneo Martell & Partners *Bedford*
Brachers *Maidstone*
Brain & Brain *Reading*
Breeze and Wyles *Enfield*
Coffin Mew & Clover *Portsmouth*
Cole and Cole *Oxford*
Darby & Son *Oxford*
Girlings *Herne Bay*
Hart Reade & Co *Eastbourne*
Neves *Luton*
Paris Smith & Randall *Southampton*
Rowberry Morris & Co *Reading*
Thomson Snell & Passmore *Tunbridge Wells*
Warner Goodman & Streat *Fareham*

Rowberry Morris & Co *Reading*, **Girlings** *Herne Bay*, and **Breeze and Wyles** *Enfield*.

In addition, there are **Snow & Bispham** *Basingstoke* and **Max Barford & Co** *Tunbridge Wells*, as well as **Cripps & Shone** *Marlow*, **Spon-Smith & Co** *Bromley*, **Thomas Mallam** *Oxford*, **Barlows** *Guildford*, **Gepp & Sons** *Chelmsford*, **Boyes Turner & Burrows** *Reading*, **Stevens Drake & Pope** *Crawley*, and **Cripps Harries Hall** *Tunbridge Wells*. To complete the picture we would also suggest **Hatten Wyatt & Co** *Gravesend*, **Balderston Warren** *Letchworth*, **Barker Son & Isherwood** *Andover*, **Larcomes** *Portsmouth*, the small firm of **John Pearson** *New Malden*, **Smith Morton & Long** *Colchester*, and the well-regarded specialist practice of **Richard White & Michael Sherwin** *Croydon*.

Personal injury litigation: Once again, it is **Thomson Snell & Passmore** *Tunbridge Wells* that seems to be the most recommended firm. Other firms that figure prominently are **Cole and Cole** *Oxford*, **Brachers** *Maidstone*, **Girlings** *Herne Bay*, **Henman Ballad & Co** *Oxford*, **Lamport**

Bassitt *Southampton*, **King & Franckeiss** *Portsmouth*, and **Gepp & Sons** *Chelmsford*. Also recommended are **Rowberry Morris & Co** *Reading*, **Bells** *Kingston upon Thames*, **Allan Janes & Co** *High Wycombe*, **Marsh & Ferriman** *Worthing*, **Redfern & Stigant** *Gillingham*, **Borneo Martell & Partners** *Bedford*, **Blake Lapthorn** *Portsmouth*, **Glanvilles** *Portsmouth*, and **Sherwins** *Fareham*.

We should also not forget **Brutton & Co** *Fareham*, **Kidd Rapinet** *Slough*, **Mackrell Turner Garret** *Woking*, **Stokes** *Portsmouth*, as well as **Coffin Mew & Clover** *Portsmouth*, **Warner Goodman & Streat** *Fareham* and the smaller firms of **Gardner & Croft** *Canterbury*, **CA Norris** *Ringwood*, and **Barry Lewis** *Guildford*.

Crime: As always, it is the smaller firms that dominate criminal practice. Whilst most of the larger firms still accept criminal cases, it does seem to be regarded as very much second-rate work — especially when legal aid is paying the bill!

Our lead firms for crime in the South East are **Cole and Cole** *Oxford*, **Berry & Berry**

Personal injury
SOUTH EAST

Allan Janes & Co *High Wycombe*
Bells *Kingston upon Thames*
Blake Lapthorn *Portsmouth*
Borneo Martell & Partners *Bedford*
Brachers *Maidstone*
Cole and Cole *Oxford*
Gepp & Sons *Chelmsford*
Girlings *Herne Bay*
Glanvilles *Portsmouth*
Henman Ballad & Co *Oxford*
King & Franckeiss *Portsmouth*
Lamport Bassitt *Southampton*
Marsh & Ferriman *Worthing*
Redfern & Stigant *Gillingham*
Rowberry Morris & Co *Reading*
Sherwin Oliver *Portsmouth*
Thomson Snell & Passmore *Tunbridge Wells*

Crime
SOUTH EAST

Allan Janes & Co *High Wycombe*
Bernard Chill & Axtell *Southampton*
Berry & Berry *Tunbridge Wells*
Blandy & Blandy *Reading*
Burroughs *Maidstone*
Cole and Cole *Oxford*
Darby & Son *Oxford*
Donne Mileham & Haddock *Brighton*
Gepp & Sons *Chelmsford*
Girlings *Herne Bay*
Hart Brown & Co *Guildford*
Kidd Rapinet *Slough*
Lamb Brooks Wills Chandler *Basingstoke*
Max Barford & Co *Tunbridge Wells*
Mayo & Perkins *Eastbourne*
Pictons *St Albans*
Staffurth & Bray *Bognor Regis*
Stokes *Portsmouth*
Talbot Davies & Copner *Andover*
Wannop & Falconer *Chichester*
Whiskers *Epping*
Woodford & Ackroyd *Southampton*

Tunbridge Wells, **Allan Janes & Co** *High Wycombe*, and **Max Barford & Co** *Tunbridge Wells* — which received a particularly high number of recommendations.

Other leading criminal practitioners include **Stokes** *Portsmouth*, **Bernard Chill & Axtell** *Southampton*, **Girlings** *Herne Bay*, **Lamb Brooks Wills Chandler** *Basingstoke*, **Woodford & Ackroyd** *Southampton*, **Blandy & Blandy** *Reading*, **Pictons** *St Albans*, **Mayo & Perkins** *Eastbourne*, **Larcomes** *Portsmouth*, and **Whiskers** *Epping*.

In addition, there are firms such as **Darby & Son** *Oxford*, **Gepp & Sons** *Chelmsford*, **Kidd Rapinet** *Slough*, **Wannop & Falconer** *Chichester*, **Hart Brown & Co** *Guildford*, **Staffurth & Bray** *Bognor Regis*, **Donne Mileham & Haddock** *Brighton*, **Burroughs** *Maidstone*, and **Talbot Davies & Copner** *Andover*. Also worthy of mention are **Foinette Quinn** *Milton Keynes*, **Knowles Cave & Co** *Luton*, **DJ Griffiths and Co**

Bromley, **Dexter Montague & Partners** *Reading*, **Brignall White & Orchard** *Stevenage*, **Burr & Company** *Farnham*, **Simms & Co** *Oxford*, **Kingsford Flower & Pain** *Ashford*, and **Hatten Wyatt & Co** *Gravesend*.

To complete the picture we would also suggest **Boys & Maughan** *Margate*, **Breeze and Wyles** *Enfield*, **Brutton & Co** *Fareham*, and Redfern & Stigant *Gillingham*. Finally, should you have the misfortune to need a criminal lawyer on the Isle of Wight, then we would suggest you try **Robinson Jarvis & Rolf** *Ryde*!

Agriculture: Many of the major commercial firms are experienced in agricultural matters. In addition, we would mention **Furley Page Fielding & Barton** *Canterbury*, **Brachers** *Maidstone*, **Smith Morton & Long** *Colchester*, as well as **Baldocks** *Guildford* and **Burley & Geach** *Petersfield*.

Firms going from strength to strength:
The name most frequently mentioned to us — and, indeed, the name that features most prominently in our lists — is **Thomson Snell & Passmore** *Tunbridge Wells*. Few would argue that this is the most prominent firm in the region.

The consensus of opinion would seem to make **Blake Lapthorn** *Portsmouth* and **Thomas Eggar Verrall Bowles** *Chichester* the other lead firms. After these three major firms, it is a wide-open race. Of the medium sized firms, there is much support for **Cole and Cole** *Oxford*, whereas if you wish to go for a smaller firm, there is backing for **Sherwins** *Fareham*.

Other names that were frequently mentioned include **Stevens & Bolton** *Farnham*, **Donne Mileham & Haddock** *Brighton*, **Girlings** *Herne Bay*, **Paris Smith & Randall** *Southampton*, and **Brachers** *Maidstone*.

The South West

In the South West the largest firm is **Clarke Willmott & Clarke** *Taunton*, with the second largest being **Bevan Ashford** (which has several major offices in the West Country). However, **Bevan Ashford** does have a relatively high number of partners in relation to its overall size – indeed, on the basis of partnership size alone it would qualify as the largest firm in the region. However, as we have often repeated, we prefer to look at total staff as a more reliable indicator of overall size. Either way, it is these two firms that are the largest in the region, although it should be borne in mind

SOUTH WEST: Top firms by total number of staff

		Total staff	Partners	Assistant solicitors	Articled clerks
1	Clarke Willmott & Clarke *Taunton*	384	36	31	14
2	Bevan Ashford *West Country*	350	49	35	20
3	Bond Pearce *Plymouth*	247	31	41	15
4	Osborne Clarke *Bristol*	201	27	40	11
5	Veale Wasbrough *Bristol*	200	27	21	13
6	Lester Aldridge *Bournemouth*	194	26	15	10
7	Burges Salmon *Bristol*	190	17	42	14
8	Stephens & Scown *St Austell*	167	22	11	4
9	JW Ward & Son *Bristol*	149	18	17	8
10	Batten & Co *Yeovil*	145	16	6	3
11	Cartwrights *Bristol*	135	20	18	7
12	Porter Bartlett & Mayo *Yeovil*	122	13	6	4
13	Wansbroughs *Bristol*	121	21	24	6
14	Foot & Bowden *Plymouth*	110	19	12	8
15	Townsends *Swindon*	108	12	13	4
16	Lawrence Tucketts *Bristol*	96	11	18	4
17	Woollcombe Watts *Newton Abbot*	95	13	9	3
18	Stones *Exeter*	95	12	13	4
19	Turners *Bournemouth*	92	12	2	1
20	Trethowans *Salisbury*	90	15	4	3
21	Tozers *Teignmouth*	90	14	10	2
22	Burroughs Day Robert Smith *Bristol*	86	12	5	4
23	Dodson Harding *Taunton*	80	14	3	1
24	Boyce Hatton *Torquay*	80	13	4	3
25	Lyons Davidson *Bristol*	80	12	12	3

that both have a considerable number of offices, and thus each individual office may not be particularly large.

This is not the case with **Bond Pearce** *Plymouth* (indeed, many people may be surprised by the relative size of the firm). It has only one branch office and yet has 247 total staff. Similarly, **Osborne Clarke** *Bristol* (the fourth largest firm in the region) has only one other office (in fact, in London). Of similar size to **Osborne Clarke** is **Veale Wasbrough** *Bristol*, with 200 staff.

Other large firms include **Lester Aldridge** *Bournemouth*, **Burges Salmon** *Bristol*, **Stephens & Scown** *St Austell* (all with over 150 total staff), as well as **JW Ward & Son** *Bristol*, **Batten & Co** *Yeovil*, **Cartwrights** *Bristol*, **Porter Bartlett & Mayo** *Yeovil*, **Wansbroughs** *Bristol*, **Foot & Bowden** *Plymouth*, and **Townsends** *Swindon* (all with over 100 total staff).

As can be seen from the table, some of these firms have a relatively large number of partners in relation to their overall size. Conversely, it is interesting to note that **Slee Blackwell** *Braunton* has only five partners and yet has a total staff of 75.

Company and commercial: There are four firms that dominate the commercial work of the region. Of these four, it is **Osborne Clarke** *Bristol* that we would regard as pre-eminent, followed by **Bond Pearce** *Plymouth*, **Burges Salmon** *Bristol*, and **Bevan Ashford** (which has a chain of offices across the South West).

There are, however, many other well-known commercial firms. Recommended are **Clarke Willmott & Clarke** *Taunton*, **Veale Wasbrough** *Bristol*, **Lester Mooring Aldridge & Russell** *Bournemouth*, **Boyce Hatton** *Torquay*, and **Stephens & Scown** *St Austell*. Also highly regarded are **Pardoes** *Bridgwater*, **Wansbroughs** *Bristol*, **Flint Hand** *Gloucester*, **Lawrence Tucketts** *Bristol*, **Lyons Davidson** *Bristol*, and **Steele Raymond** *Bournemouth*.

Company
SOUTH WEST
Bevan Ashford *West Country*
Bond Pearce *Plymouth*
Boyce Hatton *Torquay*
Burges Salmon *Bristol*
Clarke Willmott & Clarke *Taunton*
Flint Hand *Gloucester*
Lawrence Tucketts *Bristol*
Lester Aldridge *Bournemouth*
Lyons Davidson *Bristol*
Osborne Clarke *Bristol*
Pardoes *Bridgwater*
Steele Raymond *Bournemouth*
Stephens & Scown *St Austell*
Veale Wasbrough *Bristol*
Wansbroughs *Bristol*

The smaller firm of **John Lindley & Company** *Bristol* is also suggested, as are **Townsends** *Swindon* and **Wiggin and Co** *Cheltenham*. Finally, we would mention firms such as **Coles** *Poole*, **James & Dennis** *Plymouth*, **Peake & Co** *Swindon*, **Stones** *Exeter*, and **Philip Evans & Co** *Bournemouth*.

Most of these firms would also claim to be fairly experienced in employment matters. Perhaps special mention should to go to **Bevan Ashford** *West Country*, **Bond Pearce** *Plymouth*, and **Burges Salmon** *Bristol*. Less obvious suggestions might include **Cartwrights** *Bristol*, **Lester Mooring Aldridge & Russell** *Bournemouth*, **Pardoes** *Bridgwater*, and **Porter Bartlett & Mayo** *Yeovil*.

For licensing we should really refer only to **Cartwrights** *Bristol*. We take the view that the firm is pre-eminent in licensing matters throughout England and Wales – certainly as regards firms outside London (and probably even including the major London firms). Otherwise, firms to mention include **Holt Phillips** *Bristol*, **Clarke Willmott & Clarke** *Taunton*, **JW Ward & Son** *Bristol*, **Crosse & Crosse** *Exeter*, as well as **Bond Pearce** *Plymouth*, **Foot & Bowden** *Plymouth*, and **Gill Akaster** *Plymouth*.

Commercial property
SOUTH WEST

Batten & Co *Yeovil*
Bevan Ashford *West Country*
Bishop Longbotham & Bagnall *Trowbridge*
Bond Pearce *Plymouth*
Boyce Hatton *Torquay*
Burges Salmon *Bristol*
Clarke Willmott & Clarke *Taunton*
Crosse & Crosse *Exeter*
Foot & Bowden *Plymouth*
Holt Phillips *Bristol*
Lester Aldridge *Bournemouth*
Michelmores *Exeter*
Osborne Clarke *Bristol*
Rickerby Jessop *Cheltenham*
Steele Raymond *Bournemouth*
Trump & Partners *Bristol*
Turners *Bournemouth*
Veale Wasbrough *Bristol*
Wansbroughs *Bristol*

Commercial Property: This is another area in which the South West has many firms of considerable experience. In our view the lead firms are **Burges Salmon** *Bristol*, **Osborne Clarke** *Bristol*, and **Bond Pearce** *Plymouth*. Other leading names include **Bevan Ashford** *West Country*, **Veale Wasbrough** *Bristol*, **Foot & Bowden** *Plymouth*, **Wansbroughs** *Bristol*, **Clarke Willmott & Clarke** *Taunton*, **Steele Raymond** *Bournemouth*, **Crosse & Crosse** *Exeter*, **Lester Mooring Aldridge & Russell** *Bournemouth*, **Trump & Partners** *Bristol*, **Boyce Hatton** *Torquay*, and **Bishop Longbotham & Bagnall** *Trowbridge*. Also recommended are **Holt Phillips** *Bristol*, **Michelmores** *Exeter*, **Batten & Co** *Yeovil*, **Rickerby Jessop** *Cheltenham*, and **Turners** *Bournemouth*.

Other firms worthy of mention include **Lawrence Tucketts** *Bristol*, **Lyons Davidson** *Bristol*, **Burd Pearse** *Okehampton*, **Dickinson Manser & Co** *Poole*, **Gould & Swayne** *Glastonbury*, **Hancock & Lawrence** *Truro*, **JW Ward & Son** *Bristol*, **Nicholas Tanner & Co** *Cirencester*, **Parker Bullen**

Salisbury, **Slee Blackwell** *Braunton*, **Trethowans** *Salisbury*, **Peter Peter & Wright** *Holsworthy*, **Wilsons** *Salisbury*, and **Withy King & Lee** *Bath*.

Planning: Naturally, any firm that claims to have expertise in commercial property work will, presumably, have a planning department. Thus most of the firms mentioned above should be able to advise satisfactorily on planning matters. However, certain firms are regularly mentioned as being especially skilled in this area. In particular we would mention **Bond Pearce** *Plymouth*, **Clarke Willmott & Clarke** *Taunton*, **Foot & Bowden** *Plymouth*, and **Bevan Ashford** *West Country*. Other strongly recommended firms include **Lawrence Tucketts** *Bristol*, **Tozers** *Teignmouth*, **Osborne Clarke** *Bristol*, **Burges Salmon** *Bristol*, **Veale Wasbrough** *Bristol*, **Cartwrights** *Bristol*, **Boyce Hatton** *Torquay*, **Lester Mooring Aldridge & Russell** *Bournemouth*, **Watterson Todman** *Cheltenham*, and the smaller firm of **Rawlins Davy and Wells** *Bournemouth*.

Other suggestions might include **Burd Pearse** *Okehampton*, **Gould & Swayne** *Glastonbury*, **Lawrence Tucketts** *Bristol*, **Lyons Davidson** *Bristol*, **Stephens & Scown** *St Austell*, and **Trethowans** *Salisbury*.

Planning
SOUTH WEST

Bevan Ashford *West Country*
Bond Pearce *Plymouth*
Boyce Hatton *Torquay*
Burges Salmon *Bristol*
Cartwrights *Bristol*
Clarke Willmott & Clarke *Taunton*
Foot & Bowden *Plymouth*
Lawrence Tucketts *Bristol*
Lester Aldridge *Bournemouth*
Osborne Clarke *Bristol*
Rawlins Davy and Wells *Bournemouth*
Tozers *Teignmouth*
Veale Wasbrough *Bristol*
Watterson Todman *Cheltenham*

Commercial litigation
SOUTH WEST

Bevan Ashford *West Country*
Bond Pearce *Plymouth*
Boyce Hatton *Torquay*
Burges Salmon *Bristol*
Clarke Willmott & Clarke *Taunton*
Crosse & Crosse *Exeter*
Lawrence Tucketts *Bristol*
Lester Aldridge *Bournemouth*
Osborne Clarke *Bristol*
Stephens & Scown *St Austell*
Turners *Bournemouth*
Veale Wasbrough *Bristol*
Wansbroughs *Bristol*
Wilsons *Salisbury*

Commercial litigation: There is a wide spread of firms with expertise in commercial litigation. Particularly prominent are **Burges Salmon** *Bristol*, **Wansbroughs** *Bristol*, **Osborne Clarke** *Bristol*, and **Bond Pearce** *Plymouth*. Also strong are **Bevan Ashford** *West Country*, **Veale Wasbrough** *Bristol*, **Clarke Willmott & Clarke** *Taunton*, **Stephens & Scown** *St Austell*, **Crosse & Crosse** *Exeter*, **Lester Mooring Aldridge & Russell** *Bournemouth*, and **Boyce Hatton** *Torquay*.

Other firms to be mentioned include **Lawrence Tucketts** *Bristol*, **Turners** *Bournemouth*, **Wilsons** *Salisbury*, **Lyons Davidson** *Bristol*, and **Gill Akaster** *Plymouth*.

Building and construction litigation: In the more specialist area of building litigation **Veale Wasbrough** *Bristol* is highly recommended, as are **Bevan Ashford** *West Country* and **Bond Pearce** *Plymouth*. Also strong are **Wansbroughs** *Bristol*, **Burges Salmon** *Bristol*, **Clarke Willmott & Clarke** *Taunton*, **Cartwrights** *Bristol*, **Boyce Hatton** *Torquay*, **Stones** *Exeter*, **Turners** *Bournemouth*, and **Osborne Clarke** *Bristol*. Not to be forgotten are **Lester Mooring Aldridge & Russell** *Bournemouth*, whilst

other suggestions might include **Nalder & Son** *Truro*, **Harper & Co** *Bristol*, and **Lyons Davidson** *Bristol*.

Insolvency and debt collection: **Bond Pearce** *Plymouth* is our first choice for insolvency work, followed by **Sargent & Probert** *Exeter*. Both firms can be strongly recommended.

Other suggestions include **Burges Salmon** *Bristol*, **Osborne Clarke** *Bristol*, **Trump & Partners** *Bristol*, **Veale Wasbrough** *Bristol*, **Lester Mooring Aldridge & Russell** *Bournemouth*, **Flint Hand** *Gloucester*, and **Laytons and Ingham Clegg & Crowther** *Bristol*. Also suggested are **Lawrence Tucketts** *Bristol*, **Stones** *Exeter*, and **Wilsons** *Salisbury*.

Most of these firms are also highly experienced at general debt collection.

Insolvency
SOUTH WEST

Bond Pearce *Plymouth*
Burges Salmon *Bristol*
Flint Hand *Gloucester*
Laytons & Ingham Clegg & Crowther *Bristol*
Lester Aldridge *Bournemouth*
Osborne Clarke *Bristol*
Sargent & Probert *Exeter*
Trump & Partners *Bristol*
Veale Wasbrough *Bristol*

Construction
SOUTH WEST

Bevan Ashford *West Country*
Bond Pearce *Plymouth*
Boyce Hatton *Torquay*
Burges Salmon *Bristol*
Cartwrights *Bristol*
Clarke Willmott & Clarke *Taunton*
Osborne Clarke *Bristol*
Stones *Exeter*
Turners *Bournemouth*
Veale Wasbrough *Bristol*
Wansbroughs *Bristol*

Intellectual property
SOUTH WEST

Bevan Ashford *West Country*
Bond Pearce *Plymouth*
Burges Salmon *Bristol*
Crosse & Crosse *Exeter*
Lester Aldridge *Bournemouth*
Osborne Clarke *Bristol*
Veale Wasbrough *Bristol*

Names that have not been mentioned so far, but might be added to a debt-collection list, include **Trethowans** *Salisbury*, **Turners** *Bournemouth*, and **Wansbroughs** *Bristol*.

Intellectual property: This is an area in which many firms are now claiming expertise. Indeed, it is one of those fields of law in which a number of firms like to claim that they have a knowledge, but the reality is that there are relatively few practices that have in-depth specialist knowledge. In the South West we would put **Osborne Clarke** *Bristol* in that category. In addition, we would mention **Bond Pearce** *Plymouth*, **Bevan Ashford** *West Country*, **Burges Salmon** *Bristol*, **Veale Wasbrough** *Bristol*, **Lester Mooring Aldridge & Russell** *Bournemouth*, and **Crosse & Crosse** *Exeter*. Also worth considering is the smaller firm of **Humphreys & Co** *Bristol*.

It is often the case that strength in intellectual property law will lead to some experience in entertainment law. This is a rough generalisation: it does not necessarily follow that the two go together (especially in London, where there are many more specialist entertainment practices). But, in this instance, it is no surprise to see that our suggested firms for entertainment law are largely the same as those we recommend for intellectual property. Once again, **Osborne Clarke** *Bristol* would seem to be the appropriate choice. Other names include **Crosse & Crosse** *Exeter*, **Cartwrights**

Bristol, **Veale Wasbrough** *Bristol*, and **Bevan Ashford** *West Country*.

Tax: It will surprise no one to learn that we regard **Burges Salmon** *Bristol* as the leading tax firm in the South West. What may be more surprising, however, is our second choice — **Wiggin and Co** *Cheltenham*. Despite the relatively small size of the firm, and its location, it might almost be described as a specialist City practice, when one considers the nature of the clientele and the work done.

Otherwise, our suggestions contain no surprises. For instance, there is **Osborne Clarke** *Bristol*, **Lester Mooring Aldridge & Russell** *Bournemouth*, **Bond Pearce** *Plymouth*, **Burd Pearse** *Okehampton*, **Stones** *Exeter*, **Bevan Ashford** *West Country*, and **Wilsons** *Salisbury*. Also suggested is **Clarke Willmott & Clarke** *Taunton*.

Family: As always, there is a wide choice when it comes to family and matrimonial work. It is an area in which most firms

Entertainment
SOUTH WEST

Bevan Ashford *West Country*
Cartwrights *Bristol*
Crosse & Crosse *Exeter*
Osborne Clarke *Bristol*
Veale Wasbrough *Bristol*

Tax
SOUTH WEST

Bevan Ashford *West Country*
Bond Pearce *Plymouth*
Burd Pearse *Okehampton*
Burges Salmon *Bristol*
Lester Aldridge *Bournemouth*
Osborne Clarke *Bristol*
Wiggin and Co *Cheltenham*
Wilsons *Salisbury*

Family
SOUTH WEST

Bevan Ashford *West Country*
Bond Pearce *Plymouth*
Clarke Willmott & Clarke *Taunton*
Coles *Poole*
Foot & Bowden *Plymouth*
Ford Simey & Ford *Exeter*
Gill Akaster *Devonport*
Lester Aldridge *Bournemouth*
Osborne Clarke *Bristol*
Rundle McDonald & Rendle's *Plymouth*
Stones *Exeter*
Trump & Partners *Bristol*
Veale Wasbrough *Bristol*
Wansbroughs *Bristol*

---

practise – even the major commercial ones. Our research indicates that **Veale Wasbrough** *Bristol*, **Trump & Partners** *Bristol*, and **Osborne Clarke** *Bristol* are the prominent firms. Also strong are **Lester Mooring Aldridge & Russell** *Bournemouth*, **Gill Akaster** *Plymouth*, **Rundle McDonald & Rendle's** *Plymouth*, as well as **Ford Simey & Ford** *Exeter*, **Stones** *Exeter*, **Wansbroughs** *Bristol*, **Bond Pearce** *Plymouth*, **Foot & Bowden** *Plymouth*, **Clarke Willmott & Clarke** *Taunton*, **Coles** *Poole*, and **Bevan Ashford** *West Country*. Other suggestions might include the small firms of **Watson Sinnott** *Bristol*, **Moriarty & Co** *Torquay*, and **Anstey & Thompson** *Exeter*. **Crosse & Crosse** *Exeter*, **JW Ward & Son** *Bristol*, **Wolferstans** *Plymouth*, **Wellingtons** *Gloucester*, **Thralls** *Truro*, and **Hooper & Wollen** *Torquay* are other names to mention.

Personal injury litigation: Amongst the major insurance litigation practices in the region are **Wansbroughs** *Bristol* and **Veale Wasbrough** *Bristol*. Well regarded for personal injury work are **Bond Pearce** *Plymouth*, **Bevan Ashford** *West Country*, **Clarke Willmott & Clarke** *Taunton*, **Crosse**

& Crosse *Exeter*, **Cartwrights** *Bristol*, **Wolferstans** *Plymouth*, **Lester Mooring Aldridge & Russell** *Bournemouth*, **Stones** *Exeter*, and **Stephens & Scown** *St Austell*. Less well-known suggestions include **Nash & Co** *Plymouth*, plus the smaller firms of **Sansbury Hill** *Bristol* and **Macfarlane Guy** *Bath*. In addition, we would mention **JW Ward & Son** *Bristol*, **Russell Jones & Walker** *Bristol*, **Ford Simey & Ford** *Exeter*, **Lyons Davidson** *Bristol*, **Moore Brown & Dixon** *Tewkesbury*, **Pardoes** *Bridgwater*, and **GD Cann & Hallett** *Exeter*.

Crime: As always, it is the smaller firms that tend to dominate any list of recommended criminal practitioners. Whilst many of the large firms do crime, it is not unusual to find that they refuse legal aid cases; in any event, they tend not to emphasise this aspect of their work as much as they do their commercial practice. Besides, it is one area in which the small firm can often compete on equal terms.

As if to confirm this, our lead firm for criminal work is relatively small – **Bobbetts** *Bristol* has only six partners. Also recommended are **Woollcombe Watts** *Newton Abbot*, **Andrews McQueen** *Bournemouth*, the one-partner firm of **W Anthony Daniel** *Plymouth*, **Macfarlane Guy**

Personal injury
SOUTH WEST

Bevan Ashford *West Country*
Bond Pearce *Plymouth*
Cartwrights *Bristol*
Clarke Willmott & Clarke *Taunton*
Crosse & Crosse *Exeter*
Lester Aldridge *Bournemouth*
Nash & Co *Plymouth*
Sansbury Hill *Bristol*
Stephens & Scown *St Austell*
Stones *Exeter*
Veale Wasbrough *Bristol*
Wansbroughs *Bristol*
Wolferstans *Plymouth*

Crime
SOUTH WEST

Andrews McQueen *Bournemouth*
Bishop Longbotham & Bagnall *Trowbridge*
Bobbetts *Bristol*
Crosse & Crosse *Exeter*
Ford Simey & Ford *Exeter*
Stones *Exeter*
Townsends *Swindon*
Veale Wasbrough *Bristol*
Wolferstans *Plymouth*
Woollcombe Watts *Newton Abbot*

Bath, **Veale Wasbrough** *Bristol*, **Wolferstans** *Plymouth*, **Crosse & Crosse** *Exeter*, **Bishop Longbotham & Bagnall** *Trowbridge*, **Ford Simey & Ford** *Exeter*, **Stones** *Exeter*, and **Townsends** *Swindon*. Other names are **Gordon & Penney** *Weston super Mare*, **Clutton Moore & Lavington** *Bristol*, and **Bretherton & Price** *Cheltenham*.

To this list we would add the more well-known firms of **Bond Pearce** *Plymouth*, **Foot & Bowden** *Plymouth*, **Gill Akaster** *Plymouth*, **JW Ward & Son** *Bristol*, and the smaller firm of **Thralls** *Truro*.

Agriculture: In our view **Burges Salmon** *Bristol* can claim to have one of the strongest agricultural departments in England and Wales. In fact, we would suggest that it is the leading agricultural firm nationally. Certainly we have no hesitation in recommending it for agricultural work. Also strong is **Bevan Ashford** *West Country*. Other firms to mention in this regard are **Clarke Willmott & Clarke** *Taunton*, **Stephens & Scown** *St Austell*, and the two Salisbury firms of **Trethowans** and **Wilsons**. Other suggestions include **Hancock & Lawrence** *Truro*, **Peter Peter & Wright** *Holsworthy*, **Slee Blackwell** *Braunton*, and **Thrings & Long** *Bath*.

Firms going from strength to strength:

It is always difficult to pick out a few names that are generally seen as going from strength to strength. But, in response to our enquiries, the general reaction has been to name **Osborne Clarke** *Bristol*, although there is also strong support for **Burges Salmon** *Bristol* and **Bevan Ashford** *West Country*. Other names that frequently crop up include **Bond Pearce** *Plymouth*, **Veale Wasbrough** *Bristol*, and **Clarke Willmott & Clarke** *Taunton*. Of the smaller practices, **Holt Phillips** *Bristol* seems to be particularly well regarded.

The West Midlands

Not surprisingly, it is the Birmingham firms that dominate the region. There are two firms that have more than 300 staff — **Evershed & Tomkinson** and **Edge & Ellison**. Both are basically the same size (with **Evershed & Tomkinson** being marginally larger — although one should not read too much into the figures!).

Otherwise there are two particularly large firms — **Wragge & Co** (300 staff) and **Needham & James** (250 staff). Next is **Pinsent & Co**, which is followed by a group of firms with between 100 and 150 total staff. These are **Blakemores** *Coventry*, **Glaisyers** *Birmingham*, **Morton Fisher** *Kidderminster*, **Haden Stretton Slater Miller**

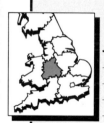

WEST MIDLANDS: Top firms by total number of staff

		Total staff	Partners	Assistant solicitors	Articled clerks
1	Evershed & Tomkinson *Birmingham*	322	32	66	40
2	Edge & Ellison *Birmingham*	320	30	50	16
3	Wragge & Co *Birmingham*	300	26	60	21
4	Needham & James *Birmingham*	250	28	26	15
5	Pinsent & Co *Birmingham*	194	27	37	20
6	Blakemores *Coventry*	146	20	11	6
7	Morton Fisher *Kidderminster*	140	20	16	6
8	Glaisyers *Birmingham*	140	20	13	8
9	Haden Stretton Slater Miller *Walsall*	138	13	10	3
10	Lanyon Bowdler *Shrewsbury*	137	17	6	4
11	Cartwright & Lewis Vernon & Shakespeare *Birmingham*	136	12	5	3
12	Martineau Johnson *Birmingham*	130	22	13	11
13	Blythe Liggins *Leamington Spa*	130	12	4	4
14	Rowley Ashworth *Birmingham*	127	9	5	2
15	Sydney Mitchell & Co *Birmingham*	110	10	5	4
16	Manby & Steward *Wolverhampton*	106	16	5	6
17	Goodger Auden *Burton on Trent*	105	15	7	3
18	Alsters Partnership *Birmingham*	104	11	7	5
19	Shakespeare Duggan Lea & Co *Birmingham*	103	15	8	8
20	Foster Baxter Cooksey *Wolverhampton*	90	15	4	8
21	Thursfield Adams & Westons *Kidderminster*	85	15	2	4
22	Higgs & Sons *Brierley Hill*	84	14	6	4
23	Darbey-Scott-Rees *Bilston*	82	12	2	7
24	R Gwynne & Sons *Wellington*	81	10	5	2
25	Rutherfords *Tamworth*	80	13	2	2

Company
WEST MIDLANDS

Edge & Ellison *Birmingham*
Evershed & Tomkinson *Birmingham*
Keely Smith & Jobson *Lichfield*
Knight & Sons *Newcastle under Lyme*
Manby & Steward *Wolverhampton*
Martineau Johnson *Birmingham*
Needham & James *Birmingham*
Pinsent & Co *Birmingham*
Rees Edwards Maddox & Co *Birmingham*
Wragge & Co *Birmingham*

Walsall, **Lanyon Bowdler** *Shrewsbury*, **Cartwright & Lewis** Vernon & **Shakespeare** *Birmingham*, **Martineau Johnson** *Birmingham*, **Blythe Liggins** *Leamington Spa*, **Rowley Ashworth** *Birmingham*, **Sydney Mitchell & Co** *Birmingham*, **Manby & Steward** *Wolverhampton*, **Goodger Auden** *Burton on Trent*, **Alsters Partnership** *Birmingham*, and **Shakespeare Duggan Lea & Co** *Birmingham*. Of these, **Rowley Ashworth** *Birmingham* has relatively few partners compared to its overall staff size.

Company and commercial: Our top six commercial firms in the West Midlands are all of undoubted strength – and all are in Birmingham. The two firms that we rate most highly, and to whom we give equal prominence, are **Evershed & Tomkinson** and **Wragge & Co**. The other firms in this group are **Pinsent & Co**, **Martineau Johnson**, **Edge & Ellison**, and **Needham & James**.

Other firms that are highly recommended – if not so well known – are **Knight & Sons** *Newcastle under Lyme*, **Manby & Steward** *Wolverhampton*, **Rees Edwards Maddox & Co** *Birmingham*, and **Keely Smith & Jobson** *Lichfield*. In addition, we would recommend **Blythe Liggins** *Leamington Spa*, **George Green & Co** *Cradley Heath*, **Blakemores** *Coventry*, **Glaisyers**

Birmingham, **Haden Stretton Slater Miller** *Walsall*, and **Rigbeys** *Birmingham*.

All of our top six commercial firms are relatively strong on employment matters; there seems to be little to choose between them. Similarly with licensing, all the major firms can be recommended – although, if one is looking for a small practice, one suggestion might be **Snape & Co** *Coventry*.

With regard to franchising, **Needham & James** *Birmingham* would seem to be in a class of its own; indeed, we would probably say that the firm is second only to **Adlers** *London* in the scope of its franchising work. Otherwise, we would suggest the other five major firms, plus **Glaisyers** – another Birmingham firm.

Commercial property: We would nominate three firms here: once again, all are in Birmingham – **Evershed & Tomkinson**, **Wragge & Co**, and **Pinsent & Co**. Other strong recommendations are **Knight & Sons** *Newcastle under Lyme*, **Martineau Johnson** *Birmingham*, **Manby & Steward** *Wolverhampton*, **Edge & Ellison** *Birmingham*, **Haden Stretton Slater Miller** *Walsall*, **Needham & James** *Birmingham*, and **Glaisyers** *Birmingham*. Other less well-known, but recommended, firms are

Commercial property
WEST MIDLANDS

Band Hatton & Co *Coventry*
Edge & Ellison *Birmingham*
Evershed & Tomkinson *Birmingham*
Glaisyers *Birmingham*
Haden Stretton Slater Miller *Walsall*
Knight & Sons *Newcastle under Lyme*
Manby & Steward *Wolverhampton*
Martineau Johnson *Birmingham*
Needham & James *Birmingham*
Newsome Vaughan & Co *Coventry*
Pinsent & Co *Birmingham*
Wragge & Co *Birmingham*

Planning
WEST MIDLANDS

Edge & Ellison *Birmingham*
Evershed & Tomkinson *Birmingham*
Knight & Sons *Newcastle under Lyme*
Pinsent & Co *Birmingham*
Wragge & Co *Birmingham*

Band Hatton & Co *Coventry*, Newsome Vaughan & Co *Coventry*, and Jagger Son & Tilley *Birmingham*.

In addition, we would mention Lanyon Bowdler *Shrewsbury*, Brindley Twist Tafft & James *Coventry*, Foster Baxter Cooksey *Wolverhampton*, Gaynor-Smith Owen & Co *Malvern*, George Green & Co *Cradley Heath*, Hatcher Rogerson *Wem*, and Martin-Kaye & Partners *Telford*.

Planning: As one would expect, it is the firms that are dominant in commercial property that are also strong on planning law. In this regard we would recommend Pinsent & Co, Evershed & Tomkinson, Edge & Ellison, Wragge & Co — all in Birmingham — and Knight & Sons *Newcastle under Lyme*. Frankly, we think there is little to choose between them. Most of the firms mentioned in commercial property could justifiably be included in this section; one small firm that has not been referred to so far and which might be of interest is Hammon & Co *Coventry*.

Commercial litigation: Once again it is Birmingham that dominates the region: Indeed, of the ten firms listed in our litigation table, seven are in Birmingham.

The general view is that Pinsent & Co is the top litigator in the region, followed by Evershed & Tomkinson and Wragge & Co. Also respected are Edge & Ellison, Martineau Johnson, Glaisyers, Needham & James, and Rutherfords *Tamworth*. Other

respected firms — although perhaps not as well known outside the region — are Varley Hibbs & Co *Coventry*, and Tinsdill Hollinshead & Moody *Stoke on Trent*. In addition, we would mention firms such as Blythe Liggins *Leamington Spa*, Cartwright & Lewis Vernon & Shakespeare *Birmingham*, Shakespeare Duggan Lea & Co *Birmingham*, George Green & Co *Cradley Heath*, Harris Cooper & Co *Solihull*, and finally Grindeys *Stoke on Trent*.

Building and construction litigation: Overall, it is the large Birmingham commercial litigation firms that dominate the more specialist area of building litigation. In particular, we would choose Wragge & Co, Evershed & Tomkinson, Pinsent & Co, Edge & Ellison, and Needham & James. One name that we have not mentioned so far is that of the relatively small Birmingham

Commercial litigation
WEST MIDLANDS

Edge & Ellison *Birmingham*
Evershed & Tomkinson *Birmingham*
Glaisyers *Birmingham*
Martineau Johnson *Birmingham*
Needham & James *Birmingham*
Pinsent & Co *Birmingham*
Rutherfords *Tamworth*
Tinsdill Hollinshead & Moody *Stoke on Trent*
Varley Hibbs & Co *Coventry*
Wragge & Co *Birmingham*

Construction
WEST MIDLANDS

Edge & Ellison. *Birmingham*
Evershed & Tomkinson *Birmingham*
Needham & James *Birmingham*
Neil F Jones & Co *Birmingham*
Pinsent & Co *Birmingham*
Wragge & Co *Birmingham*

Insolvency
WEST MIDLANDS

Edge & Ellison *Birmingham*
Evershed & Tomkinson *Birmingham*
Knight & Sons *Newcastle under Lyme*
Needham & James *Birmingham*
Pinsent & Co *Birmingham*
Whatley Weston & Fox *Worcester*
Wragge & Co *Birmingham*

firm, **Neil F Jones & Co**, which is particularly well regarded for its building litigation work. Also we would mention **Hacking Ashton Jervis & Co** *Newcastle under Lyme*.

Insolvency and debt collection: Once again, it is Birmingham that dominates. **Edge & Ellison** is clearly regarded as the leading firm for insolvency work, along with **Wragge & Co** and **Pinsent & Co**. After that trio we would recommend **Knight & Sons** *Newcastle under Lyme*, **Evershed & Tomkinson** *Birmingham*, **Needham & James** *Birmingham*, and **Whatley Weston & Fox** *Worcester*. Also suggested are **Blair Allison & Co** *Birmingham* and **Band Hatton & Co** *Coventry*.

For the less specialised work of debt collection we would add the names of **Bettinsons** *Birmingham*, **Brindley Twist Tafft & James** *Coventry*, **Goodger Auden** *Burton on Trent*, as well as **Hatcher Rogerson** *Wem*, and **Herbert Wilkes** *Birmingham*.

Intellectual property: As one would expect, most of the large commercial firms are strong in this area of work. Having said that, **Pinsent & Co** is generally regarded as being the most respected name in this particular field. Otherwise the recommended firms are **Needham & James**, **Evershed & Tomkinson**, **Wragge & Co**, **Edge & Ellison** (all in Birmingham), as well as **Shakespeare**

Duggan Lea & Co *Birmingham*, **Glaisyers** *Birmingham*, **Knight & Sons** *Newcastle under Lyme*, **Goodger Auden** *Burton on Trent*, and **Hacking Ashton Jervis & Co** *Newcastle under Lyme*.

For entertainment law the lead firms would seem to be **Pinsent & Co**, **Evershed & Tomkinson**, and **Needham & James**. Having said that, any of the other large commercial firms could probably advise in this area; as we have mentioned elsewhere, the real point is that entertainment expertise is difficult to find outside the specialist London firms.

Tax: Once again **Pinsent & Co** leads the field — in the same way that it does with intellectual property. Otherwise we would suggest that the lead firms are **Evershed & Tomkinson**, **Wragge & Co**, **Edge & Ellison**, **Glaisyers** and **Martineau Johnson**. All are in Birmingham.

Intellectual property
WEST MIDLANDS

Edge & Ellison *Birmingham*
Evershed & Tomkinson *Birmingham*
Glaisyers *Birmingham*
Hacking Ashton Jervis & Co *Newcastle under Lyme*
Knight & Sons *Newcastle under Lyme*
Needham & James *Birmingham*
Pinsent & Co *Birmingham*
Shakespeare Duggan Lea & Co *Birmingham*
Wragge & Co *Birmingham*

Tax
WEST MIDLANDS

Edge & Ellison *Birmingham*
Evershed & Tomkinson *Birmingham*
Glaisyers *Birmingham*
Martineau Johnson *Birmingham*
Pinsent & Co *Birmingham*
Wragge & Co *Birmingham*

Family
WEST MIDLANDS

Blair Allison & Co *Birmingham*
Edge & Ellison *Birmingham*
Evershed & Tomkinson *Birmingham*
Glaisyers *Birmingham*
Knight & Sons *Newcastle under Lyme*
Mander Hadley & Co *Coventry*
Martineau Johnson *Birmingham*
Wallace Robinson & Morgan *Birmingham*

Family: Family and matrimonial law is not the exclusive province of the large firms; accordingly, we are able to recommend many smaller firms, including those with mainly legal aid practices. One of our top two firms is unusually small – with only three partners. It is, however, a firm that has made a name in the specialist area of matrimonial law and, in particular, on negotiating the financial aspects of divorce. It is **Blair Allison & Co** *Birmingham*. Our other leading firm is **Glaisyers** *Birmingham*. Other leading matrimonial practices are **Knight & Sons** *Newcastle under Lyme*, **Martineau Johnson** *Birmingham*, **Edge & Ellison** *Birmingham*, **Wallace Robinson & Morgan** *Birmingham*, **Evershed & Tomkinson** *Birmingham*, and **Mander Hadley & Co** *Coventry*. Other suggestions include **Blythe Liggins** *Leamington Spa*, **Goodger Auden** *Burton on Trent*, **Manby & Steward** *Wolverhampton*, **The Smith Partnership** *Burton on Trent*, **Brendan Fleming & Co** *Birmingham*, **Challinor & Roberts** *Warley*, **Parkinson Wright** *Worcester*, and **Young & Lee** *Birmingham*.

Personal injury litigation: It is difficult to nominate an individual firm as being dominant in personal injury work in the West Midlands. Rather, it is a case of there being several firms that have acquired a good sound reputation. For instance, **Edge & Ellison** *Birmingham*, **Pinsent & Co** *Birmingham*, the smaller **Tinsdill Hollinshead & Moody** *Stoke on Trent*, and **Buller Jeffries** *Birmingham* are firms that are frequently mentioned. So also are the names of **Evershed & Tomkinson** *Birmingham*, **Cartwright & Lewis Vernon & Shakespeare** *Birmingham*, **Wright Hassall & Co** *Leamington Spa*, **Rowley Ashworth** *Birmingham*, **Glaisyers** *Birmingham* – and, of course, one should not forget the Birmingham office of **Robin Thompson & Partners**. There are, however, many other firms with personal injury expertise and we would not suggest that this is a comprehensive list. For instance, there are firms such as **Rutherfords** *Tamworth*, **William F Hatton & Co** *Dudley*, **R Gwynne & Sons** *Wellington*, **George Green & Co** *Cradley Heath*, **Foster Baxter Cooksey** *Wolverhampton*, and **Cocks Lloyd & Co** *Nuneaton*.

Crime: Criminal law is generally the province of the smaller firms, especially those which are prepared to make a living from legal aid. Having said that, our lead firm does not come into this category – it is one of the larger firms in the region and also has a significant commercial practice. It is **Glaisyers** *Birmingham*. Other recommended firms are **Mander Hadley & Co** *Coventry*, **George Jonas & Co**

Personal injury
WEST MIDLANDS

Buller Jeffries *Birmingham*
Cartwright & Lewis Vernon & Shakespeare *Birmingham*
Edge & Ellison *Birmingham*
Evershed & Tomkinson *Birmingham*
Glaisyers *Birmingham*
Pinsent & Co *Birmingham*
Robin Thompson & Partners *Birmingham*
Rowley Ashworth *Birmingham*
Tinsdill Hollinshead & Moody *Stoke on Trent*
Wright Hassall & Co *Leamington Spa*

Crime
WEST MIDLANDS

Cartwright & Lewis Vernon & Shakespeare *Birmingham*
Curtler & Hallmark *Worcester*
George Jonas & Co *Birmingham*
Glaisyers *Birmingham*
Mander Hadley & Co *Coventry*
Maurice Putsman & Co *Birmingham*
The Smith Partnership *Burton on Trent*
Tinsdill Hollinshead & Moody *Stoke on Trent*
Varley Hibbs & Co *Coventry*
Wallace Robinson & Morgan *Birmingham*

Birmingham, **The Smith Partnership** *Burton on Trent*, **Maurice Putsman & Co** *Birmingham*, **Tinsdill Hollinshead & Moody** *Stoke on Trent*, **Cartwright & Lewis Vernon & Shakespeare** *Birmingham*, **Wallace Robinson & Morgan** *Birmingham*, **Curtler & Hallmark** *Worcester*, and **Varley Hibbs & Co** *Coventry*. Other suggestions include **Challinor & Roberts** *Warley*, **Grindeys** *Stoke on Trent*, **R Gwynne & Sons** *Wellington*, **Brown & Corbishley** *Newcastle under Lyme*, **Goodger Auden** *Burton on Trent*, **McMillan Bennett** *Telford*, **Parkinson Wright** *Worcester*, and **Young & Co** *Stoke on Trent*.

Firms going from strength to strength:

It is Birmingham that dominates the region. The indications we have received are that **Evershed & Tomkinson** is generally perceived as the front-runner, although some would say that this is largely a by-product of the publicity that the creation of **Eversheds** has received. Be that as it may, **Evershed & Tomkinson** heads our list. **Wragge & Co** and **Pinsent & Co** have similar areas of practice, and are clearly in direct competition, although **Wragge & Co** would seem to be more generally favoured.

Otherwise, firms such as **Edge & Ellison**, **Needham & James**, **Martineau Johnson**, and **Shakespeare Duggan Lea & Co** all have their supporters.

The East Midlands

Here the dominant firm is **Shoosmiths & Harrison** *Northampton* — it has considerably more total staff (and partners) than its rivals. Its largest competitor is **Howes Percival** *Northampton*, and these two are easily the biggest firms within the region. Next come **Toller Hales & Collcutt** *Northampton*, **Wells & Hind** *Nottingham*, **Hunt Dickins** *Nottingham*, **Ironsides Ray & Vials** *Northampton*, **Flint Bishop & Barnett** *Derby*, **Harvey Ingram Stone & Simpson** *Leicester*, **Roythorne & Co** *Spalding*, **Truman Close Kendall & Appelby** *Grantham*, and **Browne Jacobson** *Nottingham*. Also with more than 100 staff are **Bray & Bray** *Leicester* and **Becke Phipps** *Northampton*. Of these, **Truman Close Kendall & Appelby** *Grantham* has relatively few partners in relation to its overall size; other firms with a low partnership ratio are **Chattertons** *Horncastle*, **Langleys** *Lincoln*, and **Franklins** *Northampton*.

EAST MIDLANDS: Top firms by total number of staff

		Total staff	Partners	Assistant solicitors	Articled clerks
1	Shoosmiths & Harrison *Northampton*	340	43	23	14
2	Howes Percival *Northampton*	260	27	14	10
3	Toller Hales & Collcutt *Northampton*	175	21	10	12
4	Wells & Hind *Nottingham*	135	17	24	6
5	Hunt Dickins *Nottingham*	127	18	11	9
6	Ironsides Ray & Vials *Northampton*	126	20	0	6
7	Flint Bishop & Barnett *Derby*	115	16	10	4
8	Harvey Ingram Stone & Simpson *Leicester*	110	20	6	6
9	Roythorne & Co *Spalding*	110	15	10	2
10	Truman Close Kendall & Appelby *Nottingham*	107	9	9	2
11	Browne Jacobson *Nottingham*	105	14	16	6
12	Bray & Bray *Leicester*	104	17	5	1
13	Becke Phipps *Northampton*	103	13	12	4
14	Chattertons *Horncastle*	98	7	7	3
15	Langleys *Lincoln*	98	7	6	3
16	Wilson & Wilson *Kettering*	94	15	5	4
17	Tallents Godfrey & Co *Newark*	91	12	3	2
18	Elliot Mather Smith *Chesterfield*	90	12	5	1
19	Shacklocks *Nottingham*	88	13	3	3
20	Franklins *Northampton*	87	5	4	2

Company
EAST MIDLANDS

Becke Phipps *Northampton*
Browne Jacobson *Nottingham*
Gadsby Coxon & Copestake *Derby*
Harvey Ingram Stone & Simpson *Leicester*
Howes Percival *Northampton*
Hunt Dickins *Nottingham*
Roythorne & Co *Spalding*
Shoosmiths & Harrison *Northampton*
Toller Hales & Collcutt *Northampton*
Wells & Hind *Nottingham*

Company and commercial: Our first two choices here may seem somewhat surprising — **Wells & Hind** *Nottingham* and **Becke Phipps** *Northampton*. However, we received a significant number of recommendations for both firms, and both have a strong reputation. Indeed, there is a strength in company and commercial work within the East Midlands. Thus other names that we would mention include **Roythorne & Co** *Spalding*, **Shoosmiths & Harrison** *Northampton*, and **Harvey Ingram Stone & Simpson** *Leicester*. Also there is **Hunt Dickins** *Nottingham*, **Browne Jacobson** *Nottingham*, **Howes Percival** *Northampton*, **Toller Hales & Collcutt** *Northampton*, as well as **Gadsby Coxon & Copestake** *Derby*. Other firms suggested include **J & WH Sale & Son** *Derby*, **Wilson & Wilson** *Kettering*, **Taylor Simpson & Mosley** *Derby*; for smaller firms, mention might be made of **Thomas Flavell & Sons** *Hinckley*, **Bennett Brooke-Taylor & Wright** *Buxton*, and the one-partner firm of **Oliver & Co** *Lincoln*.

For employment law, we would make special mention of **Howes Percival** *Northampton*, **Becke Phipps** *Northampton*, **Toller Hales & Collcutt** *Northampton*, and especially **Rotheras** *Nottingham* (which is also well known for road haulage and transport matters).

On the licensing front our suggestions include **Cutts and Shiers** *Chesterfield*, **Harvey Ingram Stone & Simpson** *Leicester*, **Hunt Dickins** *Nottingham*, **Ironsides Ray & Vials** *Northampton*, and **Shacklocks** *Nottingham*.

Commercial property: Amongst leading property firms we find **Wells & Hind** *Nottingham*, **Shoosmiths & Harrison** *Northampton*, **Becke Phipps** *Northampton*, and **Roythorne & Co** *Spalding*. Also strong are **Staunton Townsend** *Leicester* (now merging with **Edge & Ellison** *Birmingham*), **Howes Percival** *Northampton*, **Franklins** *Northampton*, **Flint Bishop & Barnett** *Derby*, **Toller Hales & Collcutt** *Northampton*, and we would also include **Dennis Faulkner & Alsop** *Northampton*.

Other suggestions are **Harvey Ingram Stone & Simpson** *Leicester*, **Taylor Simpson & Mosley** *Derby*, **Freeth Cartwright & Sketchley** *Nottingham*, and **Hunt Dickins** *Nottingham*.

Planning: As always, firms that are strong in commercial property are also likely to be relatively strong in town and country planning. In particular, we would mention **Shoosmiths & Harrison** *Northampton*, **Browne Jacobson** *Nottingham*, **Dennis Faulkner & Alsop** *Northampton*, **Howes Percival** *Northampton*, **Becke Phipps** *Northampton*, **Roythorne & Co** *Spalding*,

Commercial property
EAST MIDLANDS

Becke Phipps *Northampton*
Browne Jacobson *Nottingham*
Dennis Faulkner & Alsop *Northampton*
Flint Bishop & Barnett *Derby*
Franklins *Northampton*
Harvey Ingram Stone & Simpson *Leicester*
Howes Percival *Northampton*
Roythorne & Co *Spalding*
Shoosmiths & Harrison *Northampton*
Staunton Townsend *Leicester*
Wells & Hind *Nottingham*

Planning
EAST MIDLANDS

Becke Phipps *Northampton*
Browne Jacobson *Nottingham*
Chattertons *Horncastle*
Crane & Walton *Leicester*
Dennis Faulkner & Alsop *Northampton*
Howes Percival *Northampton*
R G Frisby & Small *Leicester*
Roythorne & Co *Spalding*
Shoosmiths & Harrison *Northampton*

and **Chattertons** *Horncastle*. Other suggestions include **Crane & Walton** *Leicester*, **Staunton Townsend** *Leicester*, **Gadsby Coxon & Copestake** *Derby*, as well as the less obvious choices of **RG Frisby & Small** *Leicester*, and **Marron Dodds & Waite** *Leicester*.

Commercial litigation: Here we put forward the names of **Browne Jacobson** *Nottingham* and **Shoosmiths & Harrison** *Northampton*. Other leading firms include **Wells & Hind** *Nottingham*, **Becke Phipps** *Northampton*, **Roythorne & Co** *Spalding*, **Harvey Ingram Stone & Simpson** *Leicester*, **Actons** *Nottingham*, **Flint Bishop & Barnett** *Derby*, **Howes Percival** *Northampton*, and **Toller Hales & Collcutt** *Northampton*. Other suggested names are **Ironsides Ray & Vials** *Northampton*, **Hunt Dickins** *Nottingham*, and **Dennis Faulkner & Alsop** *Northampton*. For those who prefer smaller firms we would include **Robinsons** *Ilkeston*, **Smeath Mann & Co** *Northampton*, and **Oliver & Co** *Lincoln*.

As far as building and construction litigation is concerned, we would pick **Browne Jacobson** *Nottingham*, **Shoosmiths & Harrison** *Northampton*, **Howes Percival** *Northampton*, **Harvey Ingram Stone & Simpson** *Leicester*, and **Hunt Dickins** *Nottingham*. Other suggestions would include **Roythorne & Co** *Spalding*, **Wells & Hind** *Nottingham*, **Bray & Bray** *Leicester*,

Flint Bishop & Barnett *Derby*, **Dennis Faulkner & Alsop** *Northampton*, and we would also add **Freeth Cartwright & Sketchley** *Nottingham*.

Insolvency and debt collection:
Actons *Nottingham* is a relatively small practice when compared with some of the other major commercial firms in the East Midlands. However, it is a leading insolvency practice. Other strong names include **Shoosmiths & Harrison** *Northampton*, **Flint Bishop & Barnett** *Derby*, **Wells & Hind** *Nottingham*, **Becke Phipps** *Northampton*, **Hunt Dickins** *Nottingham*, **Roythorne & Co** *Spalding*, **Shacklocks** *Nottingham*, and, of course, **Howes Percival** *Northampton*. In addition, we would mention firms such as **Browne Jacobson** *Nottingham*, **Chattertons** *Horncastle*, **Harvey Ingram Stone &**

Commercial litigation
EAST MIDLANDS

Actons *Nottingham*
Becke Phipps *Northampton*
Browne Jacobson *Nottingham*
Flint Bishop & Barnett *Derby*
Harvey Ingram Stone & Simpson *Leicester*
Howes Percival *Northampton*
Roythorne & Co *Spalding*
Shoosmiths & Harrison *Northampton*
Toller Hales & Collcutt *Northampton*
Wells & Hind *Nottingham*

Insolvency
EAST MIDLANDS

Actons *Nottingham*
Becke Phipps *Northampton*
Flint Bishop & Barnett *Derby*
Howes Percival *Northampton*
Hunt Dickins *Nottingham*
Roythorne & Co *Spalding*
Shacklocks *Nottingham*
Shoosmiths & Harrison *Northampton*
Wells & Hind *Nottingham*

Simpson *Leicester*, and **Ironsides Ray & Vials** *Leicester*. Not to be forgotten are **Wells & Hind** *Nottingham*, **Owston & Co** *Leicester*, and the less well-known firms of **Ashton Hill Bond** *Nottingham*, **Eking Manning** *Nottingham*, and **Eddowes Waldron & Cash** *Derby*.

Virtually all of these firms are experienced in debt collection matters. Perhaps we should also mention **Toller Hales & Collcutt** *Northampton* and **Franklins** *Northampton*. In addition, there is **Curtis & Parkinson** *Nottingham*, which is particularly adept at mortgage repossessions.

Intellectual property: We have little hesitation in putting forward **Wells & Hind** *Nottingham* for intellectual property. They are generally perceived to be particularly strong in this area.

For entertainment law we would suggest **Shoosmiths & Harrison** *Northampton*. In general, however, we do not believe there is any great breadth of expertise in entertainment practice within the East Midlands — it is a field of law in which the London firms still reign supreme.

Tax: Our suggestions here are **Wells & Hind** *Nottingham*, **Roythorne & Co** *Spalding*, **Shoosmiths & Harrison** *Northampton*, **Browne Jacobson** *Nottingham*, and **Howes Percival** *Northampton*. In addition, we might suggest **Chattertons** *Horncastle*, **Harvey Ingram Stone & Simpson** *Leicester*, and the smaller practice of **Thomas Flavell & Sons** *Hinckley*.

Tax
EAST MIDLANDS

Browne Jacobson *Nottingham*
Howes Percival *Northampton*
Roythorne & Co *Spalding*
Shoosmiths & Harrison *Northampton*
Wells & Hind *Nottingham*

Family
EAST MIDLANDS

Blakesley & Rooth *Chesterfield*
Dennis Faulkner & Alsop *Northampton*
Flint Bishop & Barnett *Derby*
Hollis Briggs Booth & Ashworth *Derby*
Hunt Dickins *Nottingham*
Ironsides Ray & Vials *Northampton*
Roythorne & Co *Spalding*
Shoosmiths & Harrison *Northampton*
Timms *Swadlincote*
Warren & Allen *Nottingham*
Wells & Hind *Nottingham*

Family: There are relatively few firms that do not do family and matrimonial law. Even most of the large commercial firms have a family department; in this respect it is different from criminal law which seems to have been abandoned by many of the larger commercial firms.

Our list of suggested family practitioners is, therefore, a mixture of the larger and smaller firms. For instance, there is **Blakesley & Rooth** *Chesterfield*, **Wells & Hind** *Nottingham*, **Dennis Faulkner & Alsop** *Northampton*, **Hollis Briggs Booth & Ashworth** *Derby*, **Ironsides Ray & Vials** *Northampton*, **Hunt Dickins** *Nottingham*, **Warren & Allen** *Nottingham*, **Shoosmiths & Harrison** *Northampton*, **Timms** *Swadlincote*, **Flint Bishop & Barnett** *Derby*, and **Roythorne & Co** *Spalding*.

In addition, there are firms such as **Banner Jones & Hawkins** *Chesterfield*, **German & Soar** *Nottingham*, **Nelsons** *Nottingham*, **Toller Hales & Collcutt** *Northampton*, and **Truman Close Kendall & Appelby** *Grantham*. There are also other firms such as **Bailey Morgan & Co** *Skegness* and **Franklins** *Northampton*. There really is a wide range of firms doing matrimonial law.

Personal injury litigation: The two firms we specially mentioned for commercial litigation were **Browne**

Jacobson *Nottingham* and **Shoosmiths & Harrison** *Northampton*. At the risk of being boringly repetitive, we suggest the same two firms as the leading personal injury practices in the region!

However, there are other major firms that should be mentioned. For instance, there is **Robin Thompson & Partners** *Nottingham*, **Flint Bishop & Barnett** *Derby*, **Howes Percival** *Northampton*, **Ironsides Ray & Vials** *Northampton*, and **Langleys** *Lincoln*. One should also not forget **Toller Hales & Collcutt** *Northampton*. There is the smaller firm of **Dennis Faulkner & Alsop** *Northampton*, plus firms such as **Rotheras** *Nottingham*, **Harvey Ingram Stone & Simpson** *Leicester*, **Franklins** *Northampton*, **German & Soar** *Nottingham*, and **Hunt Dickins** *Nottingham*.

Crime: As always, it is the smaller (and relatively unheard-of firms) that dominate criminal practice. Of the large commercial practices in the East Midlands, **Hunt Dickins** *Nottingham* is one of the few that still has an extensive criminal legal aid practice. Several of the other commercial firms have withdrawn from crime — or, at least, from legal aid crime. Firms to be mentioned include **Dennis Faulkner & Alsop** *Northampton*, **Woodford Robinson Williams & Co** *Northampton*, **Nelsons** *Nottingham*, **Eddowes Waldron & Cash**

Crime
EAST MIDLANDS

Dennis Faulkner & Alsop *Northampton*
Eddowes Waldron & Cash *Derby*
Hawley & Rodgers *Loughborough*
Nelsons *Nottingham*
Rotheras *Nottingham*
Roythorne & Co *Spalding*
Toller Hales & Collcutt *Northampton*
Truman Close Kendall & Appelby *Nottingham*
Wells & Hind *Nottingham*
Woodford Robinson Williams & Co *Northampton*

Construction
EAST MIDLANDS

Browne Jacobson *Nottingham*
Harvey Ingram Stone & Simpson *Leicester*
Howes Percival *Northampton*
Hunt Dickins *Nottingham*
Shoosmiths & Harrison *Northampton*

Derby, **Toller Hales & Collcutt** *Northampton*, **Wells & Hind** *Nottingham*, **Hawley & Rodgers** *Loughborough*, **Rotheras** *Nottingham*, **Truman Close Kendall & Appelby** *Nottingham*, **Roythorne & Co** *Spalding*, and **Tallents Godfrey & Co** *Newark*. Other firms worthy of mention include **Banner Jones & Hawkins** *Chesterfield* and **Elliot Mather Smith** *Chesterfield*.

Agriculture: We put forward the names of **Howes Percival** *Northampton*, **Shoosmiths & Harrison** *Northampton*, **Roythorne & Co** *Spalding*, **Hunt Dickins** *Nottingham*, **Tallents Godfrey & Co** *Newark*, and **Becke Phipps** *Northampton*.

Firms going from strength to strength:

The firm most frequently mentioned as likely to go from strength to strength is

---

Personal injury
EAST MIDLANDS

Browne Jacobson *Nottingham*
Flint Bishop & Barnett *Derby*
Freeth Cartwright & Sketchley *Nottingham*
Howes Percival *Northampton*
Ironsides Ray & Vials *Northampton*
Langleys *Lincoln*
Robin Thompson & Partners *Nottingham*
Shoosmiths & Harrison *Northampton*
Toller Hales & Collcutt *Northampton*

Howes Percival *Northampton.* The firm certainly has a higher public profile than many of its rivals in the East Midlands, but we believe its reputation is firmly based. Certainly, the general perception is that it is a firm that will go from strength to strength in the years to come. Otherwise, our two main contenders are **Wells & Hind** *Nottingham* and **Becke Phipps** *Northampton.* However, there are other strong firms as well — for instance, **Shoosmiths & Harrison** *Northampton,* **Roythorne & Co** *Spalding,* **Browne Jacobson** *Nottingham,* **Hunt Dickins** *Nottingham,* and **Langleys** *Lincoln.* Amongst the smaller firms **Dennis Faulkner & Alsop** *Northampton* should be noted.

East Anglia

There are two firms that dominate the legal scene in East Anglia: **Mills & Reeve Francis** *Norwich* and **Daynes Hill & Perks** *Norwich*. Both have a national reputation, and both are of considerable size. In terms of numbers of total staff (and numbers of partners) the firms are virtually the same, although **Daynes Hill & Perks** is slightly the larger. Interestingly, however, **Mills & Reeve Francis** employs more assistant solicitors and has the greater number of qualified lawyers. In any event, the size distinctions are small: both firms are well regarded.

In terms of size, the third and fourth largest firms in the region are **Wild Hewitson & Shaw** *Cambridge* and **Taylor Vinters** *Cambridge*. After them there is a batch of firms (all with between 100 and 150 staff) comprising **Winter Wilkinson** *Huntingdon*, **Greenwoods** *Peterborough*, **Birketts** *Ipswich*, and **Prettys** *Ipswich*. Next (with fewer than 100 staff) are **Hegarty & Co** *Peterborough*, **Overbury Steward & Eaton** *Norwich*, **Buckle Mellows** *Peterborough*, **Steele & Co** *Diss*, **Bankes Ashton** *Bury St Edmunds*, **Ward, Gethin &**

EAST ANGLIA: Top firms by total number of staff

		Total staff	Partners	Assistant solicitors	Articled clerks
1	Daynes Hill & Perks *Norwich*	304	46	29	15
2	Mills & Reeve Francis *Norwich*	300	43	42	10
3	Wild Hewitson & Shaw *Cambridge*	170	27	14	7
4	Taylor Vinters *Cambridge*	165	21	18	9
5	Winter Wilkinson *Huntingdon*	130	16	8	4
6	Greenwoods *Peterborough*	114	13	6	6
7	Birketts *Ipswich*	110	14	4	2
8	Prettys *Ipswich*	105	13	8	5
9	Hegarty & Co *Peterborough*	87	9	4	5
10	Overbury Steward & Eaton *Norwich*	85	12	8	3
11	Buckle Mellows *Peterborough*	85	12	4	3
12	Steele & Co *Diss*	82	10	0	0
13	Bankes Ashton *Bury St Edmunds*	80	16	4	4
14	Ward, Gethin & Co *King's Lynn*	80	12	1	1
15	Gotelee & Goldsmith *Ipswich*	80	9	6	0
16	Westhorp Ward & Catchpole *Ipswich*	78	14	2	2
17	Metcalfe, Copeman & Pettefar *Wisbech*	78	12	6	2
18	Greenland Houchen *Norwich*	78	5	7	0
19	Kenneth Bush & Co *King's Lynn*	73	12	1	1
20	Blocks *Ipswich*	67	9	3	2

Co *King's Lynn*, and **Gotelee & Goldsmith** *Ipswich.*

Refer to the accompanying table for a full list of firms by total staff. Once again, we would point out that we prefer to rely upon total staff figures when deciding on the relative size of firms; the alternative is to look at the number of partners within the firm, but this can be misleading. For instance, by partnership size **Hegarty & Co** *Peterborough* is only the 20th largest firm in the region, but when you look at total staff it is the ninth largest.

Finally, a word about **Winter Wilkinson** *Huntingdon.* Unfortunately, this was virtually the only major law firm in England and Wales that declined to provide us with up-to-date background information about itself; thus the staffing and other figures that we quote for that firm may be out of date. More importantly, the firm did not supply us with information about the nature of its practice; this, coupled with the fact that the firm did not feature in the results of our surveys, means that we have been unable to refer to the firm in the accompanying text.

Company and commercial: There is little doubt that **Mills & Reeve Francis** *Norwich* is the lead firm for company and commercial work. The second place must, however, go to **Daynes Hill & Perks** *Norwich.* These two lead the field

---

Commercial property
EAST ANGLIA

Birketts *Ipswich*
Daynes Hill & Perks *Norwich*
Few & Kester *Cambridge*
Gotelee & Goldsmith *Ipswich*
Greenwoods *Peterborough*
Mills & Reeve Francis *Norwich*
Overbury Steward & Eaton *Norwich*
Southwells *Wisbech*
Taylor Vinters *Cambridge*
Wild Hewitson & Shaw *Cambridge*

---

comfortably — and, indeed, both can claim to be nationally known as commercial practices. Other leading company and commercial firms within the region include **Taylor Vinters** *Cambridge*, **Greenwoods** *Peterborough*, **Birketts** *Ipswich*, and **Wild Hewitson & Shaw** *Cambridge*. We might also mention **Nicholson Cadge & Gilbert** *Lowestoft* and **Greene & Greene** *Bury St Edmunds.* In addition, there are firms such as **Ward, Gethin & Co** *King's Lynn*, **Bankes Ashton** *Bury St Edmunds*, **Gotelee & Goldsmith** *Ipswich*, **Cozens-Hardy & Jewson** *Norwich*, **Westhorp Ward & Catchpole** *Ipswich*, and also the smaller firm of **Palmer Wheeldon** *Cambridge*. For those who want an even smaller practice, one might try **Henniker-Major** *Ipswich*.

As regards employment law, mention should be made of **Wild Hewitson & Shaw** *Cambridge*, although it has to be said that the larger firms mentioned above are also experienced in employment matters. As far as licensing is concerned, specific mention should be made of **Mills & Reeve Francis** *Norwich* and **Overbury Steward & Eaton** *Norwich*; a less obvious name here is **Norton Peskett & Forward** *Lowestoft*.

Commercial property: **Mills & Reeve Francis** *Norwich* is our choice here. Also highly recommended are **Daynes Hill & Perks** *Norwich* and **Birketts** *Ipswich*. Other

---

Company
EAST ANGLIA

Birketts *Ipswich*
Daynes Hill & Perks *Norwich*
Greene & Greene *Bury St Edmunds*
Greenwoods *Peterborough*
Mills & Reeve Francis *Norwich*
Nicholson Cadge & Gilbert *Lowestoft*
Taylor Vinters *Cambridge*
Wild Hewitson & Shaw *Cambridge*

strong firms include **Wild Hewitson & Shaw** *Cambridge*, **Greenwoods** *Peterborough*, **Taylor Vinters** *Cambridge*, and also firms such as **Gotelee & Goldsmith** *Ipswich*, **Southwells** *Wisbech*, **Overbury Steward & Eaton** *Norwich*, and **Few & Kester** *Cambridge*.

Needless to say, there are many other firms in the region that are strong in commercial property. For instance, **Masters & Co** *Cambridge*, **Nicholson Cadge & Gilbert** *Lowestoft*, **Ben Pearson GJ Starling & Co** *King's Lynn*, **Cozens-Hardy & Jewson** *Norwich*, **Bankes Ashton** *Bury St Edmunds*, **Greene & Greene** *Bury St Edmunds*, **Mears Hobbs & Durrant** *Lowestoft*, **Buckle Mellows** *Peterborough*, and **Day & Son** *Huntingdon*. In addition, there are firms such as **Hegarty & Co** *Peterborough* and **Wade Gery Farr** *St Neots*.

Planning: As far as town and country planning is concerned, one would expect any firm that is strong in commercial property to also be competent at town planning. Thus there is no point in our repeating the names of the firms listed above. However, as regards firms that are particularly strong in this area we must give specific mention (once again!) to the Norwich firms of **Mills & Reeve Francis** and **Daynes Hill & Perks**. Other notables include **Wild Hewitson & Shaw** *Cambridge*, **Greene & Greene** *Bury St Edmunds*, **Birketts** *Ipswich*, **Bankes Ashton** *Bury St*

Edmunds, and **Greenwoods** *Peterborough*. Firms that we have not previously mentioned in the context of commercial property but which should not be ignored – especially for town and country planning – include **Steed & Steed** *Sudbury*, **King & Co** *Cambridge*, and **Kenneth Bush & Co** *King's Lynn*.

Commercial litigation: Once again, **Mills & Reeve Francis** *Norwich* would seem to be the leader, followed by **Daynes Hill & Perks** *Norwich*. After that formidable duo, we would suggest firms such as **Greenwoods** *Peterborough*, **Birketts** *Ipswich*, **Taylor Vinters** *Cambridge*, **Greene & Greene** *Bury St Edmunds*, and the small firm of **Rogers & Norton** *Norwich*. Other notable names include **Wild Hewitson & Shaw** *Cambridge*, **Bankes Ashton** *Bury St Edmunds*, **Nicholson Cadge & Gilbert** *Lowestoft*, **Hegarty & Co** *Peterborough*, **Gotelee & Goldsmith** *Ipswich*, **Kenneth Bush & Co** *King's Lynn*, **Barr Ellison** *Cambridge*, and **Turner Martin & Symes** *Ipswich*. **Emmet & Tacon** *Norwich* is another suggestion.

As regards building and construction litigation our two lead firms would be **Mills & Reeve Francis** *Norwich* and **Greenwoods** *Peterborough*. Also strongly recommended are **Rogers & Norton** *Norwich*, **Merricks** *Ipswich*, **Daynes Hill & Perks** *Norwich*,

Birketts *Ipswich*, **Berry & Walton** *King's Lynn*, **Wild Hewitson & Shaw** *Cambridge*, **Bankes Ashton** *Bury St Edmunds*, **Greenland Houchen** *Norwich*, **Greene & Greene** *Bury St Edmunds*, **Taylor Vinters** *Cambridge*, and **Kenneth Bush & Co** *King's Lynn*.

Insolvency and debt collection: As regards the specialist area of insolvency, we would suggest **Leathes Prior** *Norwich* as the outstanding firm. Other strong firms are **Mills & Reeve Francis** *Norwich*, **Nicholson Cadge & Gilbert** *Lowestoft*, **Berry & Walton** *King's Lynn*, **Taylor Vinters** *Cambridge*, **Overbury Steward & Eaton** *Norwich*, **Greenwoods** *Peterborough*, and **Birketts** *Ipswich*. More generally — and specifically for debt collection — we would mention **Greene & Greene** *Bury St Edmunds*, **Prettys** *Ipswich*, **Buckle Mellows** *Peterborough*, **Rogers & Norton** *Norwich*, **Daynes Hill & Perks** *Norwich*, **Barr Ellison** *Cambridge*, **Wild Hewitson & Shaw** *Cambridge*, and **Bankes Ashton** *Bury St Edmunds*.

Intellectual property: Our lead firms here would be **Wild Hewitson & Shaw** *Cambridge* and **Mills & Reeve Francis** *Norwich*. In intellectual property terms **Wild Hewitson & Shaw** seems to have benefitted from the science boom in Cambridge (in the same way that **Taylor Vinters** has benefitted from the Cambridge property boom)!

Other suggestions include **Daynes Hill &**

Insolvency
EAST ANGLIA
Berry & Walton *King's Lynn*
Birketts *Ipswich*
Greenwoods *Peterborough*
Leathes Prior *Norwich*
Mills & Reeve Francis *Norwich*
Nicholson Cadge & Gilbert *Lowestoft*
Overbury Steward & Eaton *Norwich*
Taylor Vinters *Cambridge*

Intellectual property
EAST ANGLIA
Bankes Ashton *Bury St Edmunds*
Daynes Hill & Perks *Norwich*
Greene & Greene *Bury St Edmunds*
Greenwoods *Peterborough*
Mills & Reeve Francis *Norwich*
Wild Hewitson & Shaw *Cambridge*

Perks *Norwich*, **Greenwoods** *Peterborough*, **Greene & Greene** *Bury St Edmunds*, and **Bankes Ashton** *Bury St Edmunds*.

It is often the case that firms that are strong in intellectual property are also fairly experienced in entertainment law matters (although it can be a mistake to take this generalisation too far!). Having said that, we are not sure that there is any great depth to the specialist practice of entertainment law in East Anglia, largely because the entertainment scene is so dominated by the London firms. However we should mention — at the least — **Mills & Reeve Francis** *Norwich*, **Greene & Greene** *Bury St Edmunds*, and **Bankes Ashton** *Bury St Edmunds*.

Tax: At the risk of being boring, we once again have to pick out **Mills & Reeve Francis** *Norwich*! Other leading contenders must be **Daynes Hill & Perks** *Norwich*, **Taylor Vinters** *Cambridge*, and **Greene & Greene** *Bury St Edmunds*. Other suggestions include **Wild Hewitson & Shaw** *Cambridge*, **Nicholson Cadge & Gilbert** *Lowestoft*, **Bankes Ashton** *Bury St Edmunds*, **Cozens-Hardy & Jewson** *Norwich*, **Ward, Gethin & Co** *King's Lynn*, **Greenwoods** *Peterborough*, **Birketts** *Ipswich* (which, incidentally, we would recommend for ecclesiastical work), **Westhorp Ward & Catchpole** *Ipswich*, and **Gotelee & Goldsmith** *Ipswich*.

Family: There is no shortage of firms with an expertise in family and matrimonial law.

In particular, we would mention **Overbury Steward & Eaton** *Norwich* and **Miller & Co** *Cambridge*. Other strong names include **Fosters** *Norwich*, **Buckle Mellows** *Peterborough*, **Turner Martin & Symes** *Ipswich*, **Kenneth Bush & Co** *King's Lynn*, **Ben Pearson GJ Starling & Co** *King's Lynn*, and **Gotelee & Goldsmith** *Ipswich*. The small firm of **Powleys** *Lowestoft* is also a possibility.

There are many other firms to suggest. In particular, there is **Wild Hewitson & Shaw** *Cambridge*, **Hegarty & Co** *Peterborough*, **Greene & Greene** *Bury St Edmunds*, **Ward, Gethin & Co** *King's Lynn*, **Cozens-Hardy & Jewson** *Norwich*, **Bankes Ashton** *Bury St Edmunds*, **Dawbarns** *Wisbech*, **Jackaman Smith & Mulley** *Ipswich*, **Prettys** *Ipswich*, **Day & Son** *Huntingdon*, **Hood Vores & Allwood** *Dereham*, as well as firms such as **Fraser Woodgate & Beall** *Wisbech* and **Wiltshire Sons & Tunbridge** *Great Yarmouth*.

Personal injury litigation: Once again, this is an area where there are many firms practising – although it is often open to doubt as to who really specialises in this work. Special mention must go to **Rogers &**

Tax
EAST ANGLIA

Daynes Hill & Perks *Norwich*
Greene & Greene *Bury St Edmunds*
Mills & Reeve Francis *Norwich*
Taylor Vinters *Cambridge*

Construction
EAST ANGLIA

Birketts *Ipswich*
Daynes Hill & Perks *Norwich*
Greenwoods *Peterborough*
Merricks *Ipswich*
Mills & Reeve Francis *Norwich*
Rogers & Norton *Norwich*

Family
EAST ANGLIA

Ben Pearson GJ Starling & Co *King's Lynn*
Buckle Mellows *Peterborough*
Daynes Hill & Perks *Norwich*
Fosters *Norwich*
Gotelee & Goldsmith *Ipswich*
Kenneth Bush & Co *King's Lynn*
Miller & Co (with Underwoods) *Cambridge*
Mills & Reeve Francis *Norwich*
Overbury Steward & Eaton *Norwich*
Powleys *Lowestoft*
Turner Martin & Symes *Ipswich*

Norton *Norwich*, as well as to **Mills & Reeve Francis** *Norwich*, **Daynes Hill & Perks** *Norwich*, and **Prettys** *Ipswich*. Other strong firms include **Greenwoods** *Peterborough*, **Overbury Steward & Eaton** *Norwich*, **Kenneth Bush & Co** *King's Lynn*, **Ward, Gethin & Co** *Kings Lynn*, and **Buckle Mellows** *Peterborough*.

In addition, mention should be made of firms such as **Taylor Vinters** *Cambridge*, **Metcalfe, Copeman & Pettefar** *Wisbech*, **Birketts** *Ipswich*, **Wild Hewitson & Shaw** *Cambridge*, **Powleys** *Lowestoft*, **Barr Ellison** *Cambridge*, and **Greene & Greene** *Bury St Edmunds*. Other suggestions include **Dawbarns** *Wisbech*, **Fosters** *Norwich*, and **Nicholson Cadge & Gilbert** *Lowestoft*.

Crime: It is often the case that it is the smaller, less well-known, firms that are particularly adept at crime. But our first choice is relatively large and well known – **Overbury Steward & Eaton** *Norwich*. Otherwise it is a fairly open field, although there are several smaller firms that should be picked out for recognition. In particular, we would mention **Ben Pearson GJ Starling & Co** *King's Lynn*, **Lucas & Wyllys** *Great Yarmouth*, **Masters & Co** *Cambridge*, **Prettys** *Ipswich*, **Hunt & Coombes** *Peterborough*, **Cole & Company** *Norwich*, **Kenneth Bush & Co** *King's Lynn*, and the well-respected **Peter Soar** *Cambridge*.

Other suggestions include **Nunes & Co**

Personal injury
EAST ANGLIA

Buckle Mellows *Peterborough*
Daynes Hill & Perks *Norwich*
Greenwoods *Peterborough*
Kenneth Bush & Co *King's Lynn*
Mills & Reeve Francis *Norwich*
Overbury Steward & Eaton *Norwich*
Prettys *Ipswich*
Rogers & Norton *Norwich*
Ward, Gethin & Co *King's Lynn*

Crime
EAST ANGLIA

Ben Pearson GJ Starling & Co *King's Lynn*
Cole & Company *Norwich*
Hunt & Coombes *Peterborough*
Kenneth Bush & Co *King's Lynn*
Lucas & Wyllys *Great Yarmouth*
Masters & Co *Cambridge*
Overbury Steward & Eaton *Norwich*
Peter Soar *Cambridge*
Prettys *Ipswich*

Cambridge, **Taylor Vinters** *Cambridge*, **Gotelee & Goldsmith** *Ipswich*, **Metcalfe, Copeman & Pettefar** *Wisbech*, **Greenwoods** *Peterborough*, **Russell Steward and Co** *Norwich*, **Greene & Greene** *Bury St Edmunds*, **Bankes Ashton** *Bury St Edmunds*, **Waller Needham & Co** *Peterborough*, **Birketts** *Ipswich*, and **Crotch Brenner & Dunkley** *Norwich*. Finally, no list in East Anglia can be complete without a mention of **Mills & Reeve Francis** *Norwich* and **Daynes Hill & Perks** *Norwich*!

Agriculture: In an area such as East Anglia there are several firms that can claim to be highly experienced in advising farmers and those interested in agricultural matters (including advising on milk quotas). Our lead firm would – inevitably – be **Mills & Reeve Francis** *Norwich*. But you cannot ignore firms such as **Wild Hewitson & Shaw** *Cambridge*, **Taylor Vinters**

Cambridge (which is also strong in bloodstock matters), **Steele & Co** *Diss*, **Greenland Houchen** *Norwich*, **Bankes Ashton** *Bury St Edmunds*, and **Daynes Hill & Perks** *Norwich*.

Firms going from strength to strength:

Any lawyer can tell you that there are two firms that dominate East Anglia – **Mills & Reeve Francis** *Norwich* and **Daynes Hill & Perks** *Norwich*. That much there can be no argument about. The difficulty comes in trying to choose between them. It is interesting to note that both have opted to join national groupings, and there is little doubt that both have a national reputation. **Mills & Reeve Francis** is a member of the **M5 Group**, while **Daynes Hill & Perks** has opted to join the proposed national firm of **Eversheds**.

Anyone who has read this section on East Anglia cannot fail to be impressed by the number of times that **Mills & Reeve Francis** has been strongly recommended. It is a name that keeps on recurring whenever one is discussing East Anglia, and we would pick it as the firm most likely to go from strength to strength in the years to come – with **Daynes Hill & Perks** in hot pursuit!

Excluding these two firms our choice would be **Wild Hewitson & Shaw** *Cambridge*. In addition, we would also go for **Prettys** *Ipswich*, **Taylor Vinters** *Cambridge*, and **Greenwoods** *Peterborough*. Other suggestions might be **Bankes Ashton** *Bury St Edmunds*, **Gotelee & Goldsmith** *Ipswich*, and **Hegarty & Co** *Peterborough*. There are many other firms we could mention; one only has to look at the company and commercial listings to see that there are several firms that could well be seen as going from strength to strength. In any event, the continued prosperity and expansion within East Anglia make it extremely likely that all these leading firms will continue to flourish.

The North West

The largest firms in the North West are **Lace Mawer** *Manchester*, **Cobbett Leak Almond** *Manchester*, **Weightman Rutherfords** *Liverpool*, **Deacon Goldrein Green** *Liverpool*, and **Alsop Wilkinson** *Liverpool*. All have a total staff figure of 150 or more. Incidentally, although we refer to **Alsop Wilkinson** as being in Liverpool, it has equally important offices in Manchester and London; similarly, **Lace Mawer** is in both Liverpool and Manchester. Our accompanying table (which lists the firms by size) is on the basis of staff within the North West: thus **Alsop Wilkinson's** London staff are excluded.

Otherwise the major firms (by size) are

NORTH WEST: Top firms by total number of staff

		Total staff	Partners	Assistant solicitors	Articled clerks
1	Lace Mawer *Manchester*	175	29	22	12
2	Lees Lloyd Whitley *Birkenhead*	163	25	7	7
3	Cobbett Leak Almond *Manchester*	160	29	12	10
4	Weightman Rutherfords *Liverpool*	155	22	17	10
5	Deacon Goldrein Green *Liverpool*	154	10	10	3
6	Alsop Wilkinson *Liverpool*	150	25	28	13
7	Pannone Blackburn *Manchester*	144	18	13	9
8	Addleshaw, Sons & Latham *Manchester*	137	22	25	11
9	Davies Wallis *Liverpool*	126	22	31	4
10	Walker Smith & Way *Chester*	125	18	14	6
11	Slater Heelis *Sale*	120	18	14	12
12	Stephensons *Leigh*	120	10	5	2
13	Bermans *Liverpool*	120	8	11	3
14	Ingham Clegg & Crowther and Laytons *Preston*	115	16	15	6
15	Cuff Roberts North Kirk *Liverpool*	111	18	13	12
16	Davis Campbell *Liverpool*	110	14	8	8
17	Rowlands *Manchester*	102	12	7	4
18	Elliott & Company *Manchester*	101	15	10	6
19	Fox Brooks Marshall *Hale*	100	17	6	3
20	Mace & Jones *Liverpool*	100	13	13	7
21	Alexander, Tatham & Co *Manchester*	90	17	11	11
22	Blackhurst Parker & Yates *Blackpool*	85	16	4	2
23	Russell & Russell *Bolton*	85	11	8	3
24	Foysters *Manchester*	81	13	12	8
25	Maxwell Entwistle & Byrne *Liverpool*	81	12	6	4

Pannone Blackburn *Manchester*, Addleshaw, Sons & Latham *Manchester*, Davies Wallis *Liverpool*, Walker Smith & Way *Chester*, Slater Heelis *Sale*, Stephensons *Leigh*, Bermans *Liverpool*, and Ingham Clegg & Crowther and Laytons *Preston* (incidentally, the firm trades in London as **Laytons**). Other firms with 100 or more total staff are **Cuff Roberts North Kirk** *Liverpool*, **Davis Campbell** *Liverpool*, **Rowlands** *Manchester*, **Elliott & Company** *Manchester*, **Fox Brooks Marshall** *Hale*, and **Mace & Jones** *Liverpool*. Of these firms, it is interesting to note the size of **Bermans**: despite having 120 staff, it has only eight partners — which is perhaps why it is often overlooked by people discussing law firms in the region.

Company and commercial: Not surprisingly, the North West has considerable strength in the area of commercial law. The leading firms have been established for many years and tend to have a client base that is derived from the more traditional manufacturing industries. From the strong competition we would single out **Addleshaw, Sons & Latham** *Manchester* and **Alsop Wilkinson** *Liverpool* for special mention. In addition, we would also highly recommend **Alexander, Tatham & Co** *Manchester*, **Halliwell Landau** *Manchester*, **Slater Heelis** *Sale*, **Lace Mawer** *Liverpool*,

---

Commercial property
NORTH WEST

Addleshaw, Sons & Latham *Manchester*
Alexander, Tatham & Co *Manchester*
Alsop Wilkinson *Liverpool*
Berry & Berry Cocker Smith & Co *Worsley*
Cuff Roberts North Kirk *Liverpool*
Fox Brooks Marshall *Hale*
Gorna & Co *Manchester*
Halliwell Landau *Manchester*
March Pearson & Skelton *Manchester*
Pannone Blackburn *Manchester*
Slater Heelis *Sale*
Weightman Rutherfords *Liverpool*

Mace & Jones *Liverpool*, **Fox Brooks Marshall** *Hale*, **Chaffe Street** *Manchester*, and **Brabner Holden & Co** *Liverpool*.

Other firms to be mentioned are **Aaron & Partners** *Chester*, **Berg & Co** *Manchester*, **Cuff Roberts North Kirk** *Liverpool*, **Elliott & Company** *Manchester*, **Foysters** *Manchester*, **William Prior & Company** *Manchester*, as well as **Pannone Blackburn** *Manchester*, **Walker Smith & Way** *Chester*, **Weightman Rutherfords** *Liverpool*, **Kuit Steinart Levy & Co** *Manchester*, **Ingham Clegg & Crowther and Laytons** *Preston* (especially for road haulage), and the small firm of **David Blank & Co** *Manchester*.

As far as employment matters are concerned, most of the firms mentioned above are fairly strong. We would particularly mention **Addleshaw, Sons & Latham** *Manchester* and **Alsop Wilkinson** *Liverpool*, as well as **Mace & Jones** *Liverpool*. In addition, there are firms such as **Lees Lloyd Whitley** *Birkenhead*, **March Pearson & Skelton** *Manchester*, **Cuff Roberts North Kirk** *Liverpool*, and **Deacon Goldrein Green** *Liverpool*.

For licensing we would nominate **Burton Copeland** *Manchester* and **Cobbett Leak Almond** *Manchester* as the outstanding firms. In addition, we would recommend **Weightman Rutherfords** *Liverpool* and **Blackhurst Parker & Yates** *Blackpool*; less

---

Company
NORTH WEST

Addleshaw, Sons & Latham *Manchester*
Alexander, Tatham & Co *Manchester*
Alsop Wilkinson *Liverpool*
Bermans *Liverpool*
Chaffe Street *Manchester*
Cobbett Leak Almond *Manchester*
Halliwell Landau *Manchester*
Lace Mawer *Liverpool*
Mace & Jones *Liverpool*
Slater Heelis *Sale*

well-known suggestions might be **Kevills** *Chorley*, **Alan Turner & Haddleton** *Preston*, and **Rowlands** *Manchester*.

Finally, it is worth noting that the North West contains two firms that can genuinely claim expertise in shipping matters. Both are in Liverpool — **Alsop Wilkinson** and **Weightman Rutherfords**.

Commercial property: We would suggest that pride of place must go to **Addleshaw, Sons & Latham** *Manchester*. Also strong are firms such as **Alsop Wilkinson** *Liverpool*, **Halliwell Landau** *Manchester*, **Slater Heelis** *Sale*, **Cuff Roberts North Kirk** *Liverpool*, and **Alexander, Tatham & Co** *Manchester*. In addition, we would suggest **Berry & Berry Cocker Smith & Co** *Worsley*, **Fox Brooks Marshall** *Hale*, **March Pearson & Skelton** *Manchester*, **Gorna & Co** *Manchester*, **Weightman Rutherfords** *Liverpool*, and **Pannone Blackburn** *Manchester*. Not to be overlooked are **Cobbett Leak Almond** *Manchester*, **Percy Hughes & Roberts** *Birkenhead*, and **Barker Travers & Co** *Sale*, as well as **Chaffe Street** *Manchester*, **Bullivant & Co** *Liverpool*, and **Davies Wallis** *Liverpool*.

Planning: Naturally, most of these commercial property firms will also be experienced in town and country planning

---

Construction
NORTH WEST

Addleshaw, Sons & Latham *Manchester*
Alexander, Tatham & Co *Manchester*
Alsop Wilkinson *Liverpool*
Bermans *Liverpool*
Davis Campbell *Liverpool*
Field Cunningham & Co *Manchester*
Ingham Clegg & Crowther and Laytons *Preston*
Lace Mawer *Liverpool*
Slater Heelis *Sale*
Weightman Rutherfords *Liverpool*

Planning
NORTH WEST

Addleshaw, Sons & Latham *Manchester*
Alsop Wilkinson *Liverpool*
Cobbett Leak Almond *Manchester*
Cuff Roberts North Kirk *Liverpool*
Halliwell Landau *Manchester*
Lambert Storey & Co *Manchester*

Commercial litigation
NORTH WEST

Addleshaw, Sons & Latham *Manchester*
Alexander, Tatham & Co *Manchester*
Alsop Wilkinson *Liverpool*
Bermans *Liverpool*
Davis Campbell *Liverpool*
Keogh Ritson *Bolton*
Kuit Steinart Levy & Co *Manchester*
Lace Mawer *Liverpool*
Mace & Jones *Liverpool*
Rowleys & Blewitts *Manchester*
Slater Heelis *Sale*
Walker Smith & Way *Chester*
Weightman Rutherfords *Liverpool*

---

matters. Specifically we would mention **Cobbett Leak Almond** *Manchester*, **Cuff Roberts North Kirk** *Liverpool*, **Lambert Storey & Co** *Manchester*, **Addleshaw, Sons & Latham** *Manchester*, **Alsop Wilkinson** *Liverpool*, and **Halliwell Landau** *Manchester*. Also worthy of mention are **March Pearson & Skelton** *Manchester*, **Alexander, Tatham & Co** *Manchester*, and **Aaron & Partners** *Chester*.

Commercial litigation: Alexander, **Tatham & Co** *Manchester* and **Addleshaw, Sons & Latham** *Manchester* figure most prominently here. However, amongst other major insurance practices in the region there are **Davis Campbell** *Liverpool* and **Weightman Rutherfords** *Liverpool*. In addition, there are firms such as **Lace Mawer** *Liverpool*, **Mace & Jones** *Liverpool*,

Bermans *Liverpool*, Walker Smith & Way *Chester*, Slater Heelis *Sale*, Alsop Wilkinson *Liverpool*, Kuit Steinart Levy & Co *Manchester*, and Rowleys & Blewitts *Manchester*. Other suggested firms include Abson Hall & Co *Stockport*, Halliwell Landau *Manchester*, James Chapman & Co *Manchester*, Cobbett Leak Almond *Manchester*, Foysters *Manchester*, Gorna & Co *Manchester*, March Pearson & Skelton *Manchester*, and also Percy Hughes & Roberts *Birkenhead*.

For building and construction litigation our main recommendations would be Addleshaw, Sons & Latham *Manchester* and Davis Campbell *Liverpool*. Another strongly recommended firm is Field Cunningham & Co *Manchester*.

Insolvency and debt collection: Many of the commercial firms we have referred to are expanding their insolvency departments. The firms that we would particularly mention are Slater Heelis *Sale* and Cuff Roberts North Kirk *Liverpool*. There is also the Manchester office of William Prior & Company, and other recommended firms include Alexander, Tatham & Co *Manchester*, Lees Lloyd Whitley *Birkenhead*, Bermans *Liverpool*, Alsop Wilkinson *Liverpool*, Mace & Jones *Liverpool*, plus the Manchester firms of Foysters, Pannone Blackburn, and Kirk Jackson.

Insolvency
NORTH WEST
Alexander, Tatham & Co *Manchester*
Alsop Wilkinson *Liverpool*
Bermans *Liverpool*
Cuff Roberts North Kirk *Liverpool*
Foysters *Manchester*
Lees Lloyd Whitley *Birkenhead*
Mace & Jones *Liverpool*
Pannone Blackburn *Manchester*
Slater Heelis *Sale*
William Prior & Company *Manchester*

Intellectual property
NORTH WEST
Addleshaw, Sons & Latham *Manchester*
Alexander, Tatham & Co *Manchester*
Alsop Wilkinson *Liverpool*
Halliwell Landau *Manchester*
March Pearson & Skelton *Manchester*

Entertainment
NORTH WEST
Alexander, Tatham & Co *Manchester*
Alsop Wilkinson *Liverpool*
Davies Wallis *Liverpool*
Dunderdale Wignall *Manchester*
Halliwell Landau *Manchester*

As far as general debt collection is concerned there is a wide choice of firms. Needless to say, the firms suggested for insolvency will normally do debt collection work as well. In addition to those referred to already, mention should be made of Cobbett Leak Almond *Manchester*, Berg & Co *Manchester*, Halliwell Landau *Manchester*, Addleshaw, Sons & Latham *Manchester*, Lace Mawer *Liverpool*, Chaffe Street *Manchester*, Donn & Co *Manchester*, Restons Linaker & Linaker *Runcorn*, and Wayman-Hales *Chester*.

Intellectual property: Once again, it is the same names that dominate – in particular Addleshaw, Sons & Latham *Manchester*, Alsop Wilkinson *Liverpool*, and Halliwell Landau *Manchester*. Other firms strongly recommended include Alexander, Tatham & Co *Manchester*, March Pearson & Skelton *Manchester*, and Brabner Holden & Co *Liverpool*. Also suggested are Cobbett Leak Almond and Foysters, both of Manchester.

For those concerned with entertainment the general suggestion is Alsop Wilkinson *Liverpool*, although there are also recommendations for **Halliwell Landau** *Manchester*, **Davies Wallis** *Liverpool*, **Alexander, Tatham & Co** *Manchester*, and **Dunderdale Wignall** *Manchester*. Several of the other leading commercial firms were also suggested.

Tax: Of the many firms with tax practices, particular mention must go to **Addleshaw, Sons & Latham** *Manchester*, **Alsop Wilkinson** *Liverpool*, **Slater Heelis** *Sale*, and **Alexander, Tatham & Co** *Manchester*. In addition, there are firms such as **Aaron & Partners** *Chester*, **Lace Mawer** *Liverpool*, **Davis Campbell** *Liverpool*, **Cuff Roberts North Kirk** *Liverpool*, and **Kuit Steinart Levy & Co** *Manchester*.

Family: The trio we would particularly recommend are **Pannone Blackburn** *Manchester*, **Nightingales** *Manchester*, and **Walker Smith & Way** *Chester*. However, as one would expect, there is a wide range of firms that are highly experienced in matrimonial matters. We had numerous suggestions, and there are far too many firms for us to mention here. However, there were a considerable number of recommendations for **Mace & Jones** *Liverpool*, **Lees Lloyd Whitley** *Birkenhead*, **Urquhart Knight & Broughton** *Liverpool*, **Weightman Rutherfords** *Liverpool*, **March Pearson & Skelton** *Manchester*, **Rowleys & Blewitts** *Manchester*, **Lace Mawer** *Liverpool*, **Philip Jones Hillyer & Jackson** *Chester*, **Berry & Berry Cocker Smith & Co** *Worsley*, **Glaisyers** *Manchester*, **Ingham Clegg & Crowther and Laytons** *Preston*, **Yaffe,**

Family
NORTH WEST
Berry & Berry Cocker Smith & Co *Worsley*
Burton Copeland *Manchester*
Deacon Goldrein Green *Liverpool*
Glaisyers *Manchester*
Ingham Clegg & Crowther and Laytons *Preston*
Lace Mawer *Liverpool*
Lees Lloyd Whitley *Birkenhead*
Mace & Jones *Liverpool*
March Pearson & Skelton *Manchester*
Nightingales *Manchester*
Pannone Blackburn *Manchester*
Philip Jones Hillyer & Jackson *Chester*
Rowleys & Blewitts *Manchester*
Russell & Russell *Bolton*
Stephensons *Leigh*
Urquhart Knight & Broughton *Liverpool*
Walker Smith & Way *Chester*
Weightman Rutherfords *Liverpool*
Yaffe Jackson & Ostrin *Liverpool*

Jackson & Ostrin *Liverpool*, **Russell & Russell** *Bolton*, and **Stephensons** *Leigh*.

Other firms include **Dunderdale Wignall** *Manchester*, **Deacon Goldrein Green** *Liverpool*, **Abson Hall & Co** *Stockport*, **Burton Copeland** *Manchester*, **Cobbett Leak Almond** *Manchester*, and **Maxwell Cooke & Co** *Birkenhead*.

Personal injury litigation: To the man in the street **Pannone Napier** *Manchester* is probably *the* personal injury firm. It has made its name as a disaster specialist, and probably has a higher mass-media profile than any other firm in the UK. Fortunately, most practitioners would take the view that this glamour image is actually justified by results. Accordingly, we have little hesitation in placing **Pannone Napier** *Manchester* at the top of our recommendations for personal injury work. By way of explanation, **Pannone Napier** is jointly run by the partners of **Pannone Blackburn** *Manchester* and **Irwin Mitchell** *Sheffield*, but is a separate firm in its own right (even through

Tax
NORTH WEST
Addleshaw, Sons & Latham *Manchester*
Alexander, Tatham & Co *Manchester*
Alsop Wilkinson *Liverpool*
Slater Heelis *Sale*

Personal injury
NORTH WEST

Alexander, Tatham & Co *Manchester*
Betesh Fox & Co *Bolton*
Davis Campbell *Liverpool*
E Rex Makin & Co *Liverpool*
Halliwell Landau *Manchester*
James Chapman & Co *Manchester*
John Pickering *Oldham*
Keogh Ritson *Bolton*
Lace Mawer *Liverpool*
Mace & Jones *Liverpool*
Pannone Napier *Manchester*
Percy Hughes & Roberts *Birkenhead*
Rowleys & Blewitts *Manchester*
Walker Smith & Way *Chester*
Wayman-Hales *Chester*
Weightman Rutherfords *Liverpool*

it is in the same buildings as **Pannone Blackburn!**).

Running a close second — especially close, when one considers its relative lack of publicity — is **Lace Mawer** *Liverpool*. Also highly recommended is **Davis Campbell** *Liverpool*.

There is no shortage of good personal injury firms in the North West. Presumably this is largely a reflection of the traditional manufacturing base. What is also interesting is that there are many smaller specialist firms that can be recommended. Thus **James Chapman & Co** *Manchester* is strongly recommended, as are firms such as **Wayman-Hales** *Chester*, **E Rex Makin & Co** *Liverpool*, **John Pickering** *Oldham*, and **Betesh Fox & Co** *Bolton*. Well-known names include **Alexander, Tatham & Co** *Manchester*, **Mace & Jones** *Liverpool*, **Halliwell Landau** *Manchester*, **Weightman Rutherfords** *Liverpool*, **Keogh Ritson** *Bolton*, plus the Manchester office of **Rowleys & Blewitts**, **Percy Hughes & Roberts** *Birkenhead*, and **Walker Smith & Way** *Chester*.

Other suggested names include **Whittles** *Manchester*, **Vaudrey Osborne & Mellor** *Manchester*, **David Phillips Harris & Whalley** *Bootle*, and **Silverman Livermore & Co** *Liverpool*. Finally, we would mention **Stephensons** *Leigh* , **Yaffe, Jackson & Ostrin** *Liverpool*, **Lonsdales** *Blackpool*, **Blackhurst Parker & Yates** *Blackpool*, **Deacon Goldrein Green** *Liverpool*, **Gorna & Co** *Manchester*, **J Keith Park & Co** *St Helens*, and **Porter Hope & Knipe** *Bolton*.

Crime: One name is far more frequently mentioned than any other — **Burton Copeland** *Manchester* (especially for white-collar crime). It clearly has a good, sound, reputation for criminal work. Other well-respected names are **Pannone Blackburn** *Manchester*, **E Rex Makin & Co** *Liverpool*, **Philip Jones Hillyer & Jackson** *Chester*, **Alexander, Tatham & Co** *Manchester*, **Mace & Jones** *Liverpool*, **Russell & Russell** *Bolton*, **Stephensons** *Leigh*, **Yaffe, Jackson & Ostrin** *Liverpool*, **Deacon Goldrein Green** *Liverpool*, **Canter Levin & Berg** *Liverpool*, **Paul Rooney & Co** *Liverpool*, and **Lee Brailsford & Co** *Leyland*.

Other suggestions include **Kirwan Nicholas Jones** *Wirral*, **Widdows** *Leigh*, **RM Broudie & Co** *Liverpool*, and **Slater Atkinson Cave & Stuart** *Blackpool*.

Crime
NORTH WEST

Alexander, Tatham & Co *Manchester*
Brabner Holden & Co *Liverpool*
Burton Copeland *Manchester*
Canter Levin & Berg *Liverpool*
Deacon Goldrein Green *Liverpool*
E Rex Makin & Co *Liverpool*
Lee Brailsford & Co *Leyland*
Mace & Jones *Liverpool*
Pannone Blackburn *Manchester*
Paul Rooney & Co *Liverpool*
Philip Jones Hillyer & Jackson *Chester*
Russell & Russell *Bolton*
Stephensons *Leigh*
Yaffe Jackson & Ostrin *Liverpool*

Firms going from strength to strength:

The North West contains a number of major practices. Indeed, there is considerable breadth of legal talent within the region. But there does seem to be a clear general consensus in favour of **Alsop Wilkinson**, which has offices in Liverpool and Manchester (as well as in London). Also strongly favoured are the Manchester firms of **Addleshaw, Sons & Latham, Alexander, Tatham & Co** and **Halliwell Landau**, as well as **Lace Mawer** – another firm with head offices in both Liverpool and Manchester. **Cobbett Leak Almond** *Manchester* is also a strong contender, whilst **Pannone Blackburn** *Manchester* is another obvious suggestion – although some might resent its recent leap to stardom!

Of the smaller firms, there seems to be much respect for **Chaffe Street** *Manchester*.

The North

The North contributes relatively few firms to our Legal 500: in fact, there are only 18 law firms in the region that have more than 50 total staff. Of these, half are in Newcastle.

Dickinson Dees *Newcastle* is by far the largest firm in the region, with 195 staff. The second largest is **Watson Burton** *Newcastle* with 158 staff (and 15 partners, which is relatively few for a firm of that size).

The only other firms with 100 or more total staff are **Ingledew Botterell** *Newcastle* and **Jacksons** *Middlesbrough*. Otherwise the largest firms are **Crutes** *Newcastle*, **Wilkinson Maughan** *Newcastle*, **Burnetts** *Carlisle*, **Mounseys** *Carlisle*, **Kidd & Spoor** *Newcastle*, **Hay & Kilner** *Newcastle*, and **Cartmell Mawson & Main** *Carlisle*.

Company and commercial: We would argue that **Dickinson Dees** *Newcastle* is the leading commercial firm in the North. Other notable firms include **Wilkinson Maughan** *Newcastle*, **Watson Burton** *Newcastle*, and **Ingledew Botterell** *Newcastle*. In addition, we would have to mention **Burnetts** *Carlisle*, **Crutes** *Newcastle*, and also **Cartmell Mawson & Main** *Carlisle*.

Tilly Bailey & Irvine *Hartlepool* is one of those firms that originally had a shipping client base, but which is now a general commercial practice. Smaller firms that might be suggested include **Merritt & Co** *Yarm*, **Robert Muckle Son & Hall** *Newcastle*, **Latimer Hinks Marsham & Little** *Darlington*, and **Bendle Dodds & Co**

NORTH: Top firms by total number of staff

		Total staff	Partners	Assistant solicitors	Articled clerks
1	Dickinson Dees *Newcastle*	195	23	20	12
2	Watson Burton *Newcastle*	158	15	15	8
3	Ingledew Botterell *Newcastle*	103	16	20	5
4	Jacksons *Middlesbrough*	100	14	6	4
5	Crutes *Newcastle*	90	14	7	1
6	Wilkinson Maughan *Newcastle*	82	21	3	2
7	Burnetts *Carlisle*	77	14	9	2
8	Mounseys *Carlisle*	75	12	4	3
9	Kidd & Spoor *Newcastle*	68	7	6	4
10	Hay & Kilner *Newcastle*	67	13	8	5
11	Cartmell Mawson & Main *Carlisle*	65	11	6	1
12	Askew & Askew *Redcar*	62	9	4	4
13	Mincoff Science & Gold *Newcastle*	61	7	3	4
14	Williamson & Co *Newcastle*	60	13	3	2
15	Punch Robson Gilchrist Smith *Middlesbrough*	60	10	4	4

Company
NORTH

Burnetts *Carlisle*
Cartmell Mawson & Main *Carlisle*
Crutes *Newcastle*
Dickinson Dees *Newcastle*
Ingledew Botterell *Newcastle*
Watson Burton *Newcastle*
Wilkinson Maughan *Newcastle*

Planning
NORTH

Burnetts *Carlisle*
Cartmell Mawson & Main *Carlisle*
Dickinson Dees *Newcastle*
Ingledew Botterell *Newcastle*
Punch Robson Gilchrist Smith *Middlesbrough*
Wilkinson Maughan *Newcastle*

Carlisle. Incidentally, having mentioned shipping, we should point out that Ingledew Botterell *Newcastle* is one of the few firms left in the area that can legitimately claim a shipping practice.

As regards employment law, suggested firms include **Burnetts** *Carlisle*, **Dickinson Dees** *Newcastle*, **Jacksons** *Middlesbrough*, and **Watson Burton** *Newcastle*. In addition, we would suggest **Hay & Kilner** *Newcastle*, and for a small firm one could consider **Short Richardson & Forth** *Newcastle*.

For those interested in licensing, **Mckenzie Bell & Sons** *Sunderland* is of particular note, having a considerable history of involvement in this field. Also worthy of mention are **Mincoff Science & Gold** *Newcastle*, **Newbys** *Stockton on Tees*, **Burnetts** *Carlisle*, and **Patterson Glenton & Stracey** *South Shields*.

Commercial property: **Wilkinson Maughan** *Newcastle*, **Dickinson Dees** *Newcastle*, and **Burnetts** *Carlisle* are particularly experienced in this field. In addition, we would mention **Cartmell**

Mawson & Main *Carlisle*, **Ingledew Botterell** *Newcastle*, **Punch Robson Gilchrist Smith** *Middlesbrough*, and **Tilly Bailey & Irvine** *Hartlepool*. There are also firms such as **Hay & Kilner** *Newcastle*, **Jacksons** *Middlesbrough*, **Kidd & Spoor** *Newcastle*, **Watson Burton** *Newcastle*, as well as the smaller firms of **Doberman Richardson Broady & Horsman** *Middlesbrough* and **Archer Parkin & Townsend** *Stockton on Tees*. Not to be overlooked is **Robert Muckle Son & Hall** *Newcastle*.

Most of these firms are also relatively experienced in town and country planning, although we would single out **Ingledew Botterell** *Newcastle* for special mention. Also strong on planning are **Burnetts** *Carlisle*, **Dickinson Dees** *Newcastle*, **Punch Robson Gilchrist Smith** *Middlesbrough*, **Wilkinson Maughan** *Newcastle*, and **Cartmell Mawson and Main** *Carlisle*.

Commercial litigation: Two firms with major litigation practices are **Ingledew Botterell** *Newcastle* and **Dickinson Dees** *Newcastle*. Also strong on the litigation front are **Wilkinson Maughan** *Newcastle*, **Burnetts** *Carlisle*, **Crutes** *Newcastle*, **Cartmell Mawson & Main** *Carlisle*, **Jacksons** *Middlesbrough*, and **Watson Burton** *Newcastle*. Other firms to include are **Kidd & Spoor** *Newcastle* and **Wheldon Houlsby & Scott** *South Shields*.

Commercial property
NORTH

Burnetts *Carlisle*
Cartmell Mawson & Main *Carlisle*
Dickinson Dees *Newcastle*
Ingledew Botterell *Newcastle*
Punch Robson Gilchrist Smith *Middlesbrough*
Tilly, Bailey & Irvine *Hartlepool*
Wheldon Houlsby & Scott *South Shields*
Wilkinson Maughan *Newcastle*

Commercial litigation
NORTH

Burnetts *Carlisle*
Cartmell Mawson & Main *Carlisle*
Crutes *Newcastle*
Dickinson Dees *Newcastle*
Ingledew Botterell *Newcastle*
Jacksons *Middlesbrough*
Watson Burton *Newcastle*
Wheldon Houlsby & Scott *South Shields*
Wilkinson Maughan *Newcastle*

Construction
NORTH

Burnetts *Carlisle*
Cartmell Mawson & Main *Carlisle*
Crutes *Middlesbrough*
Dickinson Dees *Newcastle*
Ingledew Botterell *Newcastle*
Jacksons *Middlesbrough*
Watson Burton *Newcastle*

For building and construction litigation our list is similar – namely, the Newcastle firms of **Ingledew Botterell**, **Dickinson Dees**, **Watson Burton**, and **Crutes**, as well as **Cartmell Mawson & Main** *Carlisle*, **Burnetts** *Carlisle*, and **Jacksons** *Middlesbrough*.

Insolvency and debt collection: **Robert Muckle Son & Hall** *Newcastle* has a strong reputation for insolvency work – which may seem surprising in view of its relatively small size when compared to the giants of the region. Other leading firms include **Dickinson Dees** *Newcastle*, **Ingledew Botterell** *Newcastle*, **Cartmell Mawson & Main** *Carlisle*, **Sinton & Co** *Newcastle*, **Wilkinson Maughan** *Newcastle*, and **Williamson & Co** *Newcastle*. For general debt collection work one should also add **Kidd & Spoor** *Newcastle* and **Mckenzie Bell & Sons** *Sunderland;* other possibilities include **Milburn Kerr** *Workington* and

Latimer Hinks Marsham & Little *Darlington.*

Intellectual property: There are not many firms in the region that can claim a real expertise in intellectual property. Amongst the exceptions to this (sweeping!) generalisation are **Dickinson Dees** *Newcastle*, **Wilkinson Maughan** *Newcastle*, **Ingledew Botterell** *Newcastle*, **Punch Robson Gilchrist Smith** *Middlesbrough*, and **Watson Burton** *Newcastle*.

For entertainment law we would suggest **Dickinson Dees** *Newcastle*.

Tax: Once again, **Dickinson Dees** *Newcastle* heads our list. The less well-known **Latimer Hinks Marsham & Little** *Darlington* is another suggestion. There are also firms such as **Wilkinson Maughan** *Newcastle*, **Cartmell Mawson & Main** *Carlisle*, and **Punch Robson Gilchrist Smith** *Middlesbrough;* in addition, of course, most of the firms recommended for company and commercial work will also have specialist tax departments.

Insolvency
NORTH

Cartmell Mawson & Main *Carlisle*
Dickinson Dees *Newcastle*
Ingledew Botterell *Newcastle*
Robert Muckle Son & Hall *Newcastle*
Sinton & Co *Newcastle*
Wilkinson Maughan *Newcastle*
Williamson & Co *Newcastle*

Intellectual property
NORTH

Dickinson Dees *Newcastle*
Ingledew Botterell *Newcastle*
Punch Robson Gilchrist Smith *Middlesbrough*
Watson Burton *Newcastle*
Wilkinson Maughan *Newcastle*

Tax
NORTH

Cartmell Mawson & Main *Carlisle*
Dickinson Dees *Newcastle*
Ingledew Botterell *Newcastle*
Latimer Hinks Marsham & Little *Darlington*
Punch Robson Gilchrist Smith *Middlesbrough*
Wilkinson Maughan *Newcastle*

Family
NORTH

Burnetts *Carlisle*
Cartmell Mawson & Main *Carlisle*
Hay & Kilner *Newcastle*
Jacksons *Middlesbrough*
Kidd & Spoor *Newcastle*
Punch Robson Gilchrist Smith *Middlesbrough*
Samuel Phillips & Co *Newcastle*
Sinton & Co *Newcastle*
Williamson & Co *Newcastle*

Family: As usual, there is a wide range of family and matrimonial practices, and you can make your choice between large and small firms. Either way we feel that **Burnetts** *Carlisle* is particularly worthy of note. In addition, there is **Williamson & Co** *Newcastle*, **Sinton & Co** *Newcastle*, **Kidd & Spoor** *Newcastle*, **Jacksons** *Middlesbrough*, **Punch Robson Gilchrist Smith** *Middlesbrough*, **Samuel Phillips & Co** *Newcastle*, and **Hay & Kilner** *Newcastle*. Other firms to suggest are **Forresters** *Barrow in Furness*, **Crutes** *Newcastle*, **Doberman Richardson Broady & Horsman** *Middlesbrough*, **Bendle Dodds & Co** *Carlisle*, **L Mulcahy Smith & Co** *Gateshead*, **Richmonds** *Newcastle*, **Hedleys & Co** *Sunderland*, **Newbys** *Stockton on Tees*, and **Tilly Bailey & Irvine** *Hartlepool*.

Personal injury litigation: **Crutes** *Newcastle* and **Sinton & Co** *Newcastle* have especially strong reputations. Also there is

Jacksons *Middlesbrough*, **Hay & Kilner** *Newcastle*, **Burnetts** *Carlisle*, **Punch Robson Gilchrist Smith** *Middlesbrough*, **Ingledew Botterell** *Newcastle*, and **Mounseys** *Carlisle*. In addition, there is the Newcastle branch of **Brian Thompson & Partners**, whilst other firms to be considered include **Samuel Phillips & Co** *Newcastle*, **Forresters** *Barrow in Furness*, **Mckenzie Bell & Sons** *Sunderland*, **Archer Parkin & Townsend** *Stockton on Tees*, and the less well-known – and smaller – firm of **Linsley & Mortimer** *Newcastle*.

Crime: Unlike some other areas of the country, it cannot be said that there are any firms that dominate the criminal scene in the North. It is a mixed picture – with a lot of small firms being recommended. We would single out for special mention **Mckeag & Co** *Newcastle*, **Mincoff Science & Gold** *Newcastle*, **Brown Beer & Co** *Redcar*, **Goodswens** *Redcar*, **Bendle Dodds & Co** *Carlisle*, and **Mounseys** *Carlisle*. There are also firms such as **Cartmell Mawson & Main** *Carlisle*, **Forresters** *Barrow in Furness*, **Samuel Phillips & Co** *Newcastle*, **Burnetts** *Carlisle*, **Hay & Kilner** *Newcastle*, **Levinsons Walker & Lister** *Hartlepool*, and **Patterson Glenton & Stracey** *South Shields*.

Agriculture: Our main suggestion here is **Cartmell Mawson & Main** *Carlisle*; for a small and less well-known practice one could consider **Little & Shepherd** *Penrith*.

Personal injury
NORTH

Burnetts *Carlisle*
Crutes *Newcastle*
Hay & Kilner *Newcastle*
Ingledew Botterell *Newcastle*
Jacksons *Middlesbrough*
Mounseys *Carlisle*
Punch Robson Gilchrist Smith *Middlesbrough*
Sinton & Co *Newcastle*

Firms going from strength to strength:

There does not seem to be any one firm that is head and shoulders above the competitors; instead there are several firms of considerable substance. Of the names mentioned to us, those most generally favoured are the Newcastle firms of **Dickinson Dees** and **Wilkinson Maughan**. However, it has to be said that **Ingledew Botterell** has its supporters, whilst **Robert Muckle Son & Hall** seems to be one of the favoured smaller firms. What is interesting is that all of these firms are in Newcastle; indeed, anyone reading this section will have noticed that there does seem to be a disproportionate number of recommendations for Newcastle firms. Why that should be, we are not sure — unless it is simply a reflection of the current optimism in the Newcastle economy!

Yorkshire and Humberside

In terms of size **Dibb Lupton Broomhead** *Leeds* dominates the region. Indeed, it is the largest provincial firm (and is the only non-London firm to have more than 400 total staff). The firm was formed in 1988 through the merger of **Broomheads** *Sheffield* with **Dibb Lupton** *Leeds*.

Otherwise the largest firm is **Hammond Suddards** *Bradford* (with 315 staff, it is also the result of a 1988 merger). In addition, there are four firms in the 200 to 300 total

staff range (all in Leeds), namely **Booth & Co, Walker Morris Scott Turnbull, Simpson Curtis**, and **Hepworth & Chadwick**.

Firms with between 100 and 200 total staff are **Irwin Mitchell** *Sheffield*, **Oxley & Coward** *Rotherham*, **Wilkin & Chapman** *Grimsby*, **Andrew M Jackson & Co** *Hull*, **Read Hind Stewart** *Bradford*, **Attey Bower & Jones** *Doncaster*, **Stamp Jackson & Procter** *Hull*, and **Castle Sanderson** *Leeds*.

YORKSHIRE AND HUMBERSIDE: Top firms by total number of staff

		Total staff	Partners	Assistant solicitors	Articled clerks
1	Dibb Lupton Broomhead *Leeds*	405	46	62	24
2	Hammond Suddards *Bradford*	315	27	46	24
3	Booth & Co *Leeds*	291	25	46	15
4	Walker Morris Scott Turnbull *Leeds*	250	21	24	14
5	Simpson Curtis *Leeds*	210	19	43	13
6	Hepworth & Chadwick *Leeds*	203	20	39	10
7	Irwin Mitchell *Sheffield*	180	23	17	11
8	Oxley & Coward *Rotherham*	125	12	5	3
9	Wilkin & Chapman *Grimsby*	121	19	6	3
10	Andrew M Jackson & Co *Hull*	110	19	13	2
11	Read Hind Stewart *Bradford*	107	14	12	3
12	Attey Bower & Jones *Doncaster*	105	12	3	3
13	Stamp Jackson & Procter *Hull*	104	15	4	4
14	Castle Sanderson *Leeds*	100	14	5	3
15	Rollit Farrell & Bladon *Hull*	94	17	10	7
16	Willey Hargrave *Leeds*	90	14	13	3
17	Gosschalk Wheldon Chambers Thomas *Hull*	89	15	3	2
18	Wake Smith & Co *Sheffield*	84	8	8	6
19	Ford & Warren *Leeds*	79	12	8	4
20	Bury & Walkers *Barnsley*	79	12	3	2

Company and commercial: We have received many recommendations for **Simpson Curtis** *Leeds* and it is clearly a firm that is well regarded. Other strong commercial contenders are **Hepworth & Chadwick** *Leeds*, **Dibb Lupton Broomhead** *Leeds*, and **Booth & Co** *Leeds*. Also there is **Andrew M Jackson & Co** *Hull*, **Rollit Farrell & Bladon** *Hull*, **Hammond Suddards** *Bradford*, **Gosschalk Wheldon Chambers Thomas** *Hull*, and **Brooke North and Goodwin** *Leeds*. Another name — not so well known nationally — is **Kershaw Tudor & Co** *Sheffield*. In addition, there are firms such as **Wilkin & Chapman** *Grimsby*, **Walker Morris Scott Turnbull** *Leeds*, **Read Hind Stewart** *Bradford*, and **David Law & Co** *Sheffield*. We would also suggest **Denison Till** *York*, **Shulmans** *Leeds*, **Ashington Denton & Co** *Sheffield*, **Castle Sanderson** *Leeds*, and **Wake Smith & Co** *Sheffield*.

As far as employment law is concerned, lead names would all seem to be in Leeds — **Simpson Curtis**, **Hepworth & Chadwick**, and **Booth & Co**.

For licensing we would once again nominate **Simpson Curtis** *Leeds*; a smaller firm with a sound reputation for this type of work is **Benson Burdekin** *Sheffield*.

Commercial property: **Booth & Co** *Leeds* dominates the commercial property sector. Otherwise, the leading firms would seem to be **Simpson Curtis** *Leeds*, **Andrew**

Company
YORKSHIRE AND HUMBERSIDE

Andrew M Jackson & Co *Hull*
Booth & Co *Leeds*
Brooke North and Goodwin *Leeds*
Dibb Lupton Broomhead *Leeds*
Gosschalk Wheldon Chambers Thomas *Hull*
Hammond Suddards *Bradford*
Hepworth & Chadwick *Leeds*
Rollit Farrell & Bladon *Hull*
Simpson Curtis *Leeds*

Commercial property
YORKSHIRE AND HUMBERSIDE

Andrew M Jackson & Co *Hull*
Booth & Co *Leeds*
Dibb Lupton Broomhead *Leeds*
Gosschalk Wheldon Chambers Thomas *Hull*
Hammond Suddards *Bradford*
Hepworth & Chadwick *Leeds*
Simpson Curtis *Leeds*
Wake Smith & Co *Sheffield*
Walker Morris Scott Turnbull *Leeds*

M Jackson & Co *Hull*, and **Hepworth & Chadwick** *Leeds*.

Other recommended firms are **Hammond Suddards** *Bradford*, **Dibb Lupton Broomhead** *Leeds*, **Gosschalk Wheldon Chambers Thomas** *Hull*, and **Wake Smith & Co** *Sheffield*.

Other suggestions include **Ford & Warren** *Leeds*, **John Barkers** *Grimsby*, **Brooke North and Goodwin** *Leeds*, **Bury & Walkers** *Barnsley*, **Cranswick Watson** *Leeds*, **Denison Till** *York*, **Finn Gledhill & Co** *Halifax*, **Lee & Priestley** *Bradford*, and **Teeman Levine & Co** *Leeds*.

As far as town and country planning is concerned, the general feeling is that **Booth & Co** *Leeds* has to take second place to **Hammond Suddards** *Bradford*. Otherwise, the main contenders are **Simpson Curtis** *Leeds*, **Walker Morris Scott Turnbull** *Leeds*, and **Dibb Lupton Broomhead** *Leeds*.

Commercial litigation: Here we select **Hepworth & Chadwick** *Leeds*, followed by **Booth & Co** *Leeds* and **Dibb Lupton Broomhead** *Leeds*. Other recommended firms are **Hammond Suddards** *Bradford*, **Simpson Curtis** *Leeds*, **Willey Hargrave** *Leeds*, **Andrew M Jackson & Co** *Hull*, **Rollit Farrell & Bladon** *Hull*, **RC Moorhouse & Co** *Leeds*, and **Irwin Mitchell** *Sheffield*.

In addition, we would mention **Walker Morris Scott Turnbull** *Leeds*, **Wilkin & Chapman** *Grimsby*, **Read Hind Stewart**

Bradford, and **Clarksons & Steele** *Halifax*. Also worth a mention is **Mason Bond** *Leeds*, which has carved out a niche in acting for tour operators and others in the holiday trade.

For building and construction litigation the firm most frequently recommended is **Booth & Co** *Leeds*. Otherwise the suggestions are **Simpson Curtis** *Leeds*, **Hammond Suddards** *Bradford*, **Gosschalk Wheldon Chambers Thomas** *Hull*, **Dibb Lupton Broomhead** *Leeds*, **Hepworth & Chadwick** *Leeds*, **Rollit Farrell & Bladon** *Hull*, and **Andrew M Jackson & Co** *Hull*.

Insolvency and debt collection: This is an area in which **Dibb Lupton Broomhead** *Leeds* is clearly the most popular choice. However, Leeds is also home of the considerably smaller specialist firm of **RC Moorhouse & Co**, and one cannot fail to strongly recommend it for insolvency work, as well as another Leeds firm, **Brooke**

Construction
YORKSHIRE AND HUMBERSIDE

Booth & Co *Leeds*
Dibb Lupton Broomhead *Leeds*
Gosschalk Wheldon Chambers Thomas *Hull*
Hammond Suddards *Bradford*
Hepworth & Chadwick *Leeds*
Rollit Farrell & Bladon *Hull*
Simpson Curtis *Leeds*

Insolvency
YORKSHIRE AND HUMBERSIDE

Booth & Co *Leeds*
Brooke North and Goodwin *Leeds*
Carrick Carr & Garwood *Hull*
Dibb Lupton Broomhead *Leeds*
Hammond Suddards *Bradford*
Hepworth & Chadwick *Leeds*
RC Moorhouse & Co *Leeds*
Simpson Curtis *Leeds*

Planning
YORKSHIRE AND HUMBERSIDE

Booth & Co *Leeds*
Dibb Lupton Broomhead *Leeds*
Hammond Suddards *Bradford*
Simpson Curtis *Leeds*
Walker Morris Scott Turnbull *Leeds*

Commercial litigation
YORKSHIRE AND HUMBERSIDE

Andrew M Jackson & Co *Hull*
Booth & Co *Leeds*
Dibb Lupton Broomhead *Leeds*
Hammond Suddards *Bradford*
Hepworth & Chadwick *Leeds*
Irwin Mitchell *Sheffield*
RC Moorhouse & Co *Leeds*
Rollit Farrell & Bladon *Hull*
Simpson Curtis *Leeds*
Willey Hargrave *Leeds*

North and Goodwin. Other firms to be recommended are **Simpson Curtis** *Leeds*, **Hammond Suddards** *Bradford*, **Carrick Carr & Garwood** *Hull*, **Booth & Co** *Leeds*, **Hepworth & Chadwick** *Leeds*, and **Andrew M Jackson & Co** *Hull*. A small firm with a licensed insolvency practitioner is **Shulmans** *Leeds*.

All of these firms would also be recommended for general debt collection. In addition, we would suggest **Walker Morris Scott Turnbull** *Leeds*, **Cranswick Watson** *Leeds*, **Dibb & Clegg** *Barnsley*, **Finn Gledhill & Co** *Halifax*, and the small firm of **Montagu J Martin & Haigh** *Scunthorpe*.

Intellectual property: Once again, this is an area in which **Dibb Lupton Broomhead** *Leeds* is pre-eminent. Other leading firms are **Simpson Curtis** *Leeds*, **Booth & Co** *Leeds*, **Hepworth & Chadwick** *Leeds*, **Hammond Suddards** *Bradford*, and **Rollit Farrell & Bladon** *Hull*.

Intellectual property
YORKSHIRE AND HUMBERSIDE

Booth & Co *Leeds*
Dibb Lupton Broomhead *Leeds*
Hammond Suddards *Bradford*
Hepworth & Chadwick *Leeds*
Rollit Farrell & Bladon *Hull*
Simpson Curtis *Leeds*

Tax
YORKSHIRE AND HUMBERSIDE

Andrew M Jackson & Co *Hull*
Booth & Co *Leeds*
Dibb Lupton Broomhead *Leeds*
Hammond Suddards *Bradford*
Hepworth & Chadwick *Leeds*
Rollit Farrell & Bladon *Hull*
Simpson Curtis *Leeds*
Walker Morris Scott Turnbull *Leeds*

As far as entertainment law is concerned, we are reluctant to make a recommendation. But, if pressed, we would probably opt for **Dibb Lupton Broomhead** *Leeds*.

Tax: It is the same firms that dominate. In particular, there is **Simpson Curtis** *Leeds*, **Dibb Lupton Broomhead** *Leeds*, **Booth & Co** *Leeds*, **Hammond Suddards** *Bradford*, **Rollit Farrell & Bladon** *Hull*, plus **Andrew M Jackson & Co** *Hull*, **Walker Morris Scott Turnbull** *Leeds*, and **Hepworth & Chadwick** *Leeds*.

Family: As is often the case, our recommendations for family work are a mixture of large and small firms. The general consensus seems to be in favour of **Booth & Co** *Leeds*, although other firms that are strongly recommended include **Irwin Mitchell** *Sheffield*, **Andrew M Jackson & Co** *Hull*, and **Victor D Zermansky & Co** *Leeds*.

Also recommended are **Hepworth & Chadwick** *Leeds*, **Hammond Suddards** *Bradford*, **Gordons and HM Dawson & Co**

Bradford, **Mills Kemp & Brown** *Barnsley*, and the smaller firm of **Parker Rhodes Field & Co** *Rotherham*.

In addition, we would mention **Grahame Stowe Bateson & Co** *Leeds*, **Mason Bond** *Leeds*, **Dibb & Clegg** *Barnsley*, **Graham & Rosen** *Hull*, **John Howell & Co** *Sheffield*, **Maycock Laverack Lewenstein** *Hull*, and **McCormicks** *Leeds*.

Personal injury litigation: The two large insurance litigation practices of **Willey Hargrave** *Leeds* and **Irwin Mitchell** *Sheffield* dominate. Also strongly recommended are **Hammond Suddards** *Bradford* and **Andrew M Jackson & Co** *Hull*.

Less well-known firms that are strong on personal injury claims include **Keeble Hawson Branson Bramley** *Sheffield*, **JH Milner & Son** *Leeds*, and **Armitage Sykes & Hinchcliffe** *Huddersfield*. Other recommendations include **Stamp Jackson &**

Family
YORKSHIRE AND HUMBERSIDE

Andrew M Jackson & Co *Hull*
Booth & Co *Leeds*
Gordons and HM Dawson & Co *Bradford*
Hammond Suddards *Bradford*
Hepworth & Chadwick *Leeds*
Irwin Mitchell *Sheffield*
Mills Kemp & Brown *Barnsley*
Victor D Zermansky & Co *Leeds*

Personal injury
YORKSHIRE AND HUMBERSIDE

Andrew M Jackson & Co *Hull*
Ford & Warren *Leeds*
Hammond Suddards *Bradford*
Irwin Mitchell *Sheffield*
JH Milner & Son *Leeds*
Keeble Hawson Branson Bramley *Sheffield*
Stamp Jackson & Procter *Hull*
Willey Hargrave *Leeds*

Crime
YORKSHIRE AND HUMBERSIDE

Ake Moore & Co *Leeds*
Irvine & Co *Bradford*
Irwin Mitchell *Sheffield*
J Levi & Co *Leeds*
John Barkers *Grimsby*
McCormicks *Leeds*
Myer Wolff & Manley *Hull*
Stamp Jackson & Procter *Hull*
Walker Morris Scott Turnbull *Leeds*

Procter *Hull*, the Sheffield office of **Brian Thompson & Partners, Kershaw Tudor & Co** *Sheffield*, **Morrish & Co** *Leeds*, **Ford & Warren** *Leeds* (especially for disaster litigation), and **John Barkers** *Grimsby*. Not to be forgotten are **Dibb & Clegg** *Barnsley*, and **Graham & Rosen** *Hull*, as well as **Wilkin & Chapman** *Grimsby* and **Gosschalk Wheldon Chambers Thomas** *Hull*.

Crime: As always, crime tends to be the province of the smaller firms – those that are prepared to get by on legal aid. Thus our list contains many names that may not be familiar to readers outside the region. The firm most generally recommended is **Myer Wolff & Manley** *Hull*. Its main competitor

in terms of reputation would seem to be **Irwin Mitchell** *Sheffield*. Other criminal firms with a strong name are **J Levi & Co** *Leeds*, **McCormicks** *Leeds*, **Ake Moore & Co** *Leeds*, **Irvine & Co** *Bradford*, and **John Barkers** *Grimsby*.

More generally known are **Stamp Jackson & Procter** *Hull* and **Walker Morris Scott Turnbull** *Leeds*. In addition, we would mention **Grahame Stowe Bateson & Co** *Leeds*, **Eaton & Co** *Bradford*, and **Lee & Priestley** *Bradford*.

Firms going from strength to strength:

Anyone reading through this section will have seen that there are four or five large firms that dominate the region, together with a few medium sized firms. The general view seems to favour **Simpson Curtis** *Leeds*, although there is much enthusiasm for the merged firm of **Dibb Lupton Broomhead** *Leeds*. Otherwise it is **Booth & Co** *Leeds*, **Hammond Suddards** *Bradford*, and **Hepworth & Chadwick** *Leeds*. Other contenders include **Walker Morris Scott Turnbull** *Leeds*, **Willey Hargrave** *Leeds*, **Andrew M Jackson & Co** *Hull*, and **Stamp Jackson & Procter** *Hull*.

Wales

No one could describe Wales as a land of large law firms! Indeed, we could only find 12 firms in the principality that had more than 50 total staff. However, this is to some extent a misleading figure, because it does imply that all firms in Wales are small. In fact, there are six firms with more than 100 total staff (and, of these, two have over 200). There is a concentration of legal talent in Cardiff, with the rest of the country being served by relatively small firms.

The largest firms in Cardiff (and thus in Wales) are **Phillips & Buck, Hugh James Jones & Jenkins, Morgan Bruce & Hardwickes**, and **Edwards Geldard**. Between them these firms dominate the commercial scene in Wales. Indeed, with the economy of south Wales enjoying a relative boom (and, in particular, with the relocation of several financial services groups to the area), these firms look set for further expansion.

Otherwise the largest firms are **Leo Abse & Cohen** *Cardiff* and **Loosemores** *Cardiff* (both with more than 100 staff), followed by **Gamlin Kelly & Beattie** *Rhyl*, **Douglas-Jones & Mercer** *Swansea*, **RL Edwards & Partners** *Bridgend*, **Dolmans** *Cardiff*, **Gartside Harding & Davies** *Newport*, and **Merrils Ede** *Cardiff*. Interestingly, **Gamlin Kelly & Beattie** *Rhyl* has 86 staff and yet has only five partners.

Company and commercial: The three big firms in Cardiff (and indeed in Wales) are **Edwards Geldard, Phillips & Buck**, and **Morgan Bruce & Hardwickes**. As one would expect, they dominate the company and commercial field in the principality. Of these, **Edwards Geldard** seems to have a particularly good reputation; it can fairly claim to be an all-round commercial firm, and has a particular experience of public and administrative law matters. For its part,

WALES: Top firms by total number of staff

		Total staff	Partners	Assistant solicitors	Articled clerks
1	Phillips & Buck *Cardiff*	240	20	32	18
2	Hugh James Jones & Jenkins *Cardiff*	215	24	17	15
3	Morgan Bruce & Hardwickes *Cardiff*	171	27	31	13
4	Edwards Geldard *Cardiff*	164	22	27	15
5	Leo Abse & Cohen *Cardiff*	118	14	12	8
6	Loosemores *Cardiff*	117	15	11	11
7	Gamlin Kelly & Beattie *Rhyl*	86	5	13	3
8	Douglas-Jones & Mercer *Swansea*	80	10	6	5
9	RL Edwards & Partners *Bridgend*	80	10	4	2
10	Dolmans *Cardiff*	68	12	5	6

Company
WALES

Collins Woods & Vaughan Jones *Swansea*
Dolmans *Cardiff*
Edwards Geldard *Cardiff*
Hugh James Jones & Jenkins *Cardiff*
Morgan Bruce & Hardwickes *Cardiff*
Phillips & Buck *Cardiff*

Commercial property
WALES

Collins Woods & Vaughan Jones *Swansea*
Dolmans *Cardiff*
Edwards Geldard *Cardiff*
Hugh James Jones & Jenkins *Cardiff*
Morgan Bruce & Hardwickes *Cardiff*
Phillips & Buck *Cardiff*

Phillips & Buck is particularly strong in banking and finance – indeed, it is one of the few firms outside the City of London that can legitimately claim to be doing any genuine banking work, and it is also one of the more internationally orientated of the Welsh firms. **Morgan Bruce & Hardwickes** is notably strong in corporate finance matters, and has an impressive client list.

Apart from these three firms – and **Hugh James Jones & Jenkins** *Cardiff* – the other commercial firms in Cardiff, such as **Dolmans** and **Edward Lewis & Co**, tend to be more general in nature. Outside Cardiff, we would mention **Collins Woods & Vaughan Jones** *Swansea* and **Allington Hughes** *Wrexham*.

For employment matters we would single out **Phillips & Buck** *Cardiff*. For those interested in licensing, **Cartwrights** *Cardiff* is particularly well known; it is the Cardiff office of the Bristol firm of that name, which is generally reckoned to be one of the country's leading licensing practices. **David and Snape** *Bridgend* is another suggestion

for licensing, whilst in north Wales there is **Gamlin Kelly & Beattie** *Rhyl*.

Commercial property: Once again, the usual firms dominate, but we would suggest that **Edwards Geldard** *Cardiff* is particularly well known for its property work. So too are firms such as **Morgan Bruce & Hardwickes** *Cardiff*, **Collins Woods & Vaughan Jones** *Swansea*, **Phillips & Buck** *Cardiff*, and **Hugh James Jones & Jenkins** *Cardiff*. Other firms that might be mentioned include **Dolmans** *Cardiff*, **Allington Hughes** *Wrexham*, **Edward Lewis & Co** *Cardiff*, **Graham Evans & Partners** *Swansea*, **Robertsons** *Cardiff*, and **Lowless & Lowless** *Pembroke*. There is also **David and Snape** *Bridgend*, **Gamlin Kelly & Beattie** *Rhyl*, and **Francis Rees & Kelly** *Swansea*.

For town and country planning the same names dominate. In this instance, **Morgan Bruce & Hardwickes** *Cardiff* has a particularly good name, and we would put it at the top of the list that includes the Cardiff firms of **Dolmans**, **Edwards Geldard**, and **Phillips & Buck**. We would also suggest **Collins Woods & Vaughan Jones** *Swansea*, and in North Wales there is **Gamlin Kelly & Beattie** *Rhyl*.

Commercial litigation: The leading firm here is **Hugh James Jones & Jenkins** *Cardiff*. Other notables are – inevitably – **Morgan Bruce & Hardwickes**, **Phillips &**

Commercial litigation
WALES

Dolmans *Cardiff*
Edwards Geldard *Cardiff*
Gamlin Kelly & Beattie *Rhyl*
Hugh James Jones & Jenkins *Cardiff*
Leo Abse & Cohen *Cardiff*
Morgan Bruce & Hardwickes *Cardiff*
Phillips & Buck *Cardiff*

Insolvency
WALES

Dolmans *Cardiff*
Edwards Geldard *Cardiff*
Hugh James Jones & Jenkins *Cardiff*
Leo Abse & Cohen *Cardiff*
Morgan Bruce & Hardwickes *Cardiff*
Phillips & Buck *Cardiff*

Intellectual property
WALES

Dolmans *Cardiff*
Edward Lewis & Co *Cardiff*
Edwards Geldard *Cardiff*
Morgan Bruce & Hardwickes *Cardiff*
Phillips & Buck *Cardiff*

Buck, and **Edwards Geldard**, all in Cardiff. Other Cardiff firms that should be mentioned are **Dolmans** and **Edward Lewis & Co**; also **Leo Abse & Cohen** is moving more into commercial litigation, as is **Loosemores**. Outside the capital, firms that might be mentioned include **Gamlin Kelly & Beattie** *Rhyl* and **Graham Evans & Partners** *Swansea.*

In the more specialist area of building and construction litigation the position is the same in that **Hugh James Jones & Jenkins** is the dominant firm. Otherwise our list is very much as before – namely **Edwards Geldard**, **Phillips & Buck**, **Morgan Bruce & Hardwickes**, and **Dolmans**.

Insolvency and debt collection:
Prominent here are **Hugh James Jones & Jenkins** and **Phillips & Buck**, both in Cardiff. As one would expect, the other firms that are particularly worthy of mention are also in Cardiff – **Edwards Geldard**, **Morgan Bruce & Hardwickes**, **Dolmans**, and **Leo Abse & Cohen**. In short, Cardiff dominates the Welsh insolvency scene;

otherwise we might mention **Collins Woods & Vaughan Jones** *Swansea.* For general debt collection our list would be very much the same – although it should also be borne in mind that most of the firms recommended for general company and commercial work will also be experienced at debt collecting.

Intellectual property: Not surprisingly, it is the large Cardiff commercial firms that have the expertise in intellectual property. **Phillips & Buck** and **Edwards Geldard** would seem to be the lead firms; otherwise the names are **Morgan Bruce & Hardwickes** and **Dolmans**. Also worthy of mention is **Edward Lewis & Co** – also in Cardiff.

For those interested in entertainment law our choice would be **Phillips & Buck**, **Dolmans**, and any other of the major Cardiff commercial firms; **Loosemores** was also recommended in this regard. Having said that, we would repeat what we have frequently said before – namely that the real expertise in entertainment law lies in London.

Tax: Once again, the Cardiff firms dominate: in particular, we would mention **Edwards Geldard** and **Phillips & Buck**.

Family: Here Leo Abse & Cohen *Cardiff* is especially strong. In addition, we would

Family
WALES

Hallinan Blackburn Gittings & Co *Cardiff*
Hugh James Jones & Jenkins *Cardiff*
Hutton's *Cardiff*
Joseph Sydney Isaacs Stewart & Dawson *Cardiff*
Leo Abse & Cohen *Cardiff*
Morgan Bruce & Hardwickes *Cardiff*
Phoenix Walters *Cardiff*
Price & Son *Haverfordwest*

Personal injury
WALES

Dolmans *Cardiff*
Edward Lewis & Co *Cardiff*
Edwards Geldard *Cardiff*
Graham Evans & Ptrs *Swansea*
Hugh James Jones & Jenkins *Cardiff*
Leo Abse & Cohen *Cardiff*
Morgan Bruce & Hardwickes *Cardiff*
Robin Thompson & Partners *Cardiff*

mention the other Cardiff firms of **Joseph Sydney Isaacs Stewart & Dawson, Morgan Bruce & Hardwickes, Hallinan Blackburn Gittings & Co, Hugh James Jones & Jenkins, Hutton's, Phoenix Walters**, plus **Price & Son** *Haverfordwest.*

However, we are now in an area of law that is not monopolised by the top four or five Cardiff commercial firms. Indeed, there are numerous small practices that could be mentioned. For instance, we received recommendations for firms such as **Holt Jones & Collins** *Swansea,* **Hambly Smith Hurley Clements** *Monmouth,* and **Marchant Harries & Co** *Aberdare.* Other firms worthy of mention include **David and Snape** *Bridgend,* **David Jones & Harvey** *Newtown,* **Loosemores** *Cardiff,* **Graeme John & Partners** *Aberdare,* **Granville-West Chivers & Morgan** *Newport,* **Gwilym Hughes & Partners** *Wrexham,* **Weaver & Co** *Caerphilly,* and **Ungoed-Thomas & King** *Carmarthen.*

Personal injury litigation: Here **Hugh James Jones & Jenkins** *Cardiff* leads: indeed, it is pre-eminent. By any standards it has an extremely large insurance company practice, especially in personal injury work. Other firms to mention are **Leo Abse & Cohen, Edward Lewis & Co, Edwards Geldard, Dolmans, Morgan Bruce & Hardwickes** (all in Cardiff), plus the Cardiff office of **Robin Thompson & Partners** and

Graham Evans & Partners *Swansea.* Other firms include **Smith Spring & Co** *Swansea,* **Loosemores** *Cardiff,* **Marchant Harries & Co** *Aberdare,* **Gamlin Kelly & Beattie** *Rhyl,* together with the smaller firms of **Grossman Hermer & Seligman** *Cardiff,* **Price & Son** *Haverfordwest,* **Simon North and Nam** *Cardiff,* and **Price & Kelway** *Milford Haven.*

Crime: This is an area in which the large commercial firms are noticeably absent. Indeed, there is a host of legal aid practices specialising in crime, many of which are very small firms indeed. The firm with the strongest reputation seems to be **Hutton's** *Cardiff.* Other strongly recommended firms are **Hallinan Blackburn Gittings & Co** *Cardiff,* **Graham Evans & Partners** *Swansea,* and **Leo Abse & Cohen** *Cardiff.* Amongst medium sized firms that should be mentioned are **David and Snape** *Bridgend,* **Gamlin Kelly & Beattie** *Rhyl,* **Collins Woods & Vaughan Jones** *Swansea,* **Robertsons** *Cardiff,* **Marchant Harries & Co** *Aberdare,* and **Loosemores** *Cardiff.* Amongst the smaller firms, it is difficult to know where to start — there are so many of them. In particular, we might suggest **Riley Mumford & Rausa** *Cardiff,* **Roy Morgan & Co** *Cardiff,* **Eaton-Evans & Morris** *Haverfordwest,* **Hodson Parsons** *Newport,* **Treasures** *Blackwood,* **Robert Render & Partners** *Cardiff,* as well as **Graeme John & Partners** *Aberdare* and **Gwilym Hughes & Partners** *Wrexham.* There are many more legal aid criminal firms that could be mentioned — but this is probably enough to be getting on with!

Crime
WALES

Graham Evans & Partners *Swansea*
Hallinan Blackburn Gittings & Co *Cardiff*
Hutton's *Cardiff*
Leo Abse & Cohen *Cardiff*

Firms going from strength to strength:

As we have seen, it is the four large Cardiff commercial firms that dominate the Welsh scene – especially when you are dealing with commercial (non-personal) work. On the basis of what we have been told, we think **Edwards Geldard** is currently the firm to beat, but hard on its heels are **Morgan Bruce & Hardwickes**, **Phillips & Buck**, and **Hugh James Jones & Jenkins**. Of the other Cardiff firms, it is clearly a competition between **Leo Abse & Cohen**, which seems to be making efforts to recover ground lost to its competitors; **Loosemores**, which would seem to be trying to convert its high-profile image into a higher quality of work; and **Dolmans**, which seems to have genuinely all-round strength.

The Provinces

The largest non-London firm is **Dibb Lupton Broomhead** *Leeds*, with 405 staff. Next in size is **Clarke Willmott & Clarke** *Taunton*, followed by **Bevan Ashford** *West Country*, **Shoosmiths & Harrison** *Northampton*, **Evershed & Tomkinson**

Birmingham, **Edge & Ellison** *Birmingham*, **Hammond Suddards** *Bradford*, **Daynes Hill & Perks** *Norwich*, **Mills & Reeve Francis** *Norwich*, and **Wragge & Co** *Birmingham*. All these firms have at least 300 total staff.

Next there is a batch of firms with over

PROVINCES: Top firms by total number of staff

		Total staff	Partners	Assistant solicitors	Articled clerks
1	Dibb Lupton Broomhead *Leeds*	405	46	62	24
2	Clarke Willmott & Clarke *Taunton*	384	36	31	14
3	Bevan Ashford *West Country*	350	49	35	20
4	Shoosmiths & Harrison *Northampton*	340	43	23	14
5	Evershed & Tomkinson *Birmingham*	322	32	66	40
6	Edge & Ellison *Birmingham*	320	30	50	16
7	Hammond Suddards *Bradford*	315	27	46	24
8	Daynes Hill & Perks *Norwich*	304	46	29	15
9	Mills & Reeve Francis *Norwich*	300	43	42	10
10	Wragge & Co *Birmingham*	300	26	60	21
11	Booth & Co *Leeds*	291	25	46	15
12	Blake Lapthorn *Portsmouth*	291	22	27	13
13	Thomas Eggar Verrall Bowles *Chichester*	290	35	20	12
14	Dundas & Wilson CS *Edinburgh*	290	33	43	21
15	Thomson Snell & Passmore *Tunbridge Wells*	260	48	14	4
16	Howes Percival *Northampton*	260	27	14	10
17	Needham & James *Birmingham*	250	28	26	15
18	Walker Morris Scott Turnbull *Leeds*	250	21	24	14
19	Bond Pearce *Plymouth*	247	31	41	15
20	Phillips & Buck *Cardiff*	240	20	32	18
21	Bird Semple Fyfe Ireland WS *Glasgow*	237	30	44	17
22	Donne Mileham & Haddock *Brighton*	235	35	13	9
23	Ross Harper & Murphy *Glasgow*	225	25	33	28
24	Durnford Ford *Hastings*	220	23	4	4
25	Argles & Court *Maidstone*	220	22	9	4

250 staff — **Booth & Co** *Leeds*, **Blake Lapthorn** *Portsmouth*, **Thomas Eggar Verrall Bowles** *Chichester*, **Dundas & Wilson CS** *Edinburgh*, **Thomson Snell & Passmore** *Tunbridge Wells*, and **Howes Percival** *Northampton*.

If you prefer to go by partnership size (a less accurate guide) the order is **Bevan Ashford, Thomson Snell & Passmore, Dibb Lupton Broomhead, Daynes Hill & Perks, Shoosmiths & Harrison,** and **Mills & Reeve Francis** (all with at least 40 partners).

Refer to the accompanying table for more detailed information. In addition, at the rear of this book is a table showing total staff figures for all our firms (whether in London or the provinces). From this it will be seen that **Dibb Lupton Broomhead**, the largest provincial firm, is the 14th largest nationally (ie including London firms). On the same basis **Clarke Willmott & Clarke** is 17th largest, **Bevan Ashford** is 23rd, and **Evershed & Tomkinson** is 28th largest.

The provincial high-flyers: Our survey of the provinces has highlighted those firms

		Total staff	Partners	Assistant solicitors	Articled clerks
26	Hugh James Jones & Jenkins *Cardiff*	215	24	17	15
27	McGrigor Donald *Glasgow*	214	36	42	19
28	Simpson Curtis *Leeds*	210	19	43	13
29	Shepherd & Wedderburn WS *Edinburgh*	205	25	32	12
30	Hepworth & Chadwick *Leeds*	203	20	39	10
31	Osborne Clarke *Bristol*	201	27	40	11
32	Coffin Mew & Clover *Portsmouth*	201	18	8	3
33	Veale Wasbrough *Bristol*	200	27	21	13
34	Dickinson Dees *Newcastle*	195	23	20	12
35	W & J Burness *Edinburgh*	195	22	27	12
36	Pinsent & Co *Birmingham*	194	27	37	20
37	Lester Aldridge *Bournemouth*	194	26	15	10
38	Brodies WS *Edinburgh*	190	27	21	12
39	Burges Salmon *Bristol*	190	17	42	14
40	Leigh Williams *Bromley*	184	17	11	9
41	Maclay Murray & Spens *Glasgow*	182	25	37	12
42	Irwin Mitchell *Sheffield*	180	23	17	11
43	Penningtons *Newbury*	178	25	18	3
44	Lace Mawer *Manchester*	175	29	22	12
45	Toller Hales & Collcutt *Northampton*	175	21	10	12
46	Cripps Harries Hall *Tunbridge Wells*	173	19	17	4
47	Morgan Bruce & Hardwickes *Cardiff*	171	27	31	13
48	Pictons *St Albans*	171	20	17	9
49	Wild Hewitson & Shaw *Cambridge*	170	27	14	7
50	Moore & Blatch *Lymington*	170	17	17	8

that seem to be particularly strong in certain areas of practice. What we are doing in this section is to draw together those various recommendations to produce a list covering the whole of the provinces for each of the major work specialisations. In effect, it is a sort of 'Top Twenty'.

As always, these tables are merely matters of opinion. They are not meant to be definitive and they are suggested by us simply as a starting point for debate. As with the other tables, there are two sources. Firstly, the comments, suggestions and recommendations made to us by the thousands of solicitors who have been in contact with us in the last year. Secondly, the editor has made his own contribution — based, as always, on feedback and opinions from fellow solicitors throughout the country. The result is not claimed to be a scientifically accurate and correct list: that would be an impossibility! Readers are welcome to let us have their comments — and make their criticisms (however hostile!) known to us.

		Total staff	Partners	Assistant solicitors	Articled clerks
51	Stephens & Scown *St Austell*	167	22	11	4
52	Taylor Vinters *Cambridge*	165	21	18	9
53	Edwards Geldard *Cardiff*	164	22	27	15
54	Lees Lloyd Whitley *Birkenhead*	163	25	7	7
55	Linnells *Oxford*	161	21	25	5
56	Cobbett Leak Almond *Manchester*	160	29	12	10
57	Brutton & Co *Fareham*	160	18	10	1
58	Watson Burton *Newcastle*	158	15	15	8
59	Weightman Rutherfords *Liverpool*	155	22	17	10
60	Deacon Goldrein Green *Liverpool*	154	10	10	3
61	Bates & Partners *Southend*	152	13	7	2
62	Alsop Wilkinson *Liverpool*	150	25	28	13
63	Cole and Cole *Oxford*	150	22	22	9
64	Biggart Baillie & Gifford *Edinburgh*	150	20	17	8
65	Stevens Drake & Pope *Crawley*	150	9	11	5
66	JW Ward & Son *Bristol*	149	18	17	8
67	Girlings *Herne Bay*	148	18	4	4
68	Kidd Rapinet *Slough*	147	27	7	5
69	Blakemores *Coventry*	146	20	11	6
70	Batten & Co *Yeovil*	145	16	6	3
71	Pannone Blackburn *Manchester*	144	18	13	9
72	Morton Fisher *Kidderminster*	140	20	16	6
73	Glaisyers *Birmingham*	140	20	13	8
74	Haden Stretton Slater Miller *Walsall*	138	13	10	3
75	Addleshaw, Sons & Latham *Manchester*	137	22	25	11

Company and commercial: If we had the room we could list more than 50 top commercial firms here. But space restricts us to a mere 20 names. If asked to narrow that list down to four, then we would choose **Osborne Clarke** *Bristol*, **Mills & Reeve Francis** *Norwich*, **Simpson Curtis** *Leeds*, and **Addleshaw, Sons & Latham** *Manchester*. Informed readers will note that honours seem to be divided equally between **M5** and **Legal Resources Group**!

If we were to produce a specialist list for licensing – which we have not – then there is no doubt that it would be headed by **Cartwrights** *Bristol*. Similarly, for franchising our list would be headed by **Needham & James** *Birmingham*.

Banking law is a specialist area that is generally confined to the City of London (note: when we talk about banking law, we mean 'pure' banking, as opposed to mortgages and securities work). There is only a handful of firms in the provinces that can claim to handle real banking work – such as **Phillips & Buck** *Cardiff*, **Pinsent & Co** *Birmingham*, and **Simpson Curtis** *Leeds*.

		Total staff	Partners	Assistant solicitors	Articled clerks
76	Lanyon Bowdler *Shrewsbury*	137	17	6	4
77	Winter-Taylors *High Wycombe*	137	15	17	5
78	Cartwright & Lewis Vernon & Shakespeare *Birmingham*	136	12	5	3
79	Cartwrights *Bristol*	135	20	18	7
80	Wells & Hind *Nottingham*	135	17	24	6
81	Martineau Johnson *Birmingham*	130	22	13	11
82	Hawkins Russell Jones *Hitchin*	130	21	10	0
83	Winter Wilkinson *Huntingdon*	130	16	8	4
84	Warner Goodman & Streat *Fareham*	130	16	4	1
85	Blythe Liggins *Leamington Spa*	130	12	4	4
86	Hunt Dickins *Nottingham*	127	18	11	9
87	Rowley Ashworth *Birmingham*	127	9	5	2
88	Davies Wallis *Liverpool*	126	22	31	4
89	Bishop and Robertson Chalmers *Glasgow*	126	20	14	11
90	Ironsides Ray & Vials *Northampton*	126	20	8	6
91	Walker Smith & Way *Chester*	125	18	14	6
92	Breeze and Wyles *Enfield*	125	14	10	11
93	Oxley & Coward *Rotherham*	125	12	5	3
94	Porter Bartlett & Mayo *Yeovil*	122	13	6	4
95	Wansbroughs *Bristol*	121	21	24	6
96	Wilkin & Chapman *Grimsby*	121	19	6	3
97	Wright Johnson & MacKenzie *Glasgow*	120	18	15	7
98	McClure Naismith Anderson & Gardiner *Glasgow*	120	18	15	7
99	Slater Heelis *Sale*	120	18	14	12
100	MacRoberts *Edinburgh*	120	16	22	10

However, it does have to be said that this is an area in which — once again — London dominates. We are currently producing a specialist report on banking lawyers which will explore this area in more detail.

Commercial property: Once again, it is a difficult choice, but our suggested shortlist is **Booth & Co** *Leeds*, **Mills & Reeve Francis** *Norwich*, **Addleshaw, Sons & Latham** *Manchester*, and **Evershed & Tomkinson** *Birmingham*. The table lists our other choices.

Planning: We have no hesitation in making our first choice for town and country planning: **Hammond Suddards** *Bradford* is the clear recommendation. **Mills & Reeve Francis** *Norwich* and **Ingledew Botterell** *Newcastle* also deserve special mention.

Commercial litigation: Here we find it a close-run thing between **Mills & Reeve Francis** *Norwich* and **Pinsent & Co** *Birmingham*. In addition, we choose **Hepworth & Chadwick** *Leeds* and **Booth & Co** *Leeds*. It will, presumably, not have escaped the attention of everyone else in Norwich that this is now the fourth consecutive list in which **Mills & Reeve Francis** has appeared as one of our top firms (and there is more to come!).

Building and construction litigation: Out of the impressive names in our list we would select **Booth & Co** *Leeds* and **Wragge & Co** *Birmingham*. Both are in **M5**.

Insolvency: William Prior & Company has offices in both London and Manchester. It has carved out a specialist niche for itself in insolvency work, and the combined strength of its two offices leads us to select it as one of our lead firms. However, another firm with an extremely strong

Company
PROVINCES

Addleshaw, Sons & Latham
Alexander, Tatham & Co
Alsop Wilkinson
Bond Pearce
Burges Salmon
Daynes Hill & Perks
Dibb Lupton Broomhead
Dickinson Dees
Edwards Geldard
Evershed & Tomkinson
Hepworth & Chadwick
Mills & Reeve Francis
Osborne Clarke
Phillips & Buck
Pinsent & Co
Simpson Curtis
Slater Heelis
Thomson Snell & Passmore
Wells & Hind
Wragge & Co

Commercial property
PROVINCES

Addleshaw, Sons & Latham
Alsop Wilkinson
Andrew M Jackson & Co
Blake Lapthorn
Bond Pearce
Booth & Co
Burges Salmon
Dickinson Dees
Edwards Geldard
Evershed & Tomkinson
Hepworth & Chadwick
Mills & Reeve Francis
Morgan Bruce & Hardwickes
Osborne Clarke
Pinsent & Co
Simpson Curtis
Thomson Snell & Passmore
Wells & Hind
Wilkinson Maughan
Wragge & Co

Planning
PROVINCES

Bevan Ashford
Bond Pearce
Booth & Co
Browne Jacobson
Clarke Willmott & Clarke
Cobbett Leak Almond
Cuff Roberts North Kirk
Daynes Hill & Perks
Evershed & Tomkinson
Foot & Bowden
Hammond Suddards
Ingledew Botterell
Lawrence Tucketts
Mills & Reeve Francis
Morgan Bruce & Hardwickes
Pinsent & Co
Pitmans
Shoosmiths & Harrison
Thomson Snell & Passmore
Wragge & Co

Commercial litigation
PROVINCES

Addleshaw, Sons & Latham
Alexander, Tatham & Co
Blake Lapthorn
Bond Pearce
Booth & Co
Browne Jacobson
Burges Salmon
Davis Campbell
Daynes Hill & Perks
Dibb Lupton Broomhead
Evershed & Tomkinson
Hepworth & Chadwick
Hugh James Jones & Jenkins
Mills & Reeve Francis
Morgan Bruce & Hardwickes
Osborne Clarke
Pinsent & Co
Thomson Snell & Passmore
Wansbroughs
Wragge & Co

reputation in this area is **Dibb Lupton Broomhead** *Leeds*. Not to be forgotten are **Edge & Ellison** *Birmingham* and **Bond Pearce** *Plymouth*.

Intellectual property: We would suggest that the leading provincial firm for intellectual property is **Pinsent & Co** *Birmingham*. Its main competitors would seem to be **Mills & Reeve Francis** *Norwich* and **Dibb Lupton Broomhead** *Leeds*. **Wells & Hind** *Nottingham* is also highly regarded.

Entertainment: We had originally intended to produce – appropriately enough – a 'Top Twenty' of entertainment lawyers in the provinces. However, we have now come to the view that this is an area in which London dominates to such an extent that it would be misleading to produce a complete list for the provinces. No doubt this statement will antagonise and annoy many provincial lawyers, and indeed there are individual provincial practitioners – as opposed to firms – who can legitimately claim an expertise in entertainment law. But our researches indicate quite clearly that London is 'where it's at'. We do not say this lightly, and, indeed, this finding was one of the reasons that led us to commission an in-depth report into entertainment lawyers. Those who disagree with our assertions should read a copy of that report when it becomes available; in the meantime we would rather not single out any provincial firms for special mention.

Tax: Our lead firms here are **Mills & Reeve Francis** *Norwich* and **Pinsent & Co** *Birmingham*, although we also highly recommend **Burges Salmon** *Bristol*.

Personal injury litigation: In terms of 'profile' there is no doubt as to the clear winner – **Pannone Napier** *Manchester*. It is a natural and well-deserved choice as one of

Construction
PROVINCES

Addleshaw, Sons & Latham
Bevan Ashford
Bond Pearce
Booth & Co
Burges Salmon
Davis Campbell
Dickinson Dees
Edge & Ellison
Edwards Geldard
Evershed & Tomkinson
Greenwoods
Hammond Suddards
Hugh James Jones & Jenkins
Ingledew Botterell
Mills & Reeve Francis
Neil F Jones & Co
Pinsent & Co
Simpson Curtis
Veale Wasbrough
Wragge & Co

Intellectual property
PROVINCES

Addleshaw, Sons & Latham
Alsop Wilkinson
Bond Pearce
Booth & Co
Dallas Brett
Dibb Lupton Broomhead
Dickinson Dees
Edwards Geldard
Evershed & Tomkinson
Hammond Suddards
Hepworth & Chadwick
Mills & Reeve Francis
Needham & James
Osborne Clarke
Phillips & Buck
Pinsent & Co
Simpson Curtis
Thomson Snell & Passmore
Wells & Hind
Wild Hewitson & Shaw

Insolvency
PROVINCES

Actons
Alexander, Tatham & Co
Bond Pearce
Burges Salmon
Cuff Roberts North Kirk
Dibb Lupton Broomhead
Dickinson Dees
Edge & Ellison
Hugh James Jones & Jenkins
Leathes Prior
Mills & Reeve Francis
Phillips & Buck
Pinsent & Co
RC Moorhouse & Co
Robert Muckle Son & Hall
Sargent & Probert
Simpson Curtis
Slater Heelis
William Prior & Company
Wragge & Co

Tax
PROVINCES

Addleshaw, Sons & Latham
Alsop Wilkinson
Blake Lapthorn
Bond Pearce
Booth & Co
Burges Salmon
Cripps Harries Hall
Daynes Hill & Perks
Dibb Lupton Broomhead
Dickinson Dees
Evershed & Tomkinson
Mills & Reeve Francis
Osborne Clarke
Pinsent & Co
Simpson Curtis
Thomas Eggar Verrall Bowles
Thomson Snell & Passmore
Wells & Hind
Wiggin and Co
Wragge & Co

our lead firms. Our other lead firm would be **Robin Thompson & Partners** which has offices in Birmingham, Cardiff, and Nottingham, as well as three in the London area. Having said that, the whole of our list is strong one — there are many prominent insurance litigation firms throughout the country.

Family and crime: In contrast to the other areas of work we have not produced full national lists for family or criminal work. This is because such work tends to be more localised; furthermore, the personal ingredient of the solicitor-client relationship is often more important in such work than it is in more commercial matters. Both family and criminal law tend to be carried out by a large number of firms — many of which are small, but have strong reputations in their immediate locality. It would, therefore, be inappropriate to recommend firms on a national basis. Certainly there are some firms that can easily be recommended; for instance, for family and matrimonial matters there is **Booth & Co** *Leeds* and **Blair Allison & Co** *Birmingham*, whereas for criminal matters one could easily suggest **Burton Copeland** *Manchester* or **Bobbetts** *Bristol*.

Personal injury
PROVINCES

Bond Pearce
Browne Jacobson
Cole and Cole
Crutes
Davis Campbell
Hammond Suddards
Hugh James Jones & Jenkins
Irwin Mitchell
James Chapman & Co
Lace Mawer
Mills & Reeve Francis
Pannone Napier
Robin Thompson & Partners
Rogers & Norton
Shoosmiths & Harrison
Sinton & Co
Thomson Snell & Passmore
Veale Wasbrough
Wansbroughs
Willey Hargrave

But even these firms have localised practices. Accordingly, whilst we have prepared regional listings for these categories, we do not think that it would be constructive to produce national listings.

Provincial firms going from strength to strength

Our provincial survey has highlighted the firms that seem to be particularly well regarded within certain specialist areas of work. But which are the firms most likely to be the market leaders in a few years time?

We asked solicitors which provincial firm 'do you think is likely to go 'from strength to strength' in the next 5-10 years?' The replies form the basis of our regional 'tips':

South East
Thomson Snell & Passmore *Tunbridge Wells*
Blake Lapthorn *Portsmouth*

South West
Osborne Clarke *Bristol*
Burges Salmon *Bristol*

West Midlands
Evershed & Tomkinson *Birmingham*
Wragge & Co *Birmingham*

East Midlands
Howes Percival *Northampton*
Wells & Hind *Nottingham*

East Anglia
Mills & Reeve Francis *Norwich*
Daynes Hill & Perks *Norwich*

North West
Alsop Wilkinson *Liverpool*
Addleshaw, Sons & Latham *Manchester*

North
Wilkinson Maughan *Newcastle*
Dickinson Dees *Newcastle*

Yorkshire & Humberside
Simpson Curtis *Leeds*
Dibb Lupton Broomhead *Leeds*

Wales
Edwards Geldard *Cardiff*
Morgan Bruce & Hardwickes *Cardiff*

But what is the national picture: which of these firms emerges as the nationwide, non-London, choice?

First it might be helpful to refer back to our conclusions in the last edition of this book. Then we had no hesitation in saying that the **M5 Group** was the popular choice. Furthermore, the constituent firms of **M5** — which then numbered five, not six — figured extremely strongly in their respective regions.

This year the position is very different, in that we now have two additional groupings of solicitors: **Eversheds** and **Legal Resources Group**, each of which has five members. Looking at the list of names above it can be seen that honours are fairly evenly distributed between these three groups (which are, between them, dominant).

We have found a considerable amount of admiration for the **Eversheds** initiative and the idea of forming a national law firm by 1991. Indeed, it would seem to be the clear favourite amongst practitioners for going from strength to strength.

But what of the individual firms in these various groups? Here the position is less clear. There are about half a dozen provincial firms that are generally regarded as the leaders. If pushed to choose from them we would give equal prominence to **Simpson Curtis** *Leeds,* **Evershed & Tomkinson** *Birmingham,* **Osborne Clarke** *Bristol,* and **Mills & Reeve Francis** *Norwich.* All have excellent reputations, and all seem to be perceived as likely to go from strength to strength. Interestingly, each of the four is already committed to one of the national groupings (see next section).

National groupings

A year ago, **M5** had the field virtually to itself: it was the only real national grouping.

There were, however, several less widely known groupings. The most important of these was **The Information Club**, although at that stage its existence was confidential and its members would even deny that it existed! Perhaps spurred on by the success of **M5**, members of **The Information Club** decided to go public in 1988 and they also decided on a more descriptive name: **Legal Resources Group**. Some might argue that the group has a northern bias, in that only one member is south of Birmingham. More important, however, is the fact that all five members are well-regarded firms — especially **Osborne Clarke** *Bristol,* and **Simpson Curtis** *Leeds.*

The purposes and aims of **Legal Resources Group** are set out more fully in the group's full-page entry in the A-Z section of this book. But at this stage it is probably fair to say that **Legal Resources Group** is very much modelled along **M5** lines, with the emphasis being upon joint recruitment, training, and pooling of resources. There is no suggestion of adopting a common identity or trading name, let alone moving towards a full-scale merger.

The other group to emerge in 1988 is much more ambitious — **Eversheds**, with its aim of creating a national firm. The goal of the members of **Eversheds** is to completely merge by the end of 1991. This would be a complete merger involving member firms abandoning their existing names, trading under the one name of **Eversheds** and — perhaps — sharing the profits. As such it is totally different from **M5** or **Legal Resources Group**, both of which concen-trate on recruitment and training, leaving the possibility of merger open for a future date.

Many thought that the initial launch of the **Eversheds** idea was mishandled. 'The first national law firm' claim was widely criticised, largely because the firm would not, in the early days, have any real presence in London or the South East. In any event, it was also pointed out that there were already firms with more branches which might arguably claim to be national! Whilst these may seem petty criticisms, they are the sort of points that tend to appeal to lawyers, with the result that some practitioners regarded the initial announcement as containing an element of hype. In fact, that initial criticism has now largely disappeared, and there is a growing realisation that **Eversheds** will almost certainly happen. Indeed, there now seems to be widespread admiration for the boldness of the decision to merge.

More fundamentally, the pessimists might say that it is all very well to talk of mergers in boom times, when one can buy one's way out of personnel problems; after all, that is certainly what has happened with some of the major London mergers. But, the critics argue, what will happen if the legal boom comes to an end, and firms have to pay more attention to their profit and loss figures? If the merger is not completed by the time any downturn arrives, then the detractors argue that the financial tensions will make merger an impossibility. Further, what about the key question of profit-sharing (about which no decision seems to have yet been made)?

What should one make of the **Eversheds** concept? For our part, we are happy to sit on the fence. But there are clearly

M5 Group

Addleshaw, Sons & Latham *Manchester*
Bond Pearce *Plymouth*
Booth & Co *Leeds*
Burges Salmon *Bristol*
Mills & Reeve Francis *Norwich*
Wragge & Co *Birmingham*

Legal Resources Group

Alsop Wilkinson *London & North West*
Dickinson Dees *Newcastle*
Osborne Clarke *Bristol*
Pinsent & Co *Birmingham*
Simpson Curtis *Leeds*

Eversheds

Alexander, Tatham & Co *Manchester*
Daynes Hill & Perks *Norwich*
Dibb Lupton Broomhead *Sheffield & Leeds*
Evershed & Tomkinson *Birmingham*
Phillips & Buck *Cardiff*

arguments for and against. Dealing with the negative side first, there are those who question the whole idea of a national chain. The parallel most frequently drawn is with accountancy — especially **Peat Marwick McLintock**, with its various branch offices, all trading under one national name. However, the critics say that the justification for **Peat Marwick McKlintock** is that accountants need a local presence throughout the country in order to carry out local audits, which are labour intensive. The provision of legal services, on the other hand, does not need to be so locally based — clients, especially commercial clients, do not necessarily expect to have their lawyer local to them. In fact, some would say that the idea of a 'national' client (needing services from offices throughout the country) is a myth. In addition, those opposed to the **Eversheds** idea would argue that it is all being done too quickly and that strains are bound to emerge. For instance, they question how it is possible for **Dibb Lupton Broomhead** to merge into **Eversheds** when **Dibb Lupton** and **Broomheads** had not even completed their own merger. In other words, the argument is that too much is being attempted in too short a time.

But there are strong arguments in favour of the **Eversheds** merger. In particular, one big benefit that will accrue is that of a national identity — which can be marketed to clients throughout the country. Secondly, the merger will allow the firms to pool resources and thus take the major step of opening a substantial London office. After all, the argument goes, you cannot claim to be national unless you have a real presence in London — and that is something that neither **M5** nor **Legal Resources Group** has. There is much to be said for the view that (for right or for wrong) London is dominant in the commercial world and it is, therefore, essential to have a proper London presence (and will not 1992 make this even more important?). The third major benefit must lie in recruitment — in the attraction of joining a new firm, with major resources, and offices throughout the country.

As we have said, we are not prepared to come off the fence on this one! All we would point out is that our survey shows great support for **Eversheds**. Those interested in **Eversheds** should refer to the full-page entry in our A-Z section.

Where does the creation of **Legal Resources Group** and **Eversheds** leave **M5**? In fact, **M5** seems — wisely in our opinion — to have not allowed itself to be hurried in its evolutionary process. What it has done, however, is strengthen its position in the North West by admitting **Addleshaw, Sons & Latham** *Manchester* as a member. At the moment, the member firms say that they have no intention of merging – but it would seem that their minds are not closed to this option, and they would do so if it was the right business decision to make. All of which seems reasonable enough.

In fact, the real strength of **M5** – and we consider that this is the main benefit to the member firms – is on the recruitment side. At the moment many provincial firms are facing appalling difficulties in recruiting solicitors. By pooling resources, the members of **M5** are able to attract a much greater number of candidates. For instance, if **M5** holds a recruitment reception in London, then a young solicitor can go to that reception knowing that he or she has the opportunity of learning about six different firms in six different areas of the country – as opposed to going to a recruitment reception held by one firm from one region. Given the current recruitment crisis, and the critical importance of recruiting the right staff, we think that the major benefit of *any* group – not just **M5** – is that it goes a long way towards solving the recruitment crisis. Added to which, of course, the member firms can collectively offer a higher standard of on-going training to their recruits than they would be able to do as individual firms. This is a benefit that all three 'national' groups enjoy.

Clearly, the announcement of **Eversheds** did put some pressure on **M5** to respond by announcing its own merger. However, we think that **M5** was right to resist that pressure. For the time being the grouping seems to work well; inevitably there will be tensions within any group, but there does seem to be a genuine belief and confidence amongst the member firms in the future of **M5**. Presumably, some within **M5** argue that it would be wrong to rock the boat by introducing the tensions and problems that are consequent upon any merger. Presumably the members of **Legal Resources Group** are thinking along similar lines.

Similarly, it may be that the same logic (or fear?) is behind **M5**'s apparent reluctance to open a London office, or admit an established London firm as a member (or is it perhaps that its overtures have been rebuffed?). Might there not be a worry that the London part of the organisation would then become dominant?

As we see it, the big attraction of any national grouping – whether or not it be a merger – is the added clout that it gives to members in the recruitment market. As it stands, there is no shortage of work for any of these firms to do, but there is a shortage of solicitors to carry out the work. Thus many would suggest that the real priority is recruitment, rather than heightening the profile to clients.

Having said all this, it may be that we are attaching too much significance to these three groups. After all, between them they comprise only 16 firms – albeit 16 major firms. The fact remains that there are many other major provincial practices that are prospering and expanding without feeling the need to join forces with other firms. Inevitably, some of the smaller and medium sized firms have thought it advisable to form their own groupings; for instance, there is a group called **The National Independent Solicitors Group** which has nine members, all small to medium sized, and there is also **Law North West**, based around high street practices in the North West. Once again, we would suggest that the benefits – if any – will be on the recruitment side.

One thing that all these groupings have in common is that they are the result of initiatives by individual firms of solicitors which have co-operated with other firms to form groups on a self-help basis (usually, as we have seen, with recruitment and training being perceived as a key benefit). An alternative approach is for a commercial organisation to set up a company which will service the needs of several different firms of solicitors; in effect, solicitors can join the 'club' run by the organisation and, having paid the membership fee, can then get advice on matters such as public relations, recruitment, training, advertising, and brochures (as well as being able to put the 'club's' logo on their notepaper).

This is an approach that is well established within the accountancy profession, but is new to solicitors. So far, the BES-funded **Law Group UK** is the only commercial operator in the legal market, and it will be interesting to see how it develops. Presumably the main concerns of potential members will be to ensure that conflicts of interest will not be a problem, and that there will be no potential overlap in the client bases of the individual competing firms (and also that they will not be competing with fellow 'club' members on the recruitment side). On the other hand, there is undoubted benefit in small firms getting together to pool resources on education and training; what individual firms have to decide is whether they would prefer to do this through their own contacts and resources (perhaps through a local Law Society), or whether they would rather sub-contract to an outside commercial body.

SCOTLAND

Scotland

Whilst Scotland still has its own separate legal system, the links between its jurisdiction and that of England and Wales are becoming closer. To some extent this is simply a reflection of the increasingly cross-frontier nature of the modern business world, which requires lawyers within the two jurisdictions to have greater dealings with each other. In addtion, there has been co-operation between the professional bodies; for instance, the Law Societies have worked together on several issues, and it can also be said that the Law Society of Scotland has recently taken on a greater

SCOTLAND: Top firms by total number of staff

		Total staff	Partners	Assistant solicitors	Articled clerks
1	**Dundas & Wilson CS** *Edinburgh*	290	33	43	21
2	**Bird Semple Fyfe Ireland WS** *Glasgow*	237	30	44	17
3	**Ross Harper & Murphy** *Glasgow*	225	25	33	28
4	**McGrigor Donald** *Glasgow*	214	36	42	19
5	**Shepherd & Wedderburn WS** *Edinburgh*	205	25	32	12
6	**W & J Burness** *Edinburgh*	195	22	27	12
7	**Brodies WS** *Edinburgh*	190	27	21	12
8	**Maclay Murray & Spens** *Glasgow*	182	25	37	12
9	**Biggart Baillie & Gifford** *Edinburgh*	150	20	17	8
10	**Bishop and Robertson Chalmers** *Glasgow*	126	20	14	11
11	**McClure Naismith Anderson & Gardiner** *Glasgow*	120	18	15	7
12	**Wright Johnson & MacKenzie** *Glasgow*	120	18	15	7
13	**MacRoberts** *Edinburgh*	120	16	22	10
14	**Paull & Williamsons** *Aberdeen*	120	16	22	5
15	**Blackadder Reid Johnston** *Dundee*	112	14	16	2
16	**Thornton Oliver WS** *Dundee*	110	19	13	6
17	**Tods Murray WS** *Edingburgh*	106	18	14	9
18	**Blair & Bryden** *Greenock*	101	16	6	2
19	**Balfour & Manson** *Edinburgh*	100	17	11	8
20	**Lindsays WS** *Edinburgh*	100	16	18	4
21	**Drummond & Co** *Edinburgh*	100	15	6	6
22	**Ketchen & Stevens WS** *Edinburgh*	100	14	10	7
23	**Morton Fraser & Milligan WS** *Edinburgh*	99	15	19	6
24	**J & F Anderson WS** *Edinburgh*	87	14	9	3
25	**Milne Mackinnon & Peterkins** *Aberdeen*	84	18	7	5

national profile especially through the work of its well-known President, Professor Ross Harper. And, of course, we now have a Scottish Lord Chancellor.

There is also the fact — regrettable from the Scottish point of view — that many Scottish lawyers have moved south after qualifying and taken jobs in London. Indeed, it is estimated that there are currently about 250 young Scottish lawyers working in London. To some extent this is not a new development. In the past it was quite common for young Scottish lawyers to take jobs in the City, acquire useful experience, and then move back home, north of the border. The difference now is that there is an increasing tendency for the young Scottish solicitors to stay in London (largely because of the much higher salaries).

The result is an increasing contact between the legal professions in the two jurisdictions — to an extent that would have been unthinkable only a decade ago. Having said that, it is still extremely difficult for lawyers in England and Wales to find out about suitably qualified lawyers in Scotland (and vice versa). The same problem exists for clients (especially those based in England or Wales who have commercial work that needs to be carried out in Scotland).

The largest firm in Scotland is **Dundas & Wilson CS** *Edinburgh*, with 290 total staff. Other firms with more than 200 staff are **Bird Semple Fyfe Ireland WS** *Glasgow*, **Ross Harper & Murphy** *Glasgow*, **McGrigor Donald** *Glasgow*, and **Shepherd & Wedderburn WS** *Edinburgh*. Incidentally, **Ross Harper & Murphy** can claim to have the largest branch network of any law firm in England, Wales or Scotland (with a total of 20 offices — this compares with the 15 of **Donne Mileham & Haddock** in the South East and of **JW Ward & Son** in the South West).

W & J Burness *Edinburgh*, **Brodies WS**

Edinburgh, **Maclay Murray & Spens** *Glasgow*, and **Biggart Baillie & Gifford** *Edinburgh* all have between 150 and 200 total staff.

Firms that have between 100 and 150 total staff include **Bishop and Robertson Chalmers** *Glasgow*, **McClure Naismith Anderson & Gardiner** *Glasgow*, **Wright Johnson & MacKensie** *Glasgow*, **MacRoberts** *Glasgow*, **Paull & Williamsons** *Aberdeen*, **Blackadder Reid Johnston** *Dundee*, **Thornton Oliver WS** *Dundee*, **Tods Murray WS** *Edinburgh*, **Blair & Bryden** *Greenock*, **Balfour & Manson** *Edinburgh*, **Lindsays WS** *Edinburgh*, **Drummond & Co** *Edinburgh*, and **Ketchen & Stevens WS** *Edinburgh*.

Company and commercial: Here there are several particularly strong firms: **Maclay Murray & Spens** *Glasgow* and **Dundas & Wilson CS** *Edinburgh* deserve special mention. In addition, **Shepherd & Wedderburn WS** *Edinburgh* is especially well regarded.

Other firms to mention include **Tods Murray WS** *Edinburgh* (particularly well known for its timesharing work), **Bird**

Company
SCOTLAND

Bird Semple Fyfe Ireland WS *Glasgow*
Bishop and Robertson Chalmers *Glasgow*
Brodies WS *Edinburgh*
Dickson Minto WS *Edinburgh*
Dundas & Wilson CS *Edinburgh*
J & F Anderson WS *Edinburgh*
MacRoberts *Edinburgh*
Maclay Murray & Spens *Glasgow*
McGrigor Donald *Glasgow*
Morton Fraser & Milligan WS *Edinburgh*
Ross Harper & Murphy *Glasgow*
Shepherd & Wedderburn WS *Edinburgh*
Tods Murray WS *Edinburgh*
W & J Burness *Edinburgh*

Semple Fyfe Ireland WS *Glasgow*, Brodies *Edinburgh*, McGrigor Donald *Glasgow*, W & J Burness *Edinburgh*, Bishop and Robertson Chalmers *Glasgow*, MacRoberts *Glasgow* (especially for franchising), McClure Naismith Anderson & Gardiner *Glasgow*, and Thornton Oliver WS *Dundee*. In addition, there are firms such as Alex Morison & Co WS *Edinburgh*, J & F Anderson WS *Edinburgh*, Lindsays WS *Edinburgh*, Morton Fraser & Milligan WS *Edinburgh*, and, of course, Ross Harper & Murphy *Glasgow*.

For employment we would specifically mention Ross Harper & Murphy *Glasgow*, Brodies *Edinburgh*, Wright Johnson & MacKenzie *Glasgow*, and Lindsays WS *Edinburgh*. The first two of these firms are also relatively strong in licensing matters, as are Blair & Bryden *Greenock* and Morton Fraser & Milligan WS *Edinburgh*.

Commercial property: Here we would suggest Shepherd & Wedderburn WS *Edinburgh*, Dundas & Wilson CS *Edinburgh*, Bird Semple Fyfe Ireland WS *Glasgow*, Tods Murray WS *Edinburgh*, Maclay Murray & Spens *Glasgow*, W & J

Burness *Edinburgh*, Brodies *Edinburgh*, McGrigor Donald *Glasgow*, and MacRoberts *Glasgow*. In addition, there is Steedman Ramage & Co WS *Edinburgh* and firms such as Bishop and Robertson Chalmers *Glasgow*, Wright Johnson & MacKenzie *Glasgow*, Thornton Oliver WS *Dundee*, and McClure Naismith Anderson & Gardiner *Glasgow*. Finally, other firms that might be mentioned include Alexander Stone & Co *Glasgow*, Thornton Oliver WS *Dundee*, Gordon & Smythe *Glasgow*, and Archibald Campbell & Harley WS *Edinburgh*.

Naturally, most of these firms are also relatively strong in town and country planning matters. This is especially true of Shepherd & Wedderburn WS *Edinburgh*, Dundas & Wilson CS *Edinburgh*, Bird Semple Fyfe Ireland WS *Glasgow*, Brodies *Edinburgh*, and W & J Burness *Edinburgh*. We would also mention Simpson & Marwick WS *Edinburgh*, Thornton Oliver WS *Dundee*, McGrigor Donald *Glasgow*, Tods Murray WS *Edinburgh*, and Archibald Campbell & Harley WS *Edinburgh*.

Commercial litigation: Here firms such as Maclay Murray & Spens *Glasgow*, Shepherd & Wedderburn WS *Edinburgh*, Dundas & Wilson CS *Edinburgh*, and McGrigor Donald *Glasgow* can all be highly recommended. In addition, there are firms such as Brodies *Edinburgh*, Simpson Marwick WS *Edinburgh*, MacRoberts *Glasgow*, Tods Murray WS *Edinburgh*, W & J Burness *Edinburgh*, Balfour & Manson *Edinburgh*, Bird Semple Fyfe Ireland WS *Glasgow*, Morton Fraser & Milligan WS *Edinburgh*, Blair & Bryden *Greenock*, Lindsays WS *Edinburgh*, Mitchells Robertson *Glasgow*, Thornton Oliver WS *Dundee*, Brechin Robb *Glasgow*, and Cochran Sayer & Cook *Glasgow*.

For the more specialist area of building and construction litigation MacRoberts

---

Commercial property
SCOTLAND

Alex Morison & Co WS *Edinburgh*
Bird Semple Fyfe Ireland WS *Glasgow*
Bishop and Robertson Chalmers *Glasgow*
Brodies WS *Edinburgh*
Dundas & Wilson CS *Edinburgh*
MacRoberts *Edinburgh*
Maclay Murray & Spens *Glasgow*
McGrigor Donald *Glasgow*
Morton Fraser & Milligan WS *Edinburgh*
Shepherd & Wedderburn WS *Edinburgh*
Steedman Ramage & Co WS *Edinburgh*
Thornton Oliver WS *Dundee*
Tods Murray WS *Edinburgh*
W & J Burness *Edinburgh*
Wright Johnson & MacKenzie *Glasgow*

Commercial litigation
SCOTLAND

Balfour & Manson *Edinburgh*
Bird Semple Fyfe Ireland WS *Glasgow*
Blair & Bryden *Greenock*
Brodies WS *Edinburgh*
Dundas & Wilson CS *Edinburgh*
MacRoberts *Edinburgh*
Maclay Murray & Spens *Glasgow*
McClure Naismith Anderson & Gardiner *Glasgow*
McGrigor Donald *Glasgow*
Mitchells Robertson *Glasgow*
Morton Fraser & Milligan WS *Edinburgh*
Shepherd & Wedderburn WS *Edinburgh*
Simpson & Marwick WS *Edinburgh*
Thornton Oliver WS *Dundee*
Tods Murray WS *Edinburgh*
W & J Burness *Edinburgh*

Glasgow, **Dundas & Wilson CS** *Edinburgh*, and **McGrigor Donald** *Glasgow* are particularly recommended. Also strong are **Brodies** *Edinburgh*, **W & J Burness** *Edinburgh*, **Bird Semple Fyfe Ireland WS** *Glasgow*, and **Tods Murray WS** *Edinburgh*. Other suggestions include **Balfour & Manson** *Edinburgh*, **Mitchells Robertson** *Glasgow*, **J & F Anderson WS** *Edinburgh*, and **Shepherd & Wedderburn WS** *Edinburgh*.

Insolvency and debt collection: Most of the firms listed in our commercial section can be recommended for general debt collection. For insolvency work we would suggest firms such as **MacRoberts** *Glasgow*, **Brodies** *Edinburgh*, **McGrigor Donald** *Glasgow*, **Shepherd & Wedderburn WS** *Edinburgh*, **Dundas & Wilson CS** *Edinburgh*, and **Bird Semple Fyfe Ireland WS** *Glasgow*. Other names to consider are **Maclay Murray & Spens** *Glasgow*, **W & J Burness** *Edinburgh*, **Dickson Minto WS** *Edinburgh*, **Tods Murray WS** *Edinburgh*, **Morton Fraser & Milligan WS** *Edinburgh*, **McClure Naismith Anderson & Gardiner**

Glasgow, **J & F Anderson WS** *Edinburgh*, and **Bishop and Robertson Chalmers** *Glasgow*. Further possibilities include **Bennett & Robertsons WS** *Edinburgh* and **West Anderson & Co** *Glasgow*.

Tax: Here **Dundas & Wilson CS** *Edinburgh* is particularly strong. Also highly recommended are **W & J Burness** *Edinburgh*, **Maclay Murray & Spens** *Glasgow*, **Brodies** *Edinburgh*, **Shepherd & Wedderburn WS** *Edinburgh*, and **Tods Murray WS** *Edinburgh*. We would also recommend firms such as **Biggart Baillie & Gifford** *Glasgow*, **Bird Semple Fyfe Ireland WS** *Glasgow*, **MacRoberts** *Glasgow*, **McGrigor Donald** *Glasgow*, **Thornton Oliver WS** *Dundee*, as well as **Murray Beith & Murray WS** *Edinburgh*.

Intellectual property: In this area of work our lead firms would be **Dundas & Wilson CS** *Edinburgh*, **McGrigor Donald** *Glasgow*, and **W & J Burness** *Edinburgh*. Also recommended are **Bird Semple Fyfe Ireland WS** *Glasgow*, **Brodies** *Edinburgh*, **MacRoberts** *Glasgow*, **Maclay Murray & Spens** *Glasgow*, **Shepherd & Wedderburn**

Insolvency
SCOTLAND

Bird Semple Fyfe Ireland WS *Glasgow*
Bishop and Robertson Chalmers *Glasgow*
Brodies WS *Edinburgh*
Dickson Minto WS *Edinburgh*
Dundas & Wilson CS *Edinburgh*
J & F Anderson WS *Edinburgh*
MacRoberts *Edinburgh*
Maclay Murray & Spens *Glasgow*
McClure Naismith Anderson & Gardiner *Glasgow*
McGrigor Donald *Glasgow*
Morton Fraser & Milligan WS *Edinburgh*
Shepherd & Wedderburn WS *Edinburgh*
Tods Murray WS *Edinburgh*
W & J Burness *Edinburgh*
Wright Johnson & MacKenzie *Glasgow*

Tax
SCOTLAND

Brodies WS *Edinburgh*
Dundas & Wilson CS *Edinburgh*
J & F Anderson WS *Edinburgh*
MacRoberts *Edinburgh*
Maclay Murray & Spens *Glasgow*
McClure Naismith Anderson & Gardiner *Glasgow*
McGrigor Donald *Glasgow*
Morton Fraser & Milligan WS *Edinburgh*
Shepherd & Wedderburn WS *Edinburgh*
Thornton Oliver WS *Dundee*
Tods Murray WS *Edinburgh*
W & J Burness *Edinburgh*

WS *Edinburgh*, and Dickson Minto WS *Edinburgh*. Other names include Morton Fraser & Milligan WS *Edinburgh*, Tods Murray WS *Edinburgh*, Steedman Ramage & Co WS *Edinburgh*, Alexander Stone & Co *Glasgow*, and Brechin Robb *Glasgow*.

Family: Most of the firms we have referred to so far also have a general private client practice. As such, there are many firms that could be recommended for family and matrimonial work. To select a few might, therefore, seem unfair. However, we do feel we should give special mention to firms such as **Balfour & Manson** *Edinburgh*, **W & J Burness** *Edinburgh*, **Brodies** *Edinburgh*, **Dundas & Wilson CS** *Edinburgh*, and **Ross Harper & Murphy** *Glasgow*. Other possibilities include Allan McDougall & Co *Edinburgh*, Morton Fraser & Milligan WS *Edinburgh*, Wright Johnson & MacKenzie *Glasgow*, Mitchells Robertson *Glasgow*, MacRoberts *Glasgow*, Simpson & Marwick WS *Edinburgh*, Russells *Glasgow*, Bell Russell & Co *Airdrie*, West Anderson & Co *Glasgow*, Brechin Robb *Glasgow*, Raeburn Christie & Co *Aberdeen*, Ross Strachan *Dundee*, Hughes Dowdall & Co *Glasgow*, Tilston MacLaurin *Glasgow*, and Warner & Co *Edinburgh*.

Personal injury litigation: One firm that is particularly well regarded here is Simpson & Marwick WS *Edinburgh* (with a reputation that belies its relatively small size). Other strong firms include Allan McDougall & Co *Edinburgh*, Balfour & Manson *Edinburgh*, Brodies *Edinburgh*, Dundas & Wilson CS *Edinburgh*, Hamilton Burns & Moore *Glasgow*, Drummond & Co *Edinburgh*, Maclay Murray & Spens *Glasgow*, MacRoberts *Glasgow*, McGrigor Donald *Glasgow*, Shepherd & Wedderburn WS *Edinburgh*, W & J Burness *Edinburgh*, Tods Murray WS *Edinburgh*, and, of course, Ross Harper & Murphy *Glasgow*. Other names to be mentioned include West Anderson & Co *Glasgow*, Raeburn Christie & Co *Aberdeen*, Ross Strachan *Dundee*, Digby Brown & Co *Glasgow*, Cochran Sayer & Cook *Glasgow*, Tilston MacLaurin *Glasgow*, and Holmes Mackillop *Glasgow*.

Crime: Here our lead firm is **Ross Harper & Murphy** *Edinburgh* – the largest firm in Scotland. Through its network of offices it has established a sound reputation in this area (and, indeed, in most areas of general practice). Having said that, of course, there are many firms that are strong at crime – and it is one area in which the small firms tend to be able to compete on equal terms

---

Intellectual property
SCOTLAND

Bird Semple Fyfe Ireland WS *Glasgow*
Brodies WS *Edinburgh*
Dundas & Wilson CS *Edinburgh*
MacRoberts *Edinburgh*
Maclay Murray & Spens *Glasgow*
McGrigor Donald *Glasgow*
Morton Fraser & Milligan WS *Edinburgh*
Shepherd & Wedderburn WS *Edinburgh*
Tods Murray WS *Edinburgh*
W & J Burness *Edinburgh*

---

with the large firms. Thus we might suggest some less well-known names. For instance, **John G Gray & Co** *Edinburgh*, **MaKay & Norwell WS** *Edinburgh*, **Balfour & Manson** *Edinburgh*, **Beltrami & Co** *Glasgow*, **More & Co** *Edinburgh*, **Hughes Dowdall & Co** *Glasgow*, **Raeburn Christie & Co** *Aberdeen*, **Ross Strachan** *Dundee*, **Levy & McRae** *Glasgow*, **Hamilton Burns & Moore** *Glasgow*, **Gilfedder & McInnes** *Edinburgh*, **Brodies** *Edinburgh*, **W & J Burness** *Edinburgh*, **Dundas & Wilson CS** *Edinburgh*, **Warner & Co** *Edinburgh*, **Tods Murray WS** *Edinburgh*, **TG Bannigan & Co** *Glasgow*, **Cochran Sayer & Cook** *Glasgow*, **J Friel & Co** *Glasgow*, and **Drummond & Co** *Edinburgh*.

Agriculture: For agricultural and farming matters we would particularly mention **Tods Murray WS** *Edinburgh*, **Brodies** *Edinburgh*, and **J & F Anderson WS** *Edinburgh*, as well as **Maclay Murray & Spens** *Glasgow*, **Blackadder Reid Johnston** *Dundee*, **Thornton Oliver WS** *Dundee*, and **Lindsays WS** *Edinburgh*.

Firms going from strength to strength:

The legal profession in Scotland is considerably smaller than that in England and Wales, and accordingly there are a relatively small number of firms that dominate the field. Various names were mentioned to us as being firms that were likely to go from strength to strength, and indeed there were recommendations for all the major Scottish practices. For instance, **MacRoberts** *Glasgow*, **Shepherd & Wedderburn WS** *Edinburgh*, **Maclay Murray & Spens** *Glasgow*, **Bird Semple Fyfe Ireland WS** *Glasgow*, **McGrigor Donald** *Glasgow*, **W & J Burness** *Edinburgh*, **Thornton Oliver WS** *Dundee*, and **Morton Fraser & Milligan WS** *Edinburgh*. Of these, our choice would be **MacRoberts** *Glasgow*.

A smaller firm that did particularly well — and which does seem to be widely tipped for the future — was **Dickson Minto WS** *Edinburgh*, and we would select it for particular mention.

LONDON

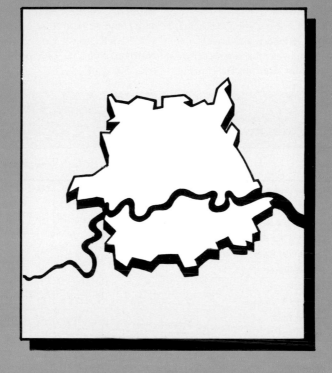

London

By whatever criteria you adopt **Clifford Chance** is by far the largest firm in London (and, indeed, in the whole country). The only other firms with more than a thousand staff are **Linklaters & Paines** and **Lovell White Durrant**. Otherwise the largest firms are **Slaughter and May**, **Denton Hall Burgin & Warrens** (both with more than 800 staff), **Allen & Overy**, **Freshfields**, **Simmons & Simmons**, **Herbert Smith** (all with over 700 staff), and **Norton Rose** (which has 660 staff). **McKenna & Co** and **Nabarro Nathanson** are the only other firms with over 500 staff.

LONDON: Top firms by total number of staff

		Total staff	Partners	Assistant solicitors	Articled clerks
1	Clifford Chance	1649	144	424	151
2	Linklaters & Paines	1250	103	325	120
3	Lovell White Durrant	1076	110	225	94
4	Slaughter and May	972	77	267	102
5	Denton Hall Burgin & Warrens	854	91	124	53
6	Allen & Overy	787	80	203	94
7	Freshfields	762	72	240	66
8	Simmons & Simmons	756	91	142	82
9	Herbert Smith	729	74	176	64
10	Norton Rose	660	77	180	66
11	McKenna & Co	554	60	114	43
12	Nabarro Nathanson	550	70	90	40
13	Richards Butler	461	64	101	71
14	Wilde Sapte	395	38	78	34
15	Clyde & Co	384	62	63	27
16	Stephenson Harwood	380	53	93	32
17	Robin Thompson & Partners	380	34	10	5
18	Theodore Goddard	377	42	94	26
19	Ashurst Morris Crisp	369	35	84	27
20	Brian Thompson & Partners	369	30	31	10
21	Cameron Markby	348	42	70	28
22	Macfarlanes	332	36	65	27
23	DJ Freeman & Co	324	52	82	19
24	Berwin Leighton	310	45	42	15
25	Turner Kenneth Brown	302	41	61	28

If you prefer to go by partnership size, the largest firms in London (after **Clifford Chance**) are **Lovell White Durrant, Linklaters & Paines, Denton Hall Burgin & Warrens, Simmons & Simmons, Allen & Overy, Slaughter and May, Norton Rose, Herbert Smith, Freshfields, Nabarro Nathanson, Richards Butler, Clyde & Co**, and **McKenna & Co**: all have at least 60 partners. However, partnership is an inaccurate measure of the relative size of firms. For instance, **Holman, Fenwick &**

Willan is the 17th largest firm if you go by partnership size; however, an examination of the total staffing figures shows that it is really the 33rd largest. Thus we prefer to rely upon total staff as an indicator of the relative size of firms. Having said that, it is important not to place too much emphasis upon mere size: what is much more important is the general reputation and 'name' of a firm, as well as its expertise in particular areas of practice. This is something that cannot be revealed by any

		Total staff	Partners	Assistant solicitors	Articled clerks
26	Rowe & Maw	302	40	78	23
27	Titmuss Sainer & Webb	294	39	73	23
28	Frere Cholmeley	283	33	66	28
29	Barlow Lyde & Gilbert	282	37	63	15
30	Lawrence Graham	282	32	60	12
31	Jaques & Lewis	279	46	43	13
32	Trowers & Hamlins	275	38	42	22
33	Holman, Fenwick & Willan	274	51	34	12
34	Baker & McKenzie	271	30	59	19
35	Masons	245	32	42	17
36	Withers Crossman Block	240	34	37	20
37	Gouldens	230	22	41	23
38	Boodle Hatfield	217	32	35	15
39	Travers Smith Braithwaite	217	29	46	16
40	SJ Berwin & Co	215	37	46	18
41	Sinclair Roche & Temperley	210	30	50	16
42	Beachcroft Stanley	200	35	29	16
43	Farrer & Co	200	33	35	12
44	Paisner & Co	190	24	30	11
45	Davies Arnold Cooper	190	19	33	13
46	Taylor Garrett	184	34	42	12
47	Ince & Co	181	34	27	11
48	Speechly Bircham	181	33	23	8
49	Charles Russell Williams & James	180	32	35	7
50	Wedlake Bell	180	30	27	8

figures. Thus, whilst the accompanying table sets out a full list of the largest firms in London, it should be treated with caution.

Company and commercial: It is difficult to know where to start! As one would expect, London is well served by company and commercial lawyers, and there is no shortage of choice.

To avoid any misunderstanding, we should explain that we use the phrase 'company and commercial' to refer to general commercial practice: we are not talking about specialist areas of work (such as banking, venture capital, or pensions). Thus in this section we are looking for an all-round strength in general commercial and corporate law.

In our view, there is one firm that is pre-eminent: **Slaughter and May**. It has a well-justified reputation for the quality of its commercial work, and we have no hesitation in putting it top of our list. After **Slaughter and May** we suggest two excellent firms — **Linklaters & Paines** and **Clifford Chance**. Together these firms make up the leading

		Total staff	Partners	Assistant solicitors	Articled clerks
51	Amery-Parkes & Co	172	21	5	3
52	Brecher & Co	168	30	23	9
53	Radcliffes & Co	165	26	20	13
54	Russell Jones & Walker	165	20	47	6
55	Reynolds Porter Chamberlain	162	25	32	11
56	Joynson-Hicks	161	27	30	14
57	Heald Nickinson	157	20	18	11
58	Field Fisher & Martineau	156	28	19	10
59	Payne Hicks Beach	155	29	15	10
60	Bristows, Cooke & Carpmael	150	18	25	9
61	Cannons	145	16	14	5
62	Saunders Sobell Leigh & Dobin	140	23	21	9
63	Alsop Wilkinson	135	26	29	17
64	Baileys Shaw & Gillett	130	23	20	8
65	Grangewoods	130	19	14	5
66	Malkin Cullis & Sumption	127	20	24	5
67	Blyth Dutton	125	18	23	10
68	Fladgate Fielder	124	27	12	8
69	Bischoff & Co	124	20	21	9
70	William Prior & Company	124	17	19	6
71	Mishcon de Reya	120	18	18	11
72	Bircham & Co	120	15	20	8
73	Forsyte Kerman	119	20	16	11
74	Nicholson Graham & Jones	118	18	25	6
75	Cartwright Cunningham Haselgrove & Co	118	10	14	6

trio of corporate law firms in this country.

Next we would suggest that there is a grouping of about half a dozen firms, all of undoubted quality and strength. At first sight, the first two names may be somewhat surprising — in view of their relative smallness (when compared to the competition). **Travers Smith Braithwaite** and **Ashurst Morris Crisp** both have a reputation that belies their size; in particular, both are particularly strong in corporate finance matters. Larger firms that we would put within this grouping are **Freshfields,**

Allen & Overy, Herbert Smith, and **Norton Rose**.

Next come some familiar names, all of which are well thought of. For instance, **SJ Berwin & Co, Macfarlanes, Stephenson Harwood, Lovell White Durrant, Frere Cholmeley, Nabarro Nathanson, Simmons & Simmons, Cameron Markby, Turner Kenneth Brown,** and **McKenna & Co.**

Refer to the table for a more complete list of firms. It will be seen that there are many firms listed in the table that we have not referred to in this text; reasons of space

		Total staff	Partners	Assistant solicitors	Articled clerks
76	Watson, Farley & Williams	115	19	32	10
77	Amhurst Brown Colombotti	115	19	10	3
78	Waltons & Morse	112	21	13	6
79	Manches & Co	112	16	26	6
80	Mackrell Turner Garrett	111	20	3	4
81	Lewis Silkin	110	20	17	20
82	Walker Martineau	110	19	18	10
83	Bird & Bird	110	18	18	8
84	Woodham Smith	110	14	16	11
85	Lawford & Co	110	10	7	4
86	Penningtons	108	19	20	10
87	Stoneham Langton & Passmore	108	19	10	5
88	Hill Dickinson & Co	107	15	18	12
89	Hewitt Woollacott & Chown	105	15	14	11
90	Laytons	105	10	10	4
91	Campbell Hooper	104	16	9	7
92	Winckworth & Pemberton	104	15	14	4
93	Birkbeck Montagu's	103	15	21	8
94	Hextall Erskine & Co	103	15	3	3
95	Hill Bailey	102	11	4	1
96	Jeffrey Green & Russell	101	18	10	9
97	Hempsons	100	16	22	5
98	Kennedys	100	16	18	8
99	Constant & Constant	96	22	14	2
100	Fox & Gibbons	96	14	12	1

Company

Allen & Overy
Alsop Wilkinson
Ashurst Morris Crisp
Baileys Shaw & Gillett
Berwin Leighton
Blyth Dutton
Boodle Hatfield
Cameron Markby
Clifford Chance
DJ Freeman & Co
Denton Hall Burgin & Warrens
Field Fisher & Martineau
Forsyte Kerman
Frere Cholmeley
Freshfields
Gouldens
Herbert Smith
Joynson-Hicks
Linklaters & Paines
Lovell White Durrant
Macfarlanes
Manches & Co
McKenna & Co
Memery Crystal
Nabarro Nathanson
Nicholson Graham & Jones
Norton Rose
Peake & Co
Penningtons
Richards Butler
Rowe & Maw
SJ Berwin & Co
Simmons & Simmons
Slaughter and May
Stephenson Harwood
Theodore Goddard
Titmuss Sainer & Webb
Travers Smith Braithwaite
Turner Kenneth Brown
Wilde Sapte
Withers Crossman Block

mean that we cannot name every firm here, although we should perhaps mention such firms as **DJ Freeman & Co**, **Gouldens**, and **Denton Hall Burgin & Warrens** as well as **Allsop Wilkinson** and **Penningtons**.

In addition, there are other firms that we have not been able to include in our table. In particular, we would mention **Hobson Audley, Trowers & Hamlins, Payne Hicks Beach, Beachcroft Stanley**, and **Adlers** (generally regarded as the country's leading firm for franchising). Also there are firms such as **Birkbeck Montagu's, Bischoff & Co, Cannons, Carter Faber, Clyde & Co, Jaques & Lewis, Lawrance, Messer & Co, Memery Crystal, Michael Freeman & Co, Pickering Kenyon, Waltons & Morse** and **Hill Bailey** (especially for consumer credit). Smaller firms that would seem to be relatively well regarded include **Calow Easton, Brooke Blain Russell**, and **Rayner De Wolfe**.

One specialist firm is **Ellison Westhorp**, which has a unique pensions practice (receiving much of its work by referrals from other solicitors). Less specialist, but well regarded within a particular niche, are **Piper Smith & Basham, Field Fisher & Martineau** (now merged into **Field Fisher Waterhouse**), and **Thornton Lynne & Lawson**, all of which of which are relatively strong on travel industry matters.

Most of the firms we have referred to have international connections, and can advise on matters within other jurisdictions. However, **Baker & McKenzie** can lay claim to being the world's most international law firm, in view of the number of its offices worldwide. But all the major English firms referred to above have an international practice; these days, corporate work in the City is international, not just national, and thus all the major firms have strong links abroad. Whilst several of the larger firms have branches in other financial centres, many of the firms have opted for the cheaper alternative of developing close links with leading local lawyers in other countries. There are also smaller firms that have acquired a reputation for dealings with particular foreign countries (eg **Pritchard Englefield & Tobin** for Germany and **Middleton Potts** for Italy: for a more general view see the section on foreign law firms in London). Another small firm with

Banking

Allen & Overy
Ashurst Morris Crisp
Baker & McKenzie
Berwin Leighton
Cameron Markby
Clifford Chance
Denton Hall Burgin & Warrens
Freshfields
Herbert Smith
Linklaters & Paines
Lovell White Durrant
Macfarlanes
McKenna & Co
Norton Rose
Richards Butler
Simmons & Simmons
Slaughter and May
Stephenson Harwood
Taylor Garrett
Travers Smith Braithwaite
Wilde Sapte

international connections is **Lane & Partners** (founded by a former senior partner of **Baker & McKenzie**).

Banking: Only a small number of firms – all within the City – can legitimately be described as having a banking practice. Note that we are referring here to 'pure' banking work (eg swaps, ECPs, and FRNs), and not general banking work (such as securities and mortgages). In fact, the City dominates to such an extent that there are hardly any firms outside London that do banking work; only a handful of provincial firms are involved in the banking sector, and generally their practices are on a considerably smaller scale than those of their London competitors.

As one might expect, the banking sector is dominated by a handful of the well-established City firms. This elite group includes **Allen & Overy**, **Clifford Chance**, **Linklaters & Paines**, **Norton Rose**, and **Slaughter and May**. Of these lead firms, we

might select **Slaughter and May** for particular mention.

Also particularly strong in banking are **Cameron Markby**, **Lovell White Durrant**, **Richards Butler**, and **Wilde Sapte**.

In addition, the following firms can be regarded as strong: **Baker & McKenzie**, **Berwin Leighton**, **Freshfields**, **Herbert Smith**, **Macfarlanes**, **Simmons & Simmons**, **Stephenson Harwood**, **Taylor Garrett**, and **Travers Smith Braithwaite**. Also with a presence in the banking sector are firms such as **Ashurst Morris Crisp**, **McKenna & Co**, and **Denton Hall Burgin & Warrens** (which has acquired extra banking expertise through the dissolution of **Oppenheimers**, and which might, therefore, be expected to increase its presence in this area). Finally, we would mention firms such as **SJ Berwin & Co**, **Nabarro Nathanson**, **Theodore Goddard**, and **Walker Martineau**.

For more details please refer to our report on banking lawyers.

For corporate finance, there is obviously a much wider choice of firms. However, to a large extent, it is still the banking firms that really dominate this sector. Of the firms mentioned so far we would give special prominence to **Ashurst Morris Crisp**, **Travers Smith Braithwaite**, **Allen & Overy**, **Clifford Chance**, **Freshfields**, **Norton Rose**, and **Slaughter and May**. **Frere Cholmeley** also has a growing reputation for this work.

Shipping: For shipping, Admiralty, and maritime matters there are several strong firms. Indeed, this is an area in which English firms probably lead the world. In particular, there are firms such as **Ince & Co**, **Clyde & Co**, **Sinclair Roche & Temperley**, **Constant & Constant**, and **Stephenson Harwood**. Also strong are **Ingledew Brown Bennison & Garrett**, **Lawrence Graham**, **Norton Rose**, **Richards Butler**, **Watson Farley & Williams**, and the smaller, specialist practices of **Elborne**

Shipping

Carter Faber
Clyde & Co
Constant & Constant
DJ Freeman & Co
Elborne Mitchell
Holman, Fenwick & Willan
Horrocks & Co
Ince & Co
Ingledew Brown Bennison & Garrett
Lawrence Graham
Middleton Potts
Norton Rose
Oswald Hickson, Collier & Co
Richards Butler
Shaw & Croft
Sinclair Roche & Temperley
Stephenson Harwood
Taylor Garrett
Waltons & Morse
Watson, Farley & Williams
Withers Crossman Block
Zaiwalla & Co

Mitchell, **Horrocks & Co**, and **Shaw & Croft**. Other names to be mentioned include **Carter Faber**, **Middleton Potts**, **Waltons & Morse**, **Withers Crossman Block**, and **Zaiwalla & Co** (largely for its Indian connections). In addition, several of the larger commercial firms would seem to be actively trying to increase their share of this work — in particular, **DJ Freeman & Co** and **Clifford Chance**.

Employment: Our suggestions here are headed by **Robin Thompson & Partners**, **Slaughter and May**, **Theodore Goddard**, **Baker & McKenzie**, and **Titmuss Sainer & Webb**. In fact, most of the major commercial practices also have specialist employment units. This is especially true of those firms with large insurance litigation departments dealing with personal injury claims. However, other firms that we would mention here include **Pattinson & Brewer**, **Simmons & Simmons**, and **William Prior & Company**. Also suggested are **Bindman &**

Partners, Cameron Markby, Field Fisher & Martineau (now **Field Fisher Waterhouse**), Gouldens, Jaques & Lewis, Lawford & Co, Lewis Silkin, Rowe & Maw, Rowley Ashworth, Russell Jones & Walker, and Travers Smith Braithwaite. Also worthy of note are **Brian Thompson & Partners**, **Amery-Parkes & Co**, Mishcon De Reya, Turner Kenneth Brown, and **Paisner & Co**.

Licensing: There are many firms that are experienced in licensing matters, but we would particularly mention **Penningtons**, **Field Fisher Martineau** (now part of **Field Fisher Waterhouse**), the small firm of **Allen & Son**, as well as **Gregory Rowcliffe & Milners, Howard Kennedy, Jeffrey Green & Russell, Joelson Wilson & Co, Kingsford Dorman & Routh Stacey, Winckworth & Pemberton**, and **Kingsley Napley**.

Commercial property: Many lawyers have benefitted from the various property booms of the last quarter-century. Indeed, rather than asking which firms do

Employment

Amery-Parkes & Co
Baker & McKenzie
Bindman & Partners
Brian Thompson & Partners
Cameron Markby
Field Fisher & Martineau
Gouldens
Jaques & Lewis
Lawford & Co
Lewis Silkin
Mishcon de Reya
Pattinson & Brewer
Robin Thompson & Partners
Rowe & Maw
Rowley Ashworth
Russell Jones & Walker
Simmons & Simmons
Slaughter and May
Theodore Goddard
Titmuss Sainer & Webb
Travers Smith Braithwaite
William Prior & Company

Licensing

Allen & Son
Field Fisher & Martineau
Gregory Rowcliffe & Milners
Howard Kennedy
Jeffrey Green & Russell
Joelson Wilson & Co
Kingsford Dorman & Routh Stacey
Kingsley Napley
Penningtons
Winckworth & Pemberton

Slaughter and May, and Jaques & Lewis. Other major firms include Simmons & Simmons, Allen & Overy, Gouldens, Freshfields, Norton Rose, Debenham & Co, Stephenson Harwood, and Denton Hall Burgin & Warrens.

Commercial property

Allen & Overy
Alsop Wilkinson
Ashurst Morris Crisp
Barlow Lyde & Gilbert
Berwin Leighton
Bischoff & Co
Boodle Hatfield
Brecher & Co
Clifford Chance
D J Freeman & Co
Debenham & Co
Denton Hall Burgin & Warrens
Fladgate Fielder
Forsyte Kerman
Frere Cholmeley
Freshfields
Gouldens
Hamlin Slowe
Herbert Smith
Howard Kennedy
Jaques & Lewis
Jeffrey Green & Russell
Lawrence Jones
Linklaters & Paines
Lovell White Durrant
Maxwell Batley
McKenna & Co
Nabarro Nathanson
Norton Rose
Paisner & Co
Rowe & Maw
S J Berwin & Co
Simmons & Simmons
Slaughter and May
Speechly Bircham
Stephenson Harwood
Stones Porter
Taylor Garrett
Theodore Goddard
Thornton Lynne & Lawson
Titmuss Sainer & Webb
Travers Smith Braithwaite
Trowers & Hamlins
Turner Kenneth Brown
Winckworth & Pemberton

commercial property work, it is much easier to ask which firms are *not* in commercial property. The simple fact is that there is hardly a firm in central London that does not have a commercial property department, and which does not claim to be highly experienced in such matters! Indeed, the amount of commercial property work around has meant that a very large number of firms have been, quite truthfully, able to make such claims. So in attempting to narrow the numbers to one list we have faced considerable difficulties. Inevitably, there are many other firms (whose names we do not have room to include) that could rightfully demand a mention.

At the top end of the market it is relatively easy to select the firms. Without doubt, pride of place must go to **Nabarro Nathanson**, which has an unrivalled reputation in the commercial property field. Although the firm practises in many other areas – indeed, one suspects that it must occasionally wish that it could shake off its 'property only' image – the firm's real strength does lie with its commercial property department. Apart from **Nabarro Nathanson**, our other three top firms would be **Linklaters & Paines**, **DJ Freeman & Co**, and **Berwin Leighton**. After that illustrious group, we would suggest firms such as **Clifford Chance**, **Titmuss Sainer & Webb**, **Lovell White Durrant**, **Herbert Smith**, **Ashurst Morris Crisp**, **McKenna & Co**,

Refer to the accompanying table for a fuller listing of firms.

Indeed, are many other firms that could be mentioned. For instance, there is **Adlers, Baileys Shaw & Gillett, Binks Stern and Partners, Bircham & Co, Cameron Markby, Kingsford Dorman & Routh Stacey, Lawrence Graham, Lewis Silkin, Macfarlanes, Michael Freeman & Co, Pickering Kenyon, Wallace & Partners,** and **Withers Crossman Block**. In addition, there are firms such as **Beachcroft Stanley, Birkbeck Montagu's, Braby & Waller, Chethams, Church Adams Tatham & Co, Davies Arnold Cooper, Glovers, Hobson Audley, Isadore Goldman & Son, Joynson-Hicks, Masons, Mishcon De Reya, Rubinstein Callingham, Russell-Cooke Potter & Chapman, Wilde Sapte, William Prior & Company,** and also **Field Fisher & Martineau** and **Gershon Young Finer & Green** (both merged into new firms — **Field Fisher Waterhouse** and **Finers** respectively).

Planning

Ashurst Morris Crisp
Berwin Leighton
Brecher & Co
Cameron Markby
Clifford Chance
DJ Freeman & Co
Denton Hall Burgin & Warrens
Gouldens
Herbert Smith
Howard Kennedy
Jaques & Lewis
Linklaters & Paines
Lovell White Durrant
Macfarlanes
Masons
McKenna & Co
Nabarro Nathanson
Norton Rose
Penningtons
Rowe & Maw
SJ Berwin & Co
Saunders Sobell Leigh & Dobin
Simmons & Simmons
Speechly Bircham
Titmuss Sainer & Webb

Finally, to complete the picture we would also mention **Blyth Dutton, Carter Faber, Farrer & Co,** and **Hicks Arnold**.

Planning: Inevitably, many of the firms that we have listed for commercial property will also be strong in town and country planning: to a large extent, the two go together. Having said that, we do take the view that there are certain firms with particularly strong planning departments. In particular, we would single out **Denton Hall Burgin & Warrens** which is widely respected for its planning expertise. Our other lead firms are **Herbert Smith, McKenna & Co, Nabarro Nathanson, Berwin Leighton,** and **Gouldens**. Also strong are **Lovell White Durrant, Clifford Chance, Norton Rose,** and **DJ Freeman & Co**.

Otherwise, we would mention **Linklaters & Paines, Ashurst Morris Crisp, Simmons & Simmons, Masons, Penningtons, Speechly Bircham, Macfarlanes, Cameron Markby, Titmuss Sainer & Webb, Rowe & Maw, Saunders Sobell Leigh & Dobin, Jaques & Lewis, SJ Berwin & Co, Brecher & Co,** and **Howard Kennedy**.

Other suggestions (not included in the accompanying table) include **Allen & Overy, Bischoff & Co, Boodle Hatfield, Forsyte Kerman, Stones Porter,** and **Theodore Goddard**.

Commercial litigation: This is a rather wide field: after all, 'commercial litigation' covers a host of different actions. Basically we are interpreting the phrase as meaning general litigation that has a commercial bias. Thus we exclude personal injury litigation, as well as criminal and family work (all of which are dealt with separately below). We also have separate sections on defamation, building and construction litigation, and insolvency and debt collection.

It is getting to the stage where **Herbert Smith** is synonymous with commercial

Commercial litigation

Allen & Overy
Alsop Wilkinson
Ashurst Morris Crisp
Barlow Lyde & Gilbert
Beachcroft Stanley
Berwin Leighton
Cameron Markby
Church Adams Tatham & Co
Clifford Chance
Clyde & Co
Collyer-Bristow
DJ Freeman & Co
Davies Arnold Cooper
Denton Hall Burgin & Warrens
Frere Cholmeley
Freshfields
Gouldens
Gregory Rowcliffe & Milners
Herbert Smith
Holman, Fenwick & Willan
Ince & Co
Jaques & Lewis
Joynson-Hicks
Kennedys
Kingsley Napley
Lawrence Graham
Lewis Silkin
Linklaters & Paines
Lovell White Durrant
Macfarlanes
Masons
McKenna & Co
Nabarro Nathanson
Norton Rose
Payne Hicks Beach
Penningtons
Reynolds Porter Chamberlain
Rowe & Maw
Russell-Cooke Potter & Chapman
Simmons & Simmons
Slaughter and May
Stephenson Harwood
Theodore Goddard
Titmuss Sainer & Webb
Turner Kenneth Brown
Vizards
Wedlake Saint

nonsense. There are many other firms of competent and tough litigators in London; **Herbert Smith** is good — but it isn't that good! So whilst we have no hesitation in naming **Herbert Smith** as our lead firm, we do have certain reservations about the very dominance of its position. Indeed, we suspect that the firm itself must have mixed feelings about the way in which it is always identified with litigation; after all, our tables show that it is strong in many other areas of practice. In short, it is not such a litigation-orientated firm as it is generally perceived to be; as such, it could be said that the firm is a victim of its own litigation success (just as **Nabarro Nathanson** has an image as a commercial property firm).

Also particularly strong is **Lovell White Durrant**, and we would complete our top three with **Linklaters & Paines**. After that, we would select **Clifford Chance, Clyde & Co, Freshfields, Allen & Overy**, and **Slaughter and May**.

Other prominent litigation firms include **Norton Rose, McKenna & Co, Stephenson Harwood, Barlow Lyde & Gilbert, Berwin Leighton, Jaques & Lewis, Nabarro Nathanson, Holman Fenwick & Willan, Macfarlanes, Cameron Markby**, and **DJ Freeman & Co**.

Refer to the accompanying table for a more complete list of commercial litigation firms. As far as agency work is concerned (ie firms acting as London litigation agents for provincial solicitors) we would particularly mention **Church Adams Tatham & Co, Collyer-Bristow**, and **Gregory Rowcliffe & Milners**.

Firms not included in our table which might also be mentioned are **Bird & Bird, Hyde Mahon Bridges, Elborne Mitchell, Sharpe Pritchard, Hill Bailey, Hopkins & Wood, Sheridans**, and **Fishburn Boxer & Co**.

litigation: inevitably, it is the first choice in any list of commercial litigation firms. We have even heard it described as 'the SAS of the legal profession' — which is, frankly,

Building and construction litigation:
Most of the major litigation firms have a building and construction practice. However,

Construction

Alastair Thomson & Partners
Allen & Overy
Beale and Company
Berwin Leighton
Clifford Chance
DJ Freeman & Co
Denton Hall Burgin & Warrens
Fenwick Elliott & Burns
Herbert Smith
Holman, Fenwick & Willan
Ince & Co
Jaques & Lewis
Kennedys
Lovell White Durrant
Macfarlanes
Masons
McKenna & Co
Nabarro Nathanson
Norton Rose
Park Nelson
Rowe & Maw
Stephenson Harwood
Titmuss Sainer & Webb
Trowers & Hamlins
Turner Kenneth Brown
Winward Fearon and Co

there are two firms that dominate this area, namely **Masons** and **McKenna & Co**. Few people would dispute their dominance, although perhaps not everyone would agree with our putting **Masons** before **McKenna & Co**. Either way, we have no hesitation in naming them as our two lead firms in this area.

Other major building litigators include **Rowe & Maw**, **Lovell White Durrant**, **Titmuss Sainer & Webb**, **DJ Freeman & Co**, **Turner Kenneth Brown**, **Stephenson Harwood**, **Nabarro Nathanson**, and **Berwin Leighton**. In addition, there is **Norton Rose**, **Herbert Smith**, **Denton Hall Burgin & Warrens**, **Holman Fenwick & Willan**, **Macfarlanes**, and the less well-known firms of **Winward Fearon and Co** and **Alastair Thomson & Partners**. Also strong are **Park Nelson**, **Clifford Chance**, **Kennedys**, **Allen & Overy**, **Beale and Company**, **Ince & Co**,

Trowers & Hamlins, **Fenwick Elliott & Burns**, and **Jaques & Lewis**.

Also suggested are **Ashurst Morris Crisp**, **Baker & McKenzie**, **Chethams**, **Freshfields**, **Oswald Hickson, Collier & Co**, and firms such as **Braby & Waller**, **Glovers**, **Hempsons**, **Warner Cranston**, and **Pritchard Englefield & Tobin**.

Defamation: Here the first choice has to be the specialist practice of **Peter Carter-Ruck & Partners**. Otherwise we would name (in no particular order) **Rubinstein Callingham Polden Gale**, **Theodore Goddard**, **Harbottle & Lewis**, **Mishcon De Reya**, **Herbert Smith**, and **Wright Webb Syrett**. In addition, there is **Oswald Hickson, Collier & Co**, **Farrer & Co**, **Goodman Derrick & Co**, **Hempsons**, **Lovell White Durrant**, **Swepstone Walsh & Son**, **Woodham Smith**, **Russell Jones & Walker**, and the small firm of **Richard CM Sykes**.

Other names that might be mentioned include two firms with civil liberties connections, namely **Bindman & Partners** and **Lewis Silkin**. In addition, one might suggest firms specialising in entertainment law – on the basis that media stars seem to be frequently embroiled in libel suits!

Defamation

Bindman & Partners
Farrer & Co
Goodman Derrick & Co
Harbottle & Lewis
Hempsons
Herbert Smith
Lewis Silkin
Lovell White Durrant
Mishcon de Reya
Oswald Hickson, Collier & Co
Peter Carter-Ruck & Partners
Rubinstein Callingham Polden Gale
Russell Jones & Walker
Theodore Goddard
Woodham Smith
Wright Webb Syrett .

Insolvency

Berwin Leighton
Binks Stern and Partners
Booth & Blackwell
Cameron Markby
Charles Russell Williams & James
Clifford Chance
DJ Freeman & Co
Edwin Coe
Farrer & Co
Freshfields
Herbert Smith
Isadore Goldman & Son
Joynson-Hicks
Laytons
Linklaters & Paines
Lovell White Durrant
McKenna & Co
Norton Rose
Slaughter and May
Stephenson Harwood
Theodore Goddard
Wilde Sapte
William Prior & Company
Withers Crossman Block

Insolvency and debt collection: This is an area in which more and more firms are claiming an expertise, although it has to be said that solicitors who are licensed insolvency practitioners are relatively few and far between. The two top insolvency firms are **Cameron Markby** and **William Prior & Company**. Frankly, it is difficult to choose between them; in our discussions with solicitors we have found that insolvency practitioners tend to choose the former, whilst the non-specialists nearly all favour **William Prior & Company**. Either way, they are our first-choice firms.

The other firms that are especially strong are **Lovell White Durrant** and **Wilde Sapte**; also prominent in the insolvency scene are **DJ Freeman & Co**, **Clifford Chance**, and **Booth & Blackwell**. In addition, there is strong support for **Herbert Smith**, **Norton Rose**, **Stephenson Harwood**, **Theodore Goddard**, and **Charles Russell Williams &**

James. Also recommended are **Laytons, Farrer & Co, Edwin Coe, Withers Crossman Block, Binks Stern and Partners, McKenna & Co, Linklaters & Paines, Freshfields, Isadore Goldman & Son, Slaughter and May, Berwin Leighton**, and **Joynson-Hicks**. Two other possibilities are **Braby & Waller** and **Carter Faber**.

For general debt collection work we do not think that it is possible to give a meaningful list. Virtually all the commercial litigation practices – as well as the insolvency specialists – will do debt collection work (assuming the sums involved are substantial enough). Generally there are no particular firms that stand out – after all, most debt collection is routine in nature.

Intellectual property: It is noticeable that many more firms are claiming an expertise in this area. In the past copyright, patents, and trademark work was generally regarded as boring and low-profile; now that there is a more glamorous name for this work, it seems to have acquired a higher profile! Be that as it may, there is little doubt that this is a growth area, and many firms are having to expand the size of their intellectual property departments. Traditionally this area of work has been dominated by **Bird & Bird** and **Bristows Cooke & Carpmael**. In our view they still reign supreme, although they are being pressed hard by **Denton Hall Burgin & Warrens**. Also with strong reputations are **Woodham Smith, McKenna & Co, Linklaters & Paines, Clifford Chance,** and **Herbert Smith**.

Also highly recommended are **Lovell White Durrant, Needham and Grant, Joynson-Hicks, Simmons & Simmons, Baker & McKenzie, Slaughter and May, Theodore Goddard, Rowe & Maw,** and **Allen & Overy**. In addition, we would recommend firms such as **Boodle Hatfield, SJ Berwin & Co, Allison & Humphreys, Norton Rose, Reynolds Porter**

Intellectual property

Allen & Overy
Allison & Humphreys
Baker & McKenzie
Bird & Bird
Boodle Hatfield
Bristows, Cooke & Carpmael
Clifford Chance
Denton Hall Burgin & Warrens
Freshfields
Harbottle & Lewis
Herbert Smith
Joynson-Hicks
Linklaters & Paines
Lovell White Durrant
McKenna & Co
Needham and Grant
Norton Rose
Reynolds Porter Chamberlain
Rowe & Maw
SJ Berwin & Co
Simmons & Simmons
Slaughter and May
Theodore Goddard
Wedlake Bell
Withers Crossman Block
Woodham Smith

Entertainment

Allison & Humphreys
Berwin Leighton
Campbell Hooper
Clintons
DJ Freeman & Co
Davenport Lyons
Denton Hall Burgin & Warrens
Frere Cholmeley
Goodman Derrick & Co
Harbottle & Lewis
Joynson-Hicks
Marriott Harrison Bloom & Norris
Mishcon de Reya
Richards Butler
Rubinstein Callingham Polden Gale
Russells
SJ Berwin & Co
Sheridans
Simon Olswang & Co
The Simkins Partnership
Theodore Goddard
Wright Webb Syrett

Chamberlain, Freshfields, Harbottle & Lewis, Withers Crossman Block, and Wedlake Bell.

Further contenders are **Norton Rose, DJ Freeman & Co, Richards Butler, Birkbeck Montagu's, Pettman Smith, Titmuss Sainer & Webb, Gouldens, Hamlin Slowe,** and **Turner Kenneth Brown.** Other possibilities include **Hobson Audley, Hopkins & Wood, Lane & Partners, Manches & Co,** and **Travers Smith Braithwaite.** Finally, it should not be forgotten that some of the specialist entertainment practices also have to be knowledgeable about intellectual property (eg **Brafman Morris, Davenport Lyons, Mishcon De Reya, Rubinstein Callingham,** and **Simons Muirhead & Burton**).

Entertainment: This is one of those areas of law about which relatively little is known by most solicitors; in practice, it is only those within the entertainment law scene who really know who is acting for whom. Further, it is an area in which there are still many small specialist practices — each of which seems to have carved out a niche in a particular aspect of entertainment (for instance, film finance, film production, or music). In this respect, entertainment law is unlike any other area of commercial law practice. It is also an area in which the expertise tends to be concentrated in London. In fact, because of the unusual nature of the entertainment law world we have undertaken a considerable amount of research to identify the firms involved, and what follows is merely a summary of a much more complex situation. Those who are interested in entertainment may find it useful to obtain our specialist report on entertainment lawyers.

The industry is, however, dominated by one firm — **Denton Hall Burgin & Warrens.** Apart from being the leading entertainment law firm in this country, it can legitimately claim to be one of the leading entertainment firms in the whole world. Needless to say, it differs from its smaller competitors in that it is able to advise in all aspects of entertainment and media law. As such, the firm does offer a 'complete' service. Two other firms that are large in entertainment law terms – and thus able to offer a relatively broad range of services – are **Frere Cholmeley** and **Richards Butler**.

Otherwise the most widely known entertainment firm is probably **Harbottle & Lewis**, which has a long-established reputation. **Theodore Goddard** and **Berwin Leighton** are both well thought of. **Simon Olswang & Co** is particularly prominent amongst the newer generation of entertainment firms. Also to be recommended are the **The Simkins Partnership**, Mishcon De Reya, **Wright Webb Syrett**, **Clintons**, **Marriott Harrison**, **Bloom & Norris**, **Joynson-Hicks**, **Davenport Lyons**, **Sheridans**, **SJ Berwin & Co**, **Allison & Humphreys**, **Russells**, **DJ Freeman & Co**, **Campbell Hooper**, **Rubinstein Callingham**, and **Goodman Derrick & Co**.

Other firms include **Beresford Lowe & Company**, **Brafman Morris**, **Brown Cooper**, **Jaques & Lewis**, **JP Kennedy & Co**, **DM Landsman & Co**, **Lee & Thompson**, **Nicholson Graham & Jones**, **Seifert Sedley Williams**, **Simons Muirhead & Burton**, **Stephenson Harwood**, **Wedlake Bell**, **Woolf Seddon Roscoe Phillips**, **Compton Carr**, **Schilling & Lom**, and **Iain Adam** (a sole practitioner).

For more details please refer to our specialist report.

Tax: This is another of those areas of legal practice in which most firms claim to have some expertise. Indeed, there is hardly a firm listed in our company and commercial section that would not claim to be experienced in tax matters. Having said that, clearly some firms are stronger than others. In particular, we have no doubt that **Freshfields** has an unrivalled reputation –

Tax

Allen & Overy
Alsop Wilkinson
Ashurst Morris Crisp
Berwin Leighton
Blyth Dutton
Boodle Hatfield
Cameron Markby
Clifford Chance
Currey & Co
Farrer & Co
Field Fisher & Martineau
Fladgate Fielder
Forsyte Kerman
Freshfields
Gouldens
Herbert Smith
Lawrence Graham
Lee & Pembertons
Linklaters & Paines
Macfarlanes
McKenna & Co
Nabarro Nathanson
Norton Rose
Paisner & Co
Payne Hicks Beach
SJ Berwin & Co
Simmons & Simmons
Slaughter and May
Speechly Bircham
Stephenson Harwood
Theodore Goddard
Trowers & Hamlins
Turner Kenneth Brown
Wedlake Saint
Withers Crossman Block

especially amongst tax specialists themselves. Second to **Freshfields** we put **Slaughter and May**, closely followed by **Clifford Chance** and **Linklaters & Paines**. They would seem to be the four dominant tax firms. Next there are the highly regarded firms of **Berwin Leighton**, **Speechly Bircham**, **Farrer & Co**, **Nabarro Nathanson**, **Boodle Hatfield**, **Herbert Smith**, **Allen & Overy**, and **Simmons & Simmons**. Also recommended are **Norton Rose**, **Theodore Goddard**, **Macfarlanes**, **Gouldens**, and **Ashurst Morris Crisp**. Refer to the accompanying table for a fuller list of our recommended firms.

Other firms that we have not been able to include in our table could also be suggested. For instance, **Joynson-Hicks, Travers Smith Braithwaite**, and **Wilde Sapte**. Other possibilities include **Frere Cholmeley, Howard Kennedy, Rowe & Maw, Titmuss Sainer & Webb**, and **Wedlake Bell**.

Family: Our lead firms here are **Charles Russell Williams & James** and **Withers Crossman Block**. Other well-known matrimonial practices are **Theodore Goddard, Gordon Dadds**, and **Farrer & Co**. Also strong are **Gamlens, Radcliffes & Co, Joynson-Hicks, Dawson Cornwell & Co, Collyer-Bristow, Payne Hicks Beach, Penningtons, Rubinstein Callingham**, and **Speechly Bircham**.

Also suggested are **Turner Kenneth Brown, Baileys Shaw & Gillett, Kingsley Napley, Fisher Meredith, Manches & Co, Hodge Jones & Allen, Jacobs & Kane,** **Malkin Cullis & Sumption, Bates Wells & Braithwaite, Simmonds Church Smiles & Co, S Rutter & Co**, and **Lewis Silkin**.

What is noticeable about this list is that we are now beginning to deal with smaller firms, many of whom are outside central London. Furthermore, several of the names on our list are quite happy to act on a legal aid basis.

Other firms (not listed on the accompanying table) might include **James and Sarch, Stephenson Harwood, Bircham & Co, Binks Stern and Partners, Forsyte Kerman, Reynolds Porter Chamberlain, Hyde Mahon Bridges**, and **Sampson Parker**.

Personal injury litigation: Inevitably, personal injury (ie accident) litigation is dominated by the insurance company solicitors (acting for the defendants) and the trade union solicitors (acting for many of the plaintiffs). From the defendant's point of view we would select **Barlow Lyde & Gilbert** as our lead firm, followed closely by **Davies Arnold Cooper**. For the plaintiff our first choice is **Robin Thompson & Partners**. Our second choice for plaintiffs is a firm that has a national reputation, namely **Pannone Napier**; despite having a very small London office (opened as recently as November 1987), we feel that it can be strongly recommended as a London firm.

Other highly recommended firms include **Brian Thompson & Partners, Herbert Smith, Russell Jones & Walker, Reynolds Porter Chamberlain, Beachcroft Stanley, Hempsons** (especially for medical and dental negligence), **Amery-Parkes & Co, Rowley Ashworth**, and **Berrymans**. Also strong are **Lawford & Co, Le Brasseur & Monier-Williams, Pattinson & Brewer, Hextall Erskine & Co, EL Murphy & Co, Hewitt Woollacott & Chown, Vizards, L Watmore & Co, Gasters, Wedlake Saint,** and **Kennedys**. Another suggestion is **RI Lewis & Co**, whose reputation is partly derived from its European accident work

Family

Baileys Shaw & Gillett
Bates Wells & Braithwaite
Charles Russell Williams & James
Collyer-Bristow
Dawson Cornwell & Co
Farrer & Co
Fisher Meredith
Gamlens
Gordon Dadds
Hodge Jones & Allen
Jacobs & Kane
Joynson-Hicks
Kingsley Napley
Lewis Silkin
Malkin Cullis & Sumption
Manches & Co
Payne Hicks Beach
Penningtons
Radcliffes & Co
Rubinstein Callingham Polden Gale
S Rutter & Co
Simmonds Church Smiles & Co
Speechly Bircham
Theodore Goddard
Turner Kenneth Brown
Withers Crossman Block

Personal injury

Amery-Parkes & Co
Barlow Lyde & Gilbert
Beachcroft Stanley
Beachcroft Stanleys
Berrymans
Brian Thompson & Partners
Davies Arnold Cooper
EL Murphy & Co
Gasters
Hempsons
Herbert Smith
Hewitt Woollacott & Chown
Hextall Erskine & Co
Kennedys
L Watmore & Co
Lawford & Co
Le Brasseur & Monier-Williams
Pannone Napier
Pattinson & Brewer
RI Lewis & Co
Reynolds Porter Chamberlain
Robin Thompson & Partners
Rowley Ashworth
Russell Jones & Walker
Vizards
Wedlake Saint

(especially France and Belgium).

To complete the picture we would suggest **Wiseman Lee, Holman Fenwick & Willan, Steggles Palmer, Sharpe Pritchard, Willey Hargrave, Radcliffes & Co, Pritchard Englefield & Tobin**, and also firms such as **Lewis Silkin, E Edwards Son & Noice, Penningtons, Seifert Sedley Williams, Simmonds Church Smiles & Co**, and **Sinclair Taylor & Martin**.

Crime: It will surprise no one to learn that our lead firm here is **Kingsley Napley**. The high profile of Sir David Napley has ensured that the firm has a pre-eminent reputation in this area; however, it does have to be noted that the firm does relatively little legal aid work (at least, when compared with other major criminal practices).

Other highly recommended firms are **Bindman & Partners, Claude Hornby &**

Cox, Peters & Peters, as well as **Powell Magrath & Spencer, Hart Fortgang, BM Birnberg & Co**, and **Fisher Meredith**. Also recommended are **TV Edwards & Co, Lewis Silkin, Reynolds Dawson, E Edwards Son & Noice, Winstanley-Burgess, Hughmans, Darlington & Parkinson, Hodge Jones & Allen, Offenbach & Co, Sears Blok, Simons Muirhead & Burton, Alexander & Partners, Christian Fisher & Co**, and **Saunders & Co**.

Other possibilities include **Mackenzie Patten, McKenna & Co, Mishcon De Reya, Russell-Cooke Potter & Chapman, Howard Kennedy, Edward Fail Bradshaw & Waterson, Wiseman Lee**, and **Freeboroughs**.

Needless to say, most of the firms listed here are small, and many are dependent on legal aid for a living.

Crime

BM Birnberg & Co
Bindman & Partners
Claude Hornby & Cox
Darlington & Parkinson
Fisher Meredith
Freeboroughs
Hart Fortgang
Hodge Jones & Allen
Hughmans
Kingsley Napley
Lewis Silkin
Mackenzie Patten
McKenna & Co
Mishcon de Reya
Offenbach & Co
Peters & Peters
Powell Magrath & Spencer
Reynolds Dawson
Russell-Cooke Potter & Chapman
Saunders & Co
Sears Blok
Simons Muirhead & Burton
TV Edwards & Co
Victor Lissack & Roscoe
Winstanley-Burgess

Private client

Baileys Shaw & Gillett
Birkbeck Montagu's
Bischoff & Co
Braby & Waller
Collyer-Bristow
Farrer & Co
Freshfields
Gamlens
Hamlin Slowe
Hunters
Jaques & Lewis
Joynson-Hicks
Kingsford Dorman & Routh Stacey
Lee & Pembertons
Lee Bolton & Lee
Macfarlanes
Manches & Co
Payne Hicks Beach
Penningtons
Radcliffes & Co
Speechly Bircham
Theodore Goddard
Titmuss Sainer & Webb
Turner Kenneth Brown
Wedlake Saint
Withers Crossman Block

Immigration: For general immigration matters our main suggestions would be **Winstanley-Burgess, Bindman & Partners, Bates Wells & Braithwaite**, and **Isadore Goldman & Son**. Other less well-known firms include **Norton and Coker, Greenhouse Stirton & Co**, and **Sheratte Caleb & Co**.

As regards 'executive immigration', several of the larger commercial firms have some experience, although it is generally a specialist area. For instance, for the USA there are firms such as **Malkin Cullis & Sumption, Powell Magrath & Spencer, Fladgate Fielder, Jaques & Lewis, Rayner De Wolfe, Reynolds Porter Chamberlain**, and **Cameron Markby** (plus, of course, some of the American firms with offices in London).

Ecclesiastical, charities, Parliamentary: For ecclesiastical matters our lead firms would be **Lee Bolton & Lee, Winckworth & Pemberton**, and **Radcliffes & Co**.

For charity law **Bates Wells & Braithwaite** has a strong name (and, indeed, it operates an advisory service for other solicitors). Also strong is **Radcliffes & Co**. The accompanying table gives other suggestions.

For Parliamentary work (eg acting on the promotion of bills for local authorities and other public bodies) we would particularly mention **Sharpe Pritchard, Bircham & Co, Vizards**, and **Lee Bolton & Lee**.

Charities

Bates Wells & Braithwaite
Bircham & Co
Currey & Co
Fairchild Greig & Co
Harbottle & Lewis
Hunters
Jaques & Lewis
Paisner & Co
Vizards

London firms going from strength to strength

Several thousand solicitors completed confidential questionnaires for us. One of the questions we asked was: 'Which firm do you think is likely to go 'from strength to strength' in the next 5-10 years (apart from your own)?' The answers received make interesting reading (as do some of the gratuitous comments made about individual firms!).

One thing is abundantly clear. In terms of prestige, and for association with 'quality', **Slaughter and May** (in particular) and **Linklaters & Paines** lead the field. In our view, when it comes to prestige these two firms have no competitors.

In terms of which firms are likely to go from strength to strength we received many suggestions. Included were a number of familiar names. For instance, **Simmons & Simmons, Penningtons, Berwin Leighton, Gouldens, Rowe & Maw, Frere Cholmeley, Alsop Wilkinson, Norton Rose, Watson Farley & Williams, Turner Kenneth Brown, Allen & Overy**, and **Cameron Markby** all received considerable support.

Next we have a group of six which are more highly recommended: **Richards Butler, Macfarlanes, Nabarro Nathanson, DJ Freeman & Co, Freshfields**, and **Ashurst Morris Crisp**. Even more strongly fancied were **Herbert Smith, SJ Berwin & Co, Lovell White Durrant**, and **McKenna & Co**.

Ahead of all these were three firms that were clearly more strongly recommended than their competitors.

On the basis of what we have been told, the third most widely tipped firm to go from strength to strength is **Denton Hall Burgin & Warrens**. Its growth within the last few years has been remarkable, and it has expanded aggressively into several new areas of practice (a process which has been helped by the quality of the lawyers recruited from the disbanded **Oppenheimers**). In our view **Denton Hall Burgin & Warrens** will, within the next few years, break through into some of the areas of work that are still jealously guarded by the select band of top City firms, and then be regarded as a leading City practice in its own right. Perhaps a litmus test for its success in this respect will be the extent to which it is able to secure high-quality banking work.

Our second-choice firm is **Travers Smith Braithwaite** (in the same position as in last year's edition). What is surprising about its success is that it is such a relatively small firm. Despite this, it carries out high-quality City work and has an excellent reputation; certainly, one hears few adverse comments about the firm. Presumably there is considerable pressure on the firm to expand (whether by merger or takeover) in an effort to transform itself into one of the large major City practices.

Our first-choice firm is way ahead of the competition. It is **Clifford Chance** and, indeed, it is interesting to note that it was also our first-choice firm last year. The general view seems to be that the 1987 merger of **Clifford Turner** and **Coward Chance** was a textbook affair in that the firms had complementary practices (ie their strengths lay in different areas, with the merger giving a combined strength on most fronts). Inevitably there are the sceptics – but their numbers would seem to have declined. Certainly, the firm was helped by merging at a time of prosperity when it was able – to some extent – to buy its way out of potentially difficult personnel and partnership problems. Now that some time has elapsed since the merger, rationalisations are being made and there are indications that the firm is being run in a more cost-conscious manner. More important-

antly, the firm's reputation continues to grow and, by any standards, the merger must be judged an overwhelming success. It would seem to be a classic case of the whole being considerably stronger and more powerful than the two original halves.

Mergers

By size, the major merger of 1988 was that of **Lovell White Durrant** (Lovell White & King *London* + Durrant Piesse *London*). Other major mergers were **Beachcroft Stanleys** (Beachcrofts *London* + Stanleys & Simpson, North *London*), **Hammond Suddards** (Last Suddards *Leeds* + AV Hammond & Co *Bradford*), **Dibb Lupton Broomhead** (Broomheads *Sheffield* + Dibb Lupton *Leeds*), **Alsop Wilkinson** (Alsop Stevens *Liverpool* + Wilkinson Kimbers *London*), **Weightman Rutherfords** (Rutherfords *Liverpool* + Weightmans *Liverpool*), **Lace Mawer** (Laces *Liverpool* + AW Mawer & Co *Manchester*), **Lanyon Bowdler** (JCH Bowdler & Sons *Shrewsbury* + Lanyons *Telford*), **Lees Lloyd Whitley** (Lees Moore & Price *Birkenhead* + Whitley and Co *Liverpool* + Edward Lloyd & Co *Liverpool*), **Harvey Ingram Stone & Simpson** (Harvey Ingram *Leicester* + Stone & Simpson *Leicester*), **Miles & Cash** (Cash Hardy Titterton & Edon *Belper* + Miles Thorpe & Oldroyd *Derby*), **Moss, Latham & Toone** (Moss Toone & Deane *Loughborough* + Latham New & Smyth *Melton Mowbray*), **Thomas Eggar Verrall Bowles** (Thomas Eggar & Son *Chichester* + Verrall Bowles & Stevens *Worthing*), and **Le Brasseur & Monier-Williams** (Le Brasseur & Bury *London* + Monier-Williams *London*).

In addition, there were serveral 'mergers' that did not involve any change of name; for instance, **Daynes Hill & Perks** *Norwich*, incorporated **Moreton Phillips & Son** *London;* **Needham & James** *Birmingham* incorporated **Byatt Michau & Smart** *London;* **Thomson Snell & Passmore** *Tunbridge Wells* incorporated **Bradfield**

Howson & Chalkley *Maidstone;* **Steele Raymond** *Bournemouth* incorporated **Luff, Raymond & Williams** *Wimborne;* **Jacksons** *Middlesbrough* joined forces with **Jacksons Monk & Rowe** *Middlesbrough;* and **Edwards Geldard** incorporated **Hollis Briggs, Booth & Ashworth** *Derby.*

Other already announced mergers that will be finalised in 1989 include **Finers** (Gershon Young Finer & Green *London* + Stein Swede Jay & Bibring *London*); **Sherwin Oliver** (Sherwins *Portsmouth* + Oliver & Co *Portsmouth*); **Field Fisher Waterhouse** (Field Fisher & Martineau *London* + Waterhouse & Co *London*); **Edge & Ellison** (Edge & Ellison *Birmingham* + Staunton Townsend *Leicester*); and **Turner Kenneth Brown** (Turner Kenneth Brown *London* + Lawrence Jones *London*).

There are, of course, many other mergers that we could have listed here. We have simply selected some of the more significant ones.

What of the future? In our view, mergers are likely to continue apace. Some will be for good reasons, and some for bad. But it should not be forgotten that the most fundamental reason for merging should be to improve the quality of the service to the client; the bottom line is whether clients (existing and future) will judge the merger as a good or bad thing. All other factors should be secondary to this.

It goes without saying that the normal reason for merging will be to unite two firms that have different but complementary skills, the aim being to produce a whole that is stronger than the two original halves.

Having said that, one only has to look at the list of mergers above to question the logic of some of them: can it really be said that all those firms have complementary skills? We doubt it.

There are other factors that can drive a merger forward; for instance, the geographical spread of offices and client bases — and well as basic economics. But, all too often, one has the impression that mergers go ahead because 'it's the thing to do', and there is clearly an element of self-delusion in thinking that a merger (and therefore greater size) will somehow transform the performance of the firm and secure its future position. If only life was that easy! Simply playing follow-my-leader, and merging because the opposition is merging, is not a sufficiently valid reason for taking such a major step. In particular, we take the view that it is not right to merge just to increase in size; safety in numbers should never be the sole reason.

Clearly the crucial aspect in any merger is finding a suitable merger partner. Usually it is advisable to use the services of an outside consultant to draw up a shortlist or to make suggestions; even if the consultant comes back and recommends the firm round the corner, at least there will be the reassurance and satisfaction of having received a second opinion. The difficulty, of course, lies in finding a suitable consultant. It has to be said that many recruitment agencies have simply changed their notepaper and jumped into the merger market! We have serious doubts about the abilities of some of those agencies to properly advise on mergers; simply sending out circular letters to thousands of solicitors asking them whether they are interested in merging (as has been done!) is not sufficient. After all, a merger between firms requiries slightly more expertise than does the filling of an individual job vacancy. Accordingly we would urge that some care be put into the choice of merger adviser or consultant.

At this stage we should, perhaps, declare an interest, in that we have been approached informally by several firms seeking advice on mergers; indeed, we do keep an informal (and confidential) list of firms that have expressed an interest in merging. Any firm that wishes to be added to that list is welcome to write to the editor with background information (in particular, the main areas of practice, strengths and weaknesses, staffing figures, and approximate gross revenue).

We should, however, conclude on a note of caution. In a time of boom and plenty (such as this) you can buy your way out of many problems. This is especially so with mergers. It is no secret that some of the largest London mergers created enormous problems with regard to personnel and, in particular, the status (and money) of the partners. Needless to say, when the firms are making a lot of money they can buy their way out of these difficulties — they can afford to be generous and keep on the unwanted partner. But, when money is not so plentiful, it is not so easy. Indeed, there are hints of what could happen in a few firms where mergers have taken place — people have been quietly paid off as the merged firm has finally had the courage to rationalise its staffing levels. So it is relatively easy to merge at a time of plenty: what needs to be done is to envisage a situation in which fee growth comes to an end, and then consider whether the merged firm could successfully ride that storm. And, in all of this, let us not forget the most important factor of all: service to the client. Client-satisfaction is the ultimate test by which the long-term success of any merger must eventually be judged.

THE LEGAL 500 A-Z

Abson Hall & Co

30 GREEK STREET
STOCKPORT
CHESHIRE
SK3 8AD
Phone: 061 480 1221

Fax: 061 480 4246
DX: 22603 STOCKPORT-2
Telex: 666413 **Other offices:** 6
Senior Partner: Mr Neville Holt
Number of Partners: 9
Total Staff: 72

Actons

2 KING STREET
NOTTINGHAM
NG1 2AX

Phone: 0602 476635

Fax: 0602 410106
DX: 10001 NOTTINGHAM
Telex: none **Other offices:** 1
Senior Partner: Mr RF Leman
Number of Partners: 6
Total Staff: 58

Adlers

22-26 PAUL STREET
LONDON
EC2A 4JH

Phone: 01 481 9100

Fax: 01 247 4701
DX: 107 LONDON CHANCERY LANE WC2
Telex: 883831
Senior Partner: Mr M Mendelsohn
Number of Partners: 11
Total Staff: 51

Aldridge & Brownlee

KINGSWAY HOUSE
13 CHRISTCHURCH ROAD
BOURNEMOUTH
DORSET BH1 3JY
Phone: 0202 294411

Fax: 0202 295944
DX: 7641 BOURNEMOUTH
Telex: none **Other offices:** 3
Senior Partner: Mr PDJ Mellowes
Number of Partners: 8
Total Staff: 57

Addleshaw, Sons & Latham *see full-page profile*

Addleshaw, Sons & Latham

DENNIS HOUSE
MARSDEN STREET
MANCHESTER
M2 1JD
Phone: 061 832 5994

Fax: 061 832 2250
DX: 14301 MANCHESTER-1
Telex: 668886
Senior Partner: Mr RGM Dykstra
Number of Partners: 22
Total Staff: 137

Addleshaw, Sons & Latham is a large Manchester firm, with a substantial commercial law practice, as well as a significant private client practice.

The firm: Established in 1865 by John William Addleshaw, today the firm is one of the leading provincial practices. The majority of Addleshaw, Sons & Latham's work is commercial. The firm is a member of the M5 Group (see separate entry).

The firm is continually expanding and has an on-going need for assistant solicitors. Enquiries to the partnership secretary.

In addition, six to ten articled clerks are recruited every year. The minimum academic requirement is a 2(2) degree, not necessarily in law. Prospects after qualification are good: nearly half of the present partners served articles with the firm. Apply by handwritten letter (with CV) to Ms DM Craven.

Agency work: The firm accepts all types of work from other solicitors.

Types of work undertaken: There are five main departments, company/commercial, litigation, property, pensions/trusts/personal taxation, intellectual property and the EEC. Major clients include well-known public and private companies, banks and institutions.

The firm is widely regarded for the work of its company/commercial department. This is the largest department, and it deals with a wide range of high-level transactions such as acquisitions, disposals, Stock Exchange listings, USM flotations, corporate finance and banking. There is a growing involvement in EEC law and intellectual property work.

The firm handles all levels of litigation, from the many aspects of commercial litigation in the High Court, Court of Appeal and House of Lords to the smaller matters dealt with by the county courts and magistrates courts, as well as arbitrations and tribunals.

The emphasis in the property department is on commercial property transactions of all types, including property investment, development, funding and letting, leases, landlord and tenant matters, and in secured lending transactions.

Addleshaw, Sons & Latham is one of the few firms outside London which provides a complete documentation service for all types of pensions; indeed, the pensions side of the practice is a significant area of growth. There is also considerable expertise in the field of retirement benefits, as well as in trusts, estates and taxation planning.

Overall, Addleshaw, Sons & Latham sees itself as a highly professional firm with wide-ranging abilities in legal matters. It is a traditional, yet forward-thinking organisation, able to look after the needs of both business and individual clients. A brochure describing the services of the firm is available on request.

ADDLESHAW
SONS & LATHAM

Alex Morison & Co WS

33 QUEEN STREET
EDINBURGH
EH2 1LE

Phone: 031 226 6541

Fax: 031 226 3156
Rutland Exchange: 38 EDINBURGH
Telex: 72547 **Other offices:** 2
Senior Partner: Mr JSB Crombie
Number of Partners: 16
Total Staff: 82

Alsters Partnership

11 WATERLOO STREET
BIRMINGHAM
B2 5TB

Phone: 021 631 4323

Fax: 021 643 8475
DX: 13007 BIRMINGHAM-1
Telex: 335568 **Other offices:** 3
Senior Partner: Mr JP Propert
Number of Partners: 11
Total Staff: 104

Amery-Parkes & Co

IMPERIAL HOUSE
15-19 KINGSWAY
LONDON
WC2B 6UU

Phone: 01 379 7246

Fax: 01 379 6052
DX: 162 LONDON CHANCERY LANE WC2
Telex: 23204 **Other offices:** 4
Senior Partner: Mr JKH Haward
Number of Partners: 21
Total Staff: 172

Amhurst Brown Colombotti

2 DUKE STREET
ST JAMES'S
LONDON
SW1Y 6BJ

Phone: 01 930 2366

Fax: 01 930 2250
DX: 412 LONDON CHANCERY LANE WC2
Telex: 261857 **Other offices:** 3
Senior Partner: Mr PD Smithson
Number of Partners: 19
Total Staff: 115

Alexander, Tatham & Co *see full-page profile*
Allan McDougall & Co *see full-page profile*
Allen & Overy *see full-page profile*
Alsop Wilkinson *see full-page profiles*

Alexander, Tatham & Co

30 ST ANN STREET
MANCHESTER
M2 3DB

Phone: 061 236 4444

Fax: 061 832 2716
DX: 14344 MANCHESTER-1
Telex: 666666 **Other office:** 1
Senior Partner: Lionel Freedman
Number of Partners: 17
Total Staff: 90

The firm is one of the region's largest legal practices, offering broadly based services to a wide range of clients.

The firm: Alexander, Tatham & Co can trace its roots to the start of the last century. It has grown into one of the leading firms in the North West and now concentrates on company/commercial work. With other major provincial firms, Alexander, Tatham & Co has initiated moves to establish the country's first national commercial law firm, Eversheds (see separate entry).

The firm is continually seeking good qualified staff, and in 1989 expects to have at least ten vacancies for assistant solicitors in all areas of practice. Enquiries should be addressed to Peter Cole.

In addition, ten articled clerks need to be recruited every year. The minimum academic requirement is a 2(2) degree. Prospects are excellent; most of the present partners were articled with the firm. Apply on standard university application form to Lou Putley.

Other offices: Warrington.

Agency work: All types of work are accepted from other solicitors; contact Mark Mattison.

Types of work undertaken: There are three main departments, namely company/ commercial, litigation and property. Clients include quoted and private companies, merchant banks, brokers, and property developers, as well as individuals.

The firm is heavily biased towards company/commercial work, involving corporate finance, acquisitions and mergers, flotations, management buy-outs and buy-ins, reconstructions and general commercial work. Indeed, the firm probably has the largest corporate services department in Manchester. The firm also has a particular skill in acting for investors (for example in relation to Barlow Clowes) and undertakes a considerable amount of franchising work.

Alexander, Tatham & Co is very active in the property field, offering advice on freehold and leasehold transactions relating to all types of commercial property in England and Wales, involving developments, funding and planning.

There is a strong litigation department concentrating on commercial matters, both in this country and internationally. The service encompasses contract and building disputes, intellectual property claims, professional negligence, and employment law. In addition, the firm has considerable experience in pensions, trusts and personal finance.

Overall, Alexander, Tatham & Co sees itself as an excellent first-class firm offering its clients a wide range of legal services. Contact John Boardman for a copy of the brochure.

ALEXANDER, TATHAM & CO.

A

Allan McDougall & Co

3 COATES CRESCENT
EDINBURGH
EH3 7AL

Phone: 031 225 2121

Fax: 031 225 8659
Rutland Exchange: none
Telex: none **Other offices:** 5
Senior Partner: John G George Jnr
Number of Partners: 11
Total Staff: 77

This medium sized Edinburgh-based firm has a wide-ranging practice, encompassing a substantial private client base and an expanding commercial practice.

The firm: Founded over 60 years ago, the firm originally specialised in litigation in all the Scottish courts, and particularly the Court of Session. Traditionally the emphasis was on private client work, but over the last ten years the corporate side has been developed, and there is now a balance of contentious and non-contentious work.

The firm is always seeking to recruit suitable qualified staff, and in 1989 expects to have three vacancies for assistant solicitors for litigation, conveyancing and corporate work. Enquiries to the staff partner.

In addition, two trainees are normally recruited annually. The minimum educational requirement is a law degree. Prospects after qualification are good; most trainees stay on with the firm. Apply in writing (with CV) to the staff partner.

Other offices: Edinburgh, Dalkeith, Glasgow, Linlithgow, Penicuik.

Agency work: The firm normally accepts all types of work from other solicitors.

Types of work undertaken: There are four main areas of practice: litigation, con-veyancing, trust and executry, and corporate.

Retaining its traditional litigation practice, the firm undertakes a wide range of work in all the Scottish courts, particularly the Court of Session and the sheriff courts. Allan McDougall & Co is well known for its expertise in dealing with personal injury claims.

The full range of conveyancing work is handled, including residential transactions (purchases, sales, mortgages and insurance), estate planning and commercial acquisitions, disposals, leases and securities. The conveyancing department advises a range of clients which encompasses individuals, small businesses and sole traders, up to the largest commercial concerns with property interests all over Scotland.

The firm is active in all other types of corporate work, including the setting up and management of businesses, incorporation, takeovers and mergers, acquisitions of companies and assets, insurance work, copyright and patent law, and pension schemes.

The strong private client side of the practice includes a substantial trust and executry workload, matrimonial and family law matters and legal aid work.

Overall, Allan McDougall & Co perceives itself as a young and energetic practice offering skilled services in defined areas, particularly to private clients.

Allan McDougall & Co. S.S.C.

Allen & Overy

9 CHEAPSIDE
LONDON
EC2V 6AD

Phone: 01 248 9898

Fax: 01 236 2192
DX: 73 LONDON CHANCERY LANE WC2
Telex: 8812801 **Other offices:** 6
Senior Partner: John Kennedy
Number of Partners: 80
Total Staff: 787

Allen & Overy is a leading City and international commercial law firm with offices in six overseas centres in addition to London.

The firm: Founded in 1930 (with only two partners and a handful of other staff) Allen & Overy now numbers 80 partners and 787 staff (of which 203 are assistant solicitors and 94 are articled clerks).

The firm's rapid expansion and reputation stem largely from its recognised ability to identify and respond readily to changes in UK and international commercial markets. For instance, Allen & Overy was highly involved in the development of the Euro-currency markets in the 1960s (including the first ever Eurobond transaction). Similarly, in recognition of the increasingly important role of EEC law, the firm opened an office in Brussels ten years ago. An office was also opened in Dubai during the 1970s. Allen & Overy is fully committed to an international practice. Thus the 1980s have seen the opening of further overseas offices.

Allen & Overy continues to expand to meet the growth in the volume and complexity of transactions in an increasingly intricate legislative and regulatory environment. The firm is always interested in receiving applications from the highest calibre applicants. In 1989 40 to 60 assistant solicitors (including those from qualifying articled

clerks) will be recruited. Enquiries to Mr CR Walford.

The firm attaches great importance to, and invests substantial resources in, its training programme for articled clerks. In 1989 some 60 articled clerks will be recruited. The firm expects a minimum of a 2(1) degree (not necessarily in law). The firm is particularly interested in applicants who can demonstrate a breadth of interests outside the law, and who have been prepared to accept positions of responsibility, whether in university or elsewhere. Prospects after qualifying are excellent: some 90 per cent of articled clerks stay on as qualified solicitors and of the current 80 partners 65 were articled with the firm. Applications should be made by recruitment brochure form (with letter, CV and names of referees) by 1 September two years in advance to Mr CR Walford.

Other offices: Brussels, Dubai, Hong Kong, New York, Paris, Tokyo.

Types of work undertaken: The greatest part of the firm's business is done in the company/commercial and international finance department, and its name is particularly well known in the areas of public company takeovers/mergers and flotations (including privatisations), international capital markets and banking, and financial services work. The department acts for private and public companies, banks and other financial and commercial institutions, and governments and governmental agencies. The work covers many specialist areas, such as publishing and the media, aerospace and satellites, and oil and gas, with particular expertise in the Financial Services Act and insolvency law. However, the work broadly breaks down into three principal categories: corporate finance, domestic and international banking, and international capital markets.

The firm has a long-recognised expertise in the field of finance. For instance, the banking group has been heavily engaged in the development of securitised and repackaged financial instruments. It also regularly advises on international project and asset-backed financings including ship and aircraft, loans and leases. The international capital markets group is one of the largest legal teams in this field in the City of London.

The corporate finance group deals with takeover bids, Stock Exchange flotations (including privatisations), and private company acquisitions and disposals. In the current climate it has witnessed a significant increase in demand for its services in the areas of management and leveraged buy-outs. The latter have included many complex transnational buy-outs, and buy-outs by way of takeover bids for listed companies.

The litigation department has acquired an international reputation, attracting a substantial proportion of direct business as well as acting on behalf of existing clients. It handles all forms of major civil litigation and national and international arbitration (particularly in areas such as banking and finance, international trade, insurance and reinsurance, the media, and industrial relations).

The property department acts principally for corporate clients such as public and private companies (including property companies), investment and other institutions, banks, government departments and agencies, and local authorities. It thus advises on a variety of commercial property investments, developments (including business parks and leisure complexes), and other major projects.

Private client work has had a special importance since the earliest days of the firm, and the emphasis in recent years has been placed strongly on tax advice and financial planning, often through the use of offshore trusts. Clients include national museums, cultural agencies of foreign states, universities and major charities, in addition to wealthy individuals and their trustees.

The EEC and competition department advises on English and EEC competition law as well as EEC law generally (largely through the Brussels office). The firm has recently established a special 1992 group to advise on the single European market programme.

The firm has a number of other specialist groups which, in drawing on expertise from a variety of legal areas within the firm, cross traditional departmental boundaries. These include: corporate taxation; intellectual property; pensions, share incentives and employee benefits; and construction law.

Overall, Allen & Overy sees itself as a major City and international commercial practice which has the experience and knowledge to advise on all areas of law that its corporate and commercial clients may require. It also prides itself on the strength of its departments, such as litigation, property, EEC/competition and private client, all of which maintain a substantial client base of their own.

Corporate and recruitment brochures are available on request.

ALLEN & OVERY

Alsop Wilkinson

INDIA BUILDINGS
WATER STREET
LIVERPOOL
L2 0NH
Phone: 051 227 3060

Fax: 051 236 9208
DX: 14103 LIVERPOOL
Telex: 627369 **Other offices:** 3
Senior Partner: Derek Morris
Number of Partners: 25
Total Staff: 150

Alsop Wilkinson is a large national firm with a significant presence both in the North West (Liverpool and Manchester) and London (see adjacent page). The firm concentrates on every aspect of commercial work and has offices in London, Manchester and Hong Kong, and an associated office in New York.

The firm: Alsop Wilkinson was formed in May 1988, the result of a merger between Alsop Stevens, founded in 1821, and Wilkinson Kimbers, which dates back to 1827 — two firms with established reputations in the commercial field and extensive client bases. Alsop Wilkinson continues to expand its client base. The firm is a member of Legal Resources Group (see separate entry).

There is a continuing need for qualified staff, especially for applicants with experience in a commercial practice. In 1989 the firm expects about 12 vacancies for assistant solicitors. Enquiries to Michael Pinfold in Liverpool; Alan Greenough in Manchester.

In addition, there are a number of vacancies for articled clerks: three in Liverpool, and four in Manchester. A 2(1) degree is required, not necessarily in law. Apply on form (available on request) in July two years in advance to David Jacks or Philip Rooney in Liverpool; Eric Quick in Manchester.

Other offices: London, Manchester, Hong Kong. Associated office in New York.

Agency work: The firm accepts specialist work only (marine and medical negligence) from other solicitors.

Types of work undertaken: This newly merged firm is one of the largest in the UK. Clients include major PLCs, pension funds and other financial institutions, public authorities, property developers and substantial private companies.

The firm's company/commercial department deals with all aspects of corporate finance and company/commercial work, with particular emphasis on pensions, acquisitions, flotations and buy-outs. The firm also handles all types of commercial property work, enjoying a high reputation in the investment and development fields. Commercial litigation work, both national and international, is a sizeable part of the firm's practice. All aspects of marine law and insurance work are also undertaken.

Intellectual property and computer law (both contentious and non-contentious) is another area of expertise. The firm's private client work is concentrated in the area of personal tax planning, with particular emphasis on trust-related tax matters (including overseas settlements).

Overall, Alsop Wilkinson perceives itself as a pre-eminent national firm offering a comprehensive quality service to all kinds of commercial clients. Brochures available.

Alsop Wilkinson

6 DOWGATE HILL
LONDON
EC4R 2SS

Phone: 01 623 5141

Fax: 01 623 8286
DX: 799 LONDON CITY EC3
Telex: 885593 **Other offices:** 3
Senior Partner: David Cooke
Number of Partners: 26
Total Staff: 135

The London office of Alsop Wilkinson forms the City presence of this national firm. The London and North West offices complement each other by adding depth and breadth to each other's commercial expertise.

The firm: Alsop Wilkinson was formed in May 1988 (see previous page). The firm now occupies a purpose-built City office resulting from the consolidation of Wilkinson Kimbers' and Alsop Stevens' London practices. Wilkinson Kimbers was itself the result of a 1960s amalgamation of three old-established City firms. The new office can therefore draw on a long and varied tradition of commercial London expertise. The firm is a member of Legal Resources Group (see separate entry).

The London office offers qualified applicants the opportunity to enjoy the benefits of working in a medium sized office whilst remaining as a member of a heavy-weight commercial team backed by the resources of a large national firm. The firm is actively recruiting qualified solicitors and is always willing to consider applications from 'quality' assistants with suitable experience. Enquiries to Simon Wethered.

Of the firm's annual intake of ten articled clerks four are London based. The minimum educational requirement is a 2(1) degree, not necessarily in law. Applications should be made by handwritten letter (with CV) to Simon Wethered two years in advance.

Other offices: Liverpoool, Manchester, Hong Kong. The firm has an associated office in New York.

Agency work: The firm accepts specialist work only (see the firm's North West entry).

Types of work undertaken: The firm is one of the largest in the UK. Clients range from individual directors and shareholders to property developers, pension funds, financial institutions and major PLCs.

The company/commercial department deals with all aspects of corporate work with emphasis on pensions, acquisitions, flotations and buy-outs and pure banking work.

The firm also handles commercial property work of every description, and has a high reputation in the investment and development side. Commercial litigation work, both in the UK and internationally, is a sizeable part of the firm's practice. Insurance and reinsurance matters are also undertaken.

Intellectual property and computer law are growing areas of the firm's practice. The private client work is primarily for individuals associated with its corporate clients, with particular emphasis on trust-related tax matters (including overseas settlements).

Overall, Alsop Wilkinson perceives itself as a pre-eminent national firm offering a high-quality service to all kinds of commercial clients. Brochures are available on request.

Andrew M Jackson & Co

VICTORIA CHAMBERS
BOWLALLEY LANE
HULL
HUMBERSIDE HU1 1XY
Phone: 0482 25242

Fax: 0482 212974
DX: 11920 HULL-1
Telex: 592419 **Other offices:** 2
Senior Partner: Mr TH Jackson
Number of Partners: 19
Total Staff: 110

Anthony Collins & Co

PEARL ASSURANCE HOUSE
4 TEMPLE ROW
BIRMINGHAM
B2 5HG
Phone: 021 200 3242

Fax: 021 2002408
DX: 13055 BIRMINGHAM-1
Telex: 312242
Senior Partner: Mr AR Collins
Number of Partners: 5
Total Staff: 68

Argles & Court

12 MILL STREET
MAIDSTONE
KENT
ME15 6XU
Phone: 0622 57461

Fax: 0622 687266
DX: 4800 MAIDSTONE
Telex: 96340 **Other offices:** 5
Senior Partner: Mr G Trevor Carney
Number of Partners: 22
Total Staff: 220

Askew & Askew

4-5 WEST TERRACE
REDCAR
CLEVELAND
TS10 3BX
Phone: 0642 475252

Fax: 0642 482793
DX: 60020 REDCAR
Telex: none **Other offices:** 2
Senior Partner: Mr DF Askew
Number of Partners: 9
Total Staff: 62

Ashurst Morris Crisp *see full-page profile*

Ashurst Morris Crisp

BROADGATE HOUSE
7 ELDON STREET
LONDON
EC2M 7HD
Phone: 01 247 7666

Fax: 01 377 5659
DX: 639 LONDON CITY EC3
Telex: 887067 **Other offices:** 1
Senior Partner: Mr MGH Bell
Number of Partners: 35
Total Staff: 369

Throughout its history Ashursts has ranked among the leading City law firms. Company and commercial law constitutes the largest part of the firm's activities.

The firm: Ashursts was founded in 1821 and rapidly gained a reputation as one of the leading City firms, a position it has retained. Ashursts is currently fifth among English law firms for the number of corporate clients listed on the Stock Exchange and in the top three for the number of listed corporate clients per partner. Stock Exchange related transactions provide the single most important area of the firm's work.

Over the years, the firm has developed its own style of operation. Great emphasis is placed internally on an informal atmosphere that allows rapid communication between all members of the firm.

The firm is always looking for high-quality fee earners, and each of the four departments has vacancies for suitably qualified solicitors.

Ashursts looks to recruit between 15 and 20 articled clerks per year. Both law and non-law graduates are sought, as are mature applicants. Applications should be made two years in advance to Alan Pannett.

Types of work undertaken: Ashurst Morris Crisp draws nearly all its clients from the business sector. It provides a full range of services for corporate clients: acquisitions, disposals, management buy-outs, taxation, pensions, commercial property and, where appropriate, litigation.

More than half of the firm's partners are involved with the company/commercial department, which has an established reputation, particularly for its mergers and acquisitions work. The firm has a number of clients in the field of energy, most notably oil and gas, and it advises both here and in the USA on substantial oil-related acquisitions.

In addition to advising clients and the other departments on the tax aspects of specific transactions, the taxation department has particular expertise in pensions and employee benefit work, and in tax litigation.

In the sphere of property and planning, the firm's property department acts for investors, developers, builders, public authorities, an urban development corporation, and many commercial clients. The firm has a first-class reputation for its urban renewal, planning and property development work.

The work undertaken by the firm's litigation department includes building and development disputes, EEC and UK competition law, insolvency and professional negligence.

This leading City firm continues to provide a swift and efficient service in all areas of company and commercial work. A brochure giving full details of the services offered by Ashurst Morris Crisp is available on request.

Attey Bower & Jones

82 CLEVELAND STREET
DONCASTER
SOUTH YORKSHIRE
DN1 3DR
Phone: 0302 340400

Fax: 0302 323710
DX: 12558 DONCASTER-1
Telex: none **Other offices:** 3
Senior Partner: Mr D Attey
Number of Partners: 12
Total Staff: 105

Attwater & Liell

147 HIGH ROAD
LOUGHTON
ESSEX
IG10 4LY
Phone: 01 508 2111

Fax: 01 508 8879
DX: 7900 LOUGHTON
Telex: none **Other offices:** 2
Senior Partner: Mr J Williams
Number of Partners: 9
Total Staff: 64

Baker & McKenzie

ALDWYCH HOUSE
ALDWYCH
LONDON
WC2B 4JP
Phone: 01 242 6531

Fax: 01 831 8611
DX: 233 LONDON CHANCERY LANE WC2
Telex: 25660
Senior Partner: Mr A Joanes
Number of Partners: 30
Total Staff: 271

Balderston Warren

BROADWAY CHAMBERS
STATION PLACE
LETCHWORTH
HERTFORDSHIRE SG6 3AD
Phone: 0462 482248

Fax: 0462 480052
DX: 31302 LETCHWORTH
Telex: none **Other offices:** 3
Senior Partner: Mr ME Gardiner
Number of Partners: 13
Total Staff: 70

Baileys Shaw & Gillett *see full-page profile*

Baileys Shaw & Gillett

17 QUEEN SQUARE
LONDON
WC1N 3RH

Phone: 01 837 5455

Fax: 01 837 0071
DX: 35704 BLOOMSBURY WC1
Telex: 28961
Senior Partner: Peter Foster
Number of Partners: 23
Total Staff: 130

This is a substantial commercial practice based in central London which provides expertise in virtually all fields of the law.

The firm: Founded in 1798 (predominantly to look after the private affairs and property interests of wealthy landed families), the firm took its present name in 1875. Property still plays an important part in the firm's recent commercially led period of expansion. The firm is divided into departments.

In line with its programme of organic growth, the firm expects to recruit up to six assistant solicitors in the litigation, commercial and property departments Address enquiries to the relevant departmental executive partner.

Up to eight articled clerks are recruited annually. Candidates should have a 2(1) degree, not necessarily in law. Prospects are good: a number of the present partners were articled to the firm. Apply (with full CV and referees) by 1 August two years in advance to Jeremy Hudson.

Agency work: The firm accepts litigation work from other solicitors: contact Simon Rawlings.

Types of work undertaken: Although structured traditionally with four principal departments (commercial, property, litigation, and tax/private client), this responsive medium sized firm specialises in advising fast-growing businesses, often solving problems by adopting a project team approach. In addition the firm acts for a large number of well-established public and private companies, institutions and charities, and has a wide-ranging private client practice (with an emphasis on tax matters).

The areas in which the firm is particularly active embrace all aspects of legal work in the fields of commercial and property law, litigation and tax planning advice. It has special expertise in commercial contract negotiation, intellectual property and technology transfer agreements, corporate finance, commercial property, construction law, bloodstock and matrimonial law.

The commercial department deals with a wide variety of corporate matters, including flotations, management buy-outs and acquisitions and disposals. As well as commercial property the firm handles residential conveyancing work. The litigation department handles all types of commercial work, as well as matrimonial and personal injury work.

Overall, Baileys Shaw & Gillett describes itself as a happy, successful and growing firm which combines all the old-fashioned virtues of integrity and professionalism with a speedy and effective response and delivery mechanism driven by top quality, commercially minded lawyers. Brochures are available.

Balfour & Manson

58 FREDERICK STREET
EDINBURGH
EH2 1LS

Phone: 031 225 8291

Fax: 031 225 5687
Rutland Exchange: 4 EDINBURGH
Telex: 72175
Senior Partner: Miss EM Houston
Number of Partners: 17
Total Staff: 100

Bankes Ashton

81A GUILDHALL STREET
BURY ST EDMUNDS
SUFFOLK
IP33 1PZ

Phone: 0284 62331

Fax: 0284 64214
DX: 57200 BURY ST EDMUNDS
Telex: 81575 **Other offices:** 1
Senior Partner: Mr RGC Freeman
Number of Partners: 16
Total Staff: 80

Barlows

55-56 QUARRY STREET
GUILDFORD
SURREY
GU1 3UE

Phone: 0483 62901

Fax: 0483 573325
DX: 2407 GUILDFORD
Telex: 859500 **Other offices:** 2
Senior Partner: Mr A Anderson
Number of Partners: 10
Total Staff: 65

Barnard & Co

HALIFAX HOUSE
77 NORTH STREET, DOWNEND
BRISTOL
AVON BS1 2AZ

Phone: 0272 561830

Fax: 0272 701121
DX: 7883 BRISTOL
Telex: none **Other offices:** 5
Senior Partner: Mr Michael Barnard
Number of Partners: 4
Total Staff: 57

Barlow Lyde & Gilbert *see full-page profile*

Barlow Lyde & Gilbert

BEAUFORT HOUSE
15 ST BOTOLPH STREET
LONDON
EC3A 7NJ

Phone: 01 247 2277

Fax: 01 782 8500
DX: 155 LONDON CITY EC3
Telex: 913281 **Other offices:** 2
Senior Partner: Mr BJ Pistorius
Number of Partners: 37
Total Staff: 282

Barlow Lyde & Gilbert is a commercial City practice with close connections with the insurance world, particularly Lloyd's of London.

The firm: The origins of Barlow Lyde & Gilbert go back as far as 1840. The firm has a strong base in the field of insurance law and has been particularly active in recent years in the fields of professional indemnity and reinsurance. From this base it has grown into a more general commercial practice with established banking, corporate and commercial property departments.

There are likely to be 20 vacancies for assistant solicitors in the next 12 months. Particular demand is likely for banking, company/commercial and litigation lawyers. Enquiries should be addressed to the personnel manager.

In addition, the firm normally recruits 10 to 12 articled clerks every year. The minimum educational requirement is a second class honours degree which need not necessarily be in law. Apply by handwritten letter (with CV and names of referees) to the personnel manager.

Other offices: Hong Kong, London (Lloyds).

Types of work undertaken: This large City firm has a substantial litigation division.

Particular areas of expertise include professional negligence work (the firm was involved in five of the ten largest claims against accountants listed in the *Financial Times* in September 1987), insurance and reinsurance disputes, personal injury, employment law, defamation and general commercial litigation. Commercial work carried out by the firm includes corporate finance, management buy-outs, joint ventures and venture capital. The firm is active in European and insolvency law and has a rapidly expanding banking department. There is a well-established commercial property department.

Barlow Lyde & Gilbert is particularly well known for its expertise in all aspects of air and space law; clients come from all parts of the aerospace industry as well as from the aviation and space insurance markets in the UK and overseas.

Much of the work of the firm is international in nature and this trend will continue with the advent of the single European market in 1992. The firm has an office in Hong Kong and through its network of overseas correspondents is able to meet the needs of clients throughout the world.

Overall, Barlow Lyde & Gilbert perceives itself as a leading practice in the insurance field, with a growing reputation in banking, company/commercial, and property work. It is firmly established, well run and second to none in its chosen fields.

BARLOW LYDE & GILBERT

Bates & Partners

BARYTA HOUSE
29 VICTORIA AVENUE
SOUTHEND
ESSEX SS2 6AR
Phone: 0702 349494

Fax: 0702 332437
DX: 2800 SOUTHEND
Telex: 995095 **Other offices:** 3
Senior Partner: Mr M Warwick
Number of Partners: 13
Total Staff: 152

Bates Wells & Braithwaite

61 CHARTERHOUSE STREET
LONDON
EC1M 6HA

Phone: 01 251 1122

Fax: 01 251 2061
DX: 46612 BARBICAN EC1
Telex: 887284 **Other offices:** 2
Senior Partner: Mr Andrew Phillips
Number of Partners: 12
Total Staff: 85

Batten & Co

CHURCH HOUSE
CHURCH STREET
YEOVIL
SOMERSET BA20 1HB
Phone: 0935 23685

Fax: 0935 706054
DX: 100503 YEOVIL
Telex: 46124 **Other offices:** 7
Managing Partner: Mr D Batten
Number of Partners: 16
Total Staff: 145

Beachcroft Stanleys

100 FETTER LANE
LONDON
EC4A 1BN

Phone: 01 242 1011

Fax: 01 430 1532
DX: 45 LONDON CHANCERY LANE WC2
Telex: 264607 **Other offices:** 1
Senior Partner: Mr G Hodson
Number of Partners: 35
Total Staff: 200

Beale and Company

GARRICK HOUSE
27-32 KING STREET
COVENT GARDEN
LONDON WC2E 8JD
Phone: 01 240 3474

Fax: 01 240 9111
DX: 595 LONDON CHANCERY LANE WC2
Telex: 912072
Senior Partner: Michael R Ludlow
Number of Partners: 9
Total Staff: 52

This medium sized central London firm is a commercially orientated practice with a varied commercial and private client base.

The firm: Established in 1838 in Birmingham, Beale and Company opened a London office 40 years later to handle railway development petitions. Since then, the firm has grown into a broadly based commercial practice well known for its extensive litigation work and a significant private client base. The firm is organised into departments.

This is an expanding firm which is always seeking qualified staff. In the next 12 months it expects to recruit three assistant solicitors, for litigation and company/commercial work. Enquiries to Antony Smith.

In addition, the firm normally has three to four vacancies for articled clerks every year. The minimum educational requirement is a 2(2) degree. Prospects after qualification are excellent: the majority of the present partners served articles with the firm. Apply by handwritten letter (with CV and names of referees) in October two years in advance to Rachel Barnes.

Types of work undertaken: The firm has long-established connections with the building and civil engineering industries. This remains a significant and renowned area of the practice, with the firm advising construction industry clients on both national and international contract conditions.

The strong litigation department handles general commercial contract disputes, and is well known for its experience and good results in UK and international litigation and arbitration cases.

There is a very strong company/commercial department, which has particular expertise in business restructuring, partnership incorporations, management buy-outs and the acquisition by and of small to medium sized enterprises (with special emphasis on 1992 single market preparation), joint venture and distribution agreements and franchises. The firm also advises major professional institutions on such matters as policy, and amendments to by-laws.

The protection of intellectual and other property rights, which may involve litigation, is a noteworthy area of the practice. In addition, there is a substantial private client department advising on tax planning and trust and estate planning, and frequently international issues such as domicile, residence, tax havens, offshore trusts and foreign property laws. A certain amount of domestic (and commercial) conveyancing work is also undertaken.

Overall, Beale and Company sees itself as accessible, providing personal attention to all clients, and above all, as a creative business source. Brochures describing the services offered are available to clients on request.

BEALE
AND COMPANY

Beaumont & Son

LLOYDS CHAMBERS
1 PORTSOKEN STREET
LONDON
E1 8AW
Phone: 01 481 3100

Fax: 01 481 3353
DX: 551 LONDON CITY EC3
Telex: 889018
Senior Partner: Mr TSB Unmack
Number of Partners: 10
Total Staff: 52

Becke Phipps

7 SPENCER PARADE
NORTHAMPTON
NN1 5AB

Phone: 0604 233233

Fax: 0604 27941
DX: 12401 NORTHAMPTON-1
Telex: 31373 **Other offices:** 2
Senior Partner: Mr KT Davidson
Number of Partners: 13
Total Staff: 103

Bell Lamb & Joynson

6 CASTLE STREET
LIVERPOOL
L2 0NB

Phone: 051 227 2626

Fax: 051 227 5937
DX: 14110 LIVERPOOL
Telex: none **Other offices:** 7
Senior Partner: Mr PH Williams
Number of Partners: 12
Total Staff: 77

Berry & Berry Cocker Smith & Co

1-5 LONGLEY ROAD
WALKDEN
WORSLEY
GREATER MANCHESTER M28 6AA
Phone: 061 790 1411

Fax: 061 790 1971
DX: none
Telex: none **Other offices:** 3
Senior Partner: Mr PT Smith
Number of Partners: 6
Total Staff: 52

Bermans *see full-page profile*

Bermans

TRIDENT HOUSE
31-33 DALE STREET
LIVERPOOL
L2 2NS
Phone: 051 227 3351

Fax: 051 236 2107
DX: 14116 LIVERPOOL
Telex: 627555 **Other offices:** 4
Senior Partner: Ian Short
Number of Partners: 8
Total Staff: 120

This Liverpool-based firm is commercially orientated, and is well known for both litigious and non-contentious work.

The firm: Established in 1970 by Keith Berman, the firm is now a leading provincial corporate and commercial practice with three offices in the UK and one in New York.

Because of its continuing expansion, Bermans is always looking for high-quality qualified staff, including qualified and trainee legal executives. In 1989 the firm expects to have six vacancies for assistant solicitors. Enquiries to Ian R Short.

In addition, the firm has vacancies for three to six articled clerks every year. The preferred educational qualification is a good class degree, usually in law. Prospects after qualification are excellent. almost all articled clerks stay on with the firm. Applications should be made by handwritten letter (with CV and names of referees) and addressed to Ian R Short two years in advance.

Other offices: Manchester, London, Glasgow, New York.

Agency work: The firm accepts commercial work only from other solicitors; contact Ian R Short (corporate/property) or John Hall (litigation).

Types of work undertaken: The work of the firm is predominantly commercial (the private client work undertaken mainly emanates from directors of client companies). Bermans deals with a wide variety of commercial clients, and is particularly well known for its work for businesses involved in factoring, leasing, banking, brewing, and building.

The firm has a high reputation for its commercial litigation work, which includes contract disputes, professional negligence claims, retention of title, mortgage actions, consumer credit and all aspects of insolvency, as well as a computerised debt collection service operated on a worldwide basis.

Non-contentious work includes the full range of corporate services (the firm has particular expertise in company start-ups, management buy-outs and insolvency), as well as commercial property work.

Much of the firm's work is international in nature, and the New York office allows companies to pursue legal and business matters on both sides of the Atlantic with the minimum of inconvenience.

Bermans sees itself as an aggressive and highly efficient commercial practice, which is pre-eminent in its chosen areas, and which utilises very advanced technology and computer-linked offices in order to provide the highest quality service to its national and international clients. A brochure describing the firm's services is available on request.

BERMANS

Berwin Leighton

ADELAIDE HOUSE
LONDON BRIDGE
LONDON
EC4R 9HA
Phone: 01 623 3144

Fax: 01 623 4416
DX: 92 LONDON CHANCERY LANE WC2
Telex: 886420 **Other offices:** 1
Chairman: Mr JR Fenner
Managing Partner: Mr L Heller
Number of Partners: 45 **Total Staff:** 310

Berwin Leighton is one of the major City firms, offering a comprehensive legal service to a wide range of commercial clients.

The firm: Founded in 1970 as the result of a merger of two successful small firms, both heavily involved in commercial work. Berwin Leighton has expanded steadily since then into a thriving medium sized firm and, despite its youth, has acquired an enviable reputation for the quality of its work. In 1983, the firm opened a New York office, dealing mainly with real estate transactions and corporate acquisitions. The firm is organised into departments with close co-operation between the experts in the different fields.

There is a continuing need for qualified staff, and in 1989 the firm expects to have about 20 vacancies for assistant solicitors. Enquiries to Freya Slade, the personnel manager.

In addition, 12 articled clerks are recruited annually. A 2(2) degree is required, not necessarily in law. Apply on form (available on request) to Hugh Homan.

Other offices: New York.

Types of work undertaken: This is a broad-based commercial practice. There are three main departments, namely company/commercial, litigation and property. The firm's wide client base includes listed and private companies, banks, insurance companies, developers, shipowners, professionals, charities, and film, TV and video producers.

Berwin Leighton is particularly well known for its expertise in the corporate and financial areas. This work includes acquisitions and takeovers, flotations, partnerships and joint ventures, contracts, pensions and insolvency matters, as well as banking, and financing (project, ship, aircraft and film).

The property department is well recognised as one of the leaders in its field. It handles the full range of commercial property development activity.

The litigation department places particular emphasis on domestic and international banking transaction disputes, insurance (contentious and non-contentious), intellectual property matters, maritime work, arbitration, employment law and defamation.

The firm is well known for its work in taxation, including tax planning and advice to individuals and corporations, litigation and negotiation on tax matters, as well as trusts, probate, wills, estates and pensions.

The practice has progressively added departments in the fields of shipping, aviation, banking, pensions, communications, entertainment, town planning and construction.

Berwin Leighton perceives itself as the most interesting major firm to have 'arrived' in the City during the last 20 years.

BERWIN LEIGHTON

Bevan Ashford

35 COLSTON AVENUE
BRISTOL
BS1 4TT

Phone: 0272 230111

Fax: 0272 291865
DX: 7828 BRISTOL
Telex: 44778
Other offices: 8
Number of Partners: 49
Total Staff: 350

This is a wide-ranging practice throughout the South West, offering the full range of legal services to commercial and private clients.

The firm: The result of a merger of three old-established firms, Bevan Ashford was formed in January 1987. Since then it has amalgamated with two other firms to become the largest practice in the south west of England. In the two years since its formation the annual expansion rate has exceeded 25 per cent. The firm is co-ordinated by a management committee, supported by a non-lawyer operations director.

Bevan Ashford expects to have more than ten vacancies for assistant solicitors, for commercial law, litigation, taxation and property. Enquiries to David Tolson (Bristol).

In addition, the firm recruits about 20 articled clerks every year. Candidates are expected to have a good degree, not necessarily in law. Apply by handwritten letter (with CV) by October two years in advance to David Tolson (Bristol).

Other offices: Exeter, Taunton, Tiverton, Swindon (2), Crediton, Cullompton, London.

Agency work: Work from other solicitors is co-ordinated by a special team, which can call on the expertise of other departments where necessary.

Types of work undertaken: Within this broad-based practice virtually every type of work is undertaken.

The clients vary from public authorities and companies requiring finance, taxation, pensions, employment law, property and litigation work, to private clients needing advice on tax, trusts and family matters, criminal law and conveyancing. Bevan Ashford is organised into departments, each of which is represented at every office.

The firm has an established reputation in the field of commercial litigation, particularly for health provision matters, insurance work, building contract law and employment law. In addition, there is extensive experience of, and expertise in, agricultural and landowning client work and related tax and trust work, intellectual property law, the full range of company/corporate work, town planning law and property development work, as well as all commercial and private conveyancing.

The firm's policy is to continue to strengthen these areas of expertise, and, at the same time, to maintain the very substantial private client base at each of the offices.

Bevan Ashford was one of the first major provincial firms to complete a comprehensive merger, making it one of the largest practices outside London. The resulting growth has proved the success of this concept and the firm intends to continue the process as part of a prudent development programme.

■ BEVAN ■
ASHFORD

Biddle & Co

1 GRESHAM STREET
LONDON
EC2V 7BU

Phone: 01 606 9301

Fax: 01 606 3305
DX: 1008 LONDON CHANCERY LANE WC2
Telex: 888197
Senior Partner: Mr RS Fawssett
Number of Partners: 19
Total Staff: 81

Biggart Baillie & Gifford

3 GLENFINLAS STREET
EDINBURGH
EH3 6YY

Phone: 031 226 5541

Fax: 031 226 2278
Rutland Exchange: 15 EDINBURGH
Telex: 727802 **Other offices:** 1
Senior Partner: Mr TN Biggart WS
Number of Partners: 20
Total Staff: 150

Bird Semple Fyfe Ireland WS

249 WEST GEORGE STREET
GLASGOW
G2 4RB

Phone: 041 221 7090

Fax: 041 204 1902
Rutland Exchange: 10 GLASGOW
Telex: 779437 **Other offices:** 1
Senior Partner: Mr JH Campbell
Number of Partners: 30
Total Staff: 237

Birketts

20-28 MUSEUM STREET
IPSWICH
SUFFOLK
IP1 1HZ
Phone: 0473 232300

Fax: 0473 230524
DX: 3206 IPSWICH
Telex: 98597 **Other offices:** 2
Senior Partner: Mr JD Mitson
Number of Partners: 14
Total Staff: 110

Binks Stern and Partners *see full-page profile*
Bircham & Co *see full-page profile*
Bird & Bird *see full-page profile*
Birkbeck Montagu's *see full-page profile*

Binks Stern and Partners

55-56 LINCOLN'S INN FIELDS
LONDON
WC2A 3LT

Phone: 01 404 4321

Fax: 01 405 5040
DX: 261 LONDON CHANCERY LANE WC2
Telex: 295408
Senior Partner: Mr WR Binks
Number of Partners: 15
Total Staff: 72

This medium sized central London firm practises in most areas of the law, and particularly in the commercial sector.

The firm: Binks Stern (originally called Harold Stern & Co) was founded in 1953. It initially concentrated on providing a service to commercial clients, particularly in the property field; today, the company/commercial and litigation departments rank equally in importance with the property department. In recent years the firm has enjoyed a period of rapid growth, partly as a result of vigorous internal expansion and partly as partners from other firms have joined the practice at partner level.

In the next 12 months, the firm expects to be looking for assistant solicitors in all areas of the practice. There is a very open recruitment policy: the firm will consider applicants of all ages, backgrounds and levels. Enquiries to Mr MP Stanley.

Two articled clerks are recruited every year. Candidates should have a sound academic background. Long-term prospects are excellent: nearly half of the present partners were articled with the firm. Apply by handwritten letter (with CV and names of two referees) to Mr JM Cantor two years in advance.

Agency work: The firm accepts work from other solicitors, and also liaises closely with foreign law firms.

Types of work undertaken: Binks Stern is firmly committed to the proposition that a firm does not have to be of giant size in order to offer a high-quality service to demanding commercial (largely corporate) clients.

A wide variety of work is undertaken, including very large matters. In addition to the normal areas of practice of interest to the commercial client, the firm has a highly active landlord and tenant litigation department and a thriving insolvency practice. Matrimonial work of the more substantial type is also undertaken.

The client base of the firm is wide and includes a number of very sizeable companies (some of which are based abroad or are subsidiaries of even larger concerns) and encompasses banking, insurance and property interests, computing, publishing, the drinks industry, manufacturing, advertising, retailing and marketing. The firm also acts for one of the Inns of Court on certain matters.

Binks Stern's particular areas of expertise are landlord and tenant work and insolvency work, both corporate and personal (the firm has acted for the trustees in bankruptcy in relation to the world's two largest ever bankruptcies).

Overall, Binks Stern sees itself as a medium sized central London firm able to compete with the giant practices in most classes of work. A brochure describing the work of the practice is available on request.

Bircham & Co

1 DEAN FARRAR STREET
WESTMINSTER
LONDON
SW1H 0DY
Phone: 01 222 8044

Fax: 01 222 3480
DX: 276 LONDON CHANCERY LANE WC2
Telex: 8954369 **Other offices:** 1
Senior Partner: James William Dolman
Number of Partners: 15
Total Staff: 120

This Westminister firm has a balanced practice with substantial private clients and an important commercial practice.

The firm: In its first years (Bircham & Co was founded in 1834 by Francis Bircham, later to become president of the Law Society), the firm's clientele included landed clients, railway companies and privately owned utilities. Building on this base, the firm has always sought to maintain the balance between private and commercial clients as it pursues a policy of steady growth.

Between six and ten assistant solicitors — in property and company/commercial — will be needed in the next year. Enquiries to Mrs CS Cotcher.

In addition, six articled clerks are recruited annually. A 2(1) degree is preferred, not necessarily in law. Apply by handwritten letter (with CV and names of referees) to Mrs CS Cotcher.

Other offices: London.

Agency work: Most of the work undertaken for other solicitors is in litigation, although other types are also accepted. For details contact Mr GH Josselyn.

Types of work undertaken: In addition to the company/commercial, property, tax and trusts, and litigation departments, there is a Parliamentary agency, an important additional service for the firm's commercial and institutional clients. Commercial property and medico-legal work represent significant growth areas in recent years.

Public and private companies, livery companies, pension funds and sundry charitable and non-charitable institutions, including a number of blue-chip companies, form the commercial and institutional client base. The firm also continues to act for many substantial private clients.

Particular areas in which Bircham & Co is well known include retail warehouse developments; city property developments; venture capital and BES schemes; employment law; charity formations and commercial/charity composite structures; capital and income tax planning; intellectual property; medico-legal work, including medical negligence; building contracts and related litigation; heritage work and agricultural and urban estates; landlord and tenant, with an emphasis on commercial and business premises; and Parliamentary agency, with an emphasis on Scotland.

Overall, Bircham & Co sees itself as a firm which is known for maintaining the highest professional standards and for the ability to respond flexibly and rapidly to the demands placed upon it. This broad, general practice aims to provide the best possible service within each area of its expertise.

BIRCHAM & CO.

Bird & Bird

2 GRAY'S INN SQUARE
LONDON
WC1R 5AF

Phone: 01 242 6681

Fax: 01 242 3643
DX: 119 LONDON CHANCERY LANE WC2
Telex: 25581
Senior Partner: Karl TC Arnold
Number of Partners: 18
Total Staff: 110

This long-established Gray's Inn firm has a primarily commercial practice with a strong technology orientation.

The firm: Bird & Bird was founded in 1835 as a general law practice. After World War II the emphasis shifted to commercial law, and now the firm is particularly well known for its work for the science and technology sectors, both in support of commercial activities and litigation.

Due to planned expansion the firm is seeking to recruit well-qualified staff and in 1989 expects to have vacancies in litigation, corporate services and property for assistant solicitors ranging from newly qualified up to five years' post-qualification experience. Enquiries to David Harriss.

In addition, four articled clerks are normally recruited annually. The firm is interested in law and non-law graduates, particularly those with languages or a scientific or technical qualification. Long-term prospects are good and most articled clerks stay after qualifying. Apply on the firm's form (available on request) in August/September two years in advance to David Harriss.

Types of work undertaken: There are four main departments, namely intellectual property and litigation, corporate services, property and private client. Clients include major multinationals, public and private companies, institutions, associations and charitable bodies, substantial individuals and organisations.

Bird & Bird is well known for its work in specialised areas of business, much of it in various technology-related fields, particularly telecommunications and computing, and the firm handles all aspects of national and international corporate affairs and commercial transactions, including competition.

The intellectual property and litigation department also handles a great deal of scientific and technology work, from traditional engineering and chemical industries to the latest computing, electronics and biotechnology developments. Many of the lawyers working in this department have scientific backgrounds. This department also covers all forms of commercial disputes, particularly in the medical and pharmaceutical fields.

The property department deals mainly with commercial property transactions, including acquisitions and disposals, leases, developments, commercial mortgages, and town and country planning work, as well as advice on the impact of related tax legislation.

In addition, there is a significant private client department providing comprehensive advice in the field of personal, financial and tax planning.

Overall, Bird & Bird is a firm that has achieved high standards in a number of specialised and developing commercial areas.

BIRD & BIRD

Birkbeck Montagu's

7 ST BRIDE STREET
LONDON
EC4A 4AT

Phone: 01 353 3222

Fax: 01 353 4761
DX: 9 LONDON CHANCERY LANE WC2
Telex: 265068 **Other offices:** 1
Senior Partner: David A Peck
Number of Partners: 15
Total Staff: 103

Birkbeck Montagu's has a typical broadly based City commercial practice together with a traditional private client base.

The firm: Birkbeck Montagu's is the result of an amalgamation in 1969 between two firms, Birkbeck Julius Coburn & Broad and Montagu's and Cox & Cardale. The Birkbeck side traces its City origins back more than 100 years, while the firm of H Montagu was started in about 1867. It has enjoyed considerable organic growth over recent years and has strong connections abroad.

This expanding firm has vacancies for assistant solicitors. Enquiries to Mr GS Bisset.

In addition, five or six articled clerks are recruited every year. The firm has a flexible approach to recruitment. Apply (with CV) in September two years ahead to Ms EM Fraenkel.

Other offices: London.

Agency work: Work from other solicitors is accepted.

Types of work undertaken: The firm's commercial base is broad, with clients ranging from small businesses and sole practitioner professionals to listed companies, multinational corporations and government agencies. The work ranges from company secretarial and small trade disputes to public

company flotations, major property developments and substantial national and international litigation. The firm also has a traditional private client base, covering trusts and probate, residential conveyancing, family law and a wide range of private litigation.

The wide range of work is divided amongst its four departments. The work of the commercial conveyancing department includes purchases and sales, developments, institutional and banking work, joint ventures and agricultural conveyancing. The company/commercial department covers the full range of business activities including acquisitions and sales, mergers, share issues and Stock Exchange work, intellectual property and immigration, and has particular expertise in management buy-outs.

The litigation department deals mainly with commercial civil litigation and arbitration, both in the UK and overseas, including insurance, construction industry, libel, employment and professional negligence and is strong in intellectual property disputes.

The private client department covers matters relating to personal wealth, including UK and overseas trusts, and financial planning.

This well-established, reputable City firm with an international outlook considers it provides a quality professional service, combining the best of traditional values with up-to-date expertise and technology. A brochure is available on request.

BIRKBECK MONTAGU'S

SOLICITORS

Bischoff & Co.

PO BOX 613
EPWORTH HOUSE
25 CITY ROAD
LONDON EC1Y 1BY
Phone: 01 628 4222

Fax: 01 638 3345
DX: 847 LONDON CITY EC3
Telex: 885062 **Other offices:** 1
Senior Partner: John Clapham
Number of Partners: 20
Total Staff: 124

This City firm's practice is directed mainly at commercial clients and also at private clients who require, in particular, a financial and fiscally orientated approach.

The firm: Founded by Charles Bischoff in 1824, the firm was closely involved in the great nineteenth-century developments in the communications and transport industries and associated financial arrangements. This tradition of commercial work has led naturally to its present-day involvement in the investment, banking and property sectors. The firm is organised into departments.

The firm is actively seeking additional solicitors for corporate and financial services and commercial property work. Enquiries to Ronald Paterson (corporate and financial services), John Pedder (property), Robby Bernstein (litigation), and James Jowitt (private client).

In addition, the firm recruits five or six articled clerks annually. Long-term prospects are excellent: two-thirds of new partners in the last decade were articled with the firm. Send applications by handwritten letter (plus CV) two years in advance to John Pedder.

Other offices: Colchester.

Types of work undertaken: The firm provides a wide range of legal advice and services to clients in the UK and abroad. In recent years the firm has been much involved in the developemnt of major office, town centre and other commercial property, and in advising banks, insurance companies, unit trust managers and financial services groups.

Particular areas of expertise include commercial property development funding, unit trusts and offshore funds, corporate finance, banking, investment management, and tax planning for individuals.

The activities of the commercial department include acquisitions, management buy-outs, flotations, regulation and supervision of financial services, pension and industrial welfare schemes, trading contracts, franchising, licensing and intellectual property.

Unlike some of its City competitors, the firm is pleased to act for private clients in such areas as taxation, property and residency, on and offshore trusts, wills, probate and tax planning, the establishment and administration of charities, the management of family farms and agricultural estates, and tax planning on divorce and separation.

The work of the litigation department includes banking problems, company disputes, international, intellectual property, trade, employment, partnership and joint ventures, landlord and tenant, building and contracting disputes, and insolvency.

Overall, the firm sees itself as providing a service which is in keeping with the highest standards of the profession.

Bischoff & Co.

Bishop Longbotham & Bagnall

RODNEY HOUSE
5 ROUNDSTONE STREET
TROWBRIDGE
WILTSHIRE BA14 8DH
Phone: 0225 755656

Fax: 0225 753266
DX: 43106 TROWBRIDGE
Telex: 449277 **Other offices:** 3
Senior Partner: Mr TA Bishop
Number of Partners: 11
Total Staff: 74

Blackadder Reid Johnston

30 & 34 REFORM STREET
DUNDEE
DD1 1RJ

Phone: 0382 29222

Fax: 0382 201132
Rutland Exchange: 2 DUNDEE
Telex: 76343 **Other offices:** 4
Senior Partners: Mr NJA Robertson and
Mr AC Clark
Number of Partners: 14 **Total Staff:** 112

Blackhurst Parker & Yates

22 EDWARD STREET
BLACKPOOL
LANCASHIRE
FY1 1BA
Phone: 0253 293061

Fax: 0253 293519
DX: 17026 BLACKPOOL-1
Telex: none **Other offices:** 6
Senior Partner: Mr JK Yates
Number of Partners: 16
Total Staff: 85

Blair & Bryden

34 UNION STREET
GREENOCK
PA16 8DJ

Phone: 0475 26411

Fax: 0475 81836
Rutland Exchange: 2 GREENOCK
Telex: none **Other offices:** 5
Senior Partner: Mr AJ Blair
Number of Partners: 16
Total Staff: 101

Bishop and Robertson Chalmers *see full-page profile*

Bishop and Robertson Chalmers

2 BLYTHSWOOD SQUARE
GLASGOW
G2 4AD

Phone: 041 248 4672

Fax: 041 248 3270
Rutland Exchange: 11 GLASGOW
Telex: 779228 **Other offices:** 1
Senior Partner: James Reid
Number of Partners: 20
Total Staff: 126

This Glasgow-based firm has a broad general practice with an equal emphasis on commercial and private client work.

The firm: Formed by the 1986 merger of two longstanding Glasgow firms – Bishop & Co and Robertson Chalmers & Auld – the new firm is one of the largest in the city. Bishop and Robertson Chalmers has an office in Edinburgh and is enjoying a period of rapid growth.

The firm's requirements for assistant solicitors are dependent on the development of the practice and the workload. Enquiries to the partnership secretary.

The firm normally recruits five trainee solicitors annually. The minimum educational requirements are a Scottish law degree and a Diploma in Legal Practice. Long-term prospects are good; most trainee solicitors stay on with the firm after qualifying. Apply to David D Whyte (with CV and names of referees).

Other offices: Edinburgh.

Agency work: The firm accepts all types of work (particularly corporate/commercial and litigation) from other solicitors; contact Hector Cameron or Alastair Lockhart.

Types of work undertaken: This broadly based practice provides the full range of legal services to individuals, small businesses and substantial commercial clients. There are four main departments, litigation, conveyancing, corporate and commercial, and private client. Although the majority of Bishop and Robertson Chalmers' clients are based in Glasgow and west Scotland, it also acts for English and foreign companies with interests in Scotland.

The strong corporate and commercial department is well known for its work in pensions law, insolvency matters, construction law and general corporate law work, including corporate restructuring, takeovers, mergers, management buy-outs and advising banks and insurance companies.

Commercial property development is the main strength of the conveyancing department, which also handles commercial sales and acquisitions, town and country planning, and commercial leases.

The private client department deals with all types of trust and probate matters as well as investment and tax planning.

The work of the litigation department covers virtually every type of contentious work, and the department has a particular reputation for insurance law litigation.

In short, Bishop and Robertson Chalmers perceives itself as providing a high standard of professional legal services within a well-organised office. A brochure for clients is available upon request.

BISHOP
AND
ROBERTSON
CHALMERS

141

Blake Lapthorn

8 LANDPORT TERRACE
PORTSMOUTH
HAMPSHIRE
PO1 2QW
Phone: 0705 822291

Fax: 0705 862972
DX: 2204 PORTSMOUTH
Telex: 86283 **Other offices:** 8
Senior Partner: David W Russell
Number of Partners: 22
Total Staff: 291

Blake Lapthorn is a major practice in Portsmouth and South Hampshire which aims to provide a complete legal service for both commercial and private clients.

The firm: Founded in 1869 as a general family firm in Gosport and Portsmouth, Blake Lapthorn began to expand after the Second World War, opening a branch in Fareham and subsequently at other locations. Commercial work always formed part of the firm's activities but has increased significantly over recent years. In addition, commercial litigation is now a substantial part of the practice making full use of the London office.

Seven to ten assistant solicitors are likely to be recruited in 1989 for commercial, litigation, probate and financial planning. Enquiries to David W Russell.

In addition, seven or eight articled clerks are recruited annually. A 2(2) degree in any subject is preferred, but other qualifications may be considered. Long-term prospects are good: half the present partners were articled with the firm. Apply by form (available on request) or by handwritten letter (plus CV) two years in advance to David W Russell.

Other offices: London, Southampton, Fareham, Gosport, Havant, Waterlooville, North End (Portsmouth), Lee on the Solent.

Agency work: The firm does litigation work for other solicitors at all offices, and commercial work on a referral basis.

Types of work undertaken: The firm offers a complete legal service in that it covers virtually all legal work (except Admiralty and ecclesiastical), with litigation, company/ commercial, commercial property, domestic property, probate, trusts and financial advice the main areas of practice. Clients range from legally aided individuals to financial institutions and multinational companies.

The firm is particularly well known for commercial work of all types, with a large proportion of the commercial work being recommendations from accountants and bankers as well as from existing clients. In litigation, professional indemnity work and personal injury claims are specialities. In addition, the town and country planning department has a high reputation. Other specialisations include crime, matrimonial and family, tax, professional negligence and building society work.

In short, Blake Lapthorn sees itself as commercial, having its clients' interests to the fore. It feels that it adheres to its original objective of offering a traditional and highly personal service which is as readily available to individuals with domestic and family problems as it is to corporate and commercial clients. Brochures detailing the firm's services are available on request.

Blake Lapthorn
——— SOLICITORS ———

Blakemores

8 DAVENPORT ROAD
COVENTRY
WEST MIDLANDS
CV5 6PY
Phone: 0203 716161

Fax: 0203 711611
DX: 11228 COVENTRY-1
Telex: 312381 **Other offices:** 12
Senior Partner: Mr RA Blakemore
Number of Partners: 20
Total Staff: 146

Blaser Mills

CARLTON HOUSE
33-35 RED LION STREET
CHESHAM
BUCKINGHAMSHIRE HP5 1DN
Phone: 0494 782291

Fax: 0494 771903
DX: 50300 CHESHAM
Telex: 83264 **Other offices:** 4
Senior Partner: Mr DM Turner
Number of Partners: 9
Total Staff: 70

Blocks

ARCADE CHAMBERS
2-6 ARCADE STREET
IPSWICH
SUFFOLK IP1 1EL
Phone: 0473 230033

Fax: 0473 232050
DX: 3207 IPSWICH
Telex: 987720 **Other offices:** 3
Senior Partner: Mr JH Collinson
Number of Partners: 9
Total Staff: 67

Blythe Liggins

DALKEITH HOUSE
7 CLARENDON PLACE
LEAMINGTON SPA
WARWICKSHIRE CV32 5QQ
Phone: 0926 831231

Fax: 0926 22607
DX: 11872 LEAMINGTON SPA-1
Telex: 312373 **Other offices:** 7
Senior Partner: Mr KCK Scott
Number of Partners: 12
Total Staff: 130

Blyth Dutton *see full-page profile*

Blyth Dutton

8 & 9 LINCOLN'S INN FIELDS
LONDON
WC2A 3DW

Phone: 01 242 3399

Fax: 01 404 4788
DX: 21 LONDON CHANCERY LANE WC2
Telex: 24531
Senior Partner: Charles Wilkinson
Number of Partners: 18
Total Staff: 125

Blyth Dutton is a very broadly based central London practice with an emphasis on company and commercial work, complemented by strong litigation and private client departments.

The firm: The origins of Blyth Dutton can be traced back to the late eighteenth century. Following mergers in the 1970s, the firm became known as Blyth Dutton in 1983. Since this time the firm has expanded rapidly in all aspects of company and commercial work and commercial property work. Its practice is now more orientated towards the needs of corporate clients, although a strong private client base is retained.

The firm is constantly recruiting competent energetic solicitors within the company/ commercial and commercial property departments, and often has vacancies in other departments. Enquiries to Mr CN Ouin/Mr JA Wrigglesworth.

Six or seven articled clerks are recruited annually. Apply by handwritten letter (plus CV) two years ahead to Mr BWD Richards.

Agency work: All litigation work, except crime, is undertaken for other firms of solicitors; contact Mr C Creagh Brown.

Types of work undertaken: The firm is particularly well known for its City-orientated work, including full listings, USM and Third Market mergers and acquisitions, takeovers, management buy-outs and venture capital schemes, commercial property and leisure industry matters. The company/commercial department acts for banks, stockbrokers and other institutions. Corporate clients range from small private companies to large fully listed companies. The department also handles general commercial work, insolvency, franchise and distribution agreements, intellectual property, service and consultancy agreements and share option schemes.

The tax department specialises in providing expert advice to corporate clients. In addition, the department provides specialist assistance to clients involved in Inland Revenue investigations.

Apart from the acquisition, disposal and leasing of commercial property, the work of the property department involves close participation in the conveyancing and financial aspects of development schemes. The department frequently advises on agricultural holdings. Litigation work is mainly in relation to civil matters, much of it substantial, with an international element. The firm handles the full range of private client work, including wills, trusts, personal taxation and estate planning.

Blyth Dutton sees itself as an efficient commercial practice going from strength to strength with emphasis on maintaining a close relationship with its clients.

Blyth Dutton

Bond Pearce

1 THE CRESCENT
PLYMOUTH
PL1 3AE

Phone: 0752 266633

Fax: 0752 225350
DX: 8251 PLYMOUTH – 2
Telex: 45404 **Other offices:** 1
Senior Partner: Jonathan Trafford
Number of Partners: 31
Total Staff: 247

Bond Pearce is one of the largest firms of solicitors in the south west of England, with a broadly based practice covering the full range of legal services from private client work to major corporate assignments.

The firm: Founded in 1881, Bond Pearce quickly became a leading firm in the area. The practice was rebuilt after suffering considerable losses during World War II, and it is now the largest firm in Plymouth with a substantial office in Exeter. It is a member of the M5 Group (see separate entry).

This expanding firm has a continuing need for high-quality assistant solicitors with two or three years post-qualification experience. In 1989 it expects to have about 15 vacancies, for litigation, property, commercial and insolvency. Enquiries to Mr WJ Price.

Ten to twelve articled clerks are recruited every year. The preferred educational qualification is a 2(1) degree, not necessarily in law. Prospects after qualification are good: about half of the present partners served articles with the firm. Apply by handwritten letter (with CV and names of referees) two years in advance to Mr VE Salomonsen.

Other offices: Exeter.

Agency work: The firm accepts litigation work from other solicitors; contact Brian Starks.

Types of work undertaken: Bond Pearce perceives itself as one of the leading practices in the south west peninsula and as serving primarily commercial and institutional clients. The firm offers a wide range of expertise and also produces excellent information booklets for its clients.

Litigation is an important part of the practice and Bond Pearce is particularly well known for its work in the fields of professional indemnity, personal injury, construction law, landlord and tenant and intellectual property.

Working in conjunction with a very experienced planning partner, the property department concentrates on commercial and industrial property and is notable for its involvement in the construction and funding of development sites. Another unit handles residential conveyancing with an emphasis on arrangements and relocation packages.

On the commercial side, the firm prides itself on joint venture and venture capital work. A separate department – including two licensed insolvency practitioners – has established an equally formidable reputation dealing with insolvency and bank recoveries.

In the private client field there is a special interest in agricultural and landed estate clients.

There are also fee-earners engaged exclusively in tax planning, employment work, shipping law and divorce.

BOND PEARCE
////////// SOLICITORS //////////

145

Boodle Hatfield

43 BROOK STREET
LONDON
W1Y 2BL

Phone: 01 629 7411

Fax: 01 629 2621
DX: 53 LONDON CHANCERY LANE WC2
Telex: 261414 **Other offices:** 1
Senior Partner: Michael Loup
Number of Partners: 32
Total Staff: 217

This medium sized central London firm handles largely commercial work on the foundation of a long-established property practice.

The firm: Boodle Hatfield, established 250 years ago as a property-based firm, has grown into a leading commercial practice with special emphasis on commercial property, corporate services and litigation. There is a strong international element and the firm works in association with large USA firms.

The firm requires seven or eight solicitors over the next year, and welcomes enquiries from newly qualified solicitors and senior solicitors seeking partnership prospects.

In addition, eight to ten articled clerks are recruited per year. Usually a 2(1) degree is required. Some trainees spend six months on secondment to ICI and Shell International. Apply by form (available on request) to Paul Pattinson.

Other offices: Southampton.

Agency work: The firm accepts agency work from solicitors in Southampton by negotiation. Contact David d'Arcy Hughes.

Types of work undertaken: The firm concentrates on commercial property; corporate and commercial; transnational, commercial and general litigation; intellectual property; and tax and financial planning. Most of these specialisations have an international dimension. Clients range from foreign governments to UK and overseas public and private companies, partnerships, wealthy individuals, financial institutions, and charities.

Historically, the firm is regarded as strong in commercial property and financial planning. Its reputation in the field of intellectual property is more recent but as significant, covering a wide range of contentious and non-contentious work relating to patents, trademarks, brand names, franchising and artistic as well as industrial copyrights. Commercial litigation is also a relatively new area but one in which it has already established a considerable reputation, particularly in relation to transnational disputes, banking and computer fraud, international arbitration and insurance matters. The firm acts for a number of sovereign states undertaking pioneering work in special fields such as sovereign immunity.

The firm considers that it has developed from its historic property base into a fully comprehensive commercial firm with specialities in commercial litigation and intellectual property. It has lawyers qualified in New York and Spain and lawyers fluent in Spanish, French and German. The firm prides itself on the level of personal contact the partners and staff maintain with clients.

Booth & Blackwell
with Samuel Tonkin & Co

3 AND 4 BERNERS STREET
LONDON
W1P 4AT

Phone: 01 580 9371

Fax: 01 631 3422
DX: 35702 BLOOMSBURY WC1
Telex: 27704
Senior Partner: Mr SAF Davies
Number of Partners: 10
Total Staff: 92

This medium sized central London firm has an expanding commercial law practice and a thriving debt recovery business.

The firm: Founded in 1915 as Samuel Tonkin & Co, the practice became Booth & Blackwell in 1940, but the name Samuel Tonkin & Co has been retained to distinguish the debt recovery work of the practice. Since the 1960s the firm has expanded rapidly; this growth has been achieved through natural growth rather than by merger or amalgamation. Booth & Blackwell is organised into departments.

There is a constant need for qualified staff, and in 1989 the firm expects to be continuing its expansion in the corporate as well as private client departments.

In addition, the firm usually recruits five articled clerks every year. A 2(2) degree is required, not necessarily in law. Prospects are excellent: most of the present partners were articled with the firm. Apply by handwritten letter (with CV and referees) to the administration partner, Mr RP Cook.

Agency work: The firm accepts litigation work from other solicitors; contact Mr TPR Sears.

Types of work undertaken: This is a commercially orientated firm which, nevertheless, retains a strong private client base.

There are five main departments, namely litigation, property, company, commercial, and private client. Clients range from large public corporations, airlines and insurance companies to individuals who are directors or executives of those companies.

A wide range of company/commercial work is undertaken to serve the various requirements of commercial clients in the UK and overseas. There is also a particularly strong commercial litigation department which handles all types of disputes, and acts for airlines and legal insurers on general commercial litigation matters, both in this jurisdiction and internationally.

The firm is particularly proud of its experience and expertise in the field of personal and corporate insolvency; indeed, the head of the department, Michael Steiner, is one of the leading lecturers on the subjects.

The debt recovery department has over 50 years' experience and is fully computerised.

There is a fast-expanding property department, which deals with the full range of commercial property transactions and has particular expertise in town and country planning. Private client work undertaken includes matrimonial and probate and trust work.

In short, Booth & Blackwell perceives itself as diligent and progressive — as a firm that has a young, forward-looking outlook combined with a commercially minded approach.

——————— SOLICITORS ———————

Booth & Blackwell

——— *with Samuel Tonkin & Co* ———

Booth & Co

SOVEREIGN HOUSE
SOUTH PARADE
LEEDS
LS1 1HQ
Phone: 0532 469655

Fax: 0532 458598
DX: 12004 LEEDS-1
Telex: 557439
Senior Partner: Mr GH Cox
Number of Partners: 25
Total Staff: 291

Booth & Co is a leading commercial practice providing a full range of legal services to both private and commercial clients.

The firm: The firm was founded in 1775. As Leeds developed into the commercial centre of the north-east of England, the firm expanded to become one of the largest in the region, serving institutions, industries and businesses, as well as private clients. Booth & Co is a member of the M5 Group.

There is a continuing need for qualified staff, and in 1989 the firm expects to recruit 20 assistant solicitors. Enquiries to Mr DM Jones.

In addition, 15 articled clerks are recruited annually. The expected educational qualification is a 2(1) degree, not necessarily in law, indeed languages and science graduates are encouraged to apply. Long-term prospects are good: half the present partners were articled with the firm. Apply by letter (with CV and names of referees) to Mr TI Roberts, from whom a brochure is available.

Types of work undertaken: This major commercial practice provides the full range of legal services to its growing list of clients, including banks and other financial institutions, PLCs and substantial private companies, and private individuals. The firm is organised into departments, namely company/commercial, commercial property, litigation, private client (comprising domestic property, financial services, taxation, and family law) and debt collection.

The company/commercial department deals with a broad range of work, particularly for listed companies (including Stock Exchange and USM issues), as well as intellectual property, banking, building society acquisitions and disposals, reorganisations, buy-outs, competition law, consumer credit, corporate and commercial taxation, employment law and commercial law.

In the field of financing, there is considerable expertise in banking and in corporate property work, and in tax planning. The commercial property department is particularly strong, and is involved in major retail, office and industrial development projects and leasing generally, as well as institutional work. Town planning work is carried out by a separate department.

The litigation department handles all aspects of civil and commercial litigation, particularly banking, intellectual property, insolvency, landlord and tenant and injunctive relief, much of it substantial and complex. Work in personal injury claims is also undertaken. Family law is also strong and is handled by a section of the private client department.

The firm sees itself as a leading provincial commercial firm, and as the leading institutional client and commercial property firm in the north of England. Brochures available.

Borneo Martell & Partners

DIXON HOUSE
77-83 HARPUR STREET
BEDFORD
MK40 2SY
Phone: 0234 53221

Fax: 0234 216272
DX: 5607 BEDFORD
Telex: 825864 **Other offices:** 3
Senior Partner: Mr KA Borneo
Number of Partners: 12
Total Staff: 67

Bower & Bailey

12 ST MICHAEL'S STREET
OXFORD
OX1 2RU

Phone: 0865 249122

Fax: 0865 248414
DX: 4315 OXFORD
Telex: 946240 **Other offices:** 8
Senior Partner: Mr DJG Bower
Number of Partners: 14
Total Staff: 110

Boys & Maughan

INDIA HOUSE
HAWLEY STREET
MARGATE
KENT CT9 1PZ
Phone: 0843 220288

Fax: 0843 299475
DX: 30551 MARGATE
Telex: none **Other offices:** 8
Senior Partner: Mr JGB Moulsdale
Number of Partners: 13
Total Staff: 110

Brachers

SOMERFIELD HOUSE
59 LONDON ROAD
MAIDSTONE
KENT ME16 8JH
Phone: 0622 690691

Fax: 0622 681430
DX: 4806 MAIDSTONE
Telex: 965008 **Other offices:** 1
Senior Partner: Mr GAW Bracher
Number of Partners: 12
Total Staff: 87

Boyce Hatton *see full-page profile*
Brabner Holden & Co *see full-page profile*
Braby & Waller *see full-page profile*

Boyce Hatton

12 TOR HILL ROAD
TORQUAY
DEVON
TQ2 5RB
Phone: 0803 25343

Fax: 0803 214876
DX: 59000 TORQUAY-1
Telex: none **Other offices:** 3
Senior Partner: Antony J Boyce
Number of Partners: 13
Total Staff: 80

Boyce Hatton, the largest law firm in Torbay, has a varied client base, including commercial and private clients, and particularly strong property and corporate departments.

The firm: Boyce Hatton was formed in 1954 by the present senior partner, Antony Boyce. Twenty years later the firm amalgamated with Carter Fisher & Co, the longest-established firm in Torquay. There were two further mergers – in 1978 with Robertson Owen & Son of Brixham and Dartmouth – and in 1979 with Parson & Outfin of Brixham.

The firm has a continuing demand for experienced staff, both newly qualified and with up to ten years' qualified experience. In particular, three assistant solicitors are required in 1989, for corporate, commercial conveyancing, and probate. Contact Mr PN Walmsley.

In addition, the firm recruits three or four articled clerks a year. The minimum educational requirements are a 2(2) law, or a 2(1) non-law, degree. Apply by handwritten letter (plus CV and two referees) between January and March to Mr PN Walmsley.

Other offices: Wellswood (Torquay), Brixham, Dartmouth.

Agency work: Boyce Hatton accepts work from other solicitors. For details, contact David J Lees (property) or Mr DJ Moss (litigation).

Types of work undertaken: The practice is a broadly based one and is divided into four main departments, namely property, litigation, company, and probate. Boyce Hatton has particular expertise in property development and in corporate work.

The property department deals with transactions for commercial and residential developers, including large public companies, from acquisition right through to dealing with sales to ultimate purchasers. In recent years the firm has undertaken commercial re-development work in various town centres, and is currently retained by the company developing the new town area adjacent to Torbay. It also deals with planning law and property taxation, residential conveyancing and work for businesses such as hotels, licensed premises, shops, and offices.

The corporate department handles a large number of acquisitions, mergers and restructuring. Boyce Hatton has acted for companies concerned with a number of BES issues, all of which were brought to successful conclusions. The firm also has strong litigation and probate departments.

Despite its location in the provinces, the firm handles a high volume of City-type work. It sees itself as one of the few firms in the South West capable of undertaking all forms of corporate and property development work.

Brabner Holden & Company

1 DALE STREET
LIVERPOOL
L2 2ET

Phone: 051 236 5821

Fax: 051 227 3185
DX: 14118 LIVERPOOL
Telex: 944-512363363
Senior Partner: Lewis L Lewis
Number of Partners: 10
Total Staff: 70

This well-established Liverpool firm offers a wide range of legal services to its broad range of commercial and private clients.

The firm: Brabner Holden was formed in 1968 by the merger of two long-established Liverpool practices which date back to the early nineteenth century. In recent years, the firm has enjoyed substantial growth, which was enhanced by a merger with Avisons in 1988.

In 1989 the firm expects to sustain its development and have vacancies for solicitors in the commercial, litigation and other departments. Enquiries to Lawrence Holden.

In addition, the firm normally recruits between two and four articled clerks annually. Candidates are assessed on individual merits rather than academic results; non-law graduates are encouraged to apply. Apply by handwritten letter (with CV and names of referees) to Mark Feeny, the partner responsible for articled clerks.

Agency work: Attendance at the Queen Elizabeth II Law Courts, Liverpool, is undertaken on behalf of other solicitors.

Types of work undertaken: This city-centre firm has an integrated range of departments, unusually organised according to the type of client — that is, corporate/commercial, public benefit organisations and individuals (private and legal aided). Each department is subdivided into contentious and non-contentious work, and for the benefit of clients active consultation between departments is encouraged.

The firm is strong in commercial work but differs from other city-centre practices by maintaining a wide range of clients and types of work rather than being narrowly commercial. It aims, by offering the full range of legal services (except crime), to meet the main requirements of the Merseyside region. The practice in fact extends beyond the local area because of the traditional and long established nature of its private client base.

Brabner Holden is particularly well known for its high quality general commercial work, for its probate, trust and taxation department, for its expertise in housing association matters and charities work, as well as in the expanding field of computer law. The firm as a matter of policy has elected to maintain a significant amount of legal aid work.

Brabner Holden's innovations in management practice have aroused considerable interest. Overall, the firm sees itself as one of the more go-ahead major Liverpool practices, which has retained its traditional base, has an extremely professional standard of work and commitment, and is highly regarded for the united nature of its partnership. In short, this is a progressive firm with very positive plans for the future.

BRABNER HOLDEN & COMPANY

Braby & Waller

82 ST JOHN STREET
LONDON
EC1M 4DP

Phone: 01 250 1884

Fax: 01 250 1698
DX: 46614 BARBICAN EC1
Telex: 8814186
Senior Partners: George Mason and
Hugh Robertson
Number of Partners: 18 **Total Staff:** 86

Braby & Waller is a medium sized City practice which is predominantly commercial with a specialist private client department.

The firm: Founded in London in the latter part of the nineteenth century, the firm provides a general legal service to a wide range of commercial and private clients. The firm is organised into a number of specialist areas, each served by a separate department.

Braby & Waller is looking for one or two assistant solicitors to work in each of the following areas: conveyancing; company/ commercial; personal tax, private client and divorce. Enquiries should be addressed to Hugh Robertson.

The firm normally recruits two articled clerks per year. The minimum academic requirement is a 2(1) degree, not necessarily in law. Applications by handwritten letter (plus CV and names of referees) should be addressed to Mr SHK Williams as early as possible.

Agency work: The firm undertakes a considerable amount of insolvency work for other solicitors; also building and civil engineering contract advice and litigation, as well as general agency work of good quality.

Types of work undertaken: While Braby & Waller is a full-service legal practice, the firm is particularly well known for its expertise in commercial property, building litigation and insolvency. It also has an active company/commercial department. The firm acts for a considerable number of large trading corporations, pension funds, banks, institutions and specialist trade associations.

The work of the commercial property department includes property development and funding, acquisitions and disposals, tenancies and agricultural holdings, taxation, rent reviews, and town and country planning. The department works closely with the debt collection and commercial departments, as well as handling residential conveyancing.

The emphasis in the litigation department is on building and civil engineering disputes at home and abroad, including the Middle East. The firm is proud of its success rate in cases that have gone to a full hearing, but derives equal satisfaction from a great many other disputes that have resulted in a commercially sensible settlement.

The insolvency department covers all aspects of personal and corporate insolvency, including investigations and sales of assets. In addition, the strong company/commercial department provides the full range of legal services, including computer contracts, intellectual property and employment.

Braby & Waller is a highly regarded medium sized firm which places a large emphasis on personal service and guaranteed partner-level attention for all clients.

Braby & Waller

Brain & Brain

ADDINGTON HOUSE
73 LONDON STREET
READING
BERKSHIRE RG1 4QB
Phone: 0734 581441

Fax: 0734 597875
DX: 4005 READING
Telex: 847645 **Other offices:** 3
Senior Partner: Mr DH Easby
Number of Partners: 13
Total Staff: 95

Bray & Bray

1 3 & 5 WELFORD ROAD
LEICESTER
LE2 7AN

Phone: 0533 548871

Fax: 0533 543056
DX: 10812 LEICESTER-1
Telex: none **Other offices:** 6
Senior Partner: Mr JR Williamson
Number of Partners: 17
Total Staff: 104

Bremner Sons & Corlett

1 CROSSHALL STREET
LIVERPOOL
L1 6DH

Phone: 051 227 1301

Fax: 051 227 1300
DX: 14119 LIVERPOOL
Telex: 629388 **Other offices:** 2
Senior Partner: Mr WR Williams
Number of Partners: 10
Total Staff: 60

Brian Thompson & Partners

102 ST GEORGES SQUARE
LONDON
SW1V 3QY

Phone: 01 828 1266

Fax: 01 630 1548
DX: none
Telex: none **Other offices:** 4
Senior Partner: Mr DB Thompson
Number of Partners: 30
Total Staff: 369

Brecher & Co *see full-page profile*
Breeze and Wyles *see full-page profile*

Brecher & Co

78 BROOK STREET
GROSVENOR SQUARE
LONDON
W1Y 2AD

Phone: 01 493 5141

Fax: 01 493 6255
DX: 13 LONDON CHANCERY LANE WC2
Telex: 263486 **Other offices:** 1
Senior Partner: David J Brecher
Number of Partners: 30
Total Staff: 168

Brecher & Co is a general practice with a strong commercial bias and has a large spread of both corporate and private clients.

The firm: Brecher & Co was founded in the mid-1950s by David and Henry Brecher on the basis that clients wanted more from a firm of solicitors than just the traditional range of legal services. Its name was soon established in the commercial property world through taking a creative role in structuring and obtaining finance for property transactions as well as dealing with the legal formalities. Today, in addition to its strength in commercial property, the firm has a broadly based general practice.

The firm is always searching for good qualified staff. In 1989 it intends to recruit at least ten assistant solicitors: five for commercial conveyancing, two for company/commercial, and three for litigation. Enquiries to Alan Wiseman.

In addition, six articled clerks are recruited annually. A good 2(2) degree, not necessarily in law, is the minimum academic qualification. Apply by handwritten letter (plus CV and names of referees) two years in advance to Geoffrey Herman.

Other offices: Paris.

Agency work: The firm undertakes agency work from other solicitors for litigation, company/commercial and property work. For details, contact Mr B Samuels (litigation), Mr THW Piper (company/commercial) and Mrs SM Freeman (property).

Types of work undertaken: The firm has substantial commercial property and corporate departments and other departments specialising in commercial litigation, entertainment law, town and country planning, taxation, probate and trusts.

The firm's client base is widespread and includes listed, USM and Third Market companies, banks and other financial institutions, private companies and individuals. It also advises on international transactions and maintains close contacts with lawyers worldwide.

The firm's extensive expertise in the property field encompasses the acquisition and realisation of property portfolios, mortgage investigations on behalf of banking and institutional clients, and town centre and out-of-town developments (including land purchase, development funding and the ultimate disposal of the completed development). Its considerable commercial practice includes acting for a number of substantial public companies in a wide variety of corporate and Stock Exchange work.

Brecher & Co is generally considered to be a firm that operates in an efficient, competent, professional and friendly manner.

BRECHER & CO
solicitors

Breeze and Wyles

37 BULLSMOOR LANE
ENFIELD
MIDDLESEX
EN3 6TF
Phone: 0992 764333

Fax: 0992 701439
DX: 51700 WALTHAM CROSS-2
Telex: 264829 **Other offices:** 6
Senior Partner: Mr GV Hyde
Number of Partners: 14
Total Staff: 125

This Enfield-based firm has six branch offices, a long-established and substantial private client base, and an expanding commercial practice.

The firm: Breeze and Wyles was established as a small family practice some 75 years ago in Bow, East London. Since then the firm has expanded rapidly, with offices stretching from north London to north Hertfordshire, and has a burgeoning commercial practice. The firm is organised into departments.

There is a constant need for good qualified staff in this expanding firm, and in the next 12 months Breeze and Wyles expects to have vacancies for two or three assistant solicitors to work in the commercial law field. All enquiries should be addressed to Mr JF Rice.

In addition, the firm normally has six vacancies for articled clerks every year. The minimum educational requirement is a 2(2) law degree or a 2(1) non-law degree. Prospects after qualification are excellent; the majority of the present partners served articles with the firm. Applications should be made by handwritten letter (with CV and names of referees) addressed to Mr I Carson (Montagu House, 68 High Street, Hoddesdon, Herts EN11 8HA).

Other offices: Palmers Green (London N13), Enfield Town, Cheshunt, Hoddesdon, Hertford, Stevenage.

Agency work: The firm accepts work from other solicitors; contact the Hertford office (litigation). In addition, the Stevenage office undertakes personal searches at the Stevenage District Land Registry.

Types of work undertaken: The firm has, traditionally, concentrated on private client work, but in recent years there has been a change of emphasis, moving away from the 'high street' approach (although still retaining its strong private client base).

There is an active litigation department, handling a wide range of civil litigation matters, and a strong criminal law department.

A recently formed company/commercial department, which offers the full range of legal services to business clients, is rapidly establishing itself at the firm's Cheshunt office.

A planning department, which was established in 1953 and is based at the head office, is able to advise on all town planning, compulsory purchase, and allied local government matters.

This is a forward-planning practice and, with new computer technology recently installed in all offices, Breeze and Wyles is looking to the future with optimism.

In short, this is an up-and-coming provincial practice offering a high level of expertise to private and commercial clients.

BREEZE
AND
WYLES
SOLICITORS

Brindley Twist Tafft & James

3 THE QUADRANT	**Fax:** 0203 632828
COVENTRY	**DX:** 11202 COVENTRY-1
WEST MIDLANDS	**Telex:** none **Other offices:** 1
CV1 2DY	**Senior Partner:** Mr GP James
	Number of Partners: 11
Phone: 0203 631632	**Total Staff:** 58

Browne Jacobson

44 CASTLE GATE	**Fax:** 0602 475246
NOTTINGHAM	**DX:** 10007 NOTTINGHAM
NG1 6EA	**Telex:** 378161 **Other offices:** 1
	Senior Partner: Mr RIA Smith
	Number of Partners: 14
Phone: 0602 500055	**Total Staff:** 105

Brutton & Co

WEST END HOUSE	**Fax:** 0329 289915
288 WEST STREET	**DX:** 40809 FAREHAM
FAREHAM	**Telex:** 86875 **Other offices:** 5
HAMPSHIRE PO16 0AJ	**Senior Partner:** Mr J Simpson
	Number of Partners: 18
Phone: 0329 236171	**Total Staff:** 160

Buckle Mellows

45-51 PRIESTGATE	**Fax:** 0733 62064
PETERBOROUGH	**DX:** 12312 PETERBOROUGH-1
CAMBRIDGESHIRE	**Telex:** none **Other offices:** 1
PE1 1LB	**Senior Partner:** Mr A Dawes
	Number of Partners: 12
Phone: 0733 68175	**Total Staff:** 85

Bristows, Cooke & Carpmael *see full-page profile*
Brodies WS *see full-page profile*
Brooke North and Goodwin *see full-page profile*

Bristows, Cooke & Carpmael

10 LINCOLN'S INN FIELDS
LONDON
WC2A 3BP

Phone: 01 242 0462

Fax: 01 242 1232
DX: 269 LONDON CHANCERY LANE WC2
Telex: 27487
Senior Partner: Ian A Scott
Number of Partners: 18
Total Staff: 150

Bristows, Cooke & Carpmael, a London firm based in Lincoln's Inn Fields, is essentially a commercial practice.

The firm: Founded in 1837 by Robert Wilson, the firm commenced practice at No 1 Copthall Buildings behind the Stock Exchange as a commercial practice specialising in intellectual property. There has been marked growth in all aspects of the firm's work in the last ten to 15 years. The firm is organised into departments.

The continuing expansion means that the firm is constantly interested in recruiting able, energetic and personable assistant solicitors; it estimates there will be ten to 15 vacancies in 1989. Enquiries to David Houlton.

In addition, seven to nine articled clerks are recruited annually. The preferred educational qualification is a 2(1) degree, not necessarily in law. Long-term prospects are excellent: about half the present partners served articles with the firm. Apply by handwritten letter (with application form, available on request, and names of referees) to Michael Rowles.

Types of work undertaken: Bristows, Cooke & Carpmael is unusually well placed to provide business and high-tech clients with intellectual property advice, having over 150 years' experience in the field. Recognising that lawyers advising science-based industries must first understand the technology themselves, the firm has a significant proportion of lawyers who trained first as scientists or engineers. It is, therefore, able to provide in-house knowledge of most major scientific disciplines – from chemistry, physics and engineering right through to information technology and molecular biology. The firm has been involved in a wide range of key cases in this field.

Bristows has, over the years, gained considerable expertise in corporate work including reorganisations, joint ventures, takeovers, mergers and similar business transactions, as well as nurturing and protecting the commercial aims of innovative companies and individuals. The firm's acquisitions and management buy-out work has grown rapidly. In addition, the firm has a group specialising in the EEC, and it is one of the leading firms advising on restrictive trade practices and monopolies referrals.

There is a strong commercial property department, and a substantial practice in the law relating to building contracts and civil engineering (including a large volume of litigation). Indeed, commercial litigation has always been an important area for Bristows, and clients include many major UK companies and foreign corporations.

This long-established firm sees itself as a reputable, highly competent and efficient practice which is pre-eminent in the intellectual property field.

BRISTOWS
COOKE &
CARPMAEL

Brodies WS

15 ATHOLL CRESCENT
EDINBURGH
EH13 8HA

Phone: 031 228 3777

Fax: 031 228 3878
Rutland Exchange: 10 EDINBURGH
Telex: 727129
Senior Partner: Mr CSR Stroyan
Number of Partners: 27
Total Staff: 190

Brodies of Edinburgh is a broadly based practice, providing a wide range of services to commercial and private clients.

The firm: John C Brodie & Son and Cuthbertson & Watson, two firms which date back to the early nineteenth century, merged in 1959 to form the present practice. Since the merger the firm has enjoyed rapid and continued growth. While maintaining its traditional private client base, the firm has built up a strong and diversified corporate and commercial practice.

The firm is always seeking to recruit assistant solicitors in all areas of the practice, but particularly for the corporate and commercial property departments; in 1989 four to six vacancies are expected. Enquiries to the partnership secretary.

Brodies recruits six to eight trainee solicitors every year. Applicants are judged as much on individual merits as academic qualifications. Prospects are good; half the present partners trained with the firm. Apply by handwritten letter (with CV) one year in advance to the partnership secretary.

Agency work: The firm undertakes work for other solicitors; contact Mr DWA Guild (corporate), Mr KPD Strachan (commercial property), Mr DS Williamson (court), Mr JG Clark (residential property), Mr MNC Gascoigne (estates, forestry and agriculture),

Mr JM Gibson (land and estate agency), and Mr AMC Dalgleish (trust and executry).

Types of work undertaken: The emphasis at Brodies is on corporate and commercial work, complemented by a substantial private client practice.

The work of the corporate department encompasses the full range of services for businesses of all sizes. The department is well known for its privatisation, employment law, banking and insolvency work.

The commercial property department has a high reputation, particularly for purchase and sale, leasing and development work, insolvency property work, liquor licensing and franchising.

There is a strong commercial litigation department undertaking building, insurance, banking, intellectual property, and employment contentious business.

On the private client side areas of expertise include agricultural and sporting estates, forestry and country houses, crime, and matrimonial disputes. The land and estate agency's wide range of services includes management and consultancy work. The firm also has a tax and accountancy association and its own insurance broking agency.

In short, Brodies sees itself as a leading and progressive Scottish firm – one which is competent, good to deal with and skilled at getting the job done. Brochures available.

BRODIES
SOLICITORS
(WS)

Brooke North and Goodwin

YORKSHIRE HOUSE
EAST PARADE
LEEDS
LS1 5SD
Phone: 0532 440411

Fax: 0532 423989
DX: 12005 LEEDS-1
Telex: 557759 **Other offices:** 1
Senior Partner: Michael C Goodwin
Number of Partners: 10
Total Staff: 54

This Leeds-based firm is an expanding, medium sized practice which deals mainly with commercial matters.

The firm: Brooke North and Goodwin's origins go back some 150 years. Over the last 30 years the firm has become mainly a commercial practice. Commercial, litigation and commercial property work have substantially increased. The firm has considerable expertise in investment advice and tax planning.

Six solicitors will be required in 1989: four for commercial work (in Leeds and Gibraltar), and one each for the litigation and private client departments. Apply to Mr MP Sutcliffe.

Two articled clerks are recruited annually. There are no specific educational requirements. Applications by handwritten letter (with CV and referees) to Richard N Parr.

Other offices: Gibraltar.

Agency work: Non-legal aid work is accepted. For Chancery and Queen's Bench matters contact Richard Parr; for Gibraltar's Court of First Instance and Supreme Court contact Stuart Frith.

Types of work undertaken: The majority of Brooke North and Goodwin's clients are based in the north of England, but the firm's funding work has drawn in a number of substantial commercial clients from the South and the London area.

The work of the commercial department encompasses both commercial and commercial property work, including Stock Exchange listing, intellectual property and the sale and acquisition of commercial premises. There is notable expertise in drafting complex commercial contracts, particularly for the high-tech electronic and telecommunications industries. In addition, funding and franchise work is handled.

While undertaking a modest amount of private client litigation (mainly larger personal injuries claims and high-value matrimonial work), most of the firm's litigation work is insolvency based; indeed, the firm considers it is one of the foremost insolvency-orientated firms in the region. It also undertakes contentious landlord and tenant work and high-value employment contract disputes.

The private client department handles trusts, tax planning, investment advice and probate. The firm's Gibraltar office enables the department to offer the private client the benefits of offshore and international strategic tax planning. The department also handles conveyancing for directors and executives of corporate clients, and gives assistance with foreign property transactions.

Brooke North and Goodwin perceives itself as a high-quality firm, with a particular reputation for integrity, efficiency, commercial awareness and, above all, for achieving results.

*Brooke North
and Goodwin*
S O L I C I T O R S

Bunker & Co

7 & 9 THE DRIVE
HOVE
EAST SUSSEX
BN3 3JS
Phone: 0273 29797

Fax: 0273 24082
DX: 59257 HOVE
Telex: 877551 **Other offices:** 2
Senior Partner: Peter J Bunker OBE
Number of Partners: 7
Total Staff: 84

Bunker & Co, a Hove-based firm, is one of the largest firms in Sussex, with a wide-ranging general practice.

The firm: Founded in 1913 as a general family practice, Bunker & Co has expanded rapidly, doubling in size in the last five years. Over the years, as well as maintaining its traditional private client base, the firm has developed a substantial commercial practice.

The firm has a continuing need to recruit good assistant solicitors, as well as encouraging those who perform well during articles to continue with the firm. Enquiries to David Bunker (32 Keymer Road, Hassocks, West Sussex BN6 8AL).

The firm currently recruits three articled clerks every year. The decisive attributes sought in candidates are personality and character rather than academic achievements or class of degree. The firm particularly welcomes non-law graduates and mature applicants. Loans (subsequently converted to grants) are available for the Finals course. Apply by letter (with CV and names of referees) two years in advance to David Bunker (32 Keymer Road, as above).

Other offices: Portslade, Hassocks.

Agency work: The firm accepts work from other solicitors; contact Mr APC Allen or Mr C Bull.

Types of work undertaken: This is a broad-based general practice. There are four main departments, namely conveyancing, probate and trusts, litigation, and commercial. In addition, Bunker's two high-street branch offices handle predominantly non-contentious work. There is a wide spread of commercial clients – from sole traders and partnerships to large companies – and individuals, including legally aided clients.

The firm is well known for the quality of the work it undertakes in its substantial company/commercial department. As well as general commercial work, commercial property development is a particular area of expertise, as are mergers, intellectual property and patents, licensing, employment, and town and country planning matters.

The large litigation department has particular experience and expertise in personal injury work (for both plaintiff and defendant), commercial and building litigation, and divorce.

As is to be expected of a long-established provincial firm, there is a strong probate and trusts department, which acts for a number of charitable trusts as well as private individuals.

In short, Bunker & Co sees itself as combining the best features of personal service associated with a family firm with a crisp and modern service to commercial clients. A brochure is available on request.

BUNKERS

Burges Salmon

NARROW QUAY HOUSE
PRINCE STREET
BRISTOL
BS1 4AH
Phone: 0272 276567

Fax: 0272 294705
DX: 7829 BRISTOL
Telex: 44736
Senior Partner: Richard Trevor Johnson
Number of Partners: 17
Total Staff: 190

Burges Salmon is a major provincial practice which, although mainly commercial, has a significant, high-quality private client base.

The firm: Founded in 1841 by Edward Burges, the firm has been known by its present name since 1947. Over the years it has expanded from an agricultural and property base into one of the leading firms in the region and was a founding member of the M5 Group (see separate entry).

The firm has a continuing need for assistant solicitors and expects to recruit about 17 new solicitors in 1989. Enquiries to Peter Kilpin.

Eight to ten articled clerks are recruited annually. A 2(1) degree is required, not necessarily in law. Candidates with ability and personality should apply on form (available on request) by September to Martin Mitchell.

Agency work: The firm accepts agency work on a normal charge-out basis; contact the agency administrator.

Types of work undertaken: Burges Salmon has gained an increasingly high reputation for the standard of its commercial work, including acquisitions and disposals, flotations, management buy-outs, BES work, establishment of unit trusts, pensions, and agricultural and corporate insolvency. The firm also handles EEC law, commercial tax matters, including VAT advice.

The firm's agricultural practice has long enjoyed a national reputation and now encompasses CAP quotas, setasides, and other EEC work. There are strong commercial and property litigation departments dealing with all aspects of agricultural, commercial, construction and engineering industry and property litigation work.

The firm is well known for its commercial property work, and has a large department which advises major landowners, developers and commercial occupiers on property matters including planning, development, housing association law and landlord and tenant. The property department also handles high-quality residential conveyancing.

Unusually for a mainstream commercial firm, a significant amount of private client work is undertaken, notably estate administration and trusts, charity law, contentious probate, and international asset protection. The firm has a large international practice.

There is also a matrimonial practice and construction and insolvency law units, plus other specialist groupings. Much of the client base is regional, although the firm acts for a number of national companies, as well as overseas residents.

Overall, Burges Salmon sees itself as a highly professional firm, quick to respond to the needs of clients and straightforward in its dealings with other professions. Contact Rebecca Wigmore for the firm's brochure.

**BURGES
SALMON**

Burley & Geach

8 SWAN STREET
PETERSFIELD
HAMPSHIRE
GU32 3AE
Phone: 0730 62401

Fax: 0730 65182
DX: 100402 PETERSFIELD
Telex: 869422 **Other offices:** 3
Senior Partner: Mr RW Burley
Number of Partners: 11
Total Staff: 66

Burnetts

6 VICTORIA PLACE
CARLISLE
CUMBRIA
CA1 1ES
Phone: 0228 20265

Fax: 0228 22399
DX: 63005 CARLISLE
Telex: 64324 **Other offices:** 1
Senior Partner: Mr DM Livingstone
Number of Partners: 14
Total Staff: 77

Burroughs Day Robert Smith

14 CHARLOTTE STREET
BRISTOL
AVON
BS1 5PT
Phone: 0272 290333

Fax: 0272 272342
DX: 7825 BRISTOL
Telex: 265871 **Other offices:** 6
Senior Partner: Mr JN Whitehead
Number of Partners: 12
Total Staff: 86

Bury & Walkers

PERMANENT BLDG
REGENT STREET
BARNSLEY
SOUTH YORKSHIRE S70 2EQ
Phone: 0226 289131

Fax: 0226 207610
DX: 12251 BARNSLEY-1
Telex: none **Other offices:** 2
Senior Partner: Mr DWG Hardy
Number of Partners: 12
Total Staff: 79

Burstows *see full-page profile*
Burt Brill & Cardens *see full-page profile*
Burton Copeland *see full-page profile*

Burstows

8 IFIELD ROAD
CRAWLEY
WEST SUSSEX
RH11 7YY
Phone: 0293 34734

Fax: 0293 552544
DX: 57100 CRAWLEY
Telex: 877468 **Other offices:** 3
Senior Partner: Mr DG Burstow
Number of Partners: 15
Total Staff: 95

This medium sized provincial practice has a strong commercial base but also provides an aggressively marketed service to individual private clients.

The firm: Burstows was established in 1975 by Tony and Donald Burstow. The firm has expanded rapidly by adopting a positive, down-to-earth commercial approach to the provision of legal services for both commercial and private clients. It has recently established a separate company/commercial division in Crawley to strengthen its commercial services to the local business community.

The continuing expansion means there is always a need for good assistant solicitors, particularly in litigation and commercial property. Contact Mr AM Burstow.

In addition, the firm recruits six or seven articled clerks per year. Candidates should have a law degree. Applications by handwritten letter (plus CV and names of referees) to Mr AM Burstow.

Other offices: Horsham, Haywards Heath, Brighton. Although this is a Sussex-based practice, many of the firm's clients operate on an international basis (and Burstows has worldwide links with foreign lawyers).

Agency work: Burstows will do conveyancing and litigation work for other firms of solicitors. Contact Mr AM Burstow.

Types of work undertaken: The firm does both commercial and non-commercial work. Proximity to Gatwick has resulted in one particular area of expertise being aviation law (including sales, leasing and CAA applications). Initially the firm concentrated on litigation, and this remains one of its specialisations. It is also strong on commercial property and town and country planning.

The firm is geared to assist business. It covers the full spectrum of company, commercial and corporate work, including company formations, reorganisations, mergers, management buy-outs, refinancing, joint ventures in the UK and abroad, distribution, agency and franchise agreements, conditions of supply and sale, obtaining venture capital, and all aspects of employment law. The firm has extensive experience of the insurance, computer and other service industries.

Burstows markets itself aggressively to the private client sector as a 'firm that gets on with it' (eg with its Solicitors' Property Centre, which offers the sale and conveyancing of residential property for an inclusive fee). The firm accepts legal aid work.

Widely regarded as a go-ahead practice, Burstows is a provincial firm not serving just the local community but a range of national and international clients as well.

Burt Brill & Cardens

30 OLD STEYNE
BRIGHTON
BN1 1FL

Phone: 0273 604123

Fax: 0273 570837
DX: 2709 BRIGHTON 1
Telex: none **Other offices:** 3
Senior Partner: Kenneth Edwards
Number of Partners: 7
Total Staff: 63

Burt Brill & Cardens is a Brighton-based firm with a long-established private client practice and an expanding commercial client base.

The firm: In 1986, the firm was formed as the result of the merger of Cardens, which was established in the 1890s, and Burt Brill & Edwards, a wide-ranging general practice founded in 1902. The firm has enjoyed rapid expansion recently. It is organised into departments.

There is a continuing need for high-calibre qualified staff, and in 1989 the firm expects to have vacancies for two to three assistant solicitors, primarily for commercial work. Address enquiries to Kenneth Edwards.

In addition, there are usually two or three vacancies for articled clerks every year. The minimum educational requirement is a 2(2) degree, not necessarily in law. Prospects after qualification are excellent; nearly half of the present partners served articles with the firm. Apply by handwritten letter (with CV and names of referees) to Kenneth Edwards.

Other offices: Hove, Hailsham, Worthing.

Agency work: The firm accepts all types of work from other solicitors; contact Kenneth Edwards.

Types of work undertaken: As an old-established provincial practice, the firm offers a wide range of legal services. There are five main departments, namely conveyancing, company/ commercial, litigation, probate and trust, and financial services. The firm has a large client base consisting of commercial and private clients, family trusts, small businesses, farmers, professionals and educational establishments.

The conveyancing department handles residential and commercial conveyancing, and the firm has a strong background in building society work (acting on the societies' behalf). Out of this work an expanding company/ commercial practice has evolved.

The firm is well known for its litigation work which covers contentious matters in a broad field, including private and commercial litigation, matrimonial matters, landlord and tenant, criminal, and debt collection work. Legal aid work is undertaken.

As is to be expected of a firm with an old-established private client base, there is a particularly strong probate and trust department handling wills, administration of estates and trusts. The financial services department deals with the compliance provisions of the Financial Services Act and investment advice for private clients and trusts.

Overall, Burt Brill & Cardens sees itself as a solid, reputable old-established firm of integrity and competence, one whose strengths are best seen in its care and support of its clients, whatever their problems.

BURT BRILL & CARDENS

Burton Copeland

ROYAL LONDON HOUSE
196 DEANSGATE
MANCHESTER
M3 3JW

Phone: 061 834 7374

Fax: 061 835 2904
DX: 14362 MANCHESTER
Telex: none
Senior Partner: Mr IR Burton
Number of Partners: 10
Total Staff: 55

This is a broadly based Manchester firm which is particulary well known for its work in commercial fraud and criminal advocacy.

The firm: Burton Copeland was founded as Burtons in 1982 by the present senior partner as a small consultancy with particular specialities. As the practice developed, additional partners were brought in, and in 1985 Nigel Copeland's practice was merged with Burtons. During 1987, two firms strong in criminal work, Millers and Crossley Mackey, were taken over; later, the Michael Green Partnership, which specialised in child care law, was merged into the practice.

Applications from assistant solicitors to work in the licensing and commercial litigation fields are sought. Enquiries to the staff partner, Michael Green.

The firm feels that its emphasis on specialised work such as commercial fraud may not be particularly appropriate for articled clerks seeking all round training. However, it welcomes approaches from bright and talented individuals with an interest in pursuing a career involving a high degree of advocacy. Apply to Michael Green.

Agency work: The firm actively encourages agency work from other solicitors, and acts throughout the country in the following fields: commercial fraud and professional misconduct (contact Mr IR Burton); liquor and gaming matters (Mr N Copeland); child care matters (Mr MG Green); and drink-driving (Mr GB Miller).

Types of work undertaken: Burton Copeland is a fast growing practice with considerable experience in handling complex, sophisticated, and specialised cases in areas such as commercial fraud, criminal law and liquor licensing.

The partnership has developed a distinct reputation for discreet, expert advocacy in fields of law — commercial fraud, insider dealing — where other firms of solicitors have been reluctant to act.

The broad client base includes many well-known individuals and companies, including a number of major breweries, large hotels and leisure establishments, but Burton Copeland is gaining particular distinction for representing clients experiencing difficulties with the police or their own professional bodies. A department dedicated to 'white collar' crime includes two ex-Fraud Squad officers and a specialist consultant.

Burton Copeland is a leading firm in the region for expertise and experience in liquor, gaming and licensing law. The firm has an extra specialisation in child care work.

Burton Copeland demonstrates that criminal advocacy should never be perceived as the poor relation, or less respectable side, of the legal profession.

BURTON COPELAND

Buss Murton Partnership

THE PRIORY
TUNBRIDGE WELLS
KENT
TN1 1JJ

Phone: 0892 510222

Fax: 0892 510333
DX: 3913 TUNBRIDGE WELLS
Telex: 95195 **Other offices:** 6
Managing Partner: Mr GC Honnywill
Number of Partners: 13
Total Staff: 95

Campbell Hooper

35 OLD QUEEN STREET
LONDON
SW1H 9JD

Phone: 01 222 9070

Fax: 01 222 5591
DX: 247 LONDON CHANCERY LANE WC2
Telex: 23518 **Other offices:** 3
Senior Partner: Mr JA Wright
Number of Partners: 16
Total Staff: 104

Cartwright & Lewis Vernon & Shakespeare

53-55 HIGH STREET
HARBORNE
BIRMINGHAM
B17 9NS

Phone: 021 426 4171

Fax: 021 427 3389
DX: 19751 HARBORNE
Telex: none **Other offices:** 7
Senior Partner: Mr AK Griesbach
Number of Partners: 12
Total Staff: 136

Cartwright Cunningham Haselgrove & Co

282-284 HOE STREET
WALTHAMSTOW
LONDON
E17 9QD

Phone: 01 520 1021

Fax: 01 520 5107
DX: 32007 WALTHAMSTOW
Telex: 262765 **Other offices:** 5
Senior Partner: Mr BG Haselgrove
Number of Partners: 10
Total Staff: 118

Cameron Markby *see full-page profile*
Cannons *see full-page profile*
Carter Faber *see full-page profile*
Cartmell Mawson & Main *see full-page profile*

Cameron Markby

SCEPTRE COURT
40 TOWER HILL
LONDON
EC3N 4BB
Phone: 01 702 2345

Fax: 01 702 2303
DX: 215 LONDON CITY EC3
Telex: 925779
Senior Partner: Russell Denoon Duncan
Number of Partners: 42
Total Staff: 348

The firm has a particular reputation in the financial field for banking, corporate finance, insolvency, real property development and investment, mergers and acquisitions.

The firm: Cameron Markby can trace its origins back to 1775. The present firm was created in 1980 when the two firms of Cameron Kemm Nordon and Markbys merged. The firm, which is growing rapidly, acts for a wide range of commercial and corporate clients, including banks, financial institutions, trading corporations and professionals.

The firm regularly recruits high-calibre solicitors with one or more year's City-type experience for property, banking, insolvency and corporate work. Enquiries to Roy Lecky-Thompson.

In addition, the firm recruits about 30 articled clerks annually. A high academic standard is expected; non-law graduates are welcome. Applications (on form available on request) should be sent to the personnel director, Roy Lecky-Thompson.

Types of work undertaken: The firm provides all legal services, but is orientated towards financial and commercial work, particularly City-type. Its client base covers a wide range of national and multinational commercial, corporate and professional clients.

Particular areas of experience include banking (domestic and international), insolvency, capital markets, venture and development capital (including BES), commercial litigation and commercial property. The large banking department acts for major UK and foreign institutions, and the firm is highly experienced in insolvency matters.

A full range of corporate work is undertaken (for both listed and unlisted companies) including management buy-outs, mergers and acquisitions, new issues, corporate finance, rescues and reconstructions (including international aspects), joint ventures, competition law, financial regulation and compliance, corporate and private tax, immigration, insurance, town and country planning, computers, intellectual property, 1992 and employment.

The property department is regularly involved in major redevelopment schemes, and acts for institutional investors as well as leading property companies. The litigation department acts mainly for corporate and banking clients in a wide range of commercial disputes, primarily in the High Court. The firm handles UK and offshore tax planning, drafting of wills and settlements for corporations and individuals and acts for charities.

The firm sees itself as a highly efficient commercial practice that is professional and friendly, aggressive when necessary and capable of creative problem solving to the benefit of clients.

CAMERON MARKBY

Cannons

11-15 ARLINGTON STREET
ST JAMES'S
LONDON
SW1A 1RD
Phone: 01 493 4205

Fax: 01 629 2143
DX: 37221 PICCADILLY-1
Telex: 27540 **Other offices:** 2
Senior Partner: Eamonn Cannon
Number of Partners: 16
Total Staff: 145

This medium sized West End firm is a major property practice in London, with strong secured lending, realisation and company/commercial departments.

The firm: Founded in 1984 by the present senior partner, the firm has expanded rapidly and established a strong reputation in property law. The firm has a growing name in secured lending and realisations and, following its May 1989 merger with North & Co, will have acquired an established and City-trained company/commercial department. Cannons is unusual in that nearly half of the partners are women.

The firm has a continuing need for assistant solicitors of quality, showing drive and a good commercial attitude, and expects to have ten vacancies in 1989. Enquiries to Antonia Brandes.

In addition, the firm has between five and eight vacancies for articled clerks every year. The minimum academic requirement is a 2(2) degree, not necessarily in law. Prospects after qualification are good, and the firm has flexible working arrangements for women with children and/or returning to the profession. Apply by letter (with CV) to Antonia Brandes.

Other offices: London (2).

Types of work undertaken: The firm is organised into three main departments, namely property, banking and company/commercial. Cannons' client base is almost entirely corporate.

Cannons' property department handles the whole spectrum of property work – especially retail superstores, both out of town and in town centres – for major developers, builders and retailers. Town and country planning is a particularly strong area of expertise.

The firm has a growing practice in banking, where it acts on behalf of a number of the major banks and financial institutions in relation to the property and security aspects of banking and insolvency.

When the merger with North & Co is effected in May 1989 Cannons will acquire an established company/commercial practice with flotation and major acquisition experience which undertakes the full range of corporate work for both listed and unlisted companies, including flotations, acquisitions and mergers.

In addition, the firm has a growing litigation practice, handling all types of contentious disputes in county courts, the High Court and tribunals.

Overall, Cannons perceives itself as a commercially minded and modern practice which offers a high-quality specialist property law service, and which is now broadening its skills to suit its clients' needs. This is a young but exceptionally experienced firm.

CANNONS

Carter Faber

10 ARTHUR STREET
LONDON
EC4R 9AY

Phone: 01 929 5555

Fax: 01 929 3637
DX: 44 LONDON CITY EC3
Telex: 887824 **Other offices:** 2
Senior Partner: Robert Rowan
Number of Partners: 14
Total Staff: 82

A medium sized City firm with a predominantly commercial law practice, Carter Faber also has two provincial offices.

The firm: The original practice of Carter & Co was formed in 1962. In 1980 JE & FE Farnfield (established in 1858 and specialising in shipping law) was acquired. Six years later Carter & Co merged with Peter Faber & Co, a City company/commercial practice.

The firm is always looking for qualified staff and is likely to recruit at least three assistant solicitors in 1989, in particular for company/commercial, banking and taxation. Enquiries to Charles Gordon.

Three or four articled clerks are required annually. The minimum requirement is a 2(2) degree, not necessarily in law. Apply by letter (plus CV and referees) to Mr P Faber.

Other offices: Sittingbourne, Maidstone.

Agency work: The firm accepts litigation work (except legal aid) from other solicitors; contact Charles Gordon.

Types of work undertaken: The City office handles mainly commercial work. It has a well established commercial property department: the firm has vast experience in acting for lenders in secured lending transactions and in commercial conveyancing generally. The company/commercial depart-

ment is very well regarded in the City and it has also developed an expertise in USM flotation and is well-established in the fields of company takeover, merger and acquisition work. The firm emphasises its insolvency work; a staff member is a licensed insolvency practitioner. It has automated its debt collection and mortgage repossession work.

The company/commercial department involves flotations, takeovers, mergers, intellectual property, insurance, banking, tax and commercial agreements of all kinds.

Clients of the property department include banks and other lenders, and property developers. The department deals with a wide range of general commercial conveyancing, and a separate department handles estate and other residential conveyancing.

The firm deals with all aspects of commercial litigation, with a strong emphasis on insolvency and debt-related litigation. There is an expanding department handling both contentious and non-contentious shipping and aviation matters and the transport industry generally. The client base is very wide, numbering about 4,000, and includes well-known public companies and large and small private companies.

Carter Faber sees itself as an expanding commercial practice able to compete with the large City firms. It sees advantage in its size, being able to offer a highly personal service with the emphasis on quality and speed.

CARTER FABER
S O L I C I T O R S

Cartmell Mawson & Main

VIADUCT HOUSE
CARLISLE
CA3 8EZ

Phone: 0228 31561

Fax: 0228 401490
DX: 63006 CARLISLE
Telex: 64106 **Other offices:** 2
Senior Partner: John AM Mawson
Number of Partners: 11
Total Staff: 65

One of Cumbria's largest law firms, Cartmell Mawson & Main has a wide-ranging provincial practice serving both commercial and private clients.

The firm: Cartmell Mawson & Main was formed in 1971 by the amalgamation of three well-respected local firms whose roots go back to the eighteenth century. Always a general practice, it has now grown to become one of the largest firms of solicitors in the area.

This expanding firm has a continuing need for high-calibre qualified staff, and expects to recruit four assistant solicitors in 1989: in civil litigation, matrimonial and family law, conveyancing and non-contentious private client (in branch office). Apply to Mr PA Clover.

In addition the firm recruits two articled clerks annually. The preferred educational qualification is a 2(1) degree; local applicants are encouraged. The firm places great emphasis on employing young professionals who will enjoy succeeding in Cumbria and the associated quality of life. Apply by letter (with CV) to Mr PA Clover two years in advance.

Other offices: Brampton, Haltwhistle, Rosehill (opens 1989).

Agency work: All types of agency work are accepted from other solicitors; contact Ian L Astle, the civil litigation partner.

Types of work undertaken: This is a wide-ranging, medium sized provincial practice. There are seven main departments: private client, conveyancing (residential), commercial non-contentious, agricultural, civil litigation (including personal injury and commercial), matrimonial, and crime.

As is to be expected of a firm located in a rural area, there is a particularly strong agricultural department offering levels of experience not available in the rest of the county. A new office to serve Cartmell Mawson & Main's agricultural clients is opening in 1989 in Rosehill, near Borderway Cattle Mart in Carlisle, indicating the firm's growing strength in this field. The firm's commercial, matrimonial and criminal departments are also particularly well thought of. Commercial work includes all matters up to and including flotations.

Overall, Cartmell Mawson & Main perceives itself as a leading firm in a prosperous, predominantly rural area, with a general practice of the highest standing. Expansionist in outlook and progressive in terms of technology and organisation, it sees changes in the economy and the legal profession as providing opportunities for further development. The firm meets these challenges in a business-like manner.

In short, Cartmell Mawson & Main can be regarded as a 'provincial City firm'. A brochure is available on request.

CARTMELL MAWSON & MAIN
SOLICITORS

Cartwrights

PO BOX 18
MARSH HOUSE
11 MARSH STREET
BRISTOL BS99 7BB
Phone: 0272 293601

Fax: 0272 262403
DX: 7851 BRISTOL
Telex: 44775 **Other offices:** 2
Senior Partner: Mr FMJ Littler
Number of Partners: 20
Total Staff: 135

This Bristol firm is a largely commercial practice and acts for a wide range of clients, from quoted PLCs to business start-ups.

The firm: Cartwrights was founded in 1836 when Thomas Danger started his solicitor's practice in Bristol. Originally a private client practice, the firm recognised the opportunities for specialisation at an early stage and developed particular expertise in licensing (liquor, gaming and cinema), insurance, employment, and transport. While growth has been largely organic, in 1988 the firm merged with the Cardiff practice of Adams & Black.

The firm has six vacancies for assistant solicitors: two each for company/commercial and private client, and one each for insurance and commercial litigation. Enquiries to Mr CL Eskell.

In addition five or six articled clerks are recruited annually. A 2(1) degree is required, not necessarily in law. Apply by handwritten letter (with CV and referees) to Mr CL Eskell two years in advance.

Other offices: Cardiff (2).

Agency work: All types of work from other solicitors accepted; contact N Puddicombe.

Types of work undertaken: Much of the firm's work is based outside the Bristol area, and it has extensive contacts with solicitors in the City and other major commercial centres.

The licensing department remains a leader in its field with probably the largest licensing practice in the country, acting for many well-known household names on a national and international basis. The department deals with a wide variety of work, ranging from entertainment centres or supermarket superstores to the one-off purchase of a corner off-licence.

The corporate client department covers commercial conveyancing, commercial litigation and company/commercial, and work varies from Stock Exchange related matters to the acquisition of commercial property and complex Chancery litigation. The firm has extensive experience and knowledge of restrictive trade practices legislation and competition law as it affects brewery and petrol companies.

The insurance department, one of the largest in the South West, acts for a large number of insurance companies, self-insuring PLCs, and loss adjusters on matters including personal injury, professional indemnity, employer's liability and public liability claims. In addition, the private client department provides a comprehensive service.

Cartwrights regards itself as professional, efficient, and firm but fair with specialist expertise within certain fields. Brochures describing the firm's services are available.

CARTWRIGHTS
S O L I C I T O R S

Castle Sanderson

RUSSELL HOUSE
19 ST PAUL'S STREET
LEEDS
LS1 2JG
Phone: 0532 434521

Fax: 0532 453967
DX: 12056 LEEDS
Telex: none **Other offices:** 2
Senior Partner: Andrew Castle
Number of Partners: 14
Total Staff: 100

This medium sized firm is a commercially orientated practice with offices in the three main Yorkshire centres.

The firm: Tracing its roots to 1839, Castle Sanderson was formed as the result of the amalgamation of a Hull firm which had built up a strong shipping practice, a Leeds general practice with an expanding commercial department, and a commercially based Sheffield practice. The new firm retains this strong commercial emphasis, combined with a considerable general practice.

The firm is expanding very rapidly, and consequently requires high-calibre assistant solicitors; in 1989 it expects to have 8 to 15 vacancies for commercial, property and litigation. Enquiries to Colin Gilbert.

In addition, Castle Sanderson recruits four or five articled clerks every year. The minimum educational requirements are a 2(2) law degree or a 2(1) non-law degree, plus all heads of Finals at first attempt. Applications should be by letter (with CV and names of referees) one year in advance to Colin Gilbert.

Other offices: Hull, Sheffield.

Agency work: The firm accepts work from other solicitors; contact Michael Nicholson (litigation), John Leahy (property) or Colin Gilbert (commercial).

Types of work undertaken: This is predominantly a commercial practice.

The company/commercial department retains its long-established shipping practice and is also well known for its work in the fields of corporate sales and purchases, and leveraged buy-outs and buy-ins. Castle Sanderson has strong contacts with development capital organisations and, indeed, acts for one in its lending and equity stakes. There is also expertise in the search for potential acquisitions and purchasers, and in commercial negotiations. The firm handles all aspects of agricultural law work.

The firm is unusual in that it has developed a successful bloodstock practice, handling the buying and selling of racehorses, and putting together and acting for syndicates. The firm has just completed a £1 million transaction for an American syndicate.

The commercial property department handles substantial real property transactions. The firm also has a thriving private client department offering domestic conveyancing, probate, trust (including the establishment of offshore trusts) and taxation work, as well as acting for developers and individuals in Iberian property sales and purchases. There is also a strong commercial litigation department and a growing international practice.

In short, Castle Sanderson sees itself as a young and vigorous practice which has placed the emphasis firmly on quality.

Challinor & Roberts

16-18 SOUTH ROAD
SMETHWICK
WARLEY
WEST MIDLANDS B67 7BW

Phone: 021 558 2351

Fax: 021 558 1814
DX: 14951 BEARWOOD
Telex: 265871 **Other offices:** 4
Senior Partner: Mr TA Lee
Number of Partners: 9
Total Staff: 72

Charles Lucas & Marshall

RADNOR HOUSE
28 BARTHOLOMEW STREET
NEWBURY
BERKSHIRE RG14 5FU

Phone: 0635 521212

Fax: 0635 37784
DX: 30802 NEWBURY
Telex: 848218 **Other offices:** 3
Senior Partner: Mr Philip Flory
Number of Partners: 18
Total Staff: 108

Charles Russell Williams & James

HALE COURT
LINCOLN'S INN
LONDON
WC2A 3UL

Phone: 01 242 1031

Fax: 01 430 0388
DX: 19 LONDON CHANCERY LANE WC2
Telex: 23521 **Other offices:** 4
Senior Partner: Mr C Russell
Number of Partners: 32
Total Staff: 180

Charsley Harrison

OLD CROWN
WINDSOR ROAD
SLOUGH
BERKSHIRE SL1 2DN

Phone: 0753 32011

Fax: 0753 691140
DX: 3402 SLOUGH
Telex: 847087 **Other offices:** 5
Senior Partner: Mr MA Ricketts
Number of Partners: 9
Total Staff: 60

Chattertons

5 SOUTH STREET
HORNCASTLE
LINCOLNSHIRE
LN9 6DS
Phone: 06582 2456

Fax: 06582 2445
DX: 26803 BOSTON
Telex: 56286 **Other offices:** 3
Senior Partner: Peter M Moran
Number of Partners: 7
Total Staff: 98

This Lincolnshire firm is a medium sized provincial practice with an emphasis on litigation, commercial and agricultural work.

The firm: Founded as a general country firm by Richard Chatterton in 1928, it remained a one-person practice until 1965 when the present senior partner joined. Since then, expansion has been steady. The firm is now based in both Horncastle and Boston (the two offices being of approximately equal size; in each town the litigation department has been hived off into separate premises). Recent growth has been rapid and the firm has virtually doubled in size in only three years.

Chattertons anticipates a continuing need for qualified staff in 1989, with four expected vacancies. Enquiries to Colin Thurston.

In addition, four articled clerks are recruited annually. The usual minimum educational qualification is a 2(2) law degree, but all suitable applicants are considered. Apply by handwritten letter (with CV and names of referees) to Caroline Mockford.

Other offices: Horncastle, Boston (2).

Agency work: Work is accepted from other solicitors. For litigation, contact Richard MacMillan or Patrick Cordingley (Horncastle), Peter Lawson (Boston); agricultural and capital taxation work, Peter Moran or Caroline Mockford (Horncastle); insolvency, Peter Moran (Horncastle), Peter Cropley (Boston); and planning, Stuart Cox (Horncastle).

Types of work undertaken: This is a broadly based provincial practice which carries out all types of work for a wide range of private clients, both nationally and locally, with some based overseas including foreign governments, as well as for agricultural and commercial clients.

There has always been a strong litigation practice, with emphasis on commercial matters but with a range from tribunals to traffic offences; mergers to matrimonials; and prosecutions to personal injuries.

Over the years the firm has expanded the work carried out for the farming and commercial client, particularly in the area of tax planning. Other areas covered on the agricultural side include land and property matters, and advising on the relevant legislation. In addition, the firm is well known for its commmercial and company work.

Town planning is another key area of strength with the firm acting for both private clients and the local authority. Chattertons boasts one of the few solicitor insolvency practitioners, and has a respected practice in this area. Legal aid work is accepted.

Overall, the firm is well managed and highly professional, with demanding standards producing consistently high quality work.

CHATTERTONS

Church Adams Tatham & Co

FULWOOD HOUSE
FULWOOD PLACE
LONDON
WC1V 6HR
Phone: 01 242 0841

Fax: 01 831 9609
DX: 183 LONDON CHANCERY LANE WC2
Telex: 28423 **Other offices:** 1
Senior Partner: Gordon R Jones
Number of Partners: 13
Total Staff: 68

This London firm has a thriving commercial practice, with a considerable amount of litigation and international work, and retains a broad private client base.

The firm: Church Adams Tatham & Co has been known by its present name since 1925 but traces its history back to the early eighteenth century. Traditionally a property-orientated firm, the emphasis in the past 25 to 30 years has been on all aspects of commercial property. Recently there has been rapid expansion into company and general commercial and international work, while retaining a broad private client base and its long-established High Court litigation practice. In 1972 an office was opened in Reigate, into which the local firm of Mole Metters & Forster was incorporated in 1986.

Two articled clerks are recruited annually. The minimum academic requirement is a 2(1) (good 2(2) law degree considered) Long-term prospects are good: half the present partners served articles with the firm. Apply by handwritten letter (plus CV and referees) to Richard Brown. Enquiries regarding vacancies for assistant solicitors should be addressed to the recruitment partner.

Other offices: Reigate, Surrey.

Agency work: The London office undertakes litigation work for other solicitors (contact Mr TW McKeown). Other agency work by arrangement.

Types of work undertaken: Generally perceived as a highly efficient and well-respected firm, Church Adams has a wide-ranging commercial and private client practice. Clients include several public companies, building societies and foreign corporate clients. In addition, there is a substantial private client base. A brochure for clients is available on request.

The firm offers comprehensive services in commercial property, ranging from setting up development funding agreements to handling property disputes and planning appeals, advising on portfolio management and acting in land transactions.

The work of the litigation department extends well beyond troubleshooting commercial property problems and includes both private and commercial litigation from the county court to the House of Lords.

The company/commercial department handles a wide variety of work for both UK and international clients, including company acquisitions, sales and restructuring, intellectual property, franchising, competition law, employment law and associated taxation advice. In addition, the firm's long-established private client department continues to handle the full range of legal services.

A brochure is available on request.

CHURCH ADAMS TATHAM & CO

Clarke Willmott & Clarke

6 HAMMET STREET
TAUNTON
SOMERSET
TA1 1RG
Phone: 0823 337474

Fax: 0823 259643
DX: 32100 TAUNTON
Telex: 46208 **Other offices:** 9
Senior Partner: Mr JM Close
Number of Partners: 36
Total Staff: 333

This thriving firm has offices throughout the south west of England, offering a truly comprehensive legal service to commercial and private clients.

The firm: Clarke Willmott & Clarke dates back to the 1880s. It expanded steadily and began opening branch offices between the wars. In the last decade, the firm has doubled in size, mainly through internal growth, to become one of the major practices in the area. Taunton remains the largest office and, with Yeovil and Bristol, undertakes a considerable amount of the firm's commercial work.

The firm is always looking for assistant solicitors, and expects to recruit about 16 in 1989. Enquiries to Roy Kerslake.

In addition, there are 12 to 15 vacancies for articled clerks every year. The minimum educational requirement is a 2(2) degree, not necessarily in law. Applications should be by handwritten letter (with CV and names of referees) to arrive by mid-August to Felicity Shakespear.

Other offices: Bridgwater, Bristol, Chard, Crewkerne, Langport, Somerton, Wellington, Worle (Weston super Mare), Yeovil.

Agency work: The firm accepts all kinds of civil and criminal litigation work from other solicitors.

Types of work undertaken: The continuing expansion of this firm reflects the increased commercial and corporate work available in the South West.

Clarke Willmott & Clarke provides wide-ranging company/commercial services to public and private companies, particularly in radio and television, in the motor and retail trades, and the licensed trade; indeed, licensing is a particular area of expertise.

There is an extensive commercial and residential conveyancing practice (including estate development) and in agricultural holdings law, all aspects of town and country planning, and in landlord and tenant matters.

The firm is well known for its personal injury litigation work, just one aspect of a substantial amount of civil litigation undertaken. The firm handles all areas of family and welfare law, employment law, consumer disputes and crime. There is a strong trust and probate department. Legal aid work is undertaken.

Clarke Willmott & Clarke sees itself as one of the leading firms in the South West, with experts in most areas of the law. The firm perceives its 'organic' growth and spread of offices not only as a solid foundation but as a source of strength, ensuring that further expansion continues to the mutual benefit of the firm and its clients. Brochures describing the firm's work are available on request.

CLARKE WILLMOTT & CLARKE

Clarks

GREAT WESTERN HOUSE
STATION ROAD
READING
BERKSHIRE RG1 1SX
Phone: 0734 585321

Fax: 0734 589859
DX: 4034 READING
Telex: 847646
Senior Partner: Hugh J Williams
Number of Partners: 9
Total Staff: 80

This medium sized provincial firm offers a wide range of legal services to business, institutional and private clients.

The firm: Founded in 1913, the firm has enjoyed a period of steady expansion since the 1960s, particularly in the areas of company/commercial, litigation and commercial property. In March 1989 the firm moved to Great Western House, Station Road, Reading, a prestigious location with ample room for expansion.

There is a continuing need for good qualified solicitors, and in 1989 the firm expects to recruit at least six assistant solicitors. Enquiries should be addressed to Michael Sippitt.

In addition, the firm generally recruits six articled clerks every year. The minimum educational requirement is a 2(2) law degree or a 2(1) non-law degree. Prospects after qualification are excellent: the majority of the partners served articles with the firm. Applications should be made by handwritten letter (with CV and names of referees) in September/October two years in advance and should be addressed to Michael Sippitt (late applications are also welcome).

Types of work undertaken: This is a broad-based practice. Clarks handles the traditional areas of legal practice as well as complex company/commercial matters and

transactions. There are four main departments, namely property, commercial litigation, company, and private client. Clients include well-known public and multinational companies and public sector bodies.

The increasing commercial importance of Reading and the Thames Valley area is reflected in the expansion of Clarks' company/commercial work, which includes joint ventures, public issues, management buy-outs, mergers and acquisitions, venture and development capital financing and banking, as well as intellectual property law, franchising, product liability and employment law.

The property department deals with the sale, purchase and letting of all types of commercial and agricultural property, the sale of businesses, mortgages and commercial lending, landlord and tenant matters, residential conveyancing, and town and country planning law.

Litigation, particularly commercial, is another area of expertise. Building disputes, industrial tribunal cases, product liability actions and all types of civil claim are handled. In addition, there is a strong private client department which handles wills, estate administration, tax planning and trusts.

In brief, Clarks sees itself as a firm with integrity and high standards, which is well known for its hard work and professionalism. Brochures are available upon request.

Clarks

Clifford Chance

ROYEX HOUSE
ALDERMANBURY SQUARE
LONDON
EC2V 7LD
Phone: 01 600 0808

Fax: 01 726 8561
DX: 606 LONDON CHANCERY LANE WC2
Telex: 8959991 **Other offices:** 15
Joint Senior Partners: Sir Max Williams
and Mr Tom Johnson-Gilbert
Number of Partners: 144 **Total Staff:** 1,649

Based in the City of London, and with offices in 14 cities around the world, this large commercial practice offers a full range of services of international scope.

The firm: Clifford Chance was formed in 1987 by the merger of Coward Chance and Clifford-Turner, two practices which had grown rapidly in the 60s and 70s. Both firms had been especially active in corporate finance, banking and international finance, commercial property law, litigation and tax advice.

Clifford Chance now provides a comprehensive range of legal services relating to: international and domestic banking and finance, securities issues, mergers and acquisitions, general corporate and commercial work, litigation and arbitration, shipping and international trade, aviation, securities regulation and investor protection, fund management, insurance, natural resources, property, taxation, trusts and personal estate planning.

The firm also owns a management consultancy company, New Bridge Street Consultants Limited, so that clients can benefit from expertise in cash and share incentives, ESOPs, pensions, personnel management and related areas.

Clients are drawn from many different industries and countries of origin – the firm acts for businesses, financiers and govern-ments throughout the world – and its lawyers accordingly have capabilities in various jurisdictions.

The firm's strength comes from the aggregation of many talented individuals. Clients are therefore offered high standards of legal expertise. They are also offered a close working relationship with their lawyers whose approach is both practical and imaginative.

Clifford Chance is a rapidly expanding firm which recruited more than 75 assistant solicitors in 1988. The growth level for 1989 is expected to be sustained if not increased. Qualified solicitors are actively sought for the company/commercial, banking and capital markets, tax, property, litigation, and intellectual property departments. Enquiries to Alistair Dawson.

In addition, approximately 120 articled clerks will be recruited in 1989. Candidates may come from the law or other disciplines. The firm seeks those who are good communicators and problem solvers with commercial as well as legal knowledge and understanding. There is no minimum academic qualification (though many recruits will have received or be expected to receive a 2(1) degree). Long-term prospects are excellent: nearly all articled clerks remain with the firm after qualification. Applications by form (available on request) should be made between August and October two years in advance to Alistair Dawson.

Other offices: Europe: Amsterdam, Brussels, London, Madrid, Paris; The Far East: Hong Kong, Singapore, Tokyo; The Middle East: Bahrain, Dubai, Jeddah, Riyadh, Sharjah; North America: New York.

Agency work: Work is accepted from other firms.

Types of work undertaken: The firm is organised into a number of broad service areas most of which are divided into smaller working groups. Since there is a frequent need for multi-disciplinary teams, there are no rigid structures.

The firm is well known for its corporate work especially mergers and acquisitions, flotations (full listings, USM and international), leveraged buy-outs, and insolvency. In addition, it acts in matters concerning government privatisations and venture capital financing.

In the field of banking and finance the firm is noted for its expertise in developing new financial techniques, in debt rescheduling, in project and asset financing, and in Euromarket issues.

The commercial department is involved in UK, EC and ECSC competition law. Entertainment and media law is another important area of activity. The work in this field includes film and television production, finance and distribution, artist management, recording and tour contracts, publishing, merchandising and sponsorship. The department also has substantial expertise in intellectual property, and in computer law including computer contracts, electronic communications and information technology, telecommunications, and cable and satellite law.

All types of English and international commercial disputes are undertaken. This includes High Court, Court of Appeal and House of Lords cases, Privy Council Appeals, and arbitrations in London and abroad. Additionally, the litigation lawyers undertake statutory inquiries/DTI, insolvency, banking litigation, insurance and reinsurance disputes, town planning applications and appeals, administrative law, compulsory purchase and construction law.

Transport, international trade and finance are dealt with by cross-departmental groups focussing on these areas. There are financial regulatory groups and a dedicated EC unit at the Brussels office.

The firm handles all aspects of corporate, personal and partnership taxation in the UK and abroad. Profit-sharing schemes and employee share schemes, pension and other retirement benefit schemes are other areas of activity.

The firm is well known for property development and financing, town and country planning including planning enquiries and appeals against planning refusals, compulsory purchase and rating.

Private clients are also served by the firm. The work includes the establishment of settlements and trusts, and the administration of estates and charities. However, welfare, criminal and matrimonial law are not part of the firm's practice.

Overall, Clifford Chance aims to be forceful and effective without being unduly aggressive in the interests of its clients. The firm sees itself as combining innovation, creativity and commercial awareness with an unstuffy style and an empathy with client problems. A brochure for clients is available on request.

CLIFFORD CHANCE

THE MERGED FIRM OF COWARD CHANCE AND CLIFFORD-TURNER

Clintons

WELLINGTON HOUSE
6-9 UPPER ST MARTIN'S LANE
LONDON
WC2H 9DF
Phone: 01 379 6080

Fax: 01 240 9310
DX: 40021 COVENT GARDEN-1
Telex: 22698
Senior Partner: Mr SB Sylvester
Number of Partners: 12
Total Staff: 75

This medium sized central London firm is broadly based, with particular expertise in the areas of entertainment law, property and international tax.

The firm: Founded in 1957, the firm has grown steadily, expanding its range of services as necessary in order to offer its commercial clients whatever legal services they require. Clintons has grown some 50 per cent since 1979. Unlike many of its competitors, the firm is not rigidly departmentalised, and there is an emphasis on close client/partner contact.

This expanding firm welcomes enquiries about vacancies for assistant solicitors; address to Sally Hamwee.

The firm normally takes two or three articled clerks each year. There are no minimum educational requirements, although a good honours degree may be an advantage; mature applicants and those with less conventional backgrounds are welcome. Apply by handwritten letter (with CV) to Laurence Middleweek.

Agency work: All types of work are accepted from other solicitors, including litigation and international commercial and tax.

Types of work undertaken: This is a broadly based commercial practice which aims to provide all the necessary services for commercial clients, as well as dealing with personal matters. Clients are often entrepreneurial, and many are in the entertainment industry. Much of the work is international in nature, and the firm includes French and Hebrew speakers.

The firm is one of the pre-eminent entertainment law practices, and is well known for its work in the fields of music, theatre, television copyright and intellectual property generally. International taxation work is also an area of particular expertise. This is part of a broad range of commmercial work undertaken which also includes company acquisitions, joint venture arrangements, liquidations and receiverships, and international contractual arrangements.

The firm has a strong property practice and special expertise in acting for banks on secured lending. Both commercial and domestic conveyancing work are handled, together with probate.

There is a substantial litigation department, dealing largely with commercial matters, though matrimonial and private client work is also undertaken. Legal aid work is accepted.

Overall, Clintons sees itself as professional without being stuffy or arrogant, and approachable with a clear appreciation of its clients' problems. It has considerable understanding of the commercial aspects of a matter, and is highly protective of the interests of its clients.

Clintons

Clyde & Co

51 EASTCHEAP
LONDON
EC3M 1JP

Phone: 01 623 1244

Fax: 01 623 5427
DX: 1071 LONDON CITY EC3
Telex: 884886 **Other offices:** 3
Senior Partner: Michael Payton
Number of Partners: 62
Total Staff: 384

Clyde & Co is a specialist commercial firm with a longstanding reputation for weighty litigation which has a rapidly growing company/commercial practice.

The firm: Founded in 1933 by RAH Clyde, the firm originally established its name through expertise in shipping law and insurance. Since then, the work of the firm has broadened and it now handles all aspects of commercial work and international trade.

The firm expects to recruit ten assistant solicitors in the next 12 months. Enquiries to the recruitment partner.

In addition, 14 to 16 articled clerks are recruited annually. A 2(1) degree, not necessarily in law, is preferred; language graduates are particularly welcome. Apply (on form available on request) to the recruitment partner.

Other offices: Guildford, Cardiff, Hong Kong.

Types of work undertaken: The firm acts for many companies in the insurance industry (both in the UK and overseas), international traders and a wide range of other commercial organisations. It has particular expertise in heavy litigation generally, especially in the insurance and shipping fields, the company and commercial aspects of insurance, and international trade work.

Shipping is a central part of Clyde & Co's practice, and the firm is one of the best known in this field. It has considerable experience of conducting cases in the commercial and Admiralty courts and before London arbitration tribunals. The work handled includes claims for loss of or damage to cargo, charterparty disputes, salvage and collision claims, transshipment agreements and problems arising from financial collapse of shipowners and shipbuilding disputes.

In the fields of insurance and reinsurance the firm advises on marine insurance policies in respect of cargoes, hulls and shipowners' liabilities. The firm also deals with many claims of a non-marine nature and has considerable experience in reinsurance markets around the world. Claims arising from the carriage of goods by road or rail, and aviation and shipping finance are also major areas of practice.

Clyde & Co handles a wide range of commercial litigation problems, including those arising in the construction industry and the fields of oil and commodity trading.

There is a strong company/commercial practice, and the firm handles all aspects of banking and finance work, as well as commercial and domestic property matters.

Overall, the firm sees itself as a leading litigation firm with an expanding company and commercial practice. Brochures describing the firm's services are available.

CLYDE & CO

Cobbett Leak Almond

SHIP CANAL HOUSE
KING STREET
MANCHESTER
M2 4WB
Phone: 061 833 3333

Fax: 061 833 3030
DX: 14374 MANCHESTER-1
Telex: 669898 **Other offices:** 4
Senior Partner: Mr JAH Fielden
Number of Partners: 29
Total Staff: 160

This large Manchester firm has a substantial commercial law practice, as well as a significant private client list.

The firm: Cobbett Leak Almond was formed in 1987 from the merger of two old-established firms, Cobbetts and Leak Almond & Parkinson, which had both been serving the Manchester business community since the Industrial Revolution. The firm is currently growing at the annual rate of 25 per cent.

The firm is seeking to recruit assistant solicitors for the commercial property and commercial departments. Enquiries should be addressed to Mr PJW Stone.

In addition, between six and nine articled clerks are recuited annually. The minimum educational requirement is a 2(2) law or a 2(1) non-law degree. Prospects after qualification are excellent; most of the present partners served articles with one of the constituent firms. Applications should be made by handwritten letter (with CV and referees) to Mr SJ White.

Other offices: Congleton, Holmes Chapel, Whaley Bridge, Wilmslow.

Agency work: The firm accepts all work from other solicitors; contact Mr RS Hawes (commercial) or Mr P Hodson (litigation).

Types of work undertaken: This is a broadly based practice, handling all types of work. There are four main departments, namely company/commercial, commercial property, litigation and private client.

The bias in the Manchester office is towards commercial work, the commercial property and company/commercial departments being particularly strong. The firm is also well known for its strong connection with the brewery trade and expertise in licensing work. While the branches specialise in private client work, the skills of the Manchester office are available to the branches at all times.

The commercial property department is well known for its planning work and its knowledge of the retail trade, particularly of large superstores.

The litigation department deals with every type of litigation, and has strengths in intellectual property, and also acts for a number of building societies handling mortgage repossession work.

This is one of the few large commercial firms that still has branches outside the City centre. The full range of private client work is undertaken, including conveyancing, tax planning, trusts and probate, and family law.

The true strength of the firm is its ability to tackle any instructions for any client, whether public company or private individual. In short, Cobbett Leak Almond sees itself as a firm of the utmost integrity — easy to deal with, efficient, young, vital and progressive.

COBBETT
LEAK ALMOND

Coffin Mew & Clover

17 HAMPSHIRE TERRACE
PORTSMOUTH
HANTS
PO1 2PU

Phone: 0705 812511

Fax: 0705 291847
DX: 2207 PORTSMOUTH
Telex: none **Other offices:** 11
Senior Partner: Murray Bell
Number of Partners: 18
Total Staff: 201

Coffin Mew & Clover is a large provincial practice providing for the needs of all types of clients throughout Hampshire.

The firm: Originally a conveyancing practice founded in 1888, since the Second World War the firm has expanded rapidly throughout the Solent region in all areas of the law. It now has a successful network of 12 offices and a client base ranging from individuals to major companies. The firm is organised into specialist departments.

In view of the firm's continuing expansion, it is always interested in interviewing well-qualified assistant solicitors, particularly those interested in the areas of commercial conveyancing and litigation. Enquiries should be addressed to Jennifer Bennett (Portsmouth).

In addition the firm is planning to recruit two or three articled clerks in the next year. Graduates are preferred but other candidates will be considered. Most articled clerks stay with the firm on admission; many have become partners. Applications by handwritten letter (plus CV and referees) should be sent to Jennifer Bennett (Portsmouth).

Other offices: Cosham, Cowplain, Emsworth, Fareham, Gosport, Havant, Leigh Park, Park Gate, Southampton, Stubbington, Totton.

Agency work: The firm undertakes work for other solicitors.

Types of work undertaken: This large Hampshire firm offers a full range of commercial and private client services through its network of regional offices. It is particularly well known for commercial and domestic conveyancing, company/commercial, all types of litigation, probate and industrial relations.

In the company/commercial field it is well equipped to guide a business through the maze of legal problems, from the formation of a company or partnership to the drawing up of commercial contracts. It also specialises in the buying and selling of companies, shops, businesses, offices and factories; employment law; and tax investments and trusts.

Commercial and residential development is on the increase in Hampshire; Coffin Mew & Clover has considerable experience advising clients on all aspects, including the related planning laws. The work of the litigation department ranges from small disputes to major trials, including accidents and personal injury claims. Private clients are offered the full range of legal services, including matrimonial and family, wills, tax planning and crime. Legal aid work is accepted.

This long-established and respected firm has a modern and forward-thinking approach and offers a comprehensive legal service throughout the Hampshire area.

Cole and Cole

ST GEORGES MANSIONS
GEORGE STREET
OXFORD
OX1 2AR
Phone: 0865 791122

Fax: 0865 721367
DX: 4303 OXFORD
Telex: 837628 **Other offices:** 9
Senior Partner: Eric Church
Number of Partners: 22
Total Staff: 150

Cole and Cole is a busy general practice with offices throughout the Oxford area, serving both business and private clients.

The firm: Cole and Cole was founded in 1945 by two brothers, RB and Maurice Cole. From the beginning, this has been a general provincial practice. Expansion has been steady, with the acquisition of established practices in Abingdon (Morland & Son), Burford (Soanes & Co) and Stow-on-the-Wold (Francis Wickens & Hill). The firm is organised into departments.

There is a continuing need for qualified staff, and in 1989 the firm expects to recruit up to ten assistant solicitors. Enquiries to Mr JC Pillman.

In addition, the firm recruits four or five articled clerks every year. The minimum educational requirement is a 2(2) degree, not necessarily in law. Prospects after qualification are excellent; about half the present partners served articles with the firm. Apply by form by the end of September two years in advance to Paul Rippon.

Other offices: Reading (commercial office), Kidlington (commercial and general offices), Abingdon (as Morland & Son), Didcot, Witney, Burford, Chipping Norton, Stow-on-the-Wold.

Agency work: The firm accepts work from other solicitors; contact Mr JPA Roche (crime and licensing) or Mr C Graham (litigation).

Types of work undertaken: There are seven departments, namely commercial, civil litigation, family, crime, property, planning, and tax and probate. The client base is varied, ranging from substantial local companies and Oxford colleges to individuals.

The firm is particularly well known for employment law (acting for employees, employers and trades unions), management buy-outs and computer contracts. Other company/commercial work includes company formations, partnerships and joint ventures, acquisitions, flotations, sale and purchase matters, insolvency work, EEC law and intellectual property.

There is wide experience and expertise in all forms of litigation: civil, criminal, licensing and matrimonial. Cole and Cole handles all types of town and country planning applications, appeals and problems, as well as commercial property matters and domestic conveyancing. There is a strong family law department, and the firm offers personal financial and tax planning advice, as well as dealing with all aspects of wills, trusts, probate and estate work. Legal aid work is accepted.

Overall, Cole and Cole is a forward-looking and enthusiastic firm, committed to supplying legal services to the highest standards, to private and business clients alike.

Collyer-Bristow

4 BEDFORD ROW
LONDON
WC1R 4DF

Phone: 01 242 7363

Fax: 01 405 0555
DX: 163 LONDON CHANCERY LANE WC2
Telex: 21615
Senior Partner: Mr AR Burdon-Cooper
Number of Partners: 9
Total Staff: 73

Cooper & Burnett

NAPIER HOUSE
14-16 MOUNT EPHRAIM ROAD
TUNBRIDGE WELLS
KENT TN1 1EE

Phone: 0892 515022

Fax: 0892 515088
DX: 3905 TUNBRIDGE WELLS
Telex: 95270 **Other offices:** 1
Senior Partner: Mr D Cooper
Number of Partners: 10
Total Staff: 66

Cozens-Hardy & Jewson

CASTLE CHAMBERS
OPIE STREET
NORWICH
NORFOLK NR1 3DP

Phone: 0603 625231

Fax: 0603 627160
DX: 5214 NORWICH
Telex: 265871
Senior Partner: Mr JA Fletcher
Number of Partners: 11
Total Staff: 56

Cripps Harries Hall

84 CALVERLEY ROAD
TUNBRIDGE WELLS
KENT
TN1 2UP

Phone: 0892 515121

Fax: 0892 515444
DX: 3912 TUNBRIDGE WELLS
Telex: none **Other offices:** 4
Senior Partner: Mr DW Rawson-Mackenzie
Number of Partners: 19
Total Staff: 173

Constant & Constant *see full-page profile*

Constant & Constant

SEA CONTAINERS HOUSE
20 UPPER GROUND
BLACKFRIARS BRIDGE
LONDON SE1 9PD
Phone: 01 261 0006

Fax: 01 401 2161
DX: 1067 LONDON CITY EC3
Telex: 927766 **Other offices:** 1
Senior Partner: John F Smith
Number of Partners: 22
Total Staff: 96

Constant & Constant is a long-established firm with an international practice and a large number of commercial clients based in this country and overseas.

The firm: Benjamin Constant founded the firm in 1911. From its beginnings the firm specialised in shipping and transport and, in addition to representing a wide range of shipping interests, the practice has traditionally maintained a close affinity with the Greek shipping community. While shipping remains a major part of the practice, Constant & Constant has expanded the scope of its work to include aviation, banking, insurance, international trade, property and general commercial matters.

The firm expects to recruit four assistant solicitors in the next 12 months – in the areas of property, company/commercial, aviation and litigation. Enquiries should be addressed to Graham Crane.

In addition, three to six articled clerks are recruited annually. A 2(2) degree is required, not necessarily in law. Apply by handwritten letter (with CV and names of referees) to Graham Crane in August/September two years in advance.

Other offices: Paris.

Agency work: The firm will occasionally undertake work (mainly specialist litigation) for other solicitors.

Types of work undertaken: Constant & Constant has developed beyond its transport law origins into an extensive general commercial and private client practice. The firm is divided into three principal areas – namely company/commercial, litigation and property – the work being concentrated in the aviation, banking and finance, corporate and commercial, insurance, marine, private client property, and taxation fields.

The client base ranges from private individuals to national governments and their agencies, and includes clearing and merchant banks and many other private and public companies in the UK and abroad. The firm's aviation clients also include national flag carriers, leasing companies and insurers, and, in the marine field, shipowners, salvage and tug companies, oil companies, shipbuilders, insurers and reinsurers, offshore services and marine engineering companies, ship and chartering brokers.

The firm is active in the fields of transport law (shipping finance, shipping litigation, aviation finance and aviation claims); banking law; and insurance and reinsurance law.

Constant & Constant prides itself on being able to provide a prompt, efficient and personal service. Overall, the firm perceives itself as being a highly efficient commercial practice. Brochures are available.

Constant & Constant

Crutes

7 OSBORNE TERRACE
JESMOND
NEWCASTLE UPON TYNE
NE2 1RQ
Phone: 091 281 5811

Fax: 091 281 3608
DX: 61013 NEWCASTLE UPON TYNE
Telex: 537681 **Other offices:** 4
Senior Partner: Mr AH Crute
Number of Partners: 14
Total Staff: 90

Curwen Carter & Evans

17 HIGH STREET
ROYSTON
HERTFORDSHIRE
SG8 9AA
Phone: 0763 241261

Fax: 0763 242125
DX: 37300 ROYSTON
Telex: 22774 **Other offices:** 5
Senior Partner: Mr T Wyndham James
Number of Partners: 13
Total Staff: 84

Dale & Newbery

CLARENCE HOUSE
31 CLARENCE STREET
STAINES
MIDDLESEX TW18 4SY
Phone: 0784 58322

Fax: 0784 63004
DX: 90402 STAINES
Telex: none **Other offices:** 5
Senior Partner: Mr SH Lloyd
Number of Partners: 9
Total Staff: 85

Darbey-Scott-Rees

17 WELLINGTON ROAD
BILSTON
WEST MIDLANDS
WV14 6AD
Phone: 0902 353535

Fax: 0902 353088
DX: 23551 BILSTON
Telex: 338490 **Other offices:** 4
Senior Partner: Mr AB Rees
Number of Partners: 12
Total Staff: 82

Cuff Roberts North Kirk *see full-page profile*
D J Freeman & Co *see full-page profile*

Cuff Roberts North Kirk
(incorporating Banks Kendall)

25 CASTLE STREET
LIVERPOOL
L2 4TD

Phone: 051 227 4181

Fax: 051 227 2584
DX: 14126 LIVERPOOL
Telex: 628169
Senior Partner: Keith Tamlin
Number of Partners: 18
Total Staff: 111

This medium sized Liverpool firm has a broadly based practice with the emphasis on commercial law work.

The firm: Cuff Roberts North Kirk was formed as the result of the 1982 amalgamation of Cuff Roberts & Co and North Kirk & Co; the first was founded in the 1920s by a partner of North Kirk, which was established well over 100 years ago. In 1987, there was a further merger, with the long-established Liverpool firm, Banks Kendall. All three firms had general practices, with North Kirk having a commercial bias. The firm is organised into departments.

In 1989 there will be two to four vacancies for assistant solicitors: for commercial (including property) and litigation work. Enquiries to the managing partner, Tony Twemlow.

In addition, the firm has four or five vacancies for articled clerks every year. The educational qualification is a 2(2) law degree or better, although the firm stresses it takes a flexible approach. Prospects after qualification are excellent; over half of the present partners served articles with the firm. Apply by letter (with CV and referees) preferably two years in advance to Peter Higgins.

Agency work: The firm accepts work from other solicitors, mainly litigation; contact Christine Aitken.

Types of work undertaken: This is a general practice with a commercial bias. There are four main departments: company/commercial, commercial property, litigation and private clients. The client base is predominantly commercial, and includes large public companies and institutions, small businesses and charities, as well as a long-established private client list.

The firm is well known for its commercial property department, which handles all types of work, including business leases for shops and offices, as well as conveyancing and property development work.

The firm has particular expertise in equal opportunities and race relations legislation, and takes cases through courts and tribunals. The full range of commercial litigation is undertaken, including building disputes, landlord and tenant, town and country planning appeals, intellectual property matters, licensing appeals, and employment law disputes. A fully computerised debt recovery service is provided.

There is a growing company/commercial department, where the emphasis is on corporate and insolvency work and the firm has a strong private client department.

Cuff Roberts North Kirk sees itself as an industrious, co-operative and go-ahead firm, with full computerised and technological back-up, fully committed to high professional standards and the regeneration of Liverpool.

DJ Freeman & Co

43 FETTER LANE
LONDON
EC4A 1NA

Phone: 01 583 4055

Fax: 01 353 7377
DX: 103 LONDON CHANCERY LANE WC2
Telex: 894579 **Other offices:** 1
Senior Partner: David John Freeman
Number of Partners: 52
Total Staff: 324

This City practice concentrates on three major areas, corporate and commercial law, property law, and commercial litigation.

The firm: Founded in 1952 by its present senior partner, David Freeman, the firm has grown rapidly – expansion has been achieved organically rather than through any mergers. Initially, the firm's reputation was primarily in litigation and it subsequently became known as a leading commercial property firm. As well as building up these specialities, Freemans has established a reputation in corporate and commercial law. Over the past two years, the firm has virtually doubled in size. Two noteworthy recent developments are the recruitment of specialists in insurance and shipping litigation, and the opening of a regional office in Reading.

The firm expects to recruit 15 to 20 assistant solicitors in 1989. It is prepared to recruit at senior levels and feels that it has a particularly enlightened attitude towards women (including permitting part-time practice). Enquiries should be addressed to Mr CS Joseph.

Twelve to 15 articled clerks are recruited annually. A high academic standard is expected. Non-law graduates are considered and candidates with wide interests and experience are welcome. Apply by letter (with CV and the names of referees) to Marcus Rutherford two years in advance.

Other offices: Reading.

Types of work undertaken: This broadly based commercial practice acts for a diverse range of corporate interests, including property construction and development companies, banks, insurance companies and other financial institutions, local authorities and government organisations, manufacturing and retail concerns, the media and high-technology companies. The firm is organised into three main departments: corporate and commercial, property and litigation.

The firm has one of the country's leading property departments which deals with some of the most important commercial and industrial developments in the country. The firm is also well known for commercial litigation, insolvency and disciplinary tribunal work, media and technology-related work.

The firm undertakes the full range of company and commercial matters (and indeed the senior partner David Freeman was the first practising solicitor appointed by the DTI for investigations under the Companies Act). In addition, there are specialist teams covering such matters as insurance and shipping, construction and entertainment law.

Freemans believes that it is perceived as a firm which has taken considerable strides within the past few years and which is continuing to develop.

Davenport Lyons

KNIGHTWAY HOUSE
20 SOHO SQUARE
LONDON
W1V 6QJ
Phone: 01 434 2255

Fax: 01 437 8216
DX: 62 LONDON CHANCERY LANE WC2
Telex: 267097
Senior Partner: Mr FDN Campailla
Number of Partners: 10
Total Staff: 50

This small but thriving central London-based firm has a strong commercial bias, with a long-established entertainment law practice.

The firm: Davenport Lyons was founded over 50 years ago as a general practice with an emphasis on litigation. The firm quickly developed wide experience in general commercial work, in all branches of media and entertainment law, and in commercial property. More recently, Davenport Lyons has built up particular expertise in computer and information technology.

In 1989, the firm expects to have vacancies for two to four assistant solicitors. Enquiries to Ms P Ellsworth.

In addition, two articled clerks are recruited annually. The minimum academic requirement is a 2(2) degree; non-law graduates and older candidates are welcome. Apply by letter (with CV) to Graham Atkins.

Agency work: Specialist entertainment litigation is the only type of work accepted from other solicitors.

Types of work undertaken: The firm has a substantial company/commercial practice, with particular emphasis on formations and reorganisations, acquisitions, venture capital, business start-ups and financing, joint ventures and corporate tax planning. It is well known for its work for small and growing companies up to and including USM and Stock Exchange quotations.

Davenport Lyons' wide experience in the media and entertainment law field is reflected in its client list, which includes substantial television production companies, music publishers, record companies and advertising agencies. There is an emphasis on commercial work, particularly in music and television production. The firm is well known for its expertise in British copyright law, and is familiar with a number of overseas copyright systems, as well as having wide experience of international fiscal and taxation issues, and computer and information technology.

There is a strong property department. It has a commercial bias and acts for major property developers, lending institutions and banks in a broad range of substantial property and property-related transactions. The department also offers a comprehensive domestic conveyancing service.

Civil litigation remains a significant element of the practice, and the firm has experience of every division of the English courts and tribunal systems. The litigation department also handles matrimonial and family law work. In addition, a separate department deals with tax planning, trust and probate.

Overall, Davenport Lyons sees itself as a competent company/commercial firm, and as as one of the older and better established entertainment law practices.

DAVENPORT LYONS

David Law & Co

TELEGRAPH HOUSE
HIGH STREET
SHEFFIELD
S1 1PT
Phone: 0742 700999

Fax: 0742 739292
DX: 10545 SHEFFIELD
Telex: 54317 **Other offices:** 2
Senior Partner: Mr DC Law
Number of Partners: 7
Total Staff: 55

Davies Wallis

5 CASTLE STREET
LIVERPOOL
L2 4XE

Phone: 051 236 6226

Fax: 051 236 3088
DX: 14128 LIVERPOOL
Telex: 627685 **Other offices:** 6
Senior Partner: Mr JCM Davies
Number of Partners: 22
Total Staff: 126

Davis Campbell

PEARL ASSURANCE HOUSE
DERBY SQUARE
LIVERPOOL
L2 9XL
Phone: 051 236 5400

Fax: 051 236 2175
DX: 14129 LIVERPOOL
Telex: none
Senior Partner: Mr WBC Lister
Number of Partners: 14
Total Staff: 110

Dawbarns

1 & 2 YORK ROW
WISBECH
CAMBRIDGESHIRE
PE13 1EA
Phone: 0945 61456

Fax: 0945 61364
DX: 41351 WISBECH
Telex: none **Other offices:** 2
Senior Partner: Mr ODG Barr
Number of Partners: 9
Total Staff: 51

Davies Arnold Cooper *see full-page profile*

Davies Arnold Cooper

12 BRIDEWELL PLACE
LONDON
EC4V 6AD

Phone: 01 353 6555

Fax: 01 353 0574
DX: 172 LONDON CHANCERY LANE WC2
Telex: 262894
Senior Partner: David A McIntosh
Number of Partners: 19
Total Staff: 190

This medium sized City firm has a high-profile broadly based UK and international commercial law practice.

The firm: Davies Arnold Cooper was established in 1927; since then it has acted for major insurance companies. This solid foundation has been the basis of the firm's rapid development; it has doubled in size over the last three years and is expanding particularly fast in the company/commercial and commercial property areas. Coupled with its 60 years' experience, the firm has a young, energetic approach; indeed, most of its partners are in their thirties.

This expanding firm expects to recruit ten assistant solicitors in 1989 for all departments. Enquiries to Nicholas Rochez or Kenneth McKenzie.

In addition, 12 to 14 articled clerks are recruited annually. The preferred educational qualification is a 2(1) degree, usually in law. Prospects after qualification are good: a number of the partners were articled with the firm. Applications should be made by form (available on request) with names of referees to Kenneth McKenzie.

Types of work undertaken: This broadly based commercial practice undertakes work in the following areas: corporate; commercial; banking; tax; insolvency; competition and anti-trust; intellectual property; commercial property and funding; town planning; construction; commercial litigation; marine and aviation; insurance and reinsurance; product liability; personal injury; and professional indemnity.

The client base consists of major UK and international public and private corporations and their subsidiary companies, and professional partnerships involved in manufacturing and service industries including, in particular, international insurance and reinsurance companies, Lloyd's underwriters and major pharmaceutical companies.

The firm's particular areas of expertise include commercial property development and funding; BES issues, funds and prospectuses; acquisitions and disposals; USM and full listings; joint ventures; corporate transactions; construction, and professional indemnity; marine and non-marine insurance.

In commercial litigation, Davies Arnold Cooper is particularly prominent for its involvement in practically all recent mass tort litigation (relating to both pharmaceuticals and single incident catastrophes); most major problems in the London insurance market over the last decade; and personal injury (for both defendants and plaintiffs).

Overall, this high-profile City firm sees itself as young, forceful but fair, unpretentious and approachable. It considers itself a leader not a follower. A brochure is available.

DAVIES
ARNOLD
COOPER

Dawson & Co

2 NEW SQUARE
LINCOLN'S INN
LONDON
WC2A 3RZ
Phone: 01 404 5941

Fax: 01 831 6924
DX: 38 LONDON CHANCERY LANE WC2
Telex: 27360 **Other offices:** 2
Senior Partner: Mr Charles Cunningham
Number of Partners: 24
Total Staff: 93

Denison Till

CHANCERY HOUSE
143 HOLGATE ROAD
YORK
NORTH YORKSHIRE YO2 4DF
Phone: 0904 610820

Fax: 0904 646972
DX: 61502 YORK
Telex: none **Other offices:** 6
Senior Partner: Mr EAK Denison
Number of Partners: 14
Total Staff: 65

Dibb & Clegg

31 REGENT STREET
BARNSLEY
SOUTH YORKSHIRE
S70 2HJ
Phone: 0226 241444

Fax: 0226 283583
DX: 12254 BARNSLEY-1
Telex: none **Other offices:** 3
Senior Partner: Mr JN Dobbin
Number of Partners: 8
Total Staff: 56

Dibbens

3 WEST BOROUGH
WIMBORNE
DORSET
BH21 1LU
Phone: 0202 882456

Fax: 0202 884552
DX: 45306 WIMBORNE
Telex: 417240 **Other offices:** 3
Senior Partner: Mr M Barrett
Number of Partners: 8
Total Staff: 70

Daynes Hill & Perks *see full-page profile*
Deacon Goldrein Green *see full-page profile*
Denton Hall Burgin & Warrens *see full-page profile*
Dibb Lupton Broomhead *see full-page profile*

Daynes Hill & Perks

HOLLAND COURT
THE CLOSE
NORWICH
NR1 4DX
Phone: 0603 611212

Fax: 0603 610535
DX: 5206 NORWICH
Telex: 975366 **Other offices:** 4
Senior Partner: Michael Churchouse
Number of Partners: 46
Total Staff: 304

This is a large regional firm based in Norwich which has an expanding commercial practice and a substantial private client base.

The firm: Daynes Hill & Perks was formed in 1987 as a result of a merger between two respected, established Norwich firms, Daynes Chittock and Hill & Perks. The firm has expanded its commercial business, which, although firmly rooted in East Anglia, includes a significant number of national and international clients. In May 1988 the firm merged with Moreton Phillips & Son in London and Daynes Hill & Perks is currently a member of Eversheds (see separate entry).

There is a continuing need for talented assistant solicitors. Enquiries to the personnel manager.

In addition, the firm usually has 12 to 15 vacancies for articled clerks every year. A good honours degree is required. Prospects after qualification are good. Apply by handwritten letter (with CV) two years in advance to Andrew Croome.

Other offices: London, Great Yarmouth, Amsterdam, Norwich.

Agency work: The firm accepts work from other solicitors; contact the client relations partner.

Types of work undertaken: Daynes Hill & Perks is a broadly based practice. The firm acts for listed companies, sole traders, professional firms and private individuals, local industries, North Sea offshore industries, as well as the high-tech and service sectors. There are four main departments, namely company/commercial, litigation, trust, probate and tax, and property services, as well as an estate agency.

The firm's company/commercial department is well known for the quality of its work, which includes acquisitions and mergers, business start-ups, corporate finance and venture capital, share issues, employment matters, town planning, intellectual property and insolvency.

There is a particularly strong property department handling commercial, residential and general conveyancing, site acquisitions, estate development and associated tax advice.

Daynes Hill & Perks has a large and varied litigation department, dealing with all contentious matters, including contractual, building and property disputes, personal injury claims, divorce and family law, crime, debt collection, landlord and tenant matters.

The firm sees itself as a major regional firm, which combines specialist skills across all legal disciplines with a modern, innnovative approach to problem solving. Brochures for clients describing the services the firm offers are available on request.

Deacon Goldrein Green

PRINCES BUILDING
81 DALE STREET
LIVERPOOL
L2 2JA
Phone: 051 227 4911

Fax: 051 236 3319
DX: 14144 LIVERPOOL
Telex: none **Other offices:** 12
Senior Partner: David Deacon
Number of Partners: 10
Total Staff: 154

This Liverpool-based firm is well known for its litigation practice and legal aid work, which is combined with a rapidly expanding commercial practice.

The firm: Deacon Goldrein Green was formed in May 1985 by the merger of Levy Deacon and Green, parts of the former firm of Goldrein and Co and parts of the firm of Dean Newman Green & Co. The firm has the largest network of offices in Liverpool and is currently undergoing a period of rapid expansion. The firm is organised into departments.

The firm has a particular need for five assistant solicitors to work in litigation; those with experience in litigation-based practices are preferred. Partnership prospects are excellent. Enquiries should be addressed to David Deacon.

In addition, Deacon Goldrein Green usually has two vacancies for articled clerks every year. The minimum educational requirement is a 2(2) degree, not necessarily in law; mature applicants are welcome. Applications should be made by letter (with CV) addressed to David Deacon and should normally be made two years in advance.

Other offices: 12 in Liverpool.

Agency work: Work is accepted from other solicitors; contact: Martin Green (crime); Andrew Gillespie (family); Martin Bracey (property); Neville Goldrein (commercial).

Types of work undertaken: The reputation of the firm has been traditionally founded on its strong, and extremely large, litigation practice. Deacon Goldrein Green has vast experience in all criminal and matrimonial work as well as employment law, personal injury claims, product liability claims and industrial disease and deafness cases.

The firm is about to market its Civil Litigation Agency Support System (CLASS), initially to service personal injury litigation on an agency basis (enquiries should be addressed to Graham Cunliffe).

The firm has always had an extremely wide private client base, offering one of the largest and most efficient legal aid services in the country, and the volume of this type of work continues to grow. Deacon Goldrein Green is one of the founder members of Law North West, the first regional network of 'high street' practices.

Deacon Goldrein Green is rapidly broadening its corporate client base, and 1988 saw the opening of a new commercial department in the business centre of Liverpool.

In short, Deacon Goldrein Green sees itself as radical and innovative, and feels that the firm is respected as an unpredictable predator in the legal market-place.

195

Denton Hall Burgin & Warrens

FIVE CHANCERY LANE
LONDON
WC2A 1LF

Phone: 01 242 1212

Fax: 01 404 0087
DX: 242 LONDON CHANCERY LANE WC2
Telex: 263567 **Other offices:** 6
Senior Partner: Michael Flint
Number of Partners: 91
Total Staff: 854

An international law practice, Denton Hall Burgin & Warrens serves commercial, corporate and private clients through modern offices in London and abroad.

The firm: Denton Hall Burgin & Warrens was formed in 1985, the result of a merger between two very old-established London firms: Denton Hall & Burgin, founded in 1788, and Warrens, which dates from 1742. In 1988 80 lawyers joined the firm from Herbert Oppenheimer, Nathan & Vandyk.

The firm is always looking for high-calibre solicitors and barristers with commercial experience; it expects to recruit about 40 in 1989. Enquiries to Gillian Tamsett.

The firm will recruit about 45 articled clerks by 1991. The minimum educational qualification is a 2(1) degree, not necessarily in law. Applications by handwritten letter (plus CV and name of academic referee) to Andrew Daws.

Other offices: London Docklands, Milton Keynes, Brussels, Hong Kong, Singapore, Los Angeles.

Types of work undertaken: Denton Hall Burgin & Warrens is a large international commercial law practice providing a wide range of those legal services required by corporate and commercial enterprises and international clients. Among its clients the firm numbers foreign governments and major multinational companies, as well as UK-listed companies, private companies and individuals.

The firm is well known for mergers and acquisitions, financial services, energy, entertainment and telecommunications, property development and planning plus international litigation and arbitration.

The company and commercial department advises on all aspects of corporate and commercial law, including public issues, mergers, acquisitions, joint ventures, banking, commercial agreements, tax planning, international trade, competition, employment and immigration.

The firm has the largest entertainment law practice outside California. Most of this work relates to film financing and distribution. The firm has over 50 years' experience in the energy sector, particularly in oil and gas and in electricity supply. In addition, there are strong property and litigation departments.

The Hong Kong office carries out a broad range of work throughout the Far East and Australasia; it is complemented by a small Singapore office. The Los Angeles office specialises in corporate and entertainment law, taxation, banking and immigration.

Overall, the firm perceives itself as a resourceful, imaginative and progressive practice, which is forward-looking yet retains a personal approach.

DENTON HALL
BURGIN & WARRENS

Dibb Lupton Broomhead

6 BUTTS COURT
LEEDS
LS1 5JX

Phone: 0532 439301

Fax: 0532 452632
DX: 12017 LEEDS
Telex: 557181 **Other offices:** 6
Senior Partner: Mr CS Barker
Number of Partners: 46
Total Staff: 405

This newly formed firm is a predominantly commercial practice, with a significant private client base.

The firm: Formed as the result of the November 1988 merger of the Sheffield firm of Broomheads and Dibb Lupton of Leeds, both of which were among the longest established firms in the country, and had grown dramatically in recent years to serve the commercial and financial sectors, the new firm is one of the largest firms in the provinces.

This thriving firm has a continuing need for qualified staff, and in 1989 expects to recruit across all departments 17 assistant solicitors. Enquiries should be addressed to Mr J Winkworth-Smith (Fountain Precinct, Balm Green, Sheffield S1 1RZ).

In addition, 20 to 24 articled clerks are recruited annually. The minimum educational requirement is a 2(2) degree, not necessarily in law. Prospects after qualification are excellent; the majority of the present partners served articles with the constituent firms. Apply by letter (with CV and names of referees) two years in advance to Kevin McLoughlin at the Sheffield address above.

Other offices: Bradford, Chesterfield, Doncaster, London, Rotherham, Sheffield.

Agency work: Work from other solicitors is accepted, particularly through the London office; contact Jonathan Yorke.

Types of work undertaken: Dibb Lupton Broomhead is primarily a commercial firm serving both PLCs and private companies as well as a number of financial institutions; nevertheless a personal service to the private client is maintained.

The firm is divided into a number of specialist departments, namely company, commercial property, commercial litigation, intellectual property and technology law, securities and recoveries, insolvency, employment, pensions, insurance litigation, debt collection, private client and taxation.

The firm's company department covers the broad spectrum of commercial work, and is particularly well known for its flotation and corporate finance work. The majority of the property department's work is commercially orientated. The commercial litigation department has wide experience in all areas of contract litigation, especially for the engineering and construction industries. Intellectual property and computer law is a particular area of expertise, as are pensions work, insolvency, debt collection and insurance litigation (notably professional negligence claims).

Overall, Dibb Lupton Broomhead sees itself as a national practice based in the provinces. A brochure is available.

DIBB LUPTON
BROOMHEAD
——SOLICITORS——

Dickinson Dees

CROSS HOUSE
WESTGATE ROAD
NEWCASTLE UPON TYNE
NE99 1SB
Phone: 091 261 1911

Fax: 091 261 5855
DX: 61191 NEWCASTLE UPON TYNE
Telex: 537129
Senior Partner: Robert Dickinson
Number of Partners: 23
Total Staff: 195

This broadly based Newcastle firm offers a full range of legal services in company and commercial matters, as well as all kinds of private client work. The firm is a member of the Legal Resources Group (see separate entry).

The firm: Dickinson Dees is a long-established Newcastle practice tracing its roots back to 1786. It incorporates a number of former Newcastle firms, culminating in the merger in 1975 of Dickinson, Miller & Turnbull with Dees & Thompson, Griffith & Co. The firm has expanded significantly in the last 15 years and prides itself on the blend of expertise it has achieved among its partners and staff.

At least five vacancies for assistant solicitors are expected in the next year: for company/commercial, commercial property and private client work. Enquiries should be addressed to the senior partner.

The firm recruits six articled clerks annually. A 2(2) degree or above is expected, not necessarily in law. Apply by handwritten letter (with CV and names of referees) to Graham Wright two years in advance.

Agency work: Work from other solicitors is accepted. For details contact Mr LM Rutherford (litigation), Mr CP Helm (conveyancing), Mr TGW Dinning (planning), and Mr JS North Lewis (private client).

Types of work undertaken: The wide range of commercial services offered by Dickinson Dees reflects its status as a major provincial practice, handling a large volume of work to a high degree of expertise through its specialised departments. The client base is large, with the commercial sector particularly well represented.

The firm is noted for its company and commercial work, particularly for the larger company, either having or seeking a quotation; for its private client work, including acting for substantial landowners; and for its commercial conveyancing expertise.

The firm will do all work for quoted and private companies, including USM, BES, mergers and buy-outs, and all types of litigation.

As well as its corporate and commercial business, the firm places particular emphasis on agricultural law, charities, EEC law, insolvency, employment law, insurance, intellectual property, licensing, pensions, town and country planning, and housing association work.

Among the private client work undertaken are the traditional areas of trust, probate, tax planning, and land, as well as financial planning and investments, and family law. The firm accepts all type of legal aid work.

Overall, Dickinson Dees sees itself as skilled, specialised, energetic and approachable. A brochure is available.

Dickinson Dees

Dickinson Manser & Co

5 PARKSTONE ROAD
POOLE
DORSET
BH15 2NL
Phone: 0202 673071

Fax: 0202 680470
DX: 07602 POOLE
Telex: 41142
Senior Partner: Mr LH Parkyn
Number of Partners: 6
Total Staff: 72

Dodson Harding

11 HAMMET STREET
TAUNTON
SOMERSET
TA1 1RJ
Phone: 0823 331293

Fax: 0823 252161
DX: 32111 TAUNTON
Telex: 46127 **Other offices:** 4
Senior Partner: Mr RK Mulligan
Number of Partners: 14
Total Staff: 80

Dolmans

17 WINDSOR PLACE
CARDIFF
CF1 4PA

Phone: 0222 345531

Fax: 0222 398206
DX: 33005 CARDIFF
Telex: none **Other offices:** 2
Senior Partner: Mr JM Biggs
Number of Partners: 12
Total Staff: 68

Donn & Co

26 CROSS STREET
MANCHESTER
M2 7AN

Phone: 061 834 3311

Fax: 061 834 2317
DX: 14312 MANCHESTER-1
Telex: 669161 **Other offices:** 6
Senior Partner: Mr RL Donn
Number of Partners: 6
Total Staff: 65

Donne Mileham & Haddock

FREDERICK PLACE
BRIGHTON
BN1 1AT

Phone: 0273 29833

Fax: 0273 739764
DX: 2703 BRIGHTON
Telex: 87107 **Other offices:** 14
Senior Partner: Quintin Barry
Number of Partners: 35
Total Staff: 235

This large Brighton-based firm has offices throughout the south east of England offering the full range of legal services to commercial and private clients.

The firm: Formed in 1970 as the result of an amalgamation of three long-established firms, Donne Mileham & Haddock has expanded rapidly and incorporated several other firms into the practice.

There is a continuing need for qualified staff. In 1989 the firm expects to recruit 10 to 15 assistant solicitors. Apply to Sylvia Henty.

In addition, seven articled clerks are recruited annually. Applications from mature candidates are encouraged. Prospects after qualification are good. Apply by letter (with CV) by 1 October to Sylvia Henty.

Other offices: Lewes, Hove (2), Portslade, Seaford, Shoreham, Steyning, Worthing, Burgess Hill, Newhaven, East Grinstead, Crawley, Forest Row, Gatwick Airport.

Agency work: All types of work are accepted from other solicitors.

Types of work undertaken: This large provincial firm is broadly based, with an extensive commercial law practice which is organised into departments, namely litigation, company/commercial, conveyancing, town and country planning, debt recovery, and financial services. The client base is correspondingly varied, and includes major corporate and industrial companies, banks, building societies, local authorities, employers' organisations and trade unions. There is also a substantial private client practice.

The size and scope of the practice are illustrated by the variety of work, ranging from 1,400 commercial conveyancing matters, 26 separate commercial and residential building developments to 2,000 civil litigation cases and some 250 Admiralty cases in 1988.

On the company/commercial side, the firm is especially well known for its work in mergers and acquisitions, employment law, general company law and liquor licensing. The range of work is wide, covering company and partnership formations, financing, takeovers and buy-outs, pensions, USM and Stock Exchange listings, franchises, sales and purchases, taxation, employee incentive schemes and intellectual property. The firm is developing a network of foreign law firm contacts.

The litigation practice includes contractual matters, professional negligence claims, landlord and tenant, property disputes, insurance claims and marine litigation.

There is a strong property department dealing with all aspects of commercial property law (especially town planning).

Donne Mileham & Haddock sees itself as a progressive multi-skilled organisation. A brochure is available on request.

Douglas-Jones & Mercer

147 ST HELENS ROAD
SWANSEA
SA1 4DB

Phone: 0792 650000

Fax: 0792 458212
DX: 39556 SWANSEA
Telex: none **Other offices:** 4
Senior Partner: Mr PR Douglas-Jones
Number of Partners: 10
Total Staff: 80

Drummond & Co

31-32 MORAY PLACE
EDINBURGH
EH2 6BZ

Phone: 031 226 5151

Fax: 031 225 2608
Rutland Exchange: 104 EDINBURGH
Telex: 727682 **Other offices:** 5
Senior Partner: Mr RG Ritchie
Number of Partners: 15
Total Staff: 100

Dundas & Wilson CS

25 CHARLOTTE SQUARE
EDINBURGH
EH2 4EZ

Phone: 031 225 1234

Fax: 031 225 5594
Rutland Exchange: 22 EDINBURGH
Telex: 72404
Senior Partner: Mr DB Birrell WS
Number of Partners: 33
Total Staff: 290

Durnford Ford

51 HAVELOCK ROAD
HASTINGS
EAST SUSSEX
TN34 1BE
Phone: 0424 442442

Fax: none
DX: none
Telex: 95319 **Other offices:** 9
Senior Partner: Mr GMD Ford
Number of Partners: 23
Total Staff: 220

Druces & Attlee *see full-page profile*

Druces & Attlee

SALISBURY HOUSE
LONDON WALL
LONDON
EC2M 5PS
Phone: 01 638 9271

Fax: 01 628 7525
DX: 534 LONDON CITY EC3
Telex: 8956278
Senior Partner: Mr AJH Weber
Number of Partners: 13
Total Staff: 73

Druces & Attlee has a broad-based City practice combining a strong property, corporate and commercial practice with a substantial private client department.

The firm: Tracing its origins to 1767, Druces & Attlee is one of the very oldest City practices. The firm still acts for many of its earliest clients including substantial life companies and City organisations. Druces & Attlee has expanded dramatically in recent years and in 1988 acquired City solicitors Hickmans.

The firm is expecting to recruit solicitors (particularly those qualified from two to four years) in the company and litigation departments. Enquiries to Mr PR Campbell.

In addition, the firm normally recruits two articled clerks per year. The minimum educational qualification is a 2(1) degree, not necessarily in law. Apply by handwritten letter (plus CV) two years in advance to the staff partner, Mr PR Campbell.

Agency work: The firm accepts litigation work from other firms; contact Mr R Sherrin.

Types of work undertaken: Druces & Attlee has a broad City-orientated client base encompassing commercial property, company/commercial, domestic and agricultural property, private client (including tax planning), and commercial and private client litigation. It is particularly well known for heavy commercial conveyancing embracing institutional funding and property development.

The fastest growing department is company/commercial which deals with the full range of legal services for corporate and commercial clients, including banking and financial services.

The property department handles institutional and investment (development funding, acquisition, sale and letting), property development, and commercial, residential and agricultural conveyancing.

The litigation department offers independent expertise in contentious matters in the areas of property (including construction and building disputes, landlord and tenant disputes, mortgage repossession), commercial (contract disputes, arbitrations, insurance, debt collection and insolvency), private client and employment (including restraint of trade, redundancy and dismissal claims).

The emphasis is on ensuring that the client has access to high-quality expertise with close partner involvement. The firm has long-standing associations throughout the world which can be called upon in international matters.

Overall, this long-established firm is generally regarded as having an innovative, forward-looking and commercial approach.

DRUCES & ATTLEE

Dutton Gregory & Williams

TRUSSELL HOUSE
23 ST PETER STREET
WINCHESTER
HAMPSHIRE SO23 8BT
Phone: 0962 66363

Fax: 0962 63582
DX: 2515 WINCHESTER
Telex: 477921 **Other offices:** 4
Senior Partner: Mr PC Gregory
Number of Partners: 10
Total Staff: 71

E Edwards Son & Noice

100-102 HIGH STREET NORTH
EAST HAM
LONDON
E6 2HU
Phone: 01 471 5231

Fax: 01 552 1864
DX: 4702 EAST HAM
Telex: 262768 **Other offices:** 1
Senior Partner: Mr CF Newman
Number of Partners: 5
Total Staff: 77

E Rex Makin & Co

WHITECHAPEL
LIVERPOOL
L1 1HQ

Phone: 051 709 4491

Fax: 051 708 8638
DX: 14168 LIVERPOOL
Telex: none
Senior Partner: Mr E Rex Makin
Number of Partners: 5
Total Staff: 52

Elliot Mather Smith

THE COURTYARD
49 LOW PAVEMENT
CHESTERFIELD
DERBYSHIRE S40 1PB
Phone: 0246 231288

Fax: 0246 204081
DX: 12362 CHESTERFIELD-1
Telex: none **Other offices:** 2
Managing Partner: Mr PA Hollyer
Number of Partners: 12
Total Staff: 90

Edge & Ellison *see full-page profile*
Edwards Geldard *see full-page profile*
Edwin Coe *see full-page profile*

Elborne Mitchell *see full-page profile*
Elgoods *see full-page profile*

Edge & Ellison

RUTLAND HOUSE
148 EDMUND STREET
BIRMINGHAM
B3 2JR
Phone: 021 200 2001

Fax: 021 200 1991
DX: 13006 BIRMINGHAM-1
Telex: 336370 **Other offices:** 1
Senior Partner: John Wardle
Number of Partners: 35
Total Staff: 370

Edge & Ellison, a Birmingham-based practice, is one of the leading provincial firms, and aims to offer a complete service to public and private companies.

The firm: Founded in 1870, Edge & Ellison has continued to grow rapidly to become one of the largest provincial practices. The firm grew by 40 per cent in 1988. The firm has merged with Staunton Townsend of Leicester and the ultimate aim is a national firm strongly represented in all major commercial centres. It is essentially a commercial practice with a substantial private client base.

High-calibre staff are always needed, and in 1989 the firm expects to recruit 30 assistant solicitors. Enquiries to Digby M Jones.

In addition, 10 to 12 articled clerks are recruited annually. A 2(1) degree, not necessarily in law, is preferred. Prospects are excellent: two-thirds of the present partners served articles with the firm. Apply by letter (with CV) in final year to Digby H Rose.

Other offices: Leicester.

Agency work: The firm often handles work for small firms of solicitors; contact Simon Ramshaw or Chris Rawstron.

Types of work undertaken: Clients include both public and private companies, professional firms, service industries and manufacturing firms, building societies, insurers and one of the main clearing banks. In addition, the firm acts for a substantial number of private clients. Its commercial practice consists of five main departments: corporate finance, commercial, commercial property, litigation and insolvency.

Corporate finance work includes acquisitions, disposals, mergers and joint ventures. The firm is particularly active in management buy-outs and flotations work. Commercial work includes banking and finance, taxation, EEC law and intellectual property. It is also one of the few provincial firms with a special pensions section.

The firm is particularly well known for its insolvency work and represents most of the major accountancy practices within the area.

The commercial property department acts for a substantial number of builder and developer clients, and also deals with landlord and tenant matters, property taxation, planning law, and housing association work.

The litigation department handles commercial litigation at all levels, including professional negligence, tribunals, and intellectual property work. Building litigation is a particular area of expertise. It also covers crime, personal injury and matrimonial.

Overall, Edge & Ellison sees itself as a rapidly expanding, approachable, team-orientated firm, which takes a commercial view of clients' problems. Brochure available.

Edge & Ellison
SOLICITORS

Edwards Geldard

16 ST ANDREWS CRESCENT
CARDIFF
CF1 3RD

Phone: 0222 238239

Fax: 0222 237268
DX: 33001 CARDIFF
Telex: 497913 **Other offices:** 4
Senior Partner: Keith Harrap Edwards
Number of Partners: 22
Total Staff: 164

Edwards Geldard is one of the largest commercial firms in Cardiff, but with a good private client department.

The firm: Edwards Geldard has been a successful commercial practice for over 180 years growing initially with flourishing coal and steel communities. Established in Cardiff since 1854 the firm commenced major expansion in 1976, since when the firm has increased sixfold.

Twelve assistant solicitors are likely to be recruited during 1989: five for company/commercial, three for litigation, two for commercial property, and two for private client. Enquiries to Dianne E Pearce.

About ten articled clerks are recruited annually. A 2(1) degree is usually required. Long-term prospects are excellent: approximately half of the present partners served articles with the firm. Apply (with CV and names of referees) to Mr WA Gill. For articles in London apply to the partner-in-charge, Francis Piesse at 3-4 St Andrews Hill, London EC4A 5BY.

Other offices: City of London, Derby, Hereford, Monmouth.

Agency work: Work is accepted from other solicitors. For Companies House matters, contact Karl Baranski; for litigation, William G Mills; for property, G Rowland Davies.

Types of work undertaken: In the four main departments (private client, litigation company/commercial, commercial property) individual expertise abounds. For example, in the commercial property department a great deal of planning and compulsory purchase work is done, and the firm is presently involved with Parliamentary bill drafting. Within the company/commercial department, corporate tax and intellectual property work is undertaken as well as mainstream corporate and commercial work. The litigation department handles employment work and medical negligence cases as well as heavy arbitration, building construction work and large scale commercial litigation.

The firm is particularly well known for intellectual property; public and administrative law, compulsory purchase law, and acting for public bodies on special assignments; computer contracts and technology transfer agreements; management buy-outs; corporate acquisitions; Stock Exchange work; and estate conveyancing (including building and civil engineering, commercial property development, arbitrations and litigation).

Overall, the firm is regarded as being in the first division. For a firm of its size and achievement Edwards Geldard believes that it is less marketing dependent. It is forward thinking in matters of technology, the development of individual expertises and in its approach to the changes heralding 1992.

EDWARDS GELDARD

Edwin Coe

11 STONE BUILDINGS
LINCOLN'S INN
LONDON
WC2A 3TH
Phone: 01 831 7466

Fax: 01 405 1108
DX: 191 LONDON CHANCERY LANE WC2
Telex: 298368
Senior Partner: John Graham Tomlins
Number of Partners: 13
Total Staff: 80

Edwin Coe is a medium sized Lincoln's Inn-based firm which has considerable experience in both commercial and private client work.

The firm: Edwin Coe traces its origins back to 1913, and was known as Edwin Coe and Calder Woods until 1988. While retaining its early reputation in litigation, in recent years the practice has been broadened considerably to encompass a wide range of commercial and private client work.

Edwin Coe has a continuing need for experienced staff, and in 1989 expects to recruit five assistant solicitors for commercial property, private client and company/commercial. Enquiries to David Greene.

The firm normally has three vacancies for articled clerks every year. Applicants are expected to have good academic qualifications, and the firm places great importance on the interviews, of which there are two. Common sense, personality, an understanding of clients' needs and professionalism are considered extremely important. Prospects after qualification are good; nearly half the present partners served articles with the firm. Applications should be made by letter (with CV and names of referees) 12 to 18 months in advance and addressed to David Greene.

Agency work: The firm accepts High Court litigation work from other solicitors. Contact Simon Rayment.

Types of work undertaken: Edwin Coe has a substantial private client base as well as acting for both large and small commercial clients.

The civil litigation department retains its traditional strengths and reputation. It is accustomed to dealing with actions of great complexity, including substantial commercial litigation, insolvency work, insurance claims, intellectual property matters, employment law disputes, and matrimonial work. In addition, the firm offers litigation support services and factored debt collecting.

The expanding company/commercial department handles all general company law matters, and has particular expertise in USM work, flotations, mergers and acquisitions, directorships, investments and insolvency.

The emphasis in the property department is on the commercial field and includes a substantial quantity of high-quality property investment and bank securities work.

The private client department has a strong reputation in settlements, tax and financial planning, investment advice and the establishment of overseas trusts.

This established firm perceives itself as a well-co-ordinated team of specialists working within the respected surroundings of Lincoln's Inn. A brochure is available.

Edwin Coe

Elborne Mitchell

THREE QUAYS
TOWER HILL
LONDON
EC3R 6DS
Phone: 01 283 7281

Fax: 01 283 5990
DX: 1063 LONDON CITY EC3
Telex: 885418
Managing Partner: Andrew Pincott
Number of Partners: 13
Total Staff: 80

This high-flying commercial City practice has been involved in most of the important shipping and insurance cases since the 1960s.

The firm: Elborne Mitchell was founded in 1968 when Bill Whitehouse-Vaux and Robert Elborne, well-known figures from established City practices with their roots in shipping and insurance, set up in partnership. The international nature of the firm has enabled it to build an extended network of contacts in Europe and the Far East. In recent years the firm has expanded its position in insurance and consolidated its wide variety of services.

As it is continuing to expand, Elborne Mitchell is seeking to recruit a number of assistant solicitors: five for litigation, two for company/commercial, and one for conveyancing work. Enquiries to Andrew Pincott.

The firm recruits five articled clerks annually. Long-term prospects are excellent: about half the present partners served articles with the firm. Applications by handwritten letter (plus CV) to Andrew Pincott 18 months in advance.

Agency work: The firm undertakes a considerable amount of work for other solicitors, particularly for overseas shipping, insurance and commercial law firms, and specialist work for country solicitors.

Types of work undertaken: Elborne

Mitchell has been described as real-life LA Law. Certainly the firm has handled substantial and high-profile cases with flair and skill: in the field of Admiralty law ('The Tojo Maru', 'The Betelgeuse' and 'The Salem' cases, 'The Derbyshire' inquiry and 'Piper Alpha'), Lloyd's ('Savonita', 'Sasse', 'Computer Leasing', 'Bush Fires', 'Outhwaite', and 'Warrilow'), and other cases of a complex commercial nature (such as the collapse of the International Tin Council). This litigation work is coupled with a growing reputation for handling the non-contentious side of major commercial transactions with similar efficiency and skill.

Shipping and admiralty law have formed a major part of the firm's practice. It also has considerable expertise in problems associated with the import and export of goods and international trade financing. Another specialist area is insurance and reinsurance, and the work the firm handles ranges from obtaining UK authorisation for insurance companies through the drafting of policy wordings to the litigation of complex disputes on marine, non-marine and aviation insurance and reinsurance contracts. In addition, the firm undertakes substantial company/commercial and property work.

Elborne Mitchell sees itself as a specialist commercial firm serving the shipping and insurance communities, with a particularly strong commercial litigation practice. A brochure is available on request.

Elgoods

123 PROMENADE
CHELTENHAM
GLOUCESTERSHIRE
GL50 1NW
Phone: 0242 518201

Fax: 0242 574285
DX: 7403 CHELTENHAM
Telex: 43624
Senior Partner: Mr AK Dooley
Number of Partners: 9
Total Staff: 64

This medium sized Cheltenham firm has a substantial private client base and a thriving commercial practice.

The firm: Elgoods was founded in 1968 as a one-person practice. The firm has developed into a typical broadly based provincial firm, handling most aspects of work. The firm has expanded rapidly, particularly in the commercial field. The firm is organised into departments.

This expanding firm is always seeking to recruit well-qualified staff who have experience in the commercial sector; in 1989 the firm expects to have two or more vacancies for assistant solicitors for commercial property work. Enquiries to the staff partner.

In addition, one or two articled clerks are recruited every year. A 2(1) degree is preferred. Prospects after qualification are good; several of the present partners served articles in the firm. Applications should be made by letter (with CV) at least one year in advance to Mr J Kirby.

Agency work: The firm accepts work from other solicitors; contact Ms J Boparai or Mr C Bell (litigation); Mr RD Handley (property).

Types of work undertaken: While the firm retains a very strong commitment to Cheltenham and the Gloucestershire area, the client base — both commercial and private clients — now extends substantially beyond the county boundaries to cover most of England and Wales.

The commercial side of the practice has broadened significantly in recent years which in turn has developed other aspects of the practice. There is a considerable amount of experience and expertise in all aspects of commercial property and land development work, from acquisitions and planning matters through to building contracts and disputes. It is also well known for its company/commercial work, particularly company share purchase, sales and amalgamations. The firm offers a wide legal service to a wider range of clients, from substantial companies and institutions, some operating on a national level, to smaller partnerships and sole traders. A substantial amount of commercial litigation work is undertaken, as well as personal injury litigation (both plaintiff and defendant claims, acting for insurance companies, trade unions, and individuals).

As is to be expected of an established provincial firm there is a substantial private client practice, covering a significant amount of matrimonial and domestic conveyancing work, as well as crime, wills, probate and trusts.

Elgoods sees itself as a young expanding practice which is broadly based, but with the emphasis firmly on commercial work.

Elgoods

Elliott & Company

CENTURION HOUSE
DEANSGATE
MANCHESTER
M3 3WT
Phone: 061 834 9933

Fax: 061 832 3693
DX: 14346 MANCHESTER-1
Telex: 667252 **Other offices:** 1
Senior Partner: Mr JCK Elliott
Number of Partners: 15
Total Staff: 101

Ellison & Co

HEADGATE COURT
HEAD STREET
COLCHESTER
ESSEX CO1 1NP
Phone: 0206 764477

Fax: 0206 764455
DX: 3601 COLCHESTER
Telex: 987168 **Other offices:** 1
Senior Partner: Mr PD Powell
Number of Partners: 10
Total Staff: 77

Enoch Evans

19 & 35 BRIDGE STREET
WALSALL
WEST MIDLANDS
WS1 1EA
Phone: 0922 720333

Fax: 0922 720623
DX: 12125 WALSALL
Telex: 339268
Senior Partner: Mr NJ Evans
Number of Partners: 7
Total Staff: 59

Eric Robinson & Co

18 WEST END ROAD
BITTERNE
SOUTHAMPTON
HAMPSHIRE SO9 4NJ
Phone: 0703 447734

Fax: 0703 446594
DX: 52750 BITTERNE
Telex: none **Other offices:** 7
Senior Partner: Mr G Payne
Number of Partners: 9
Total Staff: 95

Evershed & Tomkinson

10 NEWHALL STREET
BIRMINGHAM
B3 3LX

Phone: 021 233 2001

Fax: 021 236 1583
DX: 13004 BIRMINGHAM-1
Telex: 336688 **Other offices:** 1
Senior Partner: Peter Bromage
Number of Partners: 32
Total Staff: 322

This large Birmingham-based commercial firm has retained a substantial private client/financial services department.

The firm: Founded as a general practice in 1914, the firm developed a strong commercial practice in the 1960s, the emphasis of which evolved to corporate finance and commercial property work. Evershed & Tomkinson has more than doubled in size within the last decade to become one of the leading provincial practices. The firm is joining forces with other major regional practices to form a new national commercial firm known as Eversheds (see separate entry).

In 1989 this expanding firm expects to have 25 vacancies for assistant solicitors, in all areas. Enquiries should be addressed to Philip Williams.

In addition, the firm recruits 15 to 20 articled clerks every year. A 2(1) degree, not necessarily in law, is preferred. Long-term prospects are excellent: the majority of the present partners served articles with the firm. Apply on form by September two years in advance to Philip Williams.

Other offices: London.

Agency work: The firm accepts litigation work from other solicitors; contact Martin McKenna (Birmingham) or Jeff Walton (London).

Types of work undertaken: This is one of the largest provincial firms. It is a commercial practice with a national and international clientele comprising financial institutions, public and substantial companies and individual entrepreneurs.

The two largest divisions are corporate services and property. The former handles a broad range of corporate finance transactions, and has particular expertise in management buy-outs and Stock Exchange work (including the USM). BES is a major growth area. The property division is involved in commercial property and property finance work, particularly large-scale developments such as town centre retail schemes, business parks, and residential developments for consortia of major house builders.

The litigation division covers all aspects of commercial litigation, notably for banks and construction disputes. There is a small and highly specialised commercial division dealing nationally and internationally with intellectual property and other trade agreements, such as patent licensing, franchising, distribution and software contracts. The financial services department has wide experience in tax advice, financial planning, wills and trusts for corporate and private clients.

In short, this is a capable, progressive, ambitious, friendly and outward-looking firm which maintains the traditional professional virtues of integrity and straight dealing.

EVERSHED & TOMKINSON

Eversheds

A GROUP OF LEGAL PRACTICES
BASED IN BIRMINGHAM, CARDIFF,
LEEDS, LONDON, MANCHESTER,
NORWICH, AND SHEFFIELD

Principal offices: 6
Chairman: Peter Bromage
Number of Partners: 157
Total Staff: 1,200

Eversheds is currently being established by five major regional firms with the aim of becoming a single firm by the end of 1991.

The firms: The constituent members of Eversheds are: Alexander, Tatham & Co of Manchester; Daynes Hill & Perks of Norwich, London and Amsterdam; Dibb Lupton Broomhead of Leeds, Sheffield and London; Evershed and Tomkinson of Birmingham and London, and Phillips & Buck of Cardiff and London (see separate entries). Together they have a combined total of 157 partners and 1,200 staff, of whom 160 are assistant solicitors and 120 are articled clerks.

The nature of the group: The intention of the group is to create a national firm offering a comprehensive commercial service to clients anywhere in the country, and a level of expertise to rival the major City firms. The constituent firms already have high reputations in the fields of company/commercial, corporate finance, property, insolvency, litigation, and private client work.

Main activities of the group: Currently the member firms are pooling resources in relation to training, recruitment, technology, research, publications and marketing. In addition, the group is working to integrate the various London operations into one location, as well as strengthening European links.

Responsibility for developing Eversheds rests with a management board with representatives from each constituent firm, under the independent chairmanship of Peter Bromage. Directors of research and training, and marketing have been appointed; director of quality assurance and administration will be in the near future.

Each member of Eversheds has a programme for the recruitment of high-calibre articled clerks and assistant solicitors. Joint articled clerk recruitment campaigns have been initiated. A training programme is in preparation.

In 1989 a wide range of literature relating to Eversheds will be produced and copies of individual firms' brochures are available.

The future: Eversheds' strategy is to respond to the needs of clients in the 1990s and beyond by providing a comprehensive national network which will combine personal and local services with in-depth expertise. Members of the group believe that regionalisation under a single national identity, as demonstrated by major accountancy firms, is the way ahead: therefore their aim is not simply to create a loose association of independent practices but rather a close-knit structure.

Eversheds predicts that it will be seen as an innovative quality firm: the first national commercial law firm in the UK.

Every & Phillips with Dunnings

THE LAURELS
46 NEW STREET
HONITON
DEVON EX14 8BZ
Phone: 0404 43431

Fax: 0404 45493
DX: 48800 HONITON
Telex: none **Other offices:** 4
Senior Partner: Mr BA Harris
Number of Partners: 10
Total Staff: 67

Farnfield & Nicholls

THE SQUARE
GILLINGHAM
DORSET
SP8 4AX
Phone: 07476 5432

Fax: 07476 2204
DX: 46005 SHAFTESBURY
Telex: none **Other offices:** 4
Senior Partner: Mr RA Savage
Number of Partners: 10
Total Staff: 65

Fitzhugh Gates

3 PAVILION PARADE
BRIGHTON
EAST SUSSEX
BN2 1RY
Phone: 0273 686811

Fax: 0273 676837
DX: 2727 BRIGHTON-1
Telex: none **Other offices:** 4
Senior Partner: Mr JJB Buckwell
Number of Partners: 12
Total Staff: 65

Flint Bishop & Barnett

ROYAL OAK HOUSE
MARKET PLACE
DERBY
DE1 2EA
Phone: 0332 40211

Fax: 0332 47107
DX: 11504 DERBY-1
Telex: none **Other offices:** 6
Senior Partner: Mr ALH Willis
Number of Partners: 16
Total Staff: 115

Farrer & Co *see full-page profile*
Fennemores *see full-page profile*
Few & Kester *see full-page profile*
Field Fisher & Martineau *see full-page profile*

Finers *see full-page profile*
Finn Gledhill & Co *see full-page profile*
Fladgate Fielder *see full-page profile*

Farrer & Co

66 LINCOLN'S INN FIELDS
LONDON
WC2A 3LH

Phone: 01 242 2022

Fax: 01 831 9748
DX: 32 LONDON CHANCERY LANE WC2
Telex: 24318
Senior Partner: William O Farrer
Number of Partners: 33
Total Staff: 200

Farrer & Co is a firm with a broadly based practice and an interesting cross-section of prominent institutions and individuals among its clients.

The firm: Founded in 1701, the firm has been in Lincoln's Inn Fields for nearly two centuries. It has a longstanding reputation for its private client work, and its connections with the banking world. Since the late 60s it has substantially increased its commercial, litigation and institutional practices. The firm draws clients from a worldwide base and has links with lawyers in most countries.

There is a continuing need for qualified staff, and in 1989 the firm expects to expand the number of assistant solicitors in all departments.

In addition, six to ten articled clerks are recruited annually. The preferred educational qualification is a 2(1) degree, but not necessarily in law. Mature candidates are considered. Prospects after qualification are excellent: the majority of the present partners served articles with the firm. Apply on form (available on request) by summer two years in advance. All employment enquiries should be addressed to Mrs Jacqueline Hammond.

Types of work undertaken: The firm is best known for its private client work. Farrers offers tax planning and business advice for the individual in both a private and corporate context; it acts for many substantial private and corporate property owners, advising on such areas as tax, VAT, landlord and tenant, planning, development schemes and commercial leases; and it has particular expertise in relation to heritage property and agricultural law. In addition, Farrers deals with the creation and administration of trusts and probates, many with an overseas dimension. As well as individuals and large estates, Farrers' private client list includes large City institutions, charities and educational establishments.

On the commercial side, there is a wide client base, including banks, newspapers and publishing groups, professional firms, private and public companies, oil companies and sporting bodies. The firm is well known for the quality of its commercial advice in such fields as pensions, intellectual property rights, licensing and consumer law and has an active acquisitions and mergers practice. It is also strong in banking and partnership law.

The litigation work of the firm is varied, concentrating on High Court work in all Divisions and in the higher courts – including the House of Lords and the Privy Council – and serving both national and international clients. The firm now has very substantial and high-profile defamation and employment law practices.

Farrers has an expanding matrimonial and family law department.

FARRER & CO

Fennemores

BOUVERIE HOUSE
200 SILBURY BOULEVARD
GRAFTON GATE EAST
CENTRAL MILTON KEYNES MK9 1LL
Phone: 0908 678241

Fax: 0908 665985
DX: 31407 MILTON KEYNES-1
Telex: 825896 **Other offices:** 2
Senior Partner: Mr CA Hilton-Johnson
Number of Partners: 9
Total Staff: 102

Fennemores is a rapidly expanding, broadly based Milton Keynes firm serving a wide commercial and private client base.

The firm: Founded in Milton Keynes in 1966, the firm is the first and largest solicitors' practice in central Milton Keynes. The firm has expanded rapidly: in recent years, annual growth has averaged 30 per cent, and offices have been opened in Luton and Northampton. Since 1982 there has been a major shift to commercial work.

The firm is actively seeking qualified staff, and expects to recruit at least ten assistant solicitors in 1989. There are excellent prospects of partnership for solicitors of suitable ability. Enquiries should be addressed to Simon Ingram.

In addition, six articled clerks are recruited annually. The firm prefers to judge applicants on individual merits as well as academic qualifications. A brochure is available and applications by handwritten letter (with CV) should be addressed to Guy Brooks two years in advance.

Other offices: Northampton, Luton.

Agency work: Work is accepted from other solicitors; contact Miss C O'Donnell.

Types of work undertaken: The work of the firm encompasses all forms of civil work, with emphasis on the commercial side, whether contentious or non-contentious, property-based or otherwise.

In addition, the firm has an increasing ability to handle high-tech intellectual property matters.

Although the practice has a busy residential conveyancing department handling domestic property transactions on a large scale, the firm also now enjoys a reputation for commercial property, company work and quality commercial litigation. There are particular skills in the legal aspects of building development, and plaintiff orientated money recovery, including a fully computerised debt recovery system.

There is a strong private client department which offers the full range of legal services; the partners of Fennemores are committed to expanding private client facilities.

Overall, Fennemores sees itself as a growing practice committed to increasing the quality of its legal services by adding to the range of skills and resources available. It aims to be seen as a centre of excellence in Milton Keynes, particularly on the commercial front but without neglect of the private client side.

The firm is generally regarded as having a modern, forward-looking approach, fully utilising the advantages of technology and a skilled, highly motivated professional staff.

A brochure detailing the services the firm offers is available on request.

Fennemores

Few & Kester

MONTAGU HOUSE
SUSSEX STREET
CAMBRIDGE
CB1 1PB
Phone: 0223 63111

Fax: 0223 323370
DX: 5813 CAMBRIDGE
Telex: 265871 **Other offices:** 1
Senior Partner: Mr JD Tunnicliffe
Number of Partners: 8
Total Staff: 52

This medium sized Cambridge firm has a broadly based practice serving the needs of private and commercial clients.

The firm: Few & Kester was founded in 1919 by John E Few as a general practice. There is a strong and expanding base of private clients, companies and other businesses. The firm acts for several major institutions and colleges in the Cambridge area. The firm is organised into departments.

This expanding firm is continually seeking to recruit good qualified staff, and in 1989 expects to have vacancies for up to four assistant solicitors in all areas. Enquiries to the recruitment partner.

In addition, two to four articled clerks are recruited annually. The minimum educational requirement is a 2(2) degree. Prospects after qualification are good; two of the present partners served articles with the firm. Apply by handwritten letter (with CV) to the recruitment partner.

Other offices: Cambridge.

Agency work: The firm accepts instructions for all non-contentious business and civil litigation work; contact any partner in the relevant department.

Types of work undertaken: There are four main departments, namely property, company/commercial, probate/trust/tax, and litigation.

The extensive property department is well known for its commercial property work, particularly landlord and tenant and development and investment projects. Both commercial and residential conveyancing work are undertaken.

The growing company/commercial department handles all aspects of commercial business, including company formations, acquisitions and disposals, bankruptcy and insolvency, partnerships, commercial agreements, share sales and purchases, and corporate finance.

As is to be expected of a firm with a long-established private client base, there is a strong probate, trust and tax department advising upon and preparing wills and settlements, administering estates and trusts.

The litigation department deals with the full range of contentious work, particularly substantial commercial cases, personal injury claims, landlord and tenant disputes, licensing and industrial tribunal work. The firm's principal aim is to provide the highest standard of work in all fields in the conviction that quality combined with prompt service is the only form of long-term competitiveness.

In short, Few & Kester is a highly regarded provincial practice which is able to act with expertise, efficiency and integrity.

FEW & KESTER

Field Fisher Waterhouse

LINCOLN HOUSE
296-302 HIGH HOLBORN
LONDON
WC1V 7JL

Phone: 01 831 9161

Fax: 01 405 5992
DX: 98 LONDON CHANCERY LANE WC2
Telex: 262613 **Other offices:** 2
Senior Partner: Mr JA Lemkin CBE
Number of Partners: 41
Total Staff: 243

This City-based firm has a substantial corporate practice, which is combined with a strong private client base.

The firm: Field Fisher Waterhouse is the result of the 1989 merger of two long-established, medium sized City firms, Field Fisher Martineau and Waterhouse & Co, both of which have enjoyed rapid growth in recent years. Most of the firm's work is for corporate clients, both national and international, and there is a thriving private client practice. The firm is organised into departments.

The firm is constantly seeking to recruit qualified solicitors, legal executives and para-legals. In 1989, it expects to have 12 vacancies for assistant solicitors. Enquiries to Chris Andrews.

In addition, the firm usually has eight vacancies for articled clerks every year. The preferred qualification is a 1st or 2(1), not necessarily in law, although those gaining a 2(2) degree will be considered. Apply on form (available on request) two years in advance to Chris Andrews.

Other offices: London, Brussels.

Agency work: Litigation work is accepted from other solicitors.

Types of work undertaken: Field Fisher Waterhouse has a wide-ranging client base, which includes financial institutions and commercial and industrial companies, many of them household names, as well as governments, trade associations, professional partnerships and charities. In addition, the firm acts for numerous overseas clients and has particularly strong connections in the Far East and Scandinavia.

The firm's main areas of work are banking and financial, company/commercial, litigation and commercial property. Much of the work is international in nature, and the firm is particularly well known for its strength in corporate taxation, overseas investments, unit trusts, pipeline conveyancing, and cultural property law.

Other fields of special experience include intellectual property work, employment law matters, work for the retail and leisure industries, property development work, and commercial litigation disputes, as well as various categories of banking and securities work.

While most of the firm's work is on the corporate side, there is a substantial and wide-ranging private client practice, with particular expertise in tax planning and heritage property.

Overall, Field Fisher Waterhouse sees itself as a quality firm which has a strong commercial and international practice. A brochure for clients decribing the services the firm offers is available on request.

F I E L D · F I S H E R   W A T E R H O U S E

Finers

79 NEW CAVENDISH STREET
LONDON
W1M 8JJ

Phone: 01 631 4611

Fax: 01 580 7069
DX: 42739 OXFORD CIRCUS NORTH
Telex: 28465
Other offices: 2
Number of Partners: 15
Total Staff: 95

This is a medium sized central London firm with a predominantly commercial practice and a strong international presence.

The firm: In 1981, two London firms, Gershon Young & Co, which dates from 1955, and Arnold Finer & Green, established in 1935, amalgamated to form Gershon Young Finer & Green. This firm expanded rapidly and in 1987 acquired the West End office of Wurzal Singleton & Charkham. The London firm of Stein Swede Jay & Bibring has also enjoyed rapid expansion since its formation in 1984, and on 1 February 1989 merged with Gershon Young Finer & Green to form Finers.

Finers normally has up to four vacancies per annum for articled clerks. The minimum educational requirement is a degree; the ability to get on with clients, a presentable appearance, intelligence and enthusiasm for hard work are also important. Apply by letter (with CV and names of referees) to Richard Gerstein or Ruth Bross.

Other offices: London (2).

Types of work undertaken: This is a broadly based practice with a strong commercial bias. The client base ranges from individuals to quoted public companies. Although the majority of the clients are UK based, there are significant numbers of clients in Europe, the Americas and major commercial centres worldwide. This overseas element is reinforced by the firm's membership of and strong involvement in the International Lawyers' Group.

Finers is well known for its property work, particularly commercial transactions, development scheme work and security transactions for banks and financial institutions, as well as substantial mortgage debenture and guarantee arrangements for borrowers.

The litigation department is involved mainly in High Court, commercial, intellectual property proceedings and enforcement of securities. In addition, divorce and matrimonial property disputes and some criminal work are undertaken.

There is particular skill and experience in company/commercial work, general commercial contracts, including entertainment and sports law, data processing and intellectual property agreements, as well as franchising, distribution and marketing agreements, joint ventures and partnerships, public issues and flotations.

The firm also has an established wills, probate and tax department, offering advice to both private and corporate clients.

In short, Finers sees itself as a highly competent professional and compact West End law firm, which is able to deal on an equal basis with all the major firms, and has a thriving international practice.

*f***INERS**
S O L I C I T O R S

Finn, Gledhill & Co

1-4 HARRISON ROAD
HALIFAX
WEST YORKSHIRE
HX1 2AG
Phone: 0422 330000

Fax: 0422 42604
DX: 16022 HALIFAX
Telex: none **Other offices:** 1
Senior Partner: Mr MW Gledhill
Number of Partners: 9
Total Staff: 55

This is a long-established medium sized Yorkshire firm offering a wide range of legal services to local, regional and national clients.

The firm: Finn, Gledhill & Co was formed as the result of the amalgamation of three old Halifax general practices: Godfrey Rhodes & Evans, which dates back to the 1850s, Frederick Walker Son & Dickie, established in the 1700s, and Horsley Bairstow & Helliwell, which was formed in the 1880s. Finn, Gledhill & Co is organised into departments.

The firm has a continuing need for high-calibre qualified staff, and in 1989 expects to have up to five vacancies for assistant solicitors. Address enquiries to Mr MW Gledhill.

In addition, the firm recruits one or two articled clerks every year. The minimum educational requirement is a 2(2) law degree; applicants are also judged on their ability to relate to the northern clientele. Prospects after qualification are excellent: two-thirds of the present partners served articles with the firm. Apply by handwritten letter (with CV and names of referees) up to ten months in advance to Mr MW Gledhill.

Other offices: Keighley.

Agency work: The firm accepts work from other solicitors; contact Mr PR Hamlett (commercial), Mr DJL Lee (domestic conveyancing), Mr MC Nowell (criminal), Mr SJ Mattock (matrimonial and licensing), or Mr JI Helliwell, (tribunal, insolvency, and debts).

Types of work undertaken: The firm is known locally as a very progressive and sound general practice. It also has a considerable reputation for its national work, the emphasis of which is on commercial matters, especially on all types of brewery work, and estate and town centre developments.

There is a strong conveyancing department handling commercial conveyancing, leases and financing work, as well as a significant amount of domestic conveyancing. The firm also handles town and country planning work.

As is to be expected of a long-established general practice, there is a substantial probate and trust practice, and the firm is also well known for the work it undertakes on behalf of charities.

Litigation is a particular strength of the firm, which handles matrimonial disputes, licensing applications and appeals, criminal cases and civil claims. The firm has a debt collection service and also deals with insolvency matters.

In short, Finn, Gledhill & Co is a general practice operating on a local and national basis. It is competitive and highly motivated, with a strong emphasis on maintaining close client/partner contacts. Brochure available.

Finn, Gledhill & co.

Fladgate Fielder

HERON PLACE
3 GEORGE STREET
LONDON
W1H 6AD
Phone: 01 486 9231

Fax: 01 935 7358
DX: 9057 WEST END W1
Telex: 8955567 **Other offices:** 3
Senior Partner: Anthony Baker
Chairman Managing Board: Howard Keen
Number of Partners: 27 **Total Staff:** 124

This newly merged firm is one of the largest in London's West End, and incorporates a number of long-established practices.

The firm: Fladgate Fielder is the result of the 1988 merger of Walters Fladgate (which can trace its origins back to a private client practice founded in about 1760, and was an amalgamation of three of the oldest firms of London solicitors) and the well-known commercial practice of Fielder Le Riche. The new firm is a predominantly commercial practice.

The firm expects to have six vacancies in 1989 for well-qualified assistant solicitors in company/corporate and taxation, both in London and in the regional offices. Enquiries to the resources partner, Charles Wander.

In addition, eight or nine articled clerks are recruited every year. A 2(2) degree is required. Apply by handwritten letter (with CV) to Janet Keeley or Richard Selby two years in advance.

Other offices: London, Basingstoke, and (under the name Bradly Trimmer) Alton.

Agency work: Litigation work is accepted from other solicitors: contact Paul Leese.

Types of work undertaken: This major West End practice has four main departments, commercial property, corporate, litigation,

and private client. The client base ranges from individuals and small companies to the largest business organisations, banks, professional practices, institutions and charities.

The commercial property department has a great deal of experience in handling all types of property transactions for institutional investors, property dealers and developers, joint venturers and lending institutions.

The corporate department deals with all aspects of company and commercial law and corporate funding, in particular, flotations, acquisitions and mergers, disposals, BES, USM and other public company work, and all other commercial aspects of creating and running a business.

The litigation department handles substantial commercial disputes and has particular expertise in building disputes, employment law and insurance cases. Stemming from the commercial property department, the firm has a strong emphasis on landlord and tenant litigation and professional neligence claims of every description.

The private client department has extensive experience in the special field of advising family trusts and individuals on the management of their affairs, particularly in agriculture, trusts, settled estates and dealing with wills and probate and inheritance tax.

The firm sees itself as a highly competent, respected, leading West End practice, which is entrepreneurial and innovative.

FLADGATE FIELDER

Foot & Bowden

70-76 NORTH HILL
PLYMOUTH
DEVON
PL4 8HH

Phone: 0752 663416

Fax: 0752 671802
DX: none
Telex: 45223
Senior Partner: Lord Foot
Number of Partners: 19
Total Staff: 110

Foot & Bowden is a long-established general practice based in Plymouth, serving both corporate and private clients.

The firm: It was founded nearly a century ago by Isaac Foot, who became a cabinet member in the Asquith government of the 1920s. The current senior partner, Lord Foot, sits as a Liberal peer in the House of Lords. Over the years, as the firm has grown, it has merged with Shelly & Johns, TR McCready & Willis, WH Sloman, Watts Anthony Yeo & Segar, Broadbent & Huddart, Porter & Hutchings, and Lake Friend & Tarbet of Exeter.

This expanding firm is expecting to recruit at least six solicitors in 1989; two are required for the company/commercial department immediately. Enquiries to Mrs JSA Lister.

The firm recruits six to eight articled clerks annually. A grant is given to prospective trainees. Applications by handwritten letter (plus CV and references) to Mrs JSA Lister.

Agency work: Nearly 15 per cent of the firm's work is referred by other solicitors.

Types of work undertaken: The firm undertakes all types of work, except entertainment. It has a special expertise in mining and mineral law. The planning department is also worthy of note (one of the planning lawyers is a chartered town planner). There is also con-siderable commercial litigation emphasis. The client base is wide, encompassing both large and small, private and commercial.

The commercial department handles the full range of company, commercial and employment law. The commercial conveyancing department deals with everything from the purchase of a corner shop lease to the transfer of factory premises and chains of public houses. It also handles licensing and self-building conveyancing.

In an area where home ownership is growing rapidly, Foot & Bowden has developed a strong residential conveyancing team who are dedicated to the idea of a quick turn-round, while providing the kind of care that first-time buyers in particular require.

As a result of the firm's many mergers it has a large trust department which handles tax work as well as winding up an estate. The family department deals with matrimonial advice, adoption, children's problems, social security benefits and consumer matters. The work of the criminal department ranges from motoring offences to serious criminal charges. The firm also has a strong litigation team, handling everything from personal injury work to the heaviest commercial action, including media and shipping work.

Foot & Bowden sees integrity as its most valuable asset and understands the importance of earning the high regard of its professional colleagues.

FOOT & BOWDEN

Ford & Warren

5 PARK SQUARE
LEEDS
LS1 2AX

Phone: 0532 436601

Fax: 0532 420905
DX: 12064 LEEDS-1
Telex: 556371
Managing Partner: Keith Hearn
Number of Partners: 12
Total Staff: 79

Ford & Warren, a medium sized Leeds-based firm, has a strong commercial and property practice and a substantial private client base.

The firm: Founded in 1815, the firm has practised under its present name since 1878. Its original success was based upon the prosperity of its land and coal owning clients. Since the mid-nineteenth century the firm has acted extensively for charities. The original commercial and property base of the firm has expanded since the 1960s, along with its litigation practice. Ford & Warren has doubled in size in the last five years.

The firm has a continuing need for assistant solicitors and expects six or seven vacancies will be available this year. In addition, the firm will always interview solicitors with potential. Enquiries to Mr EV Brown.

Three articled clerks are recruited annually. A 2(2) law degree is required. Long-term prospects after qualification are excellent: over three-quarters of the present partners served articles with the firm. Applications should be made by handwritten letter (with CV and names of two referees) addressed to Mr EV Brown.

Agency work: The firm accepts litigation work from other solicitors; contact Gary Hodgson.

Types of work undertaken: The firm deals with the full range of private client work (except in crime, when it acts only for established clients), as well as commercial/corporate work, litigation, trusts and tax, commercial property, residential conveyancing, and employee relocation. The client base includes major insurance companies, UK-listed companies, property developers, and some of the largest landowners in the north of England.

Ford & Warren is particularly well known for corporate acquisitions, its involvement in disaster claims (for example, the Paris DC-10 crash, Tenerife air disaster, Bradford fire, Zeebrugge), and its insurance company work.

The firm acts nationally in employment matters of all kinds, including advising several multinationals; it undertook employment law co-ordination and advice for the duration of the Sullom Voe oil terminal project. It has been suggested that the firm's track record in commercial property letting arrangements is second to none. Ford & Warren is heavily involved in Leeds City Centre commercial property purchase and letting. It pioneered computerised conveyancing in the region, and handles commercial road transport problems, from public enquiries to consultancy management and systems advice.

The firm sees itself as well established and reputable with a pioneering approach to specialised fields of work and technology.

FORD & WARREN

Ford Simey & Ford

8 CATHEDRAL CLOSE
EXETER
DEVON
EX1 1EZ
Phone: 0392 74126

Fax: 0392 410933
DX: 8316 EXETER
Telex: none **Other offices:** 3
Senior Partner: Mr GRS Simey
Number of Partners: 10
Total Staff: 70

Fox & Gibbons

2 OLD BURLINGTON STREET
LONDON
W1X 2QA

Phone: 01 439 8271

Fax: 01 734 8843
DX: 37244 PICCADILLY-1
Telex: 267108 **Other offices:** 4
Senior Partner: Mr RF Gibbons
Number of Partners: 14
Total Staff: 96

Fox Brooks Marshall

BRIDGE HOUSE
157A ASHLEY ROAD
HALE
CHESHIRE WA14 2UT
Phone: 061 928 5371

Fax: 061 941 4802
DX: 22055 HALE
Telex: 265871 **Other offices:** 9
Senior Partner: Mr G Smith
Number of Partners: 17
Total Staff: 100

Frederic Hall & Co

YORK HOUSE
32 CHERITON GARDENS
FOLKESTONE
KENT CT20 2UR
Phone: 0303 851185

Fax: 0303 850700
DX: 4907 FOLKESTONE
Telex: none **Other offices:** 1
Senior Partner: Mr JP Medlicott
Number of Partners: 10
Total Staff: 51

Forsyte Kerman *see full-page profile*
Foster Baxter Cooksey *see full-page profile*
Foysters *see full-page profile*
Franklins *see full-page profile*

Forsyte Kerman

79 NEW CAVENDISH STREET
LONDON
W1M 8AQ

Phone: 01 637 8566

Fax: 01 436 6088
DX: 99 LONDON CHANCERY LANE WC2
Telex: 22122
Senior Partner: Isidore Kerman
Number of Partners: 20
Total Staff: 119

Forsyte Kerman is a central London firm recognised for its property and commercial work allied to a strong litigation and tax planning practice.

The firm: Established in 1927, Forsyte Kerman has developed into a medium sized commercial and property practice providing an efficient and effective service to its clients in the business community. The firm is run by a partnership board and a managing partner.

Because of their increasing high quality workload, coupled with expansion plans, the firm is always actively recruiting top quality lawyers at all levels from partner to newly qualified. Enquiries to the managing partner, Alan Kaufman.

There are vacancies for eight articled clerks annually. A 2(1) degree is desirable, not necessarily in law. Long-term prospects are good: over half the present partners were articled with the firm. The firm offers good training and excellent career development prospects for lawyers. Apply (on form available on request) with references to David Raff by September two years in advance.

Types of work undertaken: The firm's principal activities are in the fields of commercial property, acting for large property and retail clients, and corporate work, for mainly medium sized businesses owned and run by their managements. Arising out of these mainstream activities is a good deal of commercial, property and building litigation work. Forsyte Kerman also acts for a number of private clients, particularly in the areas of matrimonial law and tax planning.

The firm is particularly well known for property work (developments and commercial leases); company (management buy-outs and buy-ins, acquisitions and disposals; litigation (property litigation and divorce); and private client (tax planning).

The property department handles the whole range of property transactions with emphasis on major development work and shops, offices and industrial property. The work includes purchases, sales, granting and taking leases, planning matters, the financing of real property transactions and the legal aspects of managing property investments.

The work of the company/commercial department encompasses a broad spread of high-quality corporate and commercial work, including company mergers and acquisitions and takeovers, buy-outs by managements, reorganisations, amalgamations and joint ventures.

Forsyte Kerman is intent on becoming a centre-stage medium sized firm, and sees itself as pushing back the frontiers of City-dominated corporate work, being technically hard to beat, extremely businesslike and totally professional.
A brochure is available on request.

**FORSYTE
KERMAN**
SOLICITORS

Foster Baxter Cooksey

7-10 GEORGE STREET
SNOW HILL
WOLVERHAMPTON
WV2 4DN
Phone: 0902 311711

Fax: 0902 311102
DX: 10404 WOLVERHAMPTON-1
Telex: none **Other offices:** 1
Senior Partner: Peter A Tredrea
Number of Partners: 15
Total Staff: 90

Foster Baxter Cooksey is a medium sized West Midlands practice with a rapidly expanding commercial bias, having both private and business clients.

The firm: Formed by a series of mergers of three old and well-established local firms — Foster & Co, JH Baxter & Son, and Cookseys — all founded in the nineteenth century, the firm has combined substantial resources and expertise and offers sound legal advice and support to private and business clients in the West Midlands area and beyond. A major aspect of the firm's approach is its use of specialist teams headed by a partner.

The firm aims to recruit at least five solicitors in 1989 to work in the litigation, commercial, property, probate and tax departments. Enquiries to John Nash the partnership secretary.

A minimum of four articled clerks are required annually. The minimum educational requirements are a 2(2) LLB or CPE followed by a pass in all heads of Finals. Apply by handwritten letter (plus CV) to John Nash.

Other offices: Willenhall.

Agency work: The firm undertakes all types of agency work for other solicitors.

Types of work undertaken: A broad spread of work is handled, with particular emphasis on commercial (including company acquisitions, mergers, management buy-outs and intellectual property) and civil litigation (PI) specialisations. Although the firm retains its market share of residential conveyancing, it is expanding faster in other areas. Its client base is made up of a general mix of corporate and private clients.

Particular areas in which the firm's name is well known are personal injury civil litigation work, commercial company acquisitions and management buy-outs and conveyancing (including town and country planning).

The commercial team handles major activities such as the sale and purchase of companies and commercial disputes ranging over a wide area of the law (including contract disputes, trademark, patent and copyright, building disputes, and warranty and indemnity claims associated with company acquisitions and disposals). The litigation team provides expertise in representing clients in the courts, insurance and employment tribunals and higher appellate courts. The commercial property team deals with freehold and leasehold developments, town and country planning, and landlord and tenant matters for builders and developers, as well as business and corporate clients.

The firm perceives itself as an expanding, widely based, provincial firm, energetic and outward looking, yet retaining the traditional virtue of partner/client contact.

SOLICITORS

FOSTER BAXTER COOKSEY

Foysters

HARVESTER HOUSE
37 PETER STREET
MANCHESTER
M2 5GB
Phone: 061 228 3702

Fax: 061 835 2407
DX: 14313 MANCHESTER
Telex: 668928 **Other offices:** 2
Managing Partner: Richard Holman
Number of Partners: 13
Total Staff: 81

Foysters is a commercially biased practice, acting for a wide range of business and finance clients throughout the North West, while at the same time maintaining a strong private client practice.

The firm: Known as Foysters since 1962, the firm can trace its roots back to 1788. In 1985 Foysters merged with John Taylor & Co, a long-established practice with strong connections in textiles and engineering complementing Foysters' wider commercial practice both in traditional industries and new and developing areas such as computer software and advertising. The enlarged firm has continued to grow, consolidating its position as one of the leading practices in Manchester.

As a result of continuing expansion, six to eight additional assistant solicitors will be needed during the next year, both newly qualified and more experienced. Enquiries to the staff partner, Andrea McWatt.

The firm recruits four articled clerks annually. Apply (with CV and names of referees) two years ahead to the staff partner.

Other offices: Blackburn, Hale Barns.

Agency work: Work is accepted from other solicitors in litigation, insolvency, and intellectual property (plus ecclesiastical law at Hale Barns).

Types of work undertaken: Foysters is particularly well known in the areas of commercial lending, marketing agreements, intellectual property (patents, copyright and trademarks), computer contracts, insolvency (both corporate and personal), brewery work (both property and litigation), banking, leasing and finance litigation, divorce and industrial tribunals.

Being primarily a commercial firm, the practice undertakes all forms of company and commercial work, including company formations, takeovers and mergers, lending, company reconstructions, buy-outs, partnerships, marketing agreements, consumer and corporate credit, pension schemes, litigation and employment law.

The property department deals with the commercial side (leases, development schemes, and compulsory purchase), as well as the private residential side.

Besides property work, the firm offers a full range of legal services to its private clients including general and personal injury litigation, employment law, landlord and tenant, matrimonial, wills, trusts, estate administration, and tax planning.

This well-respected and long-established firm is modern in outlook and technology, providing a strong across-the-board service with the necessary expertise to deal with unusual and complex problems.

A brochure is available on request.

F O Y S T E R S

Franklins Solicitors

14 CASTILIAN STREET
NORTHAMPTON
NN1 1JX

Phone: 0604 31722

Fax: 0604 250208
DX: 12471 NORTHAMPTON
Telex: none **Other offices:** 4
Senior Partner: Michael Franklin
Number of Partners: 5
Total Staff: 87

This medium sized Northampton-based firm has a substantial private client base and a growing commercial practice.

The firm: Founded in 1982, Franklins was originally established as a private client practice, but has since expanded into the commercial law field and, at the same time, has opened four branch offices. The firm has plans to establish city-centre commercial offices in Northampton and Milton Keynes, as well as an administration and computer headquarters in Northampton.

This expanding firm is always looking for high-quality assistant solicitors, and in the next 12 months expects to have two to three vacancies. Enquiries should be addressed to Michael Franklin.

Six articled clerks are recruited annually. The minimum educational requirement is a 2(2) degree. This growing firm offers excellent long-term prospects. Apply by letter (with CV) to Michael Franklin.

Other offices: Central Milton Keynes, Leighton Buzzard, Dunstable, Towcester.

Agency work: The Milton Keynes office accepts general court work from other solicitors; contact Philip Parsons.

Types of work undertaken: Initially the firm concentrated wholly on private client work but now, while retaining this bias, it has developed strong commercial property and commercial litigation departments for a range of clients, from small private companies to several listed companies.

Franklins is particularly well known for its residential conveyancing department, which is fully computerised, as is the firm's debt collection service.

On the litigation side, there is particular expertise in plaintiff personal injury claims, magisterial law and licensing, criminal advocacy and commercial litigation matters. The firm also handles matrimonial and family work, landlord and tenant and employment law disputes and debt collection cases.

The growing company/commercial practice includes company formation, partnership deeds, business terms contracts, taxation and financial planning. The firm's involvement in the commercial property field is well known and encompasses the full range of services, including work for developers, the sale and purchase of property, financing, and lettings of business premises.

The range of private client services offered is wide ranging, and includes wills, probate, family and matrimonial law matters, and personal taxation and financial planning. Legal aid work is accepted.

Overall, Franklins sees itself as a youthful and rapidly expanding practice, which offers expertise in specialist areas of the law.

Frere Cholmeley

28 LINCOLN'S INN FIELDS
LONDON
WC2A 3HH

Phone: 01 405 7878

Fax: 01 405 9056
DX: 140 LONDON CHANCERY LANE WC2
Telex: 27623 **Other offices:** 3
Senior Partner: Michael Boreham
Number of Partners: 33
Total Staff: 283

Frere Cholmeley is one of the major London law firms, with the full range of commercial services of a City practice and a history dating from the middle of the eighteenth century.

The firm: The firm's reputation is based on its ability to offer to private, corporate and government clients an accomplished and quality service. Frere Cholmeley's offices in London, Paris, Monte Carlo and Milan each work together to support an international practice.

There is a constant need for high-calibre qualified staff in all departments, both those with general training and with specialist knowledge. Enquiries to Sophie Hamilton.

The firm will be recruiting 26 articled clerks for 1991. A 2(1) degree in any subject is required. Apply by handwritten letter (plus CV and academic referee) before 1 September 1989 to Sophie Hamilton.

Other offices: Paris, Monte Carlo, Milan.

Types of work undertaken: The firm is a predominantly corporate and commercial practice, with some high quality private client work. Specialisations are sales of professional partnerships, entertainment, employment, planning, aviation and Anglo-German. There is a varied international client base.

The largest department is the company/commercial department covering corporate finance, banking, major transactional work for listed and non-listed companies, taxation, anti-trust matters and international business transactions. The specialist aviation division advises on all aspects of air-law. The Anglo-German group offers a fully bilingual service, advising on Anglo-German and community law matters.

The entertainment group offers a comprehensive range of music business law advice to major record companies, international artists and representative bodies.

The litigation department is mainly concerned with large-scale commercial disputes and international arbitrations, and has particular experience in oil related matters. The department has advised on several major City fraud cases. Specialist areas include intellectual property disputes and industrial relations work.

The property department covers every kind of property transaction, specialising in property development and planning, and related financing/security matters.

The private client department acts for landowners, business people and celebrities, advising on tax planning, handling probate matters, and dealing with heritage property.

This highly professional firm is generally regarded as providing an excellent service that is both efficient and commercial. A brochure for clients detailing the services the firm offers is available on request.

≡ **FRERE CHOLMELEY**

Freshfields

GRINDALL HOUSE
25 NEWGATE STREET
LONDON
EC1A 7LH

Phone: 01 606 6677

Fax: 01 248 3487
DX: 23 LONDON CITY EC3
Telex: 889292 **Other offices:** 5
Senior Partner: Mr HSK Peppiatt
Number of Partners: 72
Total Staff: 762

Freshfields is one of the oldest and largest firms of solicitors in England with offices also in the Far East, Paris and New York, and an international list of clients.

The firm: Freshfields was founded in the early eighteenth century by an adviser to the Bank of England and it has acted for the bank ever since. The firm has long been at the centre of City and commercial life. It has become one of the largest firms in the City through internal growth, rather than through mergers or acquisitions.

Rapid growth promotes a continuing need for qualified staff at Freshfields, and in 1989 the firm expects to recruit between 40 and 70 assistant solicitors. Enquiries should be addressed to David Rance.

Freshfields has one of the largest intakes of articled clerks: between 55 to 65 per year. The preferred educational qualification is a 2(1) degree, not necessarily in law. Long-term prospects are excellent: a majority of the present partners served articles with the firm. Applications should be made by form (available on request) between July and September a year before graduation to Guy Whalley, the Training Principal.

Other offices: Hong Kong, Paris, New York, Singapore, Tokyo.

Types of work undertaken: Generally regarded to be one of the leading firms in London, Freshfields has an international client base, which includes large corporate entities, banks and investment institutions, and five overseas offices. Corporate and commercial work make up the main body of the firm's work. There are five departments: company/commercial, litigation, real property, tax, and private client.

Freshfields' best known areas of expertise in the corporate/commercial field are mergers and acquisitions (especially takeover bids); public offers of securities on the Stock Exchange and USM; privatisations; capital markets work (such as Eurobond issues); specialist financing (particularly, aircraft and projects); and EEC and competition law.

The firm also has a strong reputation for its work in major international arbitrations and commercial litigation; large-scale commercial real property transactions for investors and developers; and specialist corporate tax advice. In addition, the private client department is well known for its tax planning work, and also undertakes family and trust law (but does not handle divorce or criminal work).

Overall, Freshfields perceives itself as a leader in the profession, and as one of the most prestigious and best established law firms in the City, recognised for its high-quality work, high-quality people and impeccable professional standards. A brochure is available on request.

FRESHFIELDS

Furley Page Fielding & Barton

39 ST MARGARET'S STREET
CANTERBURY
KENT
CT1 2TX
Phone: 0227 763939

Fax: 0227 762829
DX: 5301 CANTERBURY
Telex: 965078 **Other offices:** 2
Senior Partner: Mr V Barton
Number of Partners: 12
Total Staff: 85

Gamlin Kelly & Beattie

31-33 RUSSELL ROAD
RHYL
CLWYD
LL18 3DB
Phone: 0745 343500

Fax: 0745 343616
DX: 17352 RHYL
Telex: none **Other offices:** 5
Senior Partner: Mr RA Salisbury
Number of Partners: 5
Total Staff: 86

Gareth Woodfine and Partners

16 ST CUTHBERTS STREET
BEDFORD
MK40 3JB

Phone: 0234 270600

Fax: 0234 210128
DX: 5619 BEDFORD
Telex: 825326 **Other offices:** 3
Senior Partner: Mr G Woodfine
Number of Partners: 6
Total Staff: 75

Gartside Harding & Davies

BRAND'S HOUSE
18-19 SKINNER STREET
NEWPORT
GWENT NP9 1HT
Phone: 0633 213411

Fax: 0633 66541
DX: 33207 NEWPORT GWENT
Telex: none **Other offices:** 3
Senior Partner: Mr D Harding
Number of Partners: 9
Total Staff: 61

Gamlens *see full-page profile*

Gamlens

3 & 4 STONE BUILDINGS
LINCOLN'S INN
LONDON
WC2A 3XS
Phone: 01 831 7345

Fax: 01 430 2566
DX: 59 LONDON CHANCERY LANE WC2
Telex: 267206
Senior Partner: Mr IR Ponsford
Number of Partners: 14
Total Staff: 83

Gamlens is among the oldest London solicitors' practices, and provides a comprehensive corporate and commercial service.

The firm: Mentioned in the first Law List in 1781, Gamlens originally had a client base dominated by individuals and owners of substantial landed estates. Since the late 1960s, the firm has expanded substantially into the company, commercial and international fields, and has developed a wide client list.

The firm is expanding and is interested in the recruitment of qualified staff, and in 1989 expects to recruit three assistant solicitors, for commercial property, company/commercial and private client tax work. Enquiries should be addressed to Ms SE Panizzo.

The firm normally has vacancies for four articled clerks. The preferred educational qualification is a 2(1) degree, not necessarily in law. Prospects are excellent: most of the present partners served articles with the firm. Apply by letter (with CV and references) two years in advance to Ms SE Panizzo.

Agency work: The firm accepts common law and Chancery litigation work from other solicitors.

Types of work undertaken: While retaining its established base of private clients and owners of landed estates, the firm has expanded to provide a comprehensive range of services, with matrimonial and civil litigation, private client, company/commercial and property departments.

Apart from its substantial private client base, the firm acts for a wide range of clients, including national clearing banks, credit and leasing groups, travel groups, film and video producers, departmental stores, substantial property-owning private companies and associated family trusts.

The work of the company/commercial department includes company, partnership, business and intellectual property law. The department is well known for its management buy-out and secured lending work.

The firm is strong in matrimonial work, dealing with divorce, foreign marriages, financial settlements, pensions, and family law matters, with special expertise in litigation. Indeed, litigation is an important area of practice, both High Court and county court.

The firm handles all aspects of commercial property work, including development and investment matters and domestic conveyancing work, as well as time sharing. Trusts and estate planning are also areas where the firm has particular expertise.

One of the partners is qualified to advise on Italian law and there are a number of Italian speakers among the firm's partners and qualified staff.

Gamlens sees itself as forward-looking, efficient and reputable.

GAMLENS

George Green & Co

195 HIGH STREET
CRADLEY HEATH
WEST MIDLANDS
B64 5HW

Phone: 0384 410410

Fax: 0384 634237
DX: 20752 CRADLEY HEATH
Telex: 337472 **Other offices:** 2
Senior Partner: Mr GP Green
Number of Partners: 9
Total Staff: 75

Gepp & Sons

58 NEW LONDON ROAD
CHELMSFORD
ESSEX
CM2 0YN

Phone: 0245 493939

Fax: 0245 493940
DX: 3306 CHELMSFORD
Telex: none
Senior Partner: Mr CL Facey
Number of Partners: 8
Total Staff: 76

Glaisyers

ST JOHN'S COURT
76 GARTSIDE STREET
MANCHESTER
M3 3EL

Phone: 061 832 4666

Fax: 061 835 4666
DX: 14381 MANCHESTER-1
Telex: none **Other offices:** 3
Senior Partner: Mr Mark Atkins
Number of Partners: 8
Total Staff: 52

Glovers

115 PARK STREET
LONDON
W1Y 4DY

Phone: 01 629 5121

Fax: 01 491 0930
DX: 115 LONDON CHANCERY LANE WC2
Telex: 261648
Senior Partner: Mr R Anstis
Number of Partners: 9
Total Staff: 55

Gill Akaster *see full-page profile*
Girlings *see full-page profile*
Glaisyers *see full-page profile*
Glanvilles *see full-page profile*

Gill Akaster

SCOTT LODGE
MILEHOUSE
PLYMOUTH
PL2 3DD
Phone: 0752 500111

Fax: 0752 563403
DX: none
Telex: 45597 **Other offices:** 3
Senior Partner: David HB Bishop
Number of Partners: 11
Total Staff: 76

Gill Akaster is a general family firm with a broad base and a growing commercial practice.

The firm: Gill Akaster can trace its history, through a series of sole practitioners, to the early nineteenth century in the Devonport area of Plymouth. The present main office in Plymouth was purpose built 20 years ago. Rapid expansion in recent years has led to the opening of three other offices.

The firm is constantly seeking assistant solicitors. Advocates are needed for the criminal department, and the firm also has vacancies in the commercial department. Enquiries should be addressed to Mr MG Pillar.

In addition, the firm usually has two or three vacancies for articled clerks every year. The recruitment policy is fairly flexible: the firm is willing to consider candidates with or without degrees. Prospects after qualification are good: indeed, five of the present partners served articles with the firm. Apply to Mr MG Pillar.

Other offices: Plymouth (3).

Agency work: Work from other solicitors is accepted in all areas. Much agency work relates to the Land Charges Registry and the District Land Registry in Plymouth: contact Tony Hunt. Litigation work: for criminal, contact Mr DHB Bishop or Mr L Cook; for matrimonial, Mrs J Ashley; and for civil, Mr MG Pillar.

Types of work undertaken: As would be expected of a general family practice, Gill Akaster offers expertise in conveyancing, litigation and probate. The firm also has strong matrimonial and criminal departments. However, in recent years, it has expanded its commercial practice in both the contentious and non-contentious fields (including licensing).

Among the type of work regularly undertaken on the commercial side are commercial leases, taxation, general company law, debt collection, town and country planning, estate development and insurance. The firm also handles employment and family law work, personal injury and defamation. All types of legal aid work are undertaken. The client base is wide and varied, ranging from large companies to individuals.

The senior partner is particularly well known for his fisheries practice (for example, representing British and foreign owners and skippers of fishing vessels charged with operating without licences, outside limits, or with under-sized nets).

Overall, the firm perceives itself as an efficient and effective family practice able to offer advice in a wide range of areas, with an increasing commercial orientation.

GILL AKASTER

Girlings

158 HIGH STREET
HERNE BAY
KENT
CT6 5NP
Phone: 0227 373874

Fax: 0227 365897
DX: 32303 HERNE BAY
Telex: 965551 **Other offices:** 4
Senior Partner: Tony Girling
Number of Partners: 18
Total Staff: 148

This is a broad-based general practice dealing primarily with private client work but including business clients.

The firm: Girlings was founded in 1881 with an office in Margate. Expansion, especially in the last two decades, has seen it become one of the largest firms in Kent. The firm has four branch offices, all of which — apart from the small office in Birchington — provide a wide spectrum of legal services.

The firm expects to have three vacancies for assistant solicitors in 1989 in conveyancing and litigation. Contact Tony Girling (at the Herne Bay office).

Generally, the firm recruits six articled clerks annually. The minimum educational requirement is A levels to take the CPE path. Applications (with CV) should be sent to Nicholas Charlesworth (3-6 Dane John, Canterbury, Kent CT1 2UG).

Other offices: Birchington, Canterbury, Margate, Ramsgate.

Agency work: Girlings undertakes a considerable amount of work for other solicitors, covering civil litigation (including matrimonial), liquor licensing, and general legal services (but excluding legal aid crime). Contact the litigation partner at any office.

Types of work undertaken: Within a general practice framework, the firm has a reputation for handling civil litigation work, including matrimonial and family law; probate, trust and management work; commercial and domestic conveyancing (as well as planning, agricultural property and rent reviews). Girlings also specialises in liquor licensing and gaming and betting.

Among the comprehensive general legal services the firm offers its substantial private client base are family law matters, including divorce, maintenance, emergency injunctions, custody and access, adoption, taxation advice, matrimonial property, and wardship and child care proceedings. There is also a private client criminal law practice, as well as domestic conveyancing, wills and probate work.

On the commercial side, Girlings handles business management; taxation planning; commercial work, including commercial leases, rent reviews, agricultural and farming matters, town and country planning, building contract disputes, estate development, and commercial property; employment law, covering redundancy, unfair dismissal, discrimination, accidents at work, employment and service contracts, and industrial tribunal representation; and company formation, sale and purchase.

This well-established firm has a modern approach and is generally regarded as being an efficient, well-managed practice serving good-quality private clients and businesses.

Girlings
SOLICITORS

Glaisyers

ROWCHESTER COURT
WHITTALL STREET
BIRMINGHAM
B4 6DZ

Phone: 021 200 2010

Fax: 021 200 2009
DX:13050 BIRMINGHAM-1
Telex: 333241 **Other offices:** 2
Senior Partner: Michael Harvey
Number of Partners: 20
Total Staff: 140

This Midlands firm has a thriving commercial practice, combined with a substantial private client base.

The firm: Glaisyers was founded in Birmingham in 1878. Since 1970, the firm has experienced rapid expansion, growing from a small practice with three partners into one of the most vigorous Midlands firms. In May 1988 the firm opened an office in Gibraltar.

There is a continuing need for qualified staff, and in 1989 the firm expects to have about ten vacancies for assistant solicitors in all departments. Enquiries should be addressed to Mr MW Cotterhill or Mr JG Loveday.

In addition, the firm recruits between six and eight articled clerks every year. The minimum educational requirement is a 2(2) degree, not necessarily in law. Prospects after qualification are good: approximately 40 per cent of the present partners served articles with the firm. Apply on form (available on request) by November in the first term of third year; address to Mr JG Loveday or Mr MW Cotterhill.

Other offices: Gibraltar, Tamworth.

Agency work: All types of work — and in particular, Gibraltar company work, Spanish property, crime and litigation — are accepted from other firms of solicitors.

Types of work undertaken: Glaisyers has a very strong private limited company base, and has wide experience and expertise in the full range of private company work, including company incorporations and administration, management buy-outs, franchising, commercial agreements, conveyancing, and commercial property and leases. In addition, the firm undertakes commercial litigation work, including breaches of agreements, intellectual property disputes, and employment disputes.

The firm also has a very significant private client base, with emphasis on criminal and matrimonial law work, as well as a competitively priced computerised domestic conveyancing service. Personal injury work is undertaken, usually with the firm acting for the plaintiff against insurance companies. Legal aid work is undertaken.

The firm's recently opened Gibraltar office offers clients advice on tax planning and residence, and sets up offshore companies and trusts. There is also a strong Anglo-Spanish department in Birmingham, dealing with the sale or purchase of Spanish property, and the firm has links with 15 different law firms throughout Spain.

Overall, Glaisyers sees itself as an aggressive, commercial practice, combining a quick, efficient service at competitive prices with the personal touch. The firm publishes an informative series of booklets for clients.

GLAISYERS

Glanvilles

16 LANDPORT TERRACE
PORTSMOUTH
HAMPSHIRE
PO1 2QT
Phone: 0705 827231

Fax: 0705 753611
DX: 2211 PORTSMOUTH
Telex: 86538 **Other offices:** 7
Senior Partner: James R Kenroy
Number of Partners: 14
Total Staff: 109

This medium sized Hampshire firm offers a wide range of legal services to commercial and private clients.

The firm: Glanvilles was founded in 1884 by John Foster Glanville as a private client practice. Since 1970, when the firm amalgamated with Sherwell Wells & Way, a network of offices has been opened across the Solent area and the emphasis in the practice has changed to accommodate an increasing commercial workload.

This rapidly expanding firm is always seeking to recruit good qualified staff, usually those with one year post-qualification experience, although more experienced applicants are always considered. On average, three or four assistant solicitors are recruited for each department each year. Enquiries to the partnership secretary.

In addition, three or four articled clerks are recruited annually. The minimum educational requirement is a 2(1) degree, not necessarily in law. Apply on form (available on request) to Mark Hepworth or Sue Craven.

Other offices: Eastleigh, Fareham, Gosport, Havant, Waterlooville, Fratton, Newport (IOW).

Agency work: The firm accepts litigation and commercial work from other solicitors; contact Mark Williams.

Types of work undertaken: This is a broadly based practice covering the full spectrum of legal expertise. In recent years the client base has expanded considerably from its private client origins to include a range of corporate and business clients, from small private businesses and partnerships to public companies.

The firm's main office in Portsmouth provides a strong company/commercial team which has wide experience and expertise in company formations, mergers, liquidations and acquisitions, as well as insolvency. Debt collection, especially mortgage repossessions, is another important area of the company/commercial practice. The firm undertakes all aspects of planning; indeed, it has three ex-council solicitors working in this area. In addition, the firm is well known for its licensing work, for clients who range from small public houses to large brewers. There is a strong criminal litigation team, and commercial conveyancing is also handled.

The experienced trust and probate department – which has particular expertise in trust accounting, taxation and personal financial planning – has been relocated to Waterlooville. The smaller offices tend to provide a 'high street' service, specialising in conveyancing and litigation.

Glanvilles sees itself as a well-established, efficient and forward-thinking practice in the forefront of South Coast legal developments.

GLANVILLES

Goodger Auden

2-4 LICHFIELD STREET
BURTON ON TRENT
STAFFORDSHIRE
DE14 3RB
Phone: 0283 44323

Fax: 0283 35448
DX: 10704 BURTON ON TRENT
Telex: none **Other offices:** 5
Senior Partner: Derek Auden
Number of Partners: 15
Total Staff: 105

This Burton on Trent firm has a strong general and commercial law practice and a long association with the brewing industry.

The firm: Goodger Auden is derived from a series of mergers that have taken place since the original firm was founded in 1852 by Henry Goodger. The firm merged with Auden & Son in 1969 and has recently amalgamated with the long established firm of Barrs. All firms involved in the various mergers had a background of general and commercial law and, with the Burton firms being located in that brewing capital, there is a long association with breweries and with brewing support industries. The firm is organised into four departments.

The firm has a continuing need for assistant solicitors, and expects to recruit about four in 1989, particularly for commercial (Burton), conveyancing (Derby and Nottingham), and litigation (Derby and Nottingham). Enquiries to Richard Cundy.

Six articled clerks are recruited annually. A 2(2) law degree or equivalent is required. Apply by handwritten letter (with CV and references) two years in advance to Richard Cundy.

Other offices: Burton (2), Lichfield, Derby, Nottingham.

Agency work: Work is accepted from other solicitors: contact Rosaleen Beck (debt collection); Tony Russell (criminal and industrial tribunal); Margaret Nickson (child care); Robert Bond (intellectual property); and Barry Challender (commercial).

Types of work undertaken: The firm is well known for its expertise in criminal, matrimonial, child care matters, company, commercial litigation, intellectual property and, most particularly, computer law. Apart from business software houses, the firm acts for six leading leisure software companies.

The litigation department handles landlord and tenant, industrial tribunal, intellectual property, personal injury, crime, child care, matrimonial and insolvency work. It also deals with litigation abroad through associates in the EEC and the USA.

The commercial/corporate department deals with non-contentious business law, and particularly company, commercial conveyancing, computer and intellectual property law.

The work of the property department encompasses residential matters, and at Burton is linked to the property sales department offering a combined estate agency/conveyancing service. There is also a strong probate department.

Goodger Auden sees itself as an up-and-coming firm providing a service in the provinces that equals that which might be expected from a London firm.

Goodman Derrick & Co

9-11 FULWOOD PLACE
GRAYS INN
LONDON
WC1V 6HQ
Phone: 01 404 0606

Fax: 831 6407
DX: 122 LONDON CHANCERY LANE WC2
Telex: 21210
Senior Partner: Lord Goodman
Number of Partners: 12
Total Staff: 70

Gordons and HM Dawson & Co

14 PICCADILLY
BRADFORD
WEST YORKSHIRE
BD1 3LX
Phone: 0274 733771

Fax: 0274 728346
DX: 11716 BRADFORD
Telex: 517593 **Other offices:** 1
Senior Partner: Mr AR Wilson
Number of Partners: 11
Total Staff: 78

Gorna & Co

VIRGINIA HOUSE
CHEAPSIDE, KING STREET
MANCHESTER
M2 4NB
Phone: 061 832 3651

Fax: 061 834 8572
DX: 14339 MANCHESTER-1
Telex: 668987
Senior Partner: Mr PG Reynolds
Number of Partners: 10
Total Staff: 55

Gosschalk Wheldon Chambers Thomas

30 SILVER STREET
HULL
HUMBERSIDE
HU1 1JR
Phone: 0482 25331

Fax: 0482 226620
DX: 11902 HULL-1
Telex: 592548 **Other offices:** 1
Senior Partner: Mr TN Wheldon
Number of Partners: 15
Total Staff: 89

Gotelee & Goldsmith

35-37 ELM STREET
IPSWICH
SUFFOLK
IP1 2AY
Phone: 0473 211121

Fax: 0473 230387
DX: 3220 IPSWICH
Telex: 987128 **Other offices:** 1
Senior Partner: Mr LJ Castle
Number of Partners: 9
Total Staff: 80

Goughs

28 CHURCH STREET
CALNE
WILTSHIRE
SN11 0HX
Phone: 0249 812086

Fax: 0249 816378
DX: 44800 CALNE
Telex: none **Other offices:** 5
Senior Partner: Mr CC Gough
Number of Partners: 12
Total Staff: 54

Grahame Stowe Bateson & Co

PORTLAND HOUSE
7 PORTLAND STREET
LEEDS
LS1 3DR
Phone: 0532 468163

Fax: 0532 426682
DX: 12022 LEEDS-1
Telex: none **Other offices:** 4
Senior Partner: Mr GC Stowe
Number of Partners: 5
Total Staff: 55

Grangewoods

1 HARLEY STREET
LONDON
W1A 4DG

Phone: 01 637 5388

Fax: 01 323 1252
DX: 223 LONDON WEST END W1
Telex: 24747
Senior Partner: Mr M Fielding
Number of Partners: 19
Total Staff: 130

Gouldens *see full-page profile*

Gouldens

22 TUDOR STREET
LONDON
EC4Y 0JJ

Phone: 01 583 7777

Fax: 01 583 3051
DX: 67 LONDON CHANCERY LANE WC2
Telex: 21520 **Other offices:** 1
Senior Partner: Hugo Scott
Number of Partners: 22
Total Staff: 230

A medium sized City firm, Gouldens offers a full range of legal services to companies, partnerships and individuals involved in commercial enterprises.

The firm: Gouldens was founded in the City during the early part of the nineteenth century and has a long history of commercial success. For its size it has always had an unusually well-balanced spread of work.

This expanding firm is looking for ten to 12 assistant solicitors specialising in the company/commercial, pension, property and tax areas. Enquiries to Neil Seaton.

Between 12 and 16 articled clerks are recruited annually. The minimum academic requirement is a 2(1) degree, not necessarily in law; applicants with language degrees are encouraged. Apply by handwritten letter (plus CV and references) to Clare Deanesly.

Other offices: Jersey; associated offices in Paris, Kuwait.

Agency work: Litigation work is accepted from other solicitors; contact Charters MacDonald-Brown.

Types of work undertaken: The firm combines expertise in the company, commercial, property development and planning areas with strong litigation, taxation and private client departments. It is well known for mergers and acquisitions (and particularly the taxation aspects); town and country planning appeals and enquiries (the firm uses its own lawyers and in-house surveyors to handle all aspects of the planning process); intellectual property; employment law; the business expansion scheme; international tax strategies for trans-national enterprises, and advertising law.

The company department advises on the establishment, financing and reconstruction of corporate entities for clients in both the industrial and financial sectors, including flotations, debt financings, venture capital, employee-incentive arrangements, intellectual property, and pension schemes.

The property and planning departments advise developers, investing institutions, banks, surveyors and estate agents on the financing, structuring and implementation of large developments as well as on the property related aspects of mergers and acquisitions.

The work of the litigation department includes all kinds of UK and international trade disputes and arbitration, particularly intellectual property, insurance and reinsurance, and construction contract and employment law disputes. The taxation and private client departments advise on such matters as BES and offshore tax planning.

This firm sees itself as dynamic, creative, commercial, forward-thinking and responsive. A brochure is available on request.

GOULDENS

Green David Conway & Co

45 CRAWFORD PLACE
LONDON
W1H 1HX

Phone: 01 258 0055

Fax: 01 724 0385
DX: 41726 MARYLEBONE-1
Telex: 24164
Senior Partners: David Conway and John Green
Number of Partners: 7 **Total Staff:** 53

This medium sized West End firm has an all-round commercial practice, with a substantial property base for which it is best known.

The firm: Green David Conway & Co was founded in 1972 by the two present senior partners. From the beginning, the emphasis has been on property work combined with a strong commercial practice. The firm's work is broadly divided into four categories: property, corporate and business services, litigation, and personal affairs.

The firm is always interested in well-qualified staff, and in 1989 expects to recruit two or three assistant solicitors for the property department. Enquiries to the recruitment partner.

In addition there are usually two vacancies for articled clerks every year. The firm has a policy of organic growth and long-term prospects are good. Every articled clerk upon qualification has, to date, remained with the firm. Applications for articles should be made one year in advance. Write directly to the recruitment partner.

Types of work undertaken: The client base is wide and varied, including merchant banks and clearing banks, listed companies, private companies, property developers and investors, liquidators and receivers, relocation agencies, residents associations, accountants and surveyors and other professional firms.

Much of the property work is associated with joint ventures, which has further accelerated an expansion of the corporate and commercial side of the practice. Client development has led to USM listings whilst other corporate/commercial work includes loan finance transactions, corporate acquisitions and disposals, mergers, partnerships, liquidations and receiverships, franchising, distribution contracts and other intellectual property matters.

There is a strong litigation department handling a broad range of commercial and private contentious work.

A multilingual ability exists within the firm, covering the main European as well as a number of oriental languages. This has been of great assistance in the development of the firm's foreign clientele, whether in the UK or abroad.

The firm has an in-house computer specialist who assists in providing the latest technology for precedent creation, document production, accounting and management information, for the benefit of partners and staff as well as clients.

Green David Conway & Co sees itself as the progressive West End practice; it seeks to provide in its field much of the expertise and resources expected from the largest firms, whilst retaining a more personal involvement in clients' affairs. A brochure describing the work of the firm is available upon request.

GREEN DAVID CONWAY & CO

Greenland Houchen

38 PRINCE OF WALES ROAD
NORWICH
NORFOLK
NR1 1HZ
Phone: 0603 660744

Fax: 0603 610700
DX: 5217 NORWICH
Telex: none **Other offices:** 2
Senior Partner: Mr Trevor Nicholls
Number of Partners: 5
Total Staff: 78

Gregory Rowcliffe & Milners

1 BEDFORD ROW
LONDON
WC1R 4BZ

Phone: 01 242 0631

Fax: 01 242 6652
DX: 95 LONDON CHANCERY LANE WC2
Telex: 261131
Senior Partner: Mr TH Drabble
Number of Partners: 12
Total Staff: 63

Grindeys

GLEBE COURT
STOKE ON TRENT
STAFFORDSHIRE
ST4 1ET
Phone: 0782 46441

Fax: 0782 416220
DX: 21053 STOKE ON TRENT
Telex: none **Other offices:** 2
Senior Partner: Mr PE Godfrey
Number of Partners: 9
Total Staff: 78

Haden Stretton Slater Miller

LEICESTER BUILDINGS
BRIDGE STREET
WALSALL
WEST MIDLANDS WS1 1EL
Phone: 0922 720000

Fax: 0922 720023
DX: 12122 WALSALL
Telex: 338625 **Other offices:** 6
Senior Partner: Mr DW Anderton OBE
Number of Partners: 13
Total Staff: 138

Greenwoods *see full-page profile*

Greenwoods

30 PRIESTGATE
PETERBOROUGH
PE1 1JE

Phone: 0733 555244

Fax: 0733 47988
DX: 12306 PETERBOROUGH-1
Telex: 32199
Senior Partner: DJ Weekes
Number of Partners: 13
Total Staff: 114

One of the largest law firms in East Anglia, Greeenwoods provides fully comprehensive legal services for a wide range of private and commercial clients.

The firm: Greenwoods was founded in Peterborough in 1927 by Charles Greenwood. From its beginnings as a small litigation practice, in what was then a medium sized market town, the firm has kept pace with the rapidly expanding city and the increasingly commercial nature of the local economy to become one of the largest and best-known firms in the region.

The firm is currently aiming to recruit two assistant solicitors in company work, and one each for commercial litigation, probate and domestic conveyancing. Enquiries to Mr J Bandaranaike.

In addition, the firm generally recruits eight articled clerks per year. Applications by hand-written letter (plus typed CV) should be addressed to Mr J Bandaranaike.

Agency work: All types of work are accepted from other solicitors; however, most of the work undertaken is conveyancing and court appearances.

Types of work undertaken: The firm's strong commercial base is complemented by an all-round traditional practice. It is structured on a departmental basis. In addition to those departments providing advice and legal services to private clients, specialist teams who have extensive experience in commercial and corporate fields work within departments and concentrate on the requirements of clients in those particular fields.

The firm undertakes virtually all types of legal work (except Admiralty). Its particular strengths lie in the building and construction arbitration areas, as well as in company takeovers and commercial conveyancing. In the non-commercial sphere it is well known for its large criminal practice. The firm is also building a sound reputation in the fields of tax planning and pension scheme work.

Apart from the usual commercial areas of work (including debt collection, franchising, planning, intellectual property, and estate development), the firm provides a full range of services for the private client (including personal injury, employment, family, and wills). Legal aid work is accepted.

Overall, Greenwoods is best perceived as an expanding provincial practice which maintains traditional standards while keeping abreast of modern changes within the legal profession. Locally, it is seen as 'the biggest', but still has a personal approach; most local firms regard Greenwoods as the leader and innovator and tend to follow where it leads. Brochures detailing the specialist and general services offered are available on request.

Greenwoods

Halliwell Landau

ST JAMES'S COURT
BROWN STREET
MANCHESTER
M2 2JF
Phone: 061 835 3003

Fax: 061 835 2994
DX: 14317 MANCHESTER-1
Telex: 666794
Senior Partner: Mr CR Garston
Number of Partners: 15
Total Staff: 80

Hammond Suddards

EMPIRE HOUSE
10 PICCADILLY
BRADFORD
WEST YORKSHIRE BD1 3LR
Phone: 0274 734700

Fax: 0274 737547
DX: 11720 BRADFORD
Telex: 517201 **Other offices:** 2
Senior Partner: Mr Alan Bottomley
Number of Partners: 27
Total Staff: 315

Harris & Cartwright

14 BATH ROAD
SLOUGH
BERKSHIRE
SL1 3SN
Phone: 0753 29944

Fax: 0753 691588
DX: 3405 SLOUGH
Telex: none **Other offices:** 4
Senior Partner: Mr JL Bayford
Number of Partners: 10
Total Staff: 52

Harrison Clark

5 DEANSWAY
WORCESTER
WR1 2JG

Phone: 0905 612001

Fax: 0905 20433
DX: 16260 WORCESTER
Telex: none
Senior Partner: Mr AD Clark
Number of Partners: 7
Total Staff: 60

Hamlin Slowe *see full-page profile*
Harbottle & Lewis *see full-page profile*

Hamlin Slowe

ROXBURGHE HOUSE
273-287 REGENT STREET
LONDON
W1A 4SQ
Phone: 01 629 1209

Fax: 01 491 2259
DX: 230 LONDON CHANCERY LANE WC2
Telex: 261337
Senior Partner: Mr AE Hoffman
Number of Partners: 14
Total Staff: 75

This medium sized London practice is property orientated with a substantial commercial client base.

The firm: Founded in 1906, the firm practised under the name of AE Hamlin & Co until 1984, when it amalgamated with Slowes.

The firm is always looking for talented qualified staff, including legal executives. There are likely to be four new positions in 1989; two in commercial property, and one each in litigation and company/commercial. Enquiries to Mr RJ Knight.

There will be seven vacancies for articled clerks in 1989 and four in 1990. A 2(2) degree, not necessarily in law, is the minimum requirement. Apply (with CV and referees) to Ms TD Gane preferably one year in advance, but late applications are considered.

Types of work undertaken: The firm has five principal departments, namely commercial property, litigation, company/commercial, entertainment and media, and residential property. The client base is wide and includes 13 PLC clients and six major private companies which are household names. Particular areas of expertise are property development, copyright and intellectual property litigation, entertainment and media law, and landlord/tenant litigation.

The property department handles all aspects of property transactions for large and small corporate clients and has considerable expertise in development and finance agreements, town and country planning, compulsory purchase, landlord/tenant law, and property taxation. It has been involved in a number of major developments and has helped to remould London's skyline.

All manner of litigation is handled by the firm. The copyright anti-piracy division is augmented by strong divisions in landlord and tenant and secured lending as well as matrimonial and general commercial litigation of a high-quality nature.

The company/commercial department has a broad commercial base and provides specialist advice on taxation issues. It has worked in an international context for many years, and acts as sole UK legal representative for a number of international clients.

The entertainment and media department provides advice on copyright, recording, publishing, management, sponsorship, film and television contracts, and all other aspects of entertainment and media law.

The lawyers in the private client department work closely with other professionals, including accountants, brokers and other advisers, in meeting a client's needs.

The firm perceives itself as a medium sized practice with a strong client base which offers a high standard of legal expertise and good rewards for staff.

Harbottle & Lewis

HANOVER HOUSE
14 HANOVER SQUARE
LONDON
W1R 0BE
Phone: 01 629 7633

Fax: 01 493 0451
DX: 44617 MAYFAIR W1
Telex: 22233
Senior Partner: G Laurence Harbottle
Number of Partners: 13
Total Staff: 91

This central London firm is pre—eminent in the entertainment industry and combines this work with strong commercial and property practices.

The firm: Founded by its present senior partner in 1954, Harbottle & Lewis initially acted almost exclusively for the entertainment industry, but has subsequently branched out into the wider commercial field. Steady expansion has forced the firm to move to larger premises in Hanover Square.

The firm is constantly looking for intelligent newly qualified solicitors and expects to recruit about six in 1989.

There are two vacancies annually for articled clerks. Applicants should have a good degree and pass the Law Society Finals first time. Apply by handwritten letter (plus CV) to G Laurence Harbottle.

Types of work undertaken: Generally recognised as a leader in the entertainment field, Harbottle & Lewis also has an extensive general commercial practice. Clients range from individuals to medium sized quoted companies; probably just under half come from the entertainment industry and the remainder from the general commercial environment and the fields of commercial property development and investment.

The firm is very well known for music, film and television work; the protection of copy-rights and other intellectual property rights, by agreement and through litigation when necessary; and commercial property work.

There are four departments, namely commercial and general, music, property, and litigation. The commercial and general department handles copyright and intellectual property, film, theatre, television, books and periodical publishing. The department also deals with the firm's considerable commercial work, including mergers and takeovers, finance, flotations, joint ventures and management buy-outs, employment, aviation law, immigration, charities, taxation and pensions.

The music department concentrates on recording contracts, video agreements, merchandising and sponsorship agreements, licensing, and tour and distribution agreements.

Much of the work of the litigation department is concerned with contract and copyright disputes, and defamation.

The property department handles both commercial and domestic conveyancing for the firm's entertainment and general clients. The department also acts for substantial clients developing and investing in shopping centres, business parks and other commercial property and handles Landlord and Tenant Act and Town and Country Planning work.

Overall, Harbottle & Lewis perceives itself as a firm of 100 per cent integrity which offers its clients a first-class personal service.

Hart Brown & Co

68 WOODBRIDGE ROAD
GUILDFORD
SURREY
GU1 4RE

Phone: 0483 68267

Fax: 0483 39313
DX: 2403 GUILDFORD
Telex: 859420 **Other offices:** 5
Senior Partner: Mr AK Preskett
Number of Partners: 15
Total Staff: 115

Hawkins Russell Jones

7-8 PORTMILL LANE
HITCHIN
HERTFORDSHIRE
SG5 1AS

Phone: 0462 51411

Fax: 0462 53169
DX: 7100 HITCHIN
Telex: none **Other offices:** 6
Senior Partner: Mr TN Heffron
Number of Partners: 21
Total Staff: 130

Hawley & Rodgers

19-23 GRANBY STREET
LOUGHBOROUGH
LEICESTERSHIRE
LE11 3DY

Phone: 0509 230333

Fax: 0509 239390
DX: 19602 LOUGHBOROUGH
Telex: 341995 **Other offices:** 2
Senior Partner: Mr CJ Coverley
Number of Partners: 10
Total Staff: 63

Hay & Kilner

33 GREY STREET
NEWCASTLE UPON TYNE
NE1 6EH

Phone: 091 232 8345

Fax: 091 261 7704
DX: 61019 NEWCASTLE UPON TYNE
Telex: 537879 **Other offices:** 3
Senior Partner: Mr JK Kilner
Number of Partners: 13
Total Staff: 67

Harvey Ingram Stone & Simpson *see full-page profile*

Harvey Ingram Stone & Simpson

20 NEW WALK
LEICESTER
LE1 6TX

Phone: 0533 545454

Fax: 0533 554559
DX: 10822 LEICESTER-1
Telex: 341622 **Other offices:** 2
Senior Partner: John Simpson
Number of Partners: 20
Total Staff: 110

This newly formed firm, one of the largest in the Midlands, has a company/commercial base combined with a substantial private client practice.

The firm: Harvey Ingram Stone & Simpson was formed in 1988 as a result of the amal gamation of two of the leading and long-established commercial firms in Leicester, Harvey Ingram and Stone & Simpson, the original founders of which began practice in Leicester over 200 years ago.

Continued expansion means that the firm is looking for a number of assistant solicitors in the next year. In particular, there are vacancies in property, litigation, and company/commercial. Enquiries should be sent to Roger Bowder.

In addition, the firm recruits four articled clerks every year. The minimum educational requirement is a 2(2) degree (2(1) preferred). Prospects after qualification are good: many of the present partners were articled with the pre-merger firms. Apply by handwritten letter (with CV and names of two referees) to Mr D Williams two years in advance.

Other offices: Oadby, Wigston.

Agency work: The firm accepts agency work from other solicitors: contact Mr D Williams (corporate); Mr PA Danby (property); and Mr JA Holland (probate and trust).

Types of work undertaken: The firm's base is company and commercial work of all types, but it also has a well-established private client base. The firm has four main departments, company/commercial, property, litigation, and probate and trust.

Particular areas of expertise are company/commercial (including acquisition, disposal, refinancing and restructuring of corporate and other businesses, and corporate insolvency); property (including Housing Corporation work, commercial leases, sales and purchases for development and licensed premises); litigation (personal injury, medical negligence, employment, licensing law, insolvency and matrimonial work); and probate and trust (especially tax planning).

As would be expected in such a wide-ranging commercial practice, all types of public and private company work and other commercial matters are handled, and the property department covers all aspects of transactions in land for both commercial and private clients. The litigation department is naturally diverse and encompasses commercial and general litigation, family matters and employment law.

Overall, this firm sees itself as an efficient leading commercial practice in the Midlands. A brochure is available on request.

HARVEY INGRAM
STONE & SIMPSON

Heald Nickinson

48 BEDFORD SQUARE
LONDON
WC1B 3DS

Phone: 01 636 8010

Fax: 01 580 7521
DX: 35700 BLOOMSBURY WC1
Telex: 268003 **Other offices:** 2
Senior Partner: Mr J Black
Number of Partners: 20
Total Staff: 157

Heckford Norton

41 HIGH STREET
ROYSTON
HERTFORDSHIRE
SG8 9AD

Phone: 0763 241144

Fax: 0763 247019
DX: 37301 ROYSTON
Telex: 265871 **Other offices:** 4
Senior Partner: Mr DJD Ritchie
Number of Partners: 15
Total Staff: 84

Hegarty & Co

16 LINCOLN ROAD
PETERBOROUGH
CAMBRIDGESHIRE
PE1 2RG

Phone: 0733 46333

Fax: 0733 62338
DX: 16850 PETERBOROUGH-2
Telex: 265871 **Other offices:** 3
Senior Partner: Mr RJ Hegarty
Number of Partners: 9
Total Staff: 87

Hepherd Winstanley & Pugh

22 KINGS PARK ROAD
SOUTHAMPTON
HAMPSHIRE
SO9 2US

Phone: 0703 632211

Fax: 0703 227469
DX: 38517 SOUTHAMPTON-3
Telex: none
Senior Partner: Mr TN MacKean
Number of Partners: 11
Total Staff: 73

Hempsons *see full-page profile*

Hempsons

33 HENRIETTA STREET
COVENT GARDEN
LONDON
WC2E 8NH
Phone: 01 836 0011

Fax: 01 836 2783
DX: 240 LONDON CHANCERY LANE WC2
Telex: 22502
Senior Partner: Mr RH James
Number of Partners: 16
Total Staff: 100

Best known for its long-established medical and dental negligence work, Hempsons also provides a full range of legal services to corporate and private clients alike.

The firm: Hempsons was founded in 1890 as a family firm. The emphasis has shifted to litigation, and the firm continues to practise from the offices where it moved in 1912, in order to be close to the Royal Courts of Justice and the Temple. The firm has expanded over the years — the number of partners has doubled since 1978 and there has been a marked increase in qualified staff over the last few years. It also includes a strong non-contentious practice.

The firm is always interested in considering suitable assistant solicitors, particularly those with experience and/or interest in the areas of medical negligence, defamation and commercial conveyancing. Enquiries to Mr JJ Taylor.

In addition, two or three articled clerks are recruited annually. Although a good academic standard is expected, each applicant is considered entirely on merit. Apply by hand-written letter (with CV and names of referees) two years in advance to Ms AS Green.

Types of work undertaken: Hempsons has a considerable reputation for its professional negligence work, particularly handling claims for medical and dental practitioners, and representing professionals before disciplinary and other tribunals.

Indeed, litigation is the firm's largest department encompassing building disputes and employment law, defamation actions, partnership disputes, matrimonial and criminal work.

There is also a thriving non-contentious practice, which includes particular expertise in all areas of professional practice, especially partnerships. An expanding property department handles commercial acquisitions, developments and disposals; commercial leases; finance; joint venture agreements, and building contracts, as well as commercial and domestic conveyancing.

As well as the medical and dental professions, clients include national charitable institutions and professional bodies, privately owned businesses and partnerships, insurance companies, and a number of longstanding corporate clients. In addition, Hempsons has a strong private client base, which is provided with the full range of legal services, including tax planning advice, wills and probate, and matrimonial matters.

Overall, Hempsons sees itself as a leading medical negligence practice. In addition, it has an expanding commercial property department and is able to provide a full range of legal services to its corporate and private clients. A brochure giving full details of the practice is available on request.

HEMPSONS

Hepworth & Chadwick

CLOTH HALL COURT
INFIRMARY STREET
LEEDS
LS1 2JB
Phone: 0532 430391

Fax: 0532 456188
DX: 12027 LEEDS-1
Telex: 557917
Senior Partner: Mr JD Ward
Number of Partners: 20
Total Staff: 203

One of the leading firms in the north of England, Hepworth & Chadwick is predominantly a commercial practice with a significant private client base.

The firm: Established in 1906, Hepworth & Chadwick has expanded — through internal growth, not amalgamation — from a two-partner practice into one of the biggest provincial firms. Indeed, the firm has grown by 50 per cent within the last 12 months. It is organised into departments.

There is a continuing need for high calibre assistant solicitors in every department, especially for corporate lawyers and town planners. Address enquiries to the head of the department involved.

At present eight articled clerks are recruited annually. A 2(1) degree, not necessarily in law, is preferred, although the firm emphasises that it judges applicants on individual merits. Long-term prospects are good: about half the present partners served articles with the firm. Apply by handwritten letter (with CV and names of referees) as early as possible to Mr JP Margerison.

Agency work: The firm accepts work of a commercial civil nature from other solicitors; contact Mr R Chapman.

Types of work undertaken: This is a broadly based commercial practice, dealing mainly with the requirements of large and medium sized PLC clients. The firm is divided into six departments, namely company, litigation, property, tax and trust, insolvency, and debt collection.

The company department is the largest in the firm, covering the full range of a business's requirements, and is well known for its consumer credit, franchising and other intellectual property work.

On the litigation side, the firm has gained a high reputation for large litigation and arbitration cases, particularly in intellectual property matters and construction law disputes. Personal injury cases (usually for insurance companies) and a certain amount of divorce and other matrimonial disputes are also undertaken. The firm's employment law team, usually acting for employers with union problems, is renowned.

There is a strong property department and the firm believes its retail property section is particularly skilled. Much of the work undertaken is on behalf of development clients. The extent of Hepworth & Chadwick's tax and pension expertise is very unusual for a non-City firm. In addition, the firm has substantial, fully computerised debt collection and insolvency departments, for both corporate and private clients.

In brief, Hepworth & Chadwick sees itself as a large, high quality commercial firm which is going from strength to strength.

Hepworth & Chadwick

Herbert Wilkes & Company

41 CHURCH STREET
BIRMINGHAM
B3 2RT

Phone: 021 233 4333

Fax: 021 233 4546
DX: 13047 BIRMINGHAM-1
Telex: 334691 **Other offices:** 2
Senior Partner: Mr CJ Turner
Number of Partners: 8
Total Staff: 55

Heringtons

23 CAMBRIDGE ROAD
HASTINGS
EAST SUSSEX
TN34 1DN

Phone: 0424 434192

Fax: 0424 444824
DX: 7006 HASTINGS
Telex: 95675 **Other offices:** 3
Senior Partner: Mr DW Chivers
Number of Partners: 11
Total Staff: 75

Hewitt Woollacott & Chown

LONDON STONE HOUSE
111 CANNON STREET
LONDON
EC4N 5AR

Phone: 01 623 7001

Fax: 01 929 3719
DX: 535 LONDON CITY EC3
Telex: 885400 **Other offices:** 2
Senior Partner: Mr RW Reiss
Number of Partners: 15
Total Staff: 105

Higgs & Sons

BLYTHE HOUSE
134 HIGH STREET
BRIERLEY HILL
WEST MIDLANDS DY5 3BG

Phone: 0384 76411

Fax: 0384 263339
DX: 22751 BRIERLEY HILL
Telex: none **Other offices:** 3
Senior Partner: Mr DH Higgs
Number of Partners: 14
Total Staff: 84

Herbert Smith *see full-page profile*
Hextall Erskine & Co *see full-page profile*

Herbert Smith

WATLING HOUSE
35 CANNON STREET
LONDON
EC4M 5SD

Phone: 01 489 8000

Fax: 01 329 0426
DX: 28 LONDON CHANCERY LANE WC2
Telex: 886633 **Other offices:** 4
Senior Partner: John A Rowson
Number of Partners: 74
Total Staff: 729

Herbert Smith is one of the leading commercial firms in the country. It is a large City firm with a substantial international practice. The firm acts for many major UK multinational corporations and foreign governments as well as smaller companies and individuals in a wide range of commercial matters.

The firm: Founded in 1882 by Norman Herbert Smith, the firm became strong, particularly in the fields of mining and commodities, acting for two of the greatest South African mining and finance houses. Despite obvious success and a move to larger premises in London Wall, the firm remained a one-partner practice until the end of World War I. At this point there was a merger with another one-partner practice, Edgar Oliver Goss, and at the same time two assistant solicitors were admitted as partners.

In 1923 the firm amalgamated with Francis and Johnson, an old-established City firm said to have had its origins in the eighteenth century. Francis and Johnson brought with it an important practice with a variety of City and private clients.

The end of World War II marked the beginning of modern times and heralded a remarkable and sustained growth for the firm. In 1958 there was a further amalgamation with Hardman, Phillips and Mann which brought to the new firm a unique practice in commercial litigation and a record of academic publications. Finally, in 1963, the firm amalgamated with Minet, May and Co, an old-established firm, which introduced many important Scottish clients.

More recently the substantial growth of the firm has come from within rather than through mergers. Today the firm has been transformed from one with a handful of partners to one with some 74 partners and over 300 other lawyers engaged in most fields of legal work.

The lawyer/client relationship remains of vital importance, however, and each client has a partner appointed to him to oversee all his legal requirements. The latest technology is used to facilitate the retrieval and storage of information, and the firm is actively involved in the development of the law through the writing and editing of articles and textbooks and through participation in the affairs of The Law Society, The City of London Law Society, and overseas international law associations.

The firm attributes its success to the outstanding flair and ability of its originators and subsequent partners, and for the future seeks men and women whose abilities match those of their predecessors.

In 1989 the firm expects to recruit approximately 43 assistant solicitors. Well-qualified solicitors with some experience of commercial work are sought to expand banking, commercial property, intellectual property and construction law work. Enquiries to Mr PH Scott.

In addition, the firm will recruit over 50

articled clerks in 1989. The minimum academic requirement is a 2(1) degree, not necessarily in law. Candidates are expected to show intelligence, a constructive approach, common sense and the ability and confidence to accept responsibility. Long term prospects are excellent: virtually all articled clerks stay on after qualifying and most of the present partners took articles with the the firm. Apply by handwritten letter (with CV and name of academic referee) between July and October to Stephen Barnard.

Other offices: Hong Kong, New York, Paris, Brussels (to open Spring 1989).

Types of work undertaken: The London practice is divided into four main departments, namely company, litigation, property, and private client/trust.

Well known as one of the top company and commercial firms in the City, Herbert Smith's company lawyers offer substantial expertise in the increasingly complex and varied areas of commercial and corporate activity. These lawyers are in tune with the commercial and financial markets and can provide a speedy, innovative and comprehensive range of services. Where necessary, a partner will co-operate and lead a team drawn from throughout the department to provide the specific expertise and experience required.

Areas of activity include corporate finance; Stock Exchange; mergers and takeovers; venture capital and management buy-outs; banking and international finance; EEC, anti-trust and competition; taxation; insolvency; investment funds; and employee benefits.

The litigation department has experience before every type of court and tribunal. In London, clients are represented before all Divisions of the High Court, the Court of Appeal and before the House of Lords. The firm also acts in international arbitrations and represents clients in the European Court of Justice and the International Court of Justice. Areas of activity include commercial disputes; international commercial arbitrations; insurance and reinsurance; banking and finance; anti-trust, competition and anti-dumping; intellectual property; property; construction and defamation.

The property department undertakes all types of legal work relating to land and buildings in England and Wales. Clients range from the private individual to the largest of multi- national corporations and institutions. Areas of activity include institutional investments; planning and compensation; development projects; and investigations and reports.

The private client/trust department advises individual and corporate clients and also specialises in all aspects of trust law and in the planning of clients' personal financial affairs. Areas of activity include tax and estate planning; Chancery litigation; probate and administration of estates; charities; and nationality and work permits.

Overall, Herbert Smith is generally acknowledged as one of the top six practices in the country and a leading firm in the City of London. Herbert Smith offers clients an international service with representation of their interests in the principal commercial centres of the world. Brochures describing all the services offered by the firm are available to clients on request.

Herbert Smith

Hextall Erskine & Co

79 ECCLESTON SQUARE
LONDON
SW1V 1PW

Phone: 01 828 7011

Fax: 01 828 8341
DX: 244 LONDON CHANCERY LANE WC2
Telex: 919135 **Other offices:** 1
Senior Partner: Grahame W Davis
Number of Partners: 15
Total Staff: 103

This central London firm is one of the leading litigation practices, and offers the full range of commercial and private client services.

The firm: Hextall Erskine & Co dates back almost 100 years to a practice established by John and George Hextall. By 1949, when the firm amalgamated with Erskine & Co, it had developed strong commercial, conveyancing and trust practices for corporate and private clients. In the mid-1950s the firm was retained by a leading insurance company to defend employers' liability cases and, within a decade, the practice had become one of London's leading litigation practices, a position it has since consolidated. As part of a major reorganisation currently taking place, the firm will be moving to 26-30 Leman Street, London E1, in the Spring of 1989.

There is an urgent need for qualified staff, and the firm is looking for three or four assistant solicitors in the litigation and commercial departments. Enquiries should be addressed to Nigel Smith (52-54 Leadenhall Street, EC3A 2AP).

In addition, four articled clerks are recruited annually. Long-term prospects are excellent: two-thirds of the present partners served articles with the firm. Apply by handwritten letter (with CV and names of referees) to Stuart White.

Other offices: London.

Agency work: The firm accepts work from established professional clients.

Types of work undertaken: Hextall Erskine & Co is organised into departments, namely litigation, commercial and property. The firm believes in consolidating its areas of expertise. One of the most notable is litigation, especially professional indemnity, building, insurance-related and personal injury claims. Litigation clients include leading UK composite insurers, foreign-based insurance companies, Lloyd's syndicates and other commercial clients.

In the company/commercial area, the firm provides a full range of services for both listed companies and private corporate clients, with particular emphasis on acquisitions, mergers, employment law, as well as issues, pension schemes and taxation planning.

There is a strong property department which handles commercial developments, planning applications and landlord and tenant matters, and also the usual conveyancing services for corporate and private clients.

For the private client, the firm provides expert advice on wills, personal tax planning, and trusts and probate matters. In addition, it will consider undertaking criminal and matrimonial work for established clients.

Overall, the firm sees itself as competent and efficient. It is resolute in advancing clients' interests yet reasonable to deal with.

HEXTALL, ERSKINE & CO.

Hill Bailey

15-16 BEDFORD ROW
LONDON
WC1R 4BX

Phone: 01 404 4114

Fax: 01 831 1695
DX: 361 LONDON CHANCERY LANE WC2
Telex: 21882 **Other offices:** 3
Senior Partner: Mr T Bailey
Number of Partners: 11
Total Staff: 102

This central London firm is essentially commercially oriented and is well known in the litigation, consumer credit and security, finance, banking, and mortgage lending sectors.

The firm: Founded in 1978 by T Bailey and R Hill, both formerly in-house finance company lawyers. The client base in the financial sector grew rapidly and has since expanded into the company, commercial, insolvency, conveyancing and litigation fields. The partners include experts in consumer credit. The firm is organised into departments.

This expanding firm is always seeking high-calibre solicitors and legal executives for all departments. Enquiries to Mr RJ Carter.

There are vacancies for three articled clerks annually. Candidates should have good general law qualifications. Prospects after qualifying are excellent. Applications by handwritten letter (plus CV and names of referees) should be addressed to Mr RJ Carter.

Other offices: Bromley, Reading, West Wickham.

Agency work: Hill Bailey undertakes a considerable amount of litigation work for other solicitors, as well as other types of agency work. Contact Michael Rapoport.

Types of work undertaken: The London office principally handles commercially oriented work with a strong bias in the finance, banking, consumer credit and financial services sectors. The litigation department is particularly strong and covers commercial as well as matrimonial matters. The conveyancing department handles all types of commercial and residential transactions, and lending and security work. The London office has a department especially established to handle mortgage possession work. In addition, there is an expanding wills, probate and trusts department.

The Bromley and West Wickham offices are more traditional, offering the type of general legal services needed in local centres.

Particular areas of expertise are consumer credit and security, finance, banking and mortgage lending; High Court litigation specialising in building, engineering and fraud-based disputes. The firm also undertakes intellectual property and immigration matters.

Certain of the partners are involved in the associated firm of Hill Bailey & Partners in Reading, which is engaged principally in mortgage processing.

Overall, Hill Bailey perceives itself as a well-run professional practice which has carved out a very distinct niche in the commercial law field. Brochure available.

Hill Bailey

Hill Dickinson & Co

IRONGATE HOUSE
DUKE'S PLACE
LONDON
EC3A 7LP
Phone: 01 283 9033

Fax: 01 283 1144
DX: 550 LONDON CITY EC3
Telex: 888470 **Other offices:** Liverpool
Chairman: Roy Hill
Number of Partners: 24
Total Staff: 164

Liverpool and London based, Hill Dickinson is a commercially oriented firm with large shipping and insurance practices.

The firm: Founded in 1810 to serve the needs of the shipping community in Liverpool, Hill Dickinson opened a London office in 1929 in order to develop its general commercial base. At the same time, the firm steadily expanded its shipping and insurance markets at home and overseas. Today, the firm is regarded as one of the foremost maritime practices in the country.

In 1989 the firm expects to recruit at least eight assistant solicitors, especially for shipping and insurance, employment and industrial relations, company/commercial including commercial conveyancing, personal injury and general litigation. Apply to Nicholas Moore, London; David Wareing, Liverpool.

There are normally eight vacancies for articled clerks every year. Candidates are judged on individual merits. Apply by handwritten letter (with CV) to Malcolm Taylor, London; Richard Martindale, Liverpool.

Other offices: Equity & Law House, 47 Castle Street, Liverpool L2 9UB (051 227 3151) which has equal status with London.

Agency work: The firm accepts complex work from other solicitors; contact David Wareing, Liverpool; David Taylor, London.

Types of work undertaken: Hill Dickinson's practice is essentially commercial. As befits its origins, shipping and insurance account for over half of its business, with a broad client base covering shipowners, their P & I clubs, and insurers and underwriters, as well as major international corporations, start-up businesses and private individuals.

The firm is also well known for its company/commercial work, particularly BES investment, finance and pensions and commercial conveyancing (mostly for institutional investors), building and civil engineering work. The firm is rapidly expanding its personal injury work, especially for shipowners and insurers, and its industrial relations employment work, for shipowners and, increasingly, for land-based employers.

Hill Dickinson places particular emphasis on identifying and pursuing clients' commercial objectives and establishing close client-partner relationships.

This is a progressive and dynamic firm, providing a broad spread of facilities to both national and international clients through its dual offices. The firm has a reputation for keeping clients' commercial interests uppermost and as an effective litigator. In short, this long-established firm sees itself as possessing an appropriate and modern approach to commercial legal problems and their resolution.

Hobson Audley

7 PILGRIM STREET
LONDON
EC4V 6DR

Phone: 01 248 2299

Fax: 01 248 0672
DX: 401 LONDON CHANCERY LANE WC2
Telex: 297005
Senior Partner: Michael Bernstein
Number of Partners: 10
Total Staff: 60

Hobson Audley is a recently established City firm which concentrates on servicing commercial clients.

The firm: Founded in 1983, the firm handles all areas of business law in the UK and overseas. In the last financial year, the company/commercial department contributed 38 per cent of fees, litigation 34 per cent and commercial conveyancing 28 per cent.

Hobson Audley requires six solicitors in 1989 and is anxious to interview at all levels. Although it prefers City-trained applicants, solicitors from provincial practices will be considered.

The firm also recruits three to four articled clerks per year. Send applications by handwritten letter (plus CV and name of referee) to Andrew Joyce.

Types of work undertaken: The client base of the practice includes public and private companies involved in manufacturing, marketing services, venture capital, publishing, the financial services and securities industry, oil and gas, and banks and other lending institutions.

The company/commercial department has considerable experience in setting up new businesses, venture capital, company acquisitions and sales, company reconstructions and amalgamations, insolvency and liquidation. It deals with Stock Exchange work, including the raising of capital and flotations on the Official List, USM and, more recently, Third Market, and also advises on joint ventures, both national and international, the regulation of restrictive trade practices and competition, banking, franchising and intellectual property rights. The department also advises on the regulatory and legal requirements which affect the everyday course of a client's business.

The litigation department deals with commercial disputes of all kinds, including those related to banking, building, employment law, intellectual property, restraints of trade, landlord and tenant, professional negligence and defamation, and also handles air transport licensing. The firm has established links with law firms in many other countries and, depending on the nature of the litigation in question, will assume responsibility for, and co-ordinate, foreign litigation on behalf of clients.

The commercial property department advises on all aspects of industrial and commercial property, handling everything from sales and acquisitions of commercial property, securing commercial mortgages, landlord and tenancy matters, to preparing and presenting planning applications.

This efficient and friendly practice adopts a commercial approach to legal matters seeking to solve them with the minimum of fuss and bother. A brochure for clients is available.

Hobson Audley
······SOLICITORS······

Holman, Fenwick & Willan

MARLOW HOUSE
LLOYDS AVENUE
LONDON
EC3N 3AL
Phone: 01 488 2300

Fax: 01 481 0316
DX: 1069 LONDON CITY EC3
Telex: 8812247 **Other offices:** 2
Senior Partner: Mr WA Bishop
Number of Partners: 51
Total Staff: 274

Holman, Fenwick & Willan is a large City-based firm with offices in Paris and Hong Kong. It has an international reputation as a major commercial and maritime practice.

The firm: Formed in 1883 by Frank Holman, son of a Devonshire shipbuilding and shipowning family, the firm adopted its present name in 1915. At that time, it offered a full range of legal services, particularly to the shipping industry. Holman, Fenwick & Willan has continued to expand in its traditional areas over the years and has consolidated its commercial sector business, especially since the 1970s. In the last decade the firm has opened two overseas offices and diversified into several other fields of expertise including reinsurance, commodities, commercial property, professional negligence and aviation.

In 1989 Holman, Fenwick & Willan expects to have ten vacancies for assistant solicitors in the company/commercial, commercial property and commercial litigation sectors. Apply to the head of personnel, Stephen Killinger.

In addition, the firm usually recruits nine articled clerks every year. Candidates who are non-law graduates, particularly those with modern language and technical degrees, are encouraged. Apply by handwritten letter (with CV and names of referees) to Gai Tetlow, articled clerk recruitment partner.

Other offices: Paris, Hong Kong.

Agency work: Work is accepted from other solicitors, particularly from overseas lawyers.

Types of work undertaken: The firm built up a substantial shipping practice in the early years of the century, which has now been extended into all aspects of international trade and transportation. Contentious and non-contentious work is undertaken including Admiralty, commercial litigation, ship finance, insurance and reinsurance, commodities and aviation – particularly route licensing, air finance and litigation.

Holman, Fenwick & Willan's commercial practice also has a high reputation. The work is diverse and is primarily undertaken on behalf of international businesses operating in the UK and for companies seeking advice on corporate law, banking, finance and trade in the UK and overseas.

Commercial property is a growing area of expertise. So, too, is professional negligence which has developed from the firm's extensive insurance work and close contacts with broking and construction professionals. In addition, Holman, Fenwick & Willan has a developing international private client practice.

Overall, the firm is a major international commercial and maritime law firm combining traditional areas of expertise with a dynamic diversification strategy. Brochures are available on request.

HOLMAN, FENWICK & WILLAN

Hooper & Wollen

CARLTON HOUSE
30 THE TERRACE
TORQUAY
DEVON TQ1 1BS
Phone: 0803 213251

Fax: 0803 26871
DX: 59204 TORQUAY-2
Telex: none **Other offices:** 1
Senior Partner: Mr JB James
Number of Partners: 7
Total Staff: 52

Hopkins & Wood

2-3 CURSITOR STREET
LONDON
EC4A 1NE

Phone: 01 404 0475

Fax: 01 430 2358
DX: 146 LONDON CHANCERY LANE WC2
Telex: 299271
Senior Partner: Mr RCB Hopkins
Number of Partners: 8
Total Staff: 60

Horwood & James

7 TEMPLE SQUARE
AYLESBURY
BUCKINGHAMSHIRE
HP20 2QB
Phone: 0296 87361

Fax: 0296 27155
DX: 4102 AYLESBURY
Telex: none **Other offices:** 1
Senior Partner: Mr AH Durrant
Number of Partners: 11
Total Staff: 70

Hunt & Hunt

LAMBOURNE HOUSE
7 WESTERN ROAD
ROMFORD
ESSEX RM1 3LT
Phone: 0708 764433

Fax: 0708 762915
DX: 4606 ROMFORD
Telex: none **Other offices:** 3
Senior Partner: Mr APD Hunt
Number of Partners: 10
Total Staff: 76

Howard Kennedy *see full-page profile*
Howes Percival *see full-page profile*
Hugh James Jones & Jenkins *see full-page profile*

Howard Kennedy

23 HARCOURT HOUSE
19 CAVENDISH SQUARE
LONDON
W1M 9AB

Phone: 01 636 1616

Fax: 01 580 7831
DX: 604 LONDON CHANCERY LANE WC2
Telex: 27169
Senior Partner: Mr RH Glick
Number of Partners: 19
Total Staff: 88

Howard Kennedy's practice, based in the West End of London, is essentially a commercial one, aimed at businesses both large and small, as well as individuals.

The firm: Founded by Harry Howard in 1936, the firm was then situated in the City of London and moved to the West End in 1950. It has grown organically, except for three small acquisitions, and is now primarily commercially orientated. The firm is organised to provide specialist services and is divided into three main departments.

Howard Kennedy expects to recruit two or three assistant solicitors in 1989 for commercial conveyancing and company work. Applicants who are three or four years' qualified and who have experience in similar or City firms are preferred. Enquiries should be addressed to Mr AG Howard, Mr AL Banes or Mr MJ Alpren.

In addition four or five articled clerks are recruited annually. Applications are welcomed from students of law or other disciplines. Prospects after qualification are good and suitable candidates are encouraged to stay on. Applications by handwritten letter (with CV) should be addressed to Mr AL Banes two years in advance.

Agency work: The firm accepts work in its areas of specialisation from other solicitors; contact Alan Howard.

Types of work undertaken: The practice consists of three departments: company/commercial and tax; conveyancing; and litigation. The client base includes public quoted companies, entrepreneurial private companies and individuals engaging in all forms of business activity.

The firm is particularly well known for its expertise in the taxation sphere and in Business Expansion Scheme matters.

The company/commercial and tax department covers the full range of business activities, including partnerships and company incorporation, management buy-outs, quoted company issues and securities, and BES flotations, as well as taxation, planning enquiries and appeals.

The conveyancing department handles all retail, industrial and office premises, advising vendors, purchasers, landlords, tenants, and organisations providing finance. Domestic conveyancing and probate work is carried out within this department, and a specialist team deals with liquor licensing.

All forms of civil and criminal litigation (except Admiralty) are handled by the litigation department, as well as commercial arbitrations, tribunals, and immigration work. Legal aid work is accepted.

Overall, Howard Kennedy perceives itself as a firm of first-rate competence and integrity, which is still small enough to retain a personal – as opposed to a 'factory' – approach.

Howard Kennedy

Howes Percival

OXFORD HOUSE
CLIFTONVILLE
NORTHAMPTON
NN1 5PN
Phone: 0604 230400

Fax: 0604 20956
DX: 12413 NORTHAMPTON-1
Telex: 311445 **Other offices:** 8
Senior Partner: Michael J Percival
Number of Partners: 27
Total Staff: 260

This medium sized Northampton firm offers a comprehensive commercial law service and also has a substantial private client base.

The firm: Howes Percival was founded almost two centuries ago by Richard Howes; the present senior partner is a seventh generation member of the founding family. Commercial organisations form the majority of the client base with the firm having specialist departments.

The firm is likely to recruit between ten and 12 assistant solicitors this year in company/commercial, tax, and commercial property.

In addition, 12 articled clerks are required each year. A 2(2) degree is required, not necessarily in law.

Applications for all vacancies by handwritten letter (plus CV) should be addressed to Peter Thompson.

Other offices: Northampton, London, Suffolk, Cambridge, Crawley, Milton Keynes, Wellingborough, Nottingham. The firm has international connections, both through established links in Europe and the Far East, and through a federation of firms in Los Angeles, Brussels, New York and Gibraltar.

Agency work: Instructions are accepted from other solicitors in all fields of work undertaken by the firm.

Types of work undertaken: Howes Percival is a broad general practice with an emphasis on commercial law. The firm is particularly well known for its tax work for commercial clients and landowners, its agricultural practice, its banking and insolvency expertise, and its employment, building, and engineering work.

Specialist support teams exist for both banking and employment/industrial relations. The company/commercial division undertakes a full range of work and provides advice on trademarks, franchising and distributorship agreements, plus guidance on company secretarial services. All commercial property services are available.

The litigation department handles crime and matrimonial, although the bulk of its work is company/commercial. Personal injury work is undertaken in the Northampton and Nottingham offices.

Other specialist divisions include American Law, Environmental Law and Single Market -1992 (dealing with EEC law and all aspects of the open market). The firm offers the full range of private client services, including tax and family law, and there is a special domestic conveyancing division.

Howes Percival perceives itself as having a tradition of values allied to a modern approach to technology and management. A brochure detailing the services of the practice and specialist leaflets are available on request.

HOWES · PERCIVAL

Hugh James Jones & Jenkins

ARLBEE HOUSE
GREYFRIARS ROAD
CARDIFF
CF1 4QB
Phone: 0222 224871

Fax: 0222 388222
DX: 33000 CARDIFF
Telex: 497018 **Other offices:** 9
Senior Partner: Michael LN Jones
Number of Partners: 24
Total Staff: 215

This Cardiff-based firm is one of the major insurance litigation practices in the UK, with substantial commercial and private client bases.

The firm: Hugh James Jones & Jenkins dates from the early 1960s. In the 70s there was a merger with the Merthyr firm of Martin Evans, which was established at the turn of the century. Since then, a number of branch offices have opened and other practices have been acquired. Traditionally, this was a general practice with a heavy bias towards litigation. In recent years commercial work has increased considerably.

The firm needs about eight to ten assistant solicitors for all areas. Enquiries to Mr MLN Jones or Mr CJ Williams.

In addition, eight to ten articled clerks are recruited every year. A 2(2) degree, preferably in law, is required. Long-term prospects are excellent: the majority of the present partners served articles with the firm. Apply by letter (with CV and names of referees) two years in advance to Miss CW Thomas.

Other offices: Bargoed, Talbot Green, Llanishen, Aberdare, Blackwood, Pontlottyn, Merthyr Tydfil, Treharris, Gurnos (the last three as Martin Evans).

Agency work: All types of work are accepted; contact Miss Phillips.

Types of work undertaken: Clients include a substantial number of large British and international insurers, property developers, together with many local and national professional practices. The firm also has a very substantial housing association clientele, one of the largest in South Wales.

As one of the major insurance litigation practices, the firm has particular expertise in construction law (including arbitrations) and in professional indemnity litigation, as well as personal injury claims (especially for insurers). There is a substantial plaintiff practice at the Merthyr and Bargoed offices.

The firm has a good reputation for insolvency work, both litigious and non-contentious, and a rapidly growing commercial property department, acting for two large national developers. Commercial mortgage work is undertaken for a number of national institutions. The firm also handles the full range of commercial work (including acquisitions and buy-outs) and the usual general solicitor's work (domestic conveyancing, family, crime, employment and probate). Legal aid work is accepted.

In brief, Hugh James Jones & Jenkins sees itself as a large general practice with a considerable reputation for commercial and insurance litigation and developing general commercial and commercial property practices. Brochures describing the work of the firm are available on request.

Hugh James Jones & Jenkins
WITH
Martin Evans
SOLICITORS CYFREITHWYR

Hunt Dickins

LEEDS HOUSE
14 CLUMBER STREET
NOTTINGHAM
NG1 3DS
Phone: 0602 418881

Fax: 0602 411471
DX: 10017 NOTTINGHAM
Telex: 377868
Managing Partner: Jeremy R Allen
Number of Partners: 18
Total Staff: 127

Hunt Dickins is a major regional firm with a predominantly commercial practice and a strong commitment to the private client.

The firm: Hunt Dickins is the result of the 1987 merger of Temple Wallis, a commercially biased six-partner practice formed in 1980, and Hunt Dickins & Willatt, a broadly based firm with heavyweight commercial property expertise formed about 1815. The business is commercially orientated, handling both contentious and non-contentious work, but retains a substantial private client base.

There is a constant need for suitably qualified solicitors, especially in company/commercial, commercial and residential conveyancing, commercial litigation and crime. Enquiries to Mr JR Allen.

Six to eight articled clerks are recruited every year. A degree is required, not necessarily in law. Applications should be made by handwritten letter (with CV) to Mr JR Allen two years ahead.

Agency work: The firm accepts work from other solicitors; contact Mr R Bullock for commercial litigation; Mr GM Bennett for crime; Mr GE Taylor for conveyancing; Mr MJ Davies for matrimonial/family; Mr JR Allen for liquor licensing; or Mr K Marlew for planning.

Types of work undertaken: Hunt Dickins has two divisions, corporate and private client, each subdivided into four departments.

The firm's corporate client base is predominantly in manufacturing industry, but also includes businesses involved in leasing, banking, brewing, computing, engineering and building, exporting and importing, factoring, as well as the motor trade and leisure industry. The commercial conveyancing department has a high reputation, as does the merger, acquisition and management buy-out work of the company/commercial department. There is considerable expertise in town and country planning matters, and a full department dealing with liquor licensing matters for major countrywide clients. Seven partners are specialist advocates; all aspects of corporate-related contentious work are handled, as well as personal injury and medical negligence claims.

Unusually for such a commercially orientated firm, Hunt Dickins has an extensive matrimonial and crime practice, a considerable part of which is legal aid work. Also handled are domestic conveyancing, wills, probate, trusts, and personal financial and tax planning (including agricultural property advice and transfers).

In short, Hunt Dickins sees itself as innovative and professional, offering a fast, efficient, broad-based and comprehensive service to all clients. A brochure detailing the firm's services is available on request.

Hunt · Dickins Solicitors

Hyde Mahon Bridges

33 ELY PLACE
LONDON
EC1N 6TS

Phone: 01 405 9455

Fax: 01 831 6649
DX: 222 LONDON CHANCERY LANE WC2
Telex: 25210
Senior Partner: Mr RE Parslow
Number of Partners: 10
Total Staff: 50

Hyde Mahon Bridges, an old-established medium sized City firm, offers a wide range of legal services to both commercial and private clients, and is a member of the NIS Group.

The firm: Hyde Mahon Bridges was formed by the merger in 1985 of Hyde Mahon & Pascall, established in 1829, and Bridges Sawtell & Adams, which dates back to 1774.

This family-style firm is a founder member of the NIS Group, formed in 1987 by independent solicitors' firms. Membership is by invitation and all the members remain completely independent. There is an inter-firm register of specialists who may be called on for advice or assistance by any member firm. The group also has regular meetings at which subjects of mutual interest are raised and ideas exchanged.

Apart from Hyde Mahon Bridges, the members are: Mellows Richard West & Boag of Reigate, Surrey; Lawrence Spear of Plymouth, Devon; Alms & Young of Taunton and Bridgwater, Somerset; Croftons of Manchester and Sheffield; Senior Calveley & Hardy of Lytham, Lancashire; Bradbury Roberts & Raby of Scunthorpe, South Humberside; Allin & Watts of Bournemouth, Dorset; and Max Engel & Co of Northampton.

The group is aiming to expand membership into areas of England and Wales where there is, as yet, no representation.

Hyde Mahon Bridges normally recruits three articled clerks each year. The firm judges applicants on individual merits as well as on academic achievements. Apply by handwritten letter (with CV and names of two referees) up to two years in advance to Mr AM Heneker.

Agency work: The firm accepts all types of work (except legal aid) from other solicitors; contact Mr CR Sels.

Types of work undertaken: Hyde Mahon Bridges is a broadly based practice, handling a wide range of private and commercial work. The firm has acted for a number of families for generations, and includes small family businesses, private companies and insurance companies among its clients.

The firm is well known for its large debt collection practice, out of which has grown a considerable amount of litigation work. Other particular areas of expertise include trust and probate matters, personal taxation planning, and housing association work.

Overall, Hyde Mahon Bridges sees itself as a firm whose competence and integrity have built up over a very long period of time. It is tenacious in the interests of its clients but, at the same time, will always be fair. With the other members of the NIS Group, the firm is taking a very positive approach to 1992, to meet developments within the EEC.

Iliffes

THE BURY
CHURCH STREET
CHESHAM
BUCKINGHAMSHIRE HP5 1JE
Phone: 0494 778822

Fax: 0494 773951
DX: 50302 CHESHAM
Telex: 837213 **Other offices:** 2
Senior Partner: Mr JCL Sweet
Number of Partners: 15
Total Staff: 83

Ingledew Botterell

MILBURN HOUSE
DEAN STREET
NEWCASTLE
NE1 1NP
Phone: 091 261 1661

Fax: 091 261 8270
DX: 61166 NEWCASTLE UPON TYNE
Telex: 53115
Senior Partner: Mr RL Allison
Number of Partners: 16
Total Staff: 103

Ingledew Brown Bennison & Garrett

INTERNATIONAL HOUSE
26 CREECHURCH LANE
LONDON
EC3A 5AL
Phone: 01 623 8899

Fax: 01 626 3073
DX: 1073 LONDON CITY EC3
Telex: 885420
Senior Partners: Mr JS Allan and
Mr AS Holmes
Number of Partners: 16 **Total Staff:** 73

Ironsides Ray & Vials

ARNCLIFFE HOUSE
9 SPENCER PARADE
NORTHAMPTON
NN1 5AH
Phone: 0604 234800

Fax: 0604 232624
DX: 12402 NORTHAMPTON-1
Telex: 312399 **Other offices:** 6
Senior Partner: Mr A Coles
Number of Partners: 20
Total Staff: 126

Ince & Co *see full-page profile*
Ingham Clegg & Crowther and Laytons *see full-page profile*

Ince & Co

KNOLLYS HOUSE
11 BYWARD STREET
LONDON
EC3R 5EN
Phone: 01 623 2011

Fax: 01 623 3225
DX: 1070 LONDON CITY EC3
Telex: 8955043 **Other offices:** 2
Senior Partner: Mr PJS Griggs
Number of Partners: 34
Total Staff: 181

Ince & Co has a worldwide reputation in maritime and insurance law and a strong commercial law practice.

The firm: Founded in 1869, Ince & Co is a medium sized firm with an international practice in commercial law. The firm's reputation, traditionally based on its maritime and shipping expertise, has now expanded to cover many areas of commercial law. Today Ince & Co handles global cases covering all aspects of commerce and business.

The firm recruits five to ten articled clerks annually. The firm generally looks for a 2(1) degree or better (though not necessarily in law). The firm is not departmentalised: each articled clerk sits at all times with a partner (moving rooms every six months) but is available to be given work from all over the firm. Cases delegated are retained, thus ensuring continuity and a steadily increasing individual case portfolio. Early responsibility is encouraged under close supervision by partners. The vast majority of articled clerks stay on after qualification. Most of the partners served articles with the firm. Apply at least two years in advance by handwritten letter (plus CV, passport-sized photo and names of two referees) to the office manager, John Brice.

Ince & Co is always seeking to recruit assistant solicitors of good ability, particularly litigation specialists.

Other offices: Hong Kong, Beijing.

Agency work: The firm accepts work from other solicitors in all departments.

Types of work undertaken: Ince & Co specialises in litigation relating to all matters of international trade and insurance (both marine and non-marine). Its speciality has always been in insurance and in international transport (by land, sea and air). The firm has one of the leading transportation practices in the world.

It also undertakes banking and corporate work and commercial conveyancing, with a thriving professional indemnity department. The client base is truly international and includes some of the world's largest shipping companies and the London insurance market.

The construction and building disputes expertise of the firm is considerable, and, in addition, Ince & Co covers the full range of company matters from traditional commerce to high technology.

The firm maintains close relations with lawyers in the world's major commercial centres, enabling it to offer clients the most efficient international service.

Ince & Co's practice is firmly based on a combination of clear legal analysis and tenacious, imaginative litigation. A brochure is available on request.

Ingham Clegg & Crowther and Laytons

GUILD CHAMBERS
4 WINCKLEY SQUARE
PRESTON
PR1 3JJ

Phone: 0772 50931

Fax: 0772 23150
DX: 17106 PRESTON-1
Telex: 67375 **Other offices:** 10
Senior Partner: Sir Walter Clegg
Number of Partners: 26
Total Staff: 220

This is a large firm combining a northern practice with a London-based southern operation and offering wide-ranging services to both commercial and private clients.

The firm: Ingham Clegg & Crowther and Laytons was formed as a result of the 1970 merger of the northern firm of Ingham Clegg & Crowther and the London firm of Laytons. The northern side of the firm traces its origins back to the Blackpool office of Charles Ingham, who started his practice in the 1930s. By the late 1940s the partnership had grown and the firm was known as Ingham Clegg & Crowther. Since then the firm has acquired a number of offices in the North West. The southern side still operates under the name of Laytons (see separate entry).

Although the 11 offices are bound together by the common corporate identity of Ingham Clegg & Crowther and Laytons with some centralised services and administration, the firm is unusual in that all the offices maintain substantial administrative autonomy. The Preston office is the main commercial centre and the largest office in terms of staffing and turnover in the North West.

The firm is seeking to recruit qualified solicitors, particularly those with experience of pure company/commercial work. Apply to Mr RA Hartley in Preston for the North West.

Because of the autonomy of the individual offices, the recruitment of articled clerks is on an ad-hoc basis and the number of available vacancies varies between offices. The minimum academic qualification is a 2(2) degree, not necessarily in law. Apply by letter (with CV) two years in advance to Mr RA Hartley.

Other offices: London, Bristol, Hampton Court, Manchester, Blackpool, St Anne's on Sea, Fleetwood, Cleveleys, Knott End, Poulton le Fylde.

Types of work undertaken: This is a broadly based practice, and the firm's size and the considerable co-operation between offices enables specialist abilities to be made available to all commercial and private clients of any office. The firm has considerable experience in all company and commercial work, including formations, mergers and acquisitions, intellectual property, employment law and insolvency. Building contract work is a major area of expertise, especially in Preston and Bristol. Clients include major civil engineering and bulding companies.

As well as commercial law, the firm's work covers commercial and domestic conveyancing, trusts, wills and settlements, taxation, civil and criminal litigation, and matrimonial.

In short, Ingham Clegg & Crowther and Laytons is an expanding firm with an individual and interesting corporate approach, providing wide-ranging legal services to its corporate and private clients.

INGHAM CLEGG & CROWTHER
and LAYTONS

Irwin Mitchell

ST PETER'S HOUSE
HARTSHEAD
SHEFFIELD
S1 2EL
Phone: 0742 739011

Fax: 0742 753306
DX: 10513 SHEFFIELD
Telex: 547367 **Other offices:** 4
Senior Partner: Mr TM Napier
Number of Partners: 23
Total Staff: 180

JE Dell & Loader

22-23 REGENCY SQUARE
BRIGHTON
EAST SUSSEX
BN1 2FS
Phone: 0273 820202

Fax: 0273 202669
DX: 36673 BRIGHTON-2
Telex: none **Other offices:** 4
Senior Partner: Mr LFT Warner
Number of Partners: 6
Total Staff: 55

J Keith Park & Co

CLAUGHTON HOUSE
39 BARROW STREET
ST HELENS
MERSEYSIDE WA10 1RX
Phone: 0744 30933

Fax: 0744 451442
DX: 19451 ST HELENS
Telex: none **Other offices:** 1
Senior Partner: Mr JK Park
Number of Partners: 3
Total Staff: 67

J M Rix and Kay

84 HIGH STREET
HEATHFIELD
EAST SUSSEX
TN21 8JG
Phone: 04352 5211

Fax: 04352 6822
DX: 39100 HEATHFIELD
Telex: none **Other offices:** 3
Senior Partner: Mr BSM Martin
Number of Partners: 9
Total Staff: 68

J & F Anderson WS *see full-page profile*

J & F Anderson WS

48 CASTLE STREET
EDINBURGH
EH2 3LX

Phone: 031 225 3912

Fax: 031 225 2668
Rutland Exchange: 3 EDINBURGH
Telex: none **Other offices:** 1
Senior Partner: Douglas F Stewart WS
Number of Partners: 14
Total Staff: 84

This long-established Edinburgh firm is broadly based with a substantial private client base and an expanding commercial practice.

The firm: Founded almost 200 years ago as a private client/estate practice, J & F Anderson still occupies its original address in the heart of Edinburgh. In the last ten years the firm has undergone rapid and continuing expansion, particularly in the company/commercial and litigation fields, and has opened an office in Haddington. The firm is organised into departments.

The firm is always seeking to recruit able solicitors, and in 1989 expects to have two or three vacancies for domestic conveyancing and commercial work. Address enquiries to the staff partner.

J & F Anderson usually takes on two legal trainees every year. The minimum educational requirement is a law degree. Prospects after qualification are good; nearly half of the present partners served apprenticeships or traineeships with the firm. Apply by letter (with CV and names of referees) in October one year in advance to Lawrence D Marshall.

Other offices: Haddington.

Agency work: The firm accepts work in all its fields of practice from other solicitors; preliminary contacts are Mr AR Watt or Mr JC Drysdale.

Types of work undertaken: This is a broadly based practice with three main departments, namely private client, commercial, and litigation.

The strongly based private client department has particular experience and expertise dealing with agricultural law matters, estate and forestry purchases, and tax planning, and is well known for the quality of its advice to landowners and farmers. In addition, the department handles domestic house purchase and sales, wills, trusts, executries, and investment work.

The work of the commercial department covers commercial conveyancing, leasing, company and corporate matters (including financing), and commercial developments. On the commercial side, the firm is particularly well known for its work in liquidation and sequestration, management buy outs, company sales and planning enquiries.

The firm has special expertise in industrial tribunal work, and the work of the substantial litigation department includes accident claims, traffic cases, matrimonial matters, family law work and arbitrations. In addition, J & F Anderson operates a sophisticated debt recovery service.

Overall, the firm sees itself as a sound, medium sized practice which offers broadly based experience and expertise to its private and commercial clients. A brochure for clients is available on request.

JW Ward & Son

52 BROAD STREET
BRISTOL
BS1 2EP

Phone: 0272 292811

Fax: 0272 290686
DX: 7824 BRISTOL
Telex: none **Other offices:** 14
Senior Partner: Mr MM Thompson
Number of Partners: 18
Total Staff: 149

One of the West Country's leading private client firms, JW Ward & Son has a network of branches throughout the area offering clients a broad range of legal services.

The firm: Founded in 1906, this family firm grew rapidly, especially the conveyancing practice after the Second World War. Other departments and areas of specialisation have been added, and in August 1988 the firm merged with the Bristol firm of Brown & Partners. JW Ward & Son has one of the largest private clienteles in the region.

This expanding firm is always recruiting assistant solicitors and always welcomes applications at any time. Contact the staff partner, Mr JF Johnston.

There are generally three or four vacancies for articled clerks a year. Candidates with a 2(1) degree, not necessarily in law, are preferred. Applications (by handwritten letter, with CV and referees) should be addressed to Mr JF Johnston 18 months in advance.

Other offices: Bristol, College Green, Filton, Staple Hill, Bradley Stoke, Winterbourne, Yate, Axbridge, Bath, Cirencester, Glastonbury, Weston super Mare, Worle, Wotton under Edge.

Agency work: The firm undertakes all types of litigation work for other solicitors; for details contact Mr JF Johnston.

Types of work undertaken: As a result of the merger with Brown & Partners the firm has strengthened its already considerable company/commercial and litigation departments. However the large and long-established private client practice still predominates.

The firm handles all aspects of property law, including building estate development and financing, commercial and residential conveyancing, leaseholds, commercial leases and transfers; commercial law; litigation, covering High Court, county court and magistrates court work and including licensing, crime and accident claims; probate, trust and tax; matrimonial and family problems; and patents and copyright.

The firm is particularly well known for property development, commercial and other conveyancing, trust and charity work, and all types of litigation.

JW Ward & Son places a great deal of emphasis on its branch offices, some of which are the size of a small firm in their own right: the offices are as self-contained as possible, while retaining access to the firm's more specialised services. In this way it can offer a wide-ranging service at the office which is most convenient for the client.

JW Ward & Son perceives itself as a well run, efficient firm which, despite continued expansion, retains its friendly 'family practice' atmosphere.

WITH
BROWN & PARTNERS

Jacksons

7-15 QUEENS SQUARE
MIDDLESBROUGH
CLEVELAND
TS2 1AL
Phone: 0642 244154

Fax: 0642 217050
DX: 60512 MIDDLESBROUGH
Telex: 587213 **Other offices:** 2
Senior Partners: John H Bloom and Brian G Potter
Number of Partners: 14 **Total Staff:** 100

This newly merged, Cleveland-based firm is able to offer its clients the benefit of both an established commercial practice and a substantial private client base.

The firm: Jacksons was formed by the January 1989 merger of the Middlesbrough firm of Jacksons Monk & Rowe and the Stockton-based practice of Cohen Jackson, both of which are over 100 years old and have established commercial practices. Jacksons Monk & Rowe was noted for its considerable personal injury litigation practice, and Cohen Jackson for its large private client base. The newly merged firm, Jacksons, is organised into departments.

This thriving firm is always seeking to recruit high-calibre qualified staff, and in 1989 expects at least seven vacancies for assistant solicitors. Enquiries should be addressed to Keith Varley.

In addition, three to four articled clerks are recruited every year. The minimum educational requirement is a 2(2) degree not necessarily in law. Prospects after qualification are good: at least a quarter of the present partners served articles with the firm. Applications should be by handwritten letter (with CV and names of referees) by 1 April and addressed to Mr N Bosher.

Other offices: Stockton on Tees, Billingham.

Agency work: The firm accepts work from other solicitors; contact Richard Clarke (Middlesbrough) or Robert C Smith (Stockton on Tees).

Types of work undertaken: This is a broadly based practice handling the full range of legal work, with emphasis on commercial work. The two constituent firms both had strong commercial departments and, by combining their experience, Jacksons is able to offer greater specialisation and better service to clients. The firm has particular expertise in company formation, takeovers and reorganisations.

In addition, a thriving civil litigation department deals with high-quality personal injury work, almost exclusively for defendant insurers. The firm is also well known for its experience in industrial tribunal law.

The property department does all types of commercial and residential work, notably commercial leasing and conveyancing for builders.

There is a particularly large private client base for whom a comprehensive range of legal services is available. Jacksons has wide experience and expertise in matrimonial law, as well as in wills, trusts, probate and crime.

Overall, Jacksons sees itself as offering the best service available to the client, while maintaining the highest possible standards of professional integrity.

JACKSONS

James Chapman & Co

CANADA HOUSE
3 CHEPSTOW STREET
MANCHESTER
M1 5ER
Phone: 061 236 7772

Fax: 061 228 3658
DX: 14358 MANCHESTER-1
Telex: none
Senior Partner: Mr JN McKenna
Number of Partners: 12
Total Staff: 53

Janners

22 UPPER BROOK STREET
LONDON
W1Y 2HD

Phone: 01 491 4484

Fax: 01 629 1577
DX: 9001 WEST END W1
Telex: 23776
Senior Partner: Mr JL Freeman
Number of Partners: 13
Total Staff: 60

John Barkers

HAMPTON HOUSE
OLD MARKET PLACE
GRIMSBY
HUMBERSIDE DN31 1JS
Phone: 0472 358686

Fax: 0472 240890
DX: 19201 GRIMSBY-1
Telex: none **Other offices:** 3
Senior Partner: Mr D Spencer
Number of Partners: 8
Total Staff: 58

Judge & Priestley

JUSTIN HOUSE
6 WEST STREET
BROMLEY
KENT BR1 1JN
Phone: 01 290 0333

Fax: 01 464 3332
DX: 5718 BROMLEY
Telex: 8955134 **Other offices:** 2
Senior Partner: Mr VG Judge
Number of Partners: 10
Total Staff: 108

Jaques & Lewis *see full-page profile*
Jeffrey Green & Russell *see full-page profile*
Joynson-Hicks *see full-page profile*

Jaques & Lewis

2 SOUTH SQUARE
GRAY'S INN
LONDON
WC1R 5HR
Phone: 01 242 9755

Fax: 01 405 4464
DX: 83 LONDON CHANCERY LANE WC2
Telex: 27938 **Other offices:** 2
Senior Partner: Mr JB Northam
Number of Partners: 46
Total Staff: 279

This City firm is predominantly a commercial practice acting for clients in all sections of the business community.

The firm: Jaques & Lewis was formed in 1982, the result of the merger of Jaques & Co, and Lewis, Lewis & Co, both long-established firms. The two firms were initially small and traditional, but both expanded substantially after World War II, becoming modern, specialist and departmental commercial firms in the process.

The firm expects to recruit between ten and 20 assistant solicitors within the next 12 months for company/commercial, litigation, and commercial property. Enquiries to the partnership executive.

Between eight and 15 articled clerks are recruited annually. A 2(1) degree is preferred, not necessarily in law. Long-term prospects are good: half the present partners served articles with the firm. Apply on form between July and September to Mr TJ Maloney.

Other offices: St Helier, Jersey; Douglas, Isle of Man.

Agency work: The firm accepts work from overseas and UK solicitors.

Types of work undertaken: Clients include large public and private companies, insurance and financial institutions, pension funds and governments, as well as substantial international clients. There are four principal departments, namely company/commercial, litigation, property and private client.

The firm is particularly well known for its commercial property work, especially that involving commercial developments, from the original site acquisition and planning aspects to building, leasing and funding agreements, and subsequent estate management.

There is a strong emphasis on company/commercial work, including USM and other Stock Exchange flotations, mergers and acquisitions, joint ventures, Yellow Book, EEC, intellectual property, franchising, banking and corporate finance, insolvency, film production, financing and distribution and other entertainment law.

The commercial litigation department deals with all manner of domestic, international, banking, insurance claims, building and engineering disputes. Tax, employment and immigration are also particular areas of expertise. In addition, the firm undertakes private client work where it is substantial, complex or international, and work in this field includes estate and tax planning, and UK and offshore trusts (where the firm has particular experience through its Jersey and Isle of Man offices).

Jaques & Lewis sees itself as a successful commercial firm with a justifiably high reputation for its professional standards.

■ JAQUES & LEWIS

Jeffrey Green & Russell

APOLLO HOUSE
56 NEW BOND STREET
LONDON
W1Y 9DG
Phone: 01 499 7020

FAX: 01 499 2449
DX: 44627 MAYFAIR W1
Telex: 298408
Senior Partner: Jeffrey I Green
Number of Partners: 18
Total Staff: 101

Jeffrey Green & Russell is a medium sized, Mayfair-based commercial firm offering business clients a wide range of services and providing a rapid and constructive response to their increasingly specialised needs. The firm's highly professional and progressive approach includes a firm commitment to developing staff potential and a major investment in sophisticated office technology.

The firm: The origins of the firm lie in Jeffrey Green & Company, founded in 1972, and in Russell and Arnholz, a City firm founded in the last century. The firm handles both national and international work and maintains professional and financial contacts in many countries.

The last few years have seen vigorous growth based on the hard work and dedication of the practising lawyers in the firm, and is not the result of succession or merger. The firm now occupies its own building in New Bond Street.

There is a particularly strong corporate-style management structure, a commitment to high technology and a comprehensive continuing legal education system, all of which have made a significant contribution to the success of the firm.

The partnership itself has a flexible 'points' based equity structure. In addition annual awards are made to partners who are judged by their peers to have achieved outstanding results.

Business clients range from sole traders to large public companies and are immensely varied in their activities: banking, computer software and hardware, music industry, airlines, leisure, franchising, licensing, freight forwarding, insurance, property investment, dealing and development are typical of the breadth and diversity of the client base.

A relatively small amount of private client work is undertaken for selected clients, mostly tax planning for wealthy individuals. Legal aid work is not undertaken.

With a combination of legal expertise and the most modern of technological systems (the firm has commissioned much of its own software), the firm offers efficiency and a determination to excel on behalf of its clients.

In 1989 the firm intends to recruit up to ten high-calibre assistant solicitors to further strengthen the company/commercial, litigation and property departments. Prospects are excellent with a definite career path to partnership. The firm offers special flexibility for women lawyers to encourage them to remain with the firm whilst allowing time for family commitments. All enquiries should be addressed to the managing partner, Clive Whitfield-Jones.

On average, ten articled clerks are recruited each year. Candidates should be intelligent, mature, able and articulate. The firm has a friendly collegiate atmosphere and working relationships are relaxed. Applications should be made by letter (plus CV) and be addressed to David R Judah.

Agency work: Jeffrey Green & Russell accepts work from other solicitors in licensing, franchising, libel, music work and commercial litigation. The firm advises other solicitors on partnership structuring and management matters.

Types of work undertaken: The firm is organised into five departments, namely company/commercial and taxation; property and conveyancing; entertainment (principally for the music industry); litigation; and licensing and leisure.

The firm's structure makes it easy for flexible, cross-disciplinary teams to be assembled rapidly to cope with complex cases or transactions involving many areas of law.

The company/commercial and taxation team provides a broad spectrum of services to the firm's highly diversified commercial client base. Examples of the department's work include mergers, acquisitions, reorganisations, BES flotations, technology licensing, insolvency franchising and international tax structuring.

The firm's property division provides a full range of services to the property industry with particular groups advising a wide range of commercial clients, from retailers to the leisure industry, on the property aspects of their businesses. The work of the property department includes all aspects of investment, management, development and funding, syndication and joint ventures and finance and security documentation.

The entertainment and media team offers a full legal service to the television and music businesses.

The litigation team at Jeffrey Green & Russell handles a wide range of commercial matters from contractual disputes to boardroom struggles. Individual groups also undertake substantial insurance related litigation, debt and insolvency work and employment litigation.

The liquor and gaming licensing team offers a nationwide service and conducts its own advocacy in courts throughout the country, including Scotland and Ireland.

The firm's long-range plans include further substantial growth both in its core business areas and in new specialisations in order to respond to long-term trends in the workplace.

Competition for able lawyers and high-quality work is expected to intensify dramatically and clients will become increasingly sophisticated and transactional in buying legal services.

The firm believes that the future belongs to larger law firms able to provide a full range of specialised services, afford the necessary technology and infrastructure and provide the right working environment and career opportunities to attract able young lawyers.

Overall, Jeffrey Green & Russell perceives itself as a highly professional and competent, progressively managed firm. Growth is anticipated to continue at an unusually rapid rate adding further breadth to its range of services. The firm sees itself as destined to become one of London's largest 50 firms. A brochure and newsletters are available on request.

JEFFREY GREEN & RUSSELL

Joynson-Hicks

10 MALTRAVERS STREET
LONDON
WC2R 3BS

Phone: 01 836 8456

Fax: 01 379 7196
DX: 41 LONDON CHANCERY LANE WC2
Telex: 268014
Senior Partner: Anthony Meredith Lewis
Number of Partners: 27
Total Staff: 161

A large, broadly based practice, Joynson-Hicks handles the full range of legal services for commercial and private clients.

The firm: Founded in 1888, Joynson-Hicks has grown into a substantial and vigorous wide-ranging firm. In recent years, there has been rapid expansion of its strong commercial practice, while retaining private client connections that go back many years. The firm has strong links with foreign lawyers, as well as many foreign-based clients. The firm is organised into four departments.

There is a continuing need for qualified staff, and in 1989 the firm expects to recruit nine assistant solicitors: three each for conveyancing, litigation and commercial. Enquiries to Mr AM Lewis.

In addition, eight articled clerks are recruited every year. A 2(2) degree is required, not necessarily in law. Long-term prospects are good: over half of the present partners served articles with the firm. Apply by handwritten letter (with CV) in July to Mr PE Mitchell.

Types of work undertaken: As one of the major practices the firm handles the full range of business services for a wide range of clients, from national and multinational public companies through to private companies and individuals. There are four main departments: company/commercial, litigation, property and private client.

Company/commercial is the largest area of practice, and indeed the firm is very well known for this work, covering the whole spectrum of corporate and commercial law. Particular areas of expertise are entertainment law, intellectual property and copyright.

The litigation department handles every type of contentious dispute within a wide variety of forums. In addition to general commercial litigation there is a particular emphasis on disputes involving intellectual property, insurance liability claims (including personal injury and medical negligence) and matrimonial work.

The work of the property department encompasses the full range of services relating to commercial property for trading companies, developers, finance institutions, and large and small investors, both national and international. A large number of residential property transactions are also handled.

On the private client side, the department deals with tax planning, drafting of wills, administration of estates, the setting up and administration of trusts, all matters relating to the family, and immigration advice.

In short, Joynson-Hicks provides a high quality of service to a wide range of clients. It perceives itself as being modern in outlook and expanionist minded, while retaining the old-fashioned virtues of trust, integrity and service to clients at the same time.

Keeble Hawson Branson Bramley

OLD CATHEDRAL VICARAGE
7 ST JAMES ROW
SHEFFIELD
S1 1XA
Phone: 0742 722061

Fax: 0742 750243
DX: 10527 SHEFFIELD
Telex: 547727 **Other offices:** 1
Senior Partner: Mr AH Gregory
Number of Partners: 11
Total Staff: 67

Keene Marsland

BOWL COURT HOUSE
225 SHOREDITCH HIGH STREET
LONDON
E1 6PB
Phone: 01 375 1581

Fax: 01 375 0318
DX: 179 LONDON EC3
Telex: none **Other offices:** 6
Senior Partner: Mr DEB Besant
Number of Partners: 18
Total Staff: 84

Kenneth Bush & Co

11 NEW CONDUIT STREET
KINGS LYNN
NORFOLK
PE30 1DG
Phone: 0553 692233

Fax: 0553 767318
DX: 57802 KING'S LYNN
Telex: none **Other offices:** 2
Senior Partner: Mr DW Hume
Number of Partners: 12
Total Staff: 73

Keogh Ritson

GOULD HOUSE
59 CHORLEY NEW ROAD
BOLTON
LANCASHIRE BL1 4QP
Phone: 0204 32611

Fax: 0204 362944
DX: 25851 BOLTON-2
Telex: none **Other offices:** 2
Senior Partner: Mr M Jowett
Number of Partners: 9
Total Staff: 71

Kennedys *see full-page profile*

Kennedys

LONGBOW HOUSE
14-20 CHISWELL STREET
LONDON
EC1Y 4TY
Phone: 01 638 3688

Fax: 01 638 2212
DX: 36607 FINSBURY EC2
Telex: 886120 **Other offices:** 2
Senior Partner: Mr E Lewis
Number of Partners: 16
Total Staff: 100

Kennedys is a City-based commercial practice which is particularly well known for its insurance litigation work.

The firm: Founded by Fred Kennedy at the turn of the century, the present City practice incorporating an insurance department dates from 1966. Expansion has been steady, especially in the insurance and commercial departments.

There is a continuing need for qualified staff, and in 1989 the firm expects to recruit eight to ten solicitors, for commercial conveyancing, company and insurance. Enquiries to the recruitment partner.

In addition, the firm usually recruits four articled clerks every year. Applicants are judged on individual merits. Prospects after qualification are excellent: seven of the present partners served articles with the firm. Apply by handwritten letter (with CV and names of referees) two years in advance to the recruitment partner.

Other offices: Brentwood, Finchley. The firm also has associated offices in Paris, New York, Karachi and Hong Kong.

Agency work: The firm accepts civil litigation work from other solicitors.

Types of work undertaken: This is a commercial practice which acts for a wide range of private and corporate clients, many of whom are internationally based.

Kennedys is one of the major insurance practices, with a very considerable expertise gained over a number of years. A large litigation department handles the whole spectrum of insurance work from product liability, personal injury, professional indemnity (including accountancy and construction) to reinsurance and policy disputes. Other specialist areas covered include employment and shipping.

The firm has a thriving construction law practice, covering building and engineering disputes often with an international element. There is considerable expertise in private international law. The firm has always retained a number of French- and German-speaking lawyers, and several partners have been admitted as solicitors in Hong Kong.

Commercial property is also an important part of the firm's business advising a variety of clients on all aspects of acquisition and building contracts.

The firm has an expanding company/commercial department which deals with all the traditional commercial work.

Overall, Kennedys perceives itself as a resourceful, competitive and expanding all-round commercial practice, with strong insurance links. It has a practical and personal approach to the particular requirements of all of its clients.

Kennedys

Ketchen & Stevens WS

55-57 QUEEN STREET
EDINBURGH
EH2 3PA

Phone: 031 226 4061

Fax: 031 220 1612
Rutland Exchange: 61 EDINBURGH
Telex: 728124 **Other offices:** 8
Senior Partner: Mr Boyd
Number of Partners: 14
Total Staff: 100

Kidd Rapinet

35 WINDSOR ROAD
SLOUGH
BERKSHIRE
SL1 2EB

Phone: 0753 32541

Fax: 0753 820501
DX: 3400 SLOUGH
Telex: 848392 **Other offices:** 6
Senior Partner: Mr GA Lewis
Number of Partners: 27
Total Staff: 147

Kirk Jackson

97 CHORLEY ROAD
SWINTON
MANCHESTER
M27 2AB

Phone: 061 794 0431

Fax: 061 794 4957
DX: 28201 SWINTON
Telex: 665216 **Other offices:** 1
Senior Partner: Mr S Ledrooke
Number of Partners: 7
Total Staff: 65

Kirwan Nicholas Jones

WYNNSTAY HOUSE
51 NEW CHESTER ROAD
WIRRAL
MERSEYSIDE L62 1AA

Phone: 051 644 8899

Fax: 051 645 0465
DX: 28621 NEW FERRY
Telex: none **Other offices:** 5
Senior Partner: Mr DS Kirwan
Number of Partners: 9
Total Staff: 80

Kidd & Spoor *see full-page profile*
Kingsford Dorman & Routh Stacey *see full-page profile*
Kingsley Napley *see full-page profile*

Kidd & Spoor

NORFOLK HOUSE
90 GREY STREET
NEWCASTLE UPON TYNE
NE1 6AG

Phone: 091 232 2020

Fax: 091 232 3372
DX: 61058 NEWCASTLE
Telex: 537226 **Other offices:** 4
Senior Partner: Kenneth Hunt
Number of Partners: 7
Total Staff: 68

This Newcastle-based firm specialises in all aspects of commercial law and has branches throughout the region.

The firm: The practice has been in existence for over 100 years under the Kidd name, and has operated as Kidd & Spoor since 1958 in the coastal area of Tyneside. Originally a broad-based firm providing advice on property, family, matrimonial, criminal and litigation matters, recently Kidd & Spoor has expanded into the city centre of Newcastle and has developed a strong property and commercial business, civil and commercial litigation practice.

Kidd & Spoor is always looking for talented and ambitious solicitors and legal executives, particularly in the company/commercial and civil litigation areas. Apply to Kenneth Hunt.

In addition, the firm recruits four articled clerks annually. The minimum academic requirement is a 2(2) law degree. Apply by handwritten letter (plus CV and referees) to Kenneth Hunt two years before starting articles.

Other offices: Newcastle upon Tyne (second office), Whitley Bay, North Shields, Wallsend.

Agency work: The firm undertakes commercial litigation work for other solicitors; contact Miss DC Harper.

Types of work undertaken: The firm specialises in corporate business, commercial property and commercial and civil litigation. The client base ranges from small family businesses to listed public companies.

The corporate department handles company formation, business start-ups, business planning and consultancy, fund raising, management buy-outs, acquisitions, mergers, and venture and development capital. The commercial department advises mainly on leasehold acquisition and disposal, sale and purchase of commercial property, and lease and tenancy agreements.

The particular expertise of the civil litigation department is plaintiff medical negligence work and contentious matters which are technical in nature. The department also handles major commercial claims ranging from breaches of warranty to non-corporate work arising out of breach of contract or tort, personal injury, and debt/possession work.

The firm sees itself as essentially problem solvers – able to identify, analyse, remedy and implement commercial solutions to commercial problems. It considers itself pro-active rather than reactive with the emphasis very much on creativity. This progressive, market-orientated practice would like to be recognised as acting for developing businesses within the region and as being able to deal with the smallest and newest ventures right through to major PLCs.

KIDD & SPOOR
S · O · L · I · C · I · T · O · R · S

Kingsford Dorman & Routh Stacey

14 OLD SQUARE
LINCOLN'S INN
LONDON
WC2A 3UB

Phone: 01 242 6784

Fax: 01 831 2915
DX: 141 LONDON CHANCERY LANE WC2
Telex: 299052 **Other offices:** 2
Senior Partner: Brian R Harvey
Number of Partners: 16
Total Staff: 82

This medium sized City-based firm has an expanding commercial practice while retaining a substantial private client base.

The firm: Formed as a result of the 1987 merger of two well-established central London firms, the firm was born of the partners' appreciation that the best way to continue providing clients with a progressive and technically skilled service in the modern legal environment was in a medium sized firm with the ability to offer a wide variety of expertise. The firm is organised into departments.

This is an expanding firm with a continuing need to recruit good quality staff. In 1989, it expects to have four or five vacancies for assistant solicitors: two for commercial conveyancing, and one each for residential conveyancing, litigation and company/commercial. Address enquiries to the practice administrator, John Silcox.

The firm recruits three or four articled clerks every year. Candidates should have a sound academic record and achievements of note in other areas. Prospects after qualification are excellent; almost all of the present partners served articles with one of the constituent firms. Apply by handwritten letter (with CV) in the autumn prior to CPEs to the practice administrator.

Other offices: London, Harpenden.

Agency work: The firm accepts High Court litigation and liquor licensing work from other solicitors; contact Charles Rankmore and Robert Edney respectively.

Types of work undertaken: This is a typical City practice with an emphasis on commercial work. There is a wide variety of public, listed and unlisted client companies, including corporations, breweries, insurance companies and retailers.

The firm is particularly strong in commercial property work, where it acts for major retailers, breweries and other PLCs with substantial property interests. Work includes acquisitions, disposals and development projects. There is also a significant residential property practice handling top-quality work.

The firm has a high reputation for its liquor licensing, undertaking work on behalf of the licensed trade throughout the country. It also has particular experience and expertise in High Court litigation, handling a broad range of commercial litigation work, especially commercial disputes, insolvency, defamation, and landlord and tenant. In addition, there is an expanding company/commercial department with extensive experience of company acquisitions, sales, and venture capital agreements.

The firm sees itself as a progressive and expanding practice offering general commercial services and particular areas of expertise.

KINGSFORD DORMAN & ROUTH STACEY

Kingsley Napley

107-115 LONG ACRE
LONDON
WC2E 9PT

Phone: 01 240 2411

Fax: 01 836 5357
DX: 22 LONDON CHANCERY LANE WC2
Telex: 28756
Senior Partner: Sir David Napley
Number of Partners: 12
Total Staff: 82

Kingsley Napley is a broadly based general practice, with a strong commercial and private client list. It is internationally known for its involvement in important cases attracting media interest.

The firm: Founded just before the Second World War by Sir David Napley and Sidney Kingsley, the firm started as a general/commercial practice and over the years has acquired and developed special expertise in complex criminal and civil litigation. In addition, the firm continues to provide a wide range of legal services for both commercial and private clients.

Although a policy of recruiting within the firm exists, at least four solicitors will be needed next year. Enquiries to Mr PB Terzeon.

There are four vacancies for articled clerks every year. Applications by handwritten letter (plus CV and referees) should be made two to three years in advance to Mr PB Terzeon.

Agency work: The firm undertakes work for other solicitors on a private basis in civil litigation and property matters. For details contact David Speker.

Types of work undertaken: Kingsley Napley emphasises the fact that it is a general practice, but one that specialises in dealing with matters of particular complexity and

difficulty in all branches of the law. The client base is wide and varied, ranging from large public companies to 'successful' businesses and individuals.

The firm is particularly well known for its criminal work, as well as all aspects of litigation, commercial law (including advice on joint ventures, partnerships, finance, flotations, rights issues, takeovers, employment, insolvency and liquidation), family, professional misconduct, private client, licensing and extradition.

The firm has a sizeable property department (handling both commercial and residential work) and a substantial matrimonial and family practice (including divorce, child custody, wills and tax planning).

There is a very strong and experienced team with particular expertise in the area of fraud, on both a large and small scale, whose services are available to both the victim and the accused. In addition, the firm is experienced in dealing with civil rights matters and immigration, nationality, extradition and deportation problems. Civil and criminal legal aid work is undertaken. A brochure detailing the firm's services is available on request.

Overall, Kingsley Napley sees itself as a medium sized general practice that is able to act with expertise and integrity in matters ranging from the mundane to the highly complex and varied.

Kingsley Napley

Knight & Sons

31 IRONMARKET
NEWCASTLE UNDER LYME
STAFFORDSHIRE
ST5 1RL
Phone: 0782 619225

Fax: 0782 661118/717260
DX: 20952 NEWCASTLE UNDER LYME
Telex: 367421 **Other offices:** 1
Senior Partner: Mr JE Cheetham
Number of Partners: 11
Total Staff: 80

This medium sized general practice, one of North Staffordshire's leading firms of solicitors, has a broad client base, both commercial and private.

The firm: Knight & Sons was founded in 1767 by John Sparrow and it still occupies offices in the original building in Newcastle under Lyme. The firm built its reputation in the fields of trusts, conveyancing and certain types of commercial work (for example, acting for coal owners and a railway company, as well as for prominent landed families). In the 1950s a deliberate policy began of broadening the client base and diversifying the types of work. Over the last few years the firm has expanded very rapidly (especially on the commercial and litigation sides).

The firm has a significant number of clients nationwide as well as some abroad.

The firm expects to recruit two or three assistant solicitors in 1989, probably for the commercial and/or litigation departments. All enquiries should be addressed to Mr JE Cheetham.

There are three vacancies for articled clerks annually. Candidates who have good degrees (not necessarily in law) are preferred. Applications by handwritten letter (plus CV and referees) should be addressed to Mr DJ Salmon.

Other office: May Bank (as Salmons).

Agency work: Most work undertaken for other solicitors is on litigation matters; contact Mr AC Bolger.

Types of work undertaken: The firm is organised into the following departments: company/commercial, litigation, probate and trusts, conveyancing and family. Knight & Sons is particularly well known for commercial work (including large-scale commercial conveyancing) and is proud of its expertise in the intellectual property and takeover spheres.

The firm also has considerable experience advising on insolvency, and has had a rapid and successful rise in the litigation field (PI commercial and insolvency). In addition, it has specialist expertise in planning work and mining subsidence compensation claims, and strong family and probate/trusts departments.

The firm feels that it is able to provide clients with an all-round service and places great emphasis on interaction between departments. Knight & Sons is unusual for a provincial firm in that it is international in outlook, and can offer clients French, German, Italian, Russian, Si Losi and Ci Nyanja.

This forward-looking firm perceives itself as both progressive and able. It is at the same time able to boast of being honest, straight forward and friendly.

KNIGHT
& SONS

Lace Mawer

KING'S HOUSE
42 KING STREET WEST
MANCHESTER
M3 2NU
Phone: 061 236 2002

Fax: 061 832 7956
DX: 14302 MANCHESTER-1
Telex: 665088 **Other offices:** 1
Senior Partner: David Turner
Number of Partners: 29
Total Staff: 175

A newly formed firm with its roots in the seventeenth century, Lace Mawer is commercially orientated and has one of the leading litigation practices in the country.

The firm: On 1 October 1988, Laces, a Liverpool practice founded in the seventeenth century, and AW Mawer & Co of Manchester, which was established in 1942, merged to form Lace Mawer. Both practices had enjoyed rapid expansion over the last two decades, and the new firm is among the largest provincial firms. There is no head office as such, although Manchester has a slightly larger staff than Liverpool.

The firm is always interested in high quality assistant solicitors in both the commercial and litigation fields; it expects to have ten vacancies in 1989. Enquiries to Louise Booth (Manchester) or John Henthorn (Liverpool).

There are normally ten to 12 articled clerks recruited each year. Applicants should have a good degree, not necessarily in law. Prospects are excellent: over three-quarters of the present partners were articled with the firm. Apply by handwritten letter (with CV) to Louise Booth (Manchester) or John Henthorn (Liverpool).

Other offices: Liverpool.

Agency work: All work (except legal aid and crime) is accepted. Contact Mark Benson (Manchester) or Jacqui Lloyd (Liverpool).

Types of work undertaken: The firm concentrates on company/commercial and European work, and civil litigation, but also has expertise in private client work, especially trust-related tax planning. Among its clients is one of the 'Top 100' public companies, for whom it works almost exclusively.

The firm is well known for its company/commercial work, especially acquisitions and disposals of companies, management buy-outs, intellectual property, computer and service agreements, employment law, contracts and pensions. There is particular expertise in EC competition and intellectual property law. Lace Mawer is one of the few UK firms to have wide practical experience of EC Commission hearings and procedures.

The work of the commercial property department includes commercial leases, sales and purchases and property development.

This is one of the major litigation practices in the country, acting for nearly all the major insurance companies, with particular expertise in civil claims, personal injury, professional negligence and contractual cases, and professional and building disputes.

Lace Mawer is a large, progressive and highly respected provincial firm, with regional, national and European connections. The emphasis of the firm is on both commercial and litigation work.

LACE · MAWER

Lamb Brooks Wills Chandler

VICTORIA HOUSE
39 WINCHESTER STREET
BASINGSTOKE
HAMPSHIRE RG21 1EQ
Phone: 0256 844888

Fax: 0256 840427
DX: 3000 BASINGSTOKE
Telex: none **Other offices:** 1
Senior Partner: Mr GE Twine
Number of Partners: 12
Total Staff: 95

Lamport Bassitt

46 THE AVENUE
SOUTHAMPTON
HAMPSHIRE
SO9 3JB
Phone: 0703 634931

Fax: 0703 222346
DX: 2012 SOUTHAMPTON
Telex: 477231
Senior Partner: Mr GN Lightfoot
Number of Partners: /
Total Staff: 72

Langleys

34 SILVER STREET
LINCOLN
LN2 1ES

Phone: 0522 531461

Fax: 0522 510476
DX: 11010 LINCOLN·1
Telex: none **Other offices:** 3
Senior Partner: Mr JR Morgan
Number of Partners: 7
Total Staff: 98

Lanyon Bowdler

23 SWAN HILL
SHREWSBURY
SHROPSHIRE
SY1 1NN
Phone: 0743 236400

Fax: 0743 54994
DX: 19721 SHREWSBURY
Telex: 35429 **Other offices:** 6
Senior Partner: Mr RJ Kelly
Number of Partners: 17
Total Staff: 137

Larcomes

168 LONDON ROAD
NORTH END
PORTSMOUTH
PO2 9DN

Phone: 0705 661531

Fax: 0705 671043
DX: 42401 PORTSMOUTH NORTH END
Telex: none **Other offices:** 1
Senior Partner: Michael Hackman
Number of Partners: 7
Total Staff: 72

This long-established Portsmouth firm is a general practice with a strong conveyancing base which is now expanding into other areas.

The firm: Larcomes was established in central Portsmouth in 1876 as a general law practice. It has always had a considerable domestic conveyancing practice which, over the years, has continued expanding along with its matrimonial and commercial work. An office was opened at Waterlooville about 40 years ago, and both offices have enjoyed rapid growth in the past few years. From 1962 until 1987 the firm practised under the name of Larcome Winter & Linington. The firm plans further development.

The firm intends to open more branch offices in the near future, and expects to recruit two or three assistant solicitors during 1989 for commercial conveyancing, commercial litigation, domestic conveyancing, probate and matrimonial. Enquiries to Martin Davies.

In addition, the firm normally recruits two articled clerks every year. Applicants are judged on individual merits rather than academic results. Prospects after qualification are good, with one 28-year-old partner appointed in May 1988 and another being appointed later this year. Apply by handwritten letter (with CV and names of referees) to Martin Davies.

Other offices: Waterlooville.

Agency work: Civil and criminal work is accepted from other solicitors; contact Mark Tooley.

Types of work undertaken: The firm has a strong conveyancing practice at its Portsmouth and Waterlooville offices, dealing with considerable volumes of residential and commercial conveyancing; indeed, it is well known for the high standard and speed of this work.

The firm's commercial department carries out a wide range of business for a varied client base which includes a major clearing bank. The volume of commercial and matrimonial work is significant, and the firm is expanding the practice further in these areas, as well as in probate. Larcomes also provides good general civil and criminal litigation advice.

The firm aims to provide an all-round service to clients, whatever their legal needs. As it grows, the firm is becoming more departmentalised.

Overall, Larcomes sees itself as a well-established yet forward-thinking firm, which is fully prepared to tackle the changes and challenges that the future holds without losing its efficient but friendly image or lowering its high professional standards. This is a small but thriving firm which is planning carefully for the future.

LARCOMES

SOLICITORS

Lawford & Co

15 DEVEREUX COURT
STRAND
LONDON
WC2R 3JJ
Phone: 01 353 5099

Fax: 01 353 5355
DX: 148 LONDON CHANCERY LANE WC2
Telex: 892303 **Other offices:** 2
Senior Partner: Mr AJ Hows
Number of Partners: 10
Total Staff: 110

Lawrance, Messer & Co

1 NOBLE STREET
LONDON
EC2V 7BJ

Phone: 01 606 7691

Fax: 01 600 8747
DX: 42607 CHEAPSIDE
Telex: 887344 **Other offices:** 1
Senior Partner: Mr NT Levison
Number of Partners: 13
Total Staff: 84

Lawrence Tucketts

SHANNON COURT
CORN STREET
BRISTOL
AVON BS99 7JZ
Phone: 0272 294861

Fax: 0272 298313
DX: 7830 BRISTOL
Telex: 44742 **Other offices:** 2
Senior Partner: Mr D Williams
Number of Partners: 11
Total Staff: 96

Le Brasseur & Monier-Williams

71 LINCOLNS INN FIELDS
LONDON
WC2A 3JF

Phone: 01 405 6195

Fax: 01 405 1453
DX: 227 LONDON CHANCERY LANE WC2
Telex: 295424
Senior Partner: Mr GA Hill
Number of Partners: 16
Total Staff: 60

Lawrence Graham *see full-page profile*
Lawrence Jones *see full-page profile*
Laytons *see full-page profile*

Lawrence Graham

190 STRAND
LONDON
WC2R 1JN

Phone: 01 379 0000

Fax: 01 379 6854
DX: 39 LONDON CHANCERY LANE WC2
Telex: 22673 **Other offices:** 1
Senior Partner: Gavin Purser
Number of Partners: 32
Total Staff: 282

This City firm has traditionally specialised in commercial conveyancing, insurance and shipping work, and has recently developed a strong corporate department.

The firm: The thrust of Lawrence Graham's development in recent years is towards the company and commercial sector, although it maintains an important private client base for which it has been well respected for over two centuries. In 1986 the firm moved to new offices at 190 Strand, which is equipped with some of the most sophisticated information technology available. The firm also has a well-established shipping department which practises under the name of a predecessor firm Middleton Lewis Lawrence Graham. It amalgamated in 1983 with Crane & Hawkins, which has a US client base.

There is a continuing need for assistant solicitors. Ten articled clerks are recruited annually. The firm welcomes graduates from a wide range of disciplines with good academic and all-round abilities. Apply by form (available on request) to Simon Randall.

Other offices: London.

Types of work undertaken: There are six principal departments, namely corporate, litigation, taxation, commercial property, private client and shipping. The firm's corporate clientele varies from the new small business

venture to the large international PLC.

A major area of the corporate department's work involves mergers and acquisitions and more issue work is now undertaken. It is strong in servicing the needs of foreign, particularly US, companies moving into the UK and Europe. It advises on financing business, PINCs property securitisation pensions work, and all commercial matters.

The commercial property department offers a comprehensive service relating to every kind of commercial property, including large private sector investments, town centre schemes, shopping centres (for which the firm is well known), high technology developments and agricultural property.

The work of the litigation department is broad-based and includes insurance and re-insurance work, as well as contentious property and general commercial, employment and matrimonial law.

The taxation department advises companies and private individuals (especially foreign domiciliaries), and the private client department deals with a wide range of topics such as financial services, trust and probate.

The shipping department handles all aspects of maritime law.

Overall, the firm sees itself as a forward-looking partnership large enough to provide a comprehensively efficient service with a personal partner-client service which is creative in its thinking.

Lawrence Jones

SEA CONTAINERS HOUSE
20 UPPER GROUND
BLACKFRIARS BRIDGE
LONDON SE1 9LH
Phone: 01 620 1311

Fax: 01 620 0860
DX: 44304 SOUTHWARK
Telex: 886804
Senior Partner: Michael Waugh
Number of Partners: 10
Total Staff: 51

This medium sized central London firm has a long-established banking, property and transport practice which is combined with general commercial work.

The firm: Formed in 1902 by William Lawrence Jones, whose uncle had founded Elder Dempster Lines and the Bank of British West Africa, the firm was at first largely concerned with shipping and banking law, especially with Canada and West Africa, specialising in Privy Council appeals. Over the years, through various City connections, the firm has expanded into heavy commercial litigation and major property work.

This expanding firm is currently seeking to recruit two assistant solicitors, experienced or wishing to specialise in corporate and personal tax and planning law. Enquiries to Colin Clark.

In addition, there are normally two vacancies for articled clerks every year. A 2(1) degree, not necessarily in law, is preferred; however, the firm prefers to judge applicants on individual merits rather than academic qualifications. Applications should be made by handwritten letter (with CV and names of referees) and addressed to Colin Clark two years in advance.

Types of work undertaken: This is a commercially orientated firm. There is an emphasis on commercial property work, particularly retail development from the retailer's point of view; the firm is very well known for its property and general commercial work for retailers.

Banking law, including financial instrument related problems and practice and security work, is another field in which the firm has wide experience and expertise.

There is a strong commercial litigation practice, with the emphasis on banking and work for the freight forwarding industry; Lawrence Jones is well known for its work for companies transporting high-value goods. Some ship financing is undertaken, and there is increasing involvement in aircraft financing, purchase, sale and leasing work.

On the company/commercial side, the firm handles corporate acquisitions, disposals and BES matters. It also acts for foreign clients, particularly in the Far and Middle East, on projects and financings in Third World countries, banking matters, as well as the setting up of branch or subsidiary businesses in the UK, either direct or as offshore tax bases. Corporate and personal tax work is undertaken, as well as other general company and commercial law, liquor licensing, and a small amount of private client work.

In short, Lawrence Jones perceives itself as an efficient and friendly firm whose experienced staff understand the commercial context in which clients operate. A brochure detailing the firm's work is available.

LAWRENCE JONES

Laytons
(London Office)

16 LINCOLN'S INN FIELDS
LONDON
WC2A 3ED

Phone: 01 404 5177

Fax: 01 405 1883
DX: 253 LONDON CHANCERY LANE WC2
Telex: 28743 **Other offices:** 10
Senior Partner: Richard Kennett
Number of Partners: 26
Total Staff: 220

The southern part of an eleven-office firm, Laytons is a commercially orientated practice, with a longstanding private client base.

The firm: Laytons, founded in the City of London in the nineteenth century, is now a national firm. Its northern offices practise as Ingham Clegg & Crowther and Laytons (see separate entry). The southern offices (London, Bristol and Hampton Court) are each autonomous, but co-operate closely with each other and with the northern offices, which is a considerable advantage to clients with interests in different parts of the country and considerably increases the resources available to individual offices.

The firm is expanding steadily and has a continuing need for good assistant solicitors.

In addition, the firm has vacancies for articled clerks. A 2(2) degree is required, not necessarily in law. Prospects are good; most articled clerks stay on with the firm. Initial applications for London, Bristol or Hampton Court to Richard Kennett, London.

Other offices: Bristol, Manchester, Hampton Court, Preston, St Anne's, Cleveleys, Blackpool, Fleetwood, Knott End, Poulton.

Types of work undertaken: Laytons is a firm of commercial lawyers whose objective is the provision of a comprehensive service in every aspect of commercial work. The firm acts for a wide variety of clients from quoted public companies and multinationals to private companies, new ventures and private individuals, in every field of the manufacturing and service industries.

The firm acts in corporate and commercial matters of every kind, including corporate finance work, land and chattel financing, employment law, intellectual property and insolvency. It handles a large variety and volume of real property matters, including developments, and general commercial and domestic land transactions. The strong litigation division handles a wide variety of work, including defamation, insurance claims, debt recovery and personal accident claims. Taxation is another area of expertise. In addition, the offices act in private client matters, including wills, trusts and estates, taxation planning, and family law.

The firm's major specialisations include building contract litigation; insolvency matters and intellectual property; the Bristol office also has experience in Admiralty and shipping law. It is, however, best regarded for its ability to serve clients closely in a wide variety of commercial matters. Laytons has close links with law firms worldwide, enabling it to offer appropriate legal advice wherever necessary.

The broad variety of the work enables a balance to be maintained between technical expertise and breadth of knowledge so as to give effective practical advice.

LAYTONS

Leathes Prior

74 THE CLOSE
NORWICH
NORFOLK
NR1 4DR
Phone: 0603 610911

Fax: 0603 610088
DX: 5205 NORWICH
Telex: 975166 **Other offices:** 1
Senior Partner: Mr GW Goodley
Number of Partners: 9
Total Staff: 63

Leeds Smith

6 BEDFORD ROAD
SANDY
BEDFORDSHIRE
SG19 1EN
Phone: 0767 80251

Fax: 0767 291 775
DX: 47801 SANDY
Telex: none **Other offices:** 4
Senior Partner: Mr TM Sills
Number of Partners: 7
Total Staff: 100

Lees Lloyd Whitley

44 & 45 HAMILTON SQUARE
BIRKENHEAD
MERSEYSIDE
L41 5AR
Phone: 051 647 9381

Fax: 051 666 1445
DX: 17856 BIRKENHEAD-1
Telex: none **Other offices:** 10
Senior Partner: Mr TD Harvey
Number of Partners: 25
Total Staff: 163

Leigh Williams

KINGS HOUSE
32-40 WIDMORE ROAD
BROMLEY
KENT BR1 1RY
Phone: 01 290 0440

Fax: 01 464 5282
DX: 5704 BROMLEY
Telex: none **Other offices:** 12
Senior Partner: Mr John Williams
Number of Partners: 17
Total Staff: 184

Lee & Pembertons *see full-page profile*
Lee & Priestley *see full-page profile*
Lee Bolton & Lee *see full-page profile*
Legal Resources Group *see full-page profile*

Lee & Pembertons

45 PONT STREET
LONDON
SW1X 0BX

Phone: 01 589 1114

Fax: 01 589 0807
DX: 245 LONDON CHANCERY LANE WC2
Telex: 22731
Senior Partner: Mr SD Staughton
Number of Partners: 15
Total Staff: 80

Lee & Pembertons is a long-established Knightsbridge firm with a substantial property based private client and growing commercial practice.

The firm: The origins of Lee & Pembertons date back to the late eighteenth century. The firm was located in and around the Inns of Court until moving to a listed building in the heart of Knightsbridge in 1975. Traditionally recognised for its wide-ranging advice and personal approach to the private client, in recent years the practice has developed to provide the full range of services required by the smaller, expanding business client.

This thriving firm has a policy of structured growth and in the next 12 months anticipates having vacancies for three assistant solicitors. Enquiries should be addressed to the partnership administrator Roger Blundell.

In addition, Lee & Pembertons recruits three articled clerks every year. The firm looks for individuals with sound academic achievements (minimum 2(2) degree, not necessarily in law), a keenness to take responsibility early and the ability to communicate well with colleagues and clients. Career prospects are excellent. Apply by handwritten letter (with CV and names of two referees) two years in advance to Roger Blundell.

Types of work undertaken: The firm provides a comprehensive service to the private client and to the business sector. A wide range of civil work is undertaken, particularly commercial and residential property matters, including landlord and tenant work for a number of substantial London estates, and general property advice, including agricultural tenancies and farming partnerships, for a number of country estates throughout England and Wales.

The firm is also well known for its involvement in the administration of trusts, particularly charitable trusts and landed estates, together with financial and tax planning, with a growing emphasis on the provision of financial services through the Solicitors Property and Financial Services Company.

There is a strong litigation and matrimonial division and a rapidly expanding company and commercial department.

The practice is broadly based and clients include many substantial individuals, their families and family trustees throughout England and Wales, and an increasing number of entrepreneurs and private companies. In addition, the firm advises a number of charities, particularly in the educational field.

Lee & Pembertons is a well-organised, professionally managed practice, long established but flexible in approach, well connected yet friendly, and provides a comprehensive service to a sophisticated and growing client base.

LEE & PEMBERTONS

Lee & Priestley

QUEEN ANNE CHAMBERS
41-43 SUNBRIDGE ROAD
BRADFORD
BD1 2AS

Phone: 0274 727757

Fax: 0274 729538
DX: 11724 BRADFORD
Telex: 51471 **Other offices:** 3
Senior Partner: Mr RM Priestley
Number of Partners: 10
Total Staff: 71

A broadly based Yorkshire practice, Lee & Priestley offers a full range of legal services to private and commercial clients.

The firm: James A Lee & Co was established in the early years of this century and in the 1930s changed its name to Lee & Priestley. The original emphasis was on litigation and criminal work to which was quickly added a full range of legal services. In the 1970s a substantial commercial conveyancing practice was developed. The firm is organised into departments.

Lee & Priestley is seeking to recruit four assistant solicitors in 1989 for its four main departments.

The firm also plans to recruit three articled clerks in 1989. Long-term prospects are good: it is the firm's established policy to recruit articled clerks of partnership potential. Apply by handwritten letter (plus CV) in June/July to Mr A Darby.

Other offices: Pudsey, Yeadon, Guiseley.

Agency work: All types of agency work are undertaken for other solicitors, particularly litigation and criminal work. For details contact Mr B Walker.

Types of work undertaken: The four main departments are property, litigation, company/commercial, and wills and probate.

Most of the departments act for a large number of firms or individuals rather than a few large clients, although the firm does have public companies and institutions in its client base. Legal aid work is undertaken, especially crime and matrimonial work. The branches provide general legal services backed up by specialist support from the Bradford office.

The firm is best known for its private client and commercial conveyancing work. The property department handles both residential and commercial conveyancing (a brochure on buying a home is available), property investment, landlord and tenant, rent reviews, planning and rating, compulsory purchase, property taxation, and mortgages and finance. The company/commercial department deals with business start-ups, partnership and joint ventures, acquisitions and disposals of businesses, reconstructions and amalgamations, industrial contracts, intellectual property, and advice on funding, tax and insurance requirements. The work of the litigation department is divided into property and commercial matters and personal litigation (including matrimonial).

The firm sees itself as one of the more substantial firms in West Yorkshire, giving a solid and wide-ranging legal service to private and commercial clients seeking a more personal and cost-effective service than that provided by many larger commercial firms. Brochures are available upon request.

LEE & PRIESTLEY

Lee Bolton & Lee

1 THE SANCTUARY
WESTMINSTER
LONDON
SW1P 3JT
Phone: 01 222 5381

Fax: 01 222 7502
DX: 2301 VICTORIA SW1
Telex: 919048 **Other offices:** 1
Senior Partner: Mr AOE Davies
Number of Partners: 13
Total Staff: 90

Based in Westminster, Lee Bolton & Lee has a general practice which handles commercial, ecclesiastical, Parliamentary agency and private client work.

The firm: This is a long-established firm, occupying its premises beside Westminster Abbey since it was founded in 1855. It originated as a family firm and the practice has grown to include Parliamentary and a wide range of general commercial work, in addition to its long-established ecclesiastical practice. In 1980 it merged with Evan Davies & Co.

Lee Bolton & Lee generally prefers to engage solicitors of some three years' experience. Enquiries to the office manager.

There are usually at least two vacancies for articled clerks every year; a number of partners were articled with the firm. Applicants should have a degree, not necessarily in law; extra-curricular interests and achievements are also important. Apply by letter (with CV) to Mr JA Durkin.

Other offices: Canterbury; and associated offices in Paris and Lille.

Agency work: The firm accepts non-criminal litigation work from other solicitors and local authorities; contact Lorna Grosse.

Types of work undertaken: The practice is a general one, having a substantial amount of conveyancing and litigation work. In addition, it has one of the largest ecclesiastical practices in the country, and is well known for its Parliamentary agency work. In recent years the firm has developed a particular expertise and reputation in the fields of charity and education law, acting for many charities and educational bodies. Housing association work is another prominent area of the practice.

The firm still has a number of family clients who have been with it for many generations, some of whom are the owners of large estates. As well as estate administration, the firm offers private clients advice on wills, probate, trusts, tax planning, divorce and family law work, as well as conveyancing.

The commercial side of the practice has expanded in recent years to encompass all aspects of company and partnership law, acquisitions and sales, commercial agreements and property transactions. A wide range of litigation work is undertaken, including commercial disputes, personal injury, insurance claims, contractual and employment problems, medical negligence, as well as divorce and family work. The firm's strong French links in the commercial and conveyancing fields are becoming increasingly important.

Overall, Lee Bolton & Lee sees itself as a firm which takes a meticulous approach to its clients' legal affairs while acting swiftly and creatively. A brochure is available on request.

Lee Bolton & Lee
—— SOLICITORS ——

Legal Resources Group

A GROUP OF INDEPENDENT
LEGAL PRACTICES BASED IN
BIRMINGHAM, BRISTOL, LEEDS,
LIVERPOOL, LONDON, MANCHESTER,
AND NEWCASTLE

Offices: 9
Co-ordinator: Peter Condon
Number of Partners: 150
Total Staff: 1,104

Legal Resources Group is a national grouping of independent law firms, made up of five of the best known commercial practices throughout the UK.

The firms: Members of the Legal Resources Group are Alsop Wilkinson of London, Liverpool and Manchester; Dickinson Dees of Newcastle upon Tyne; Osborne Clarke of Bristol and London; Pinsent & Co of Birmingham and London; and Simpson Curtis of Leeds (see separate entries). Legal Resources Group has developed into one of the largest legal organisations in the country.

The group was established in 1982 as the Information Club, but in 1988 the group formed a central management company based in Birmingham, and at the same time it changed its name to Legal Resources Group.

The nature of the group: There is a natural affinity between the firms, each of which undertakes a significant amount of quality corporate work. Each member firm retains its independence but has access to a common pool of legal expertise and experience from the group's combined resources. The shared resources enable members to expand both nationally and internationally.

The original aim of the group was the sharing of information on financial and management matters. The overall goal has changed, however, and today the group concentrates on rapidly developing its central resources (in the areas of staff training, research facilities, overseas representation, publications, marketing, new office technology, management systems, recruitment, and bulk purchasing) so that economies of scale can provide improved client services.

Co-ordination: Legal Resources Group has recently appointed chartered accountant Peter Condon as co-ordinator to organise resources, liaise between the member firms, and develop long-term strategies.

The Group's full-time national director of training is barrister Ann Andrews. She is responsible for devising, implementing and monitoring training courses for articled clerks, assistant solicitors and partners in all the participating member firms. Courses, which are organised either at a central location for all member firms or on an in-house basis, embrace general skills training on matters such as communication, drafting and negotiation, as well as technical legal subjects.

As the Chairman of Legal Resources Group, Martin Shaw of Simpson Curtis, commented: 'The legal community, especially in European and international commercial fields, is changing rapidly, and the concept of the central resource is the fulcrum of the group's philosophy, reflecting our strategy for meeting the demands of the future.'

Lewis & Dick

443 KINGSTON ROAD
EWELL
EPSOM
SURREY KT19 0DG
Phone: 01 393 0055

Fax: 01 393 3317
DX: 30715 EPSOM
Telex: none **Other offices:** 4
Senior Partner: Mr RD Millett
Number of Partners: 10
Total Staff: 70

Lindsays WS

11 ATHOLL CRESCENT
EDINBURGH
EH3 8HE

Phone: 031 229 8851

Fax: 031 229 5611
Rutland Exchange: 25 EDINBURGH
Telex: 727538 **Other offices:** 2
Senior Partner: Mr RG Shearer
Number of Partners: 16
Total Staff: 100

Linnells

12 KING EDWARD STREET
OXFORD
OX1 4HX

Phone: 0865 248607

Fax: 0865 728445
DX: 4312 OXFORD
Telex: none **Other offices:** 12
Senior Partner: Mr MJ Linnell
Number of Partners: 21
Total Staff: 161

Loosemores

ALLIANCE HOUSE
18-20 HIGH STREET
CARDIFF
CF1 2BZ

Phone: 0222 224433

Fax: 0222 373275
DX: 33008 CARDIFF
Telex: 265871 **Other offices:** 8
Senior Partner: Mr JH Loosemore
Number of Partners: 15
Total Staff: 117

Leo Abse & Cohen *see full-page profile*
Lester Aldridge *see full-page profile*
Lewis Silkin *see full-page profile*
Linklaters & Paines *see full-page profile*

Leo Abse & Cohen

40 CHURCHILL WAY
CARDIFF
SOUTH GLAMORGAN
CF1 4SS
Phone: 0222 383252

Fax: 0222 345572
DX: 33002 CARDIFF
Telex: none
Senior Partner: Isaac Cohen
Number of Partners: 14
Total Staff: 118

Leo Abse & Cohen is a broadly based practice serving the legal needs of a wide range of clients in the South Glamorgan area.

The firm: Founded in 1951, the firm has grown progressively since then, with a period of rapid expansion starting in the late 1970s and continuing still. Growth has been achieved without mergers or amalgamations, and today the firm is one of the largest firms in Wales.

This expanding firm has a continuing demand for assistant solicitors of a high calibre. Enquiries to Henry Nyman.

In addition, the firm has between four and eight vacancies for articled clerks every year. There is no minimum educational requirement — indeed, a degree is not always necessary — and the firm prefers to judge applicants on individual merits. Prospects after qualification are excellent; over half of the present partners served articles with the firm. Apply by handwritten letter (with CV) to John Sherratt. A brochure for prospective articled clerks is available on request.

Agency work: The firm accepts litigation work in all courts throughout South Wales from other solicitors.

Types of work undertaken: This is a broad-based general practice, divided into four main departments, namely civil litigation, criminal litigation, family law, and conveyancing and commercial.

Litigation is a major area of practice. The work of the civil litigation department is wide ranging. It represents two substantial trade unions and deals with litigation and other legal matters on behalf of their members, predominantly in the fields of personal injury and employment disputes; indeed, the firm has particular expertise in difficult personal injury cases and in claims involving industrial diseases such as asbestosis and deafness. The firm also acts for major insurance companies in all types of litigation.

The criminal litigation department is one of the largest of its type in the city of Cardiff with five solicitor advocates practising in the courts of South Wales and the West Country. Members of the department also specialise in child care law, both on behalf of statutory bodies and local authorities, and in representing the interests of the child. Civil and criminial legal work is always accepted.

The divorce department handles all aspects of marriage breakdown. The conveyancing and commercial department handles a large amount of domestic and commercial conveyancing, with an increasing amount of commercial work for substantial financial institutions and major banks.

In short, Leo Abse & Cohen sees itself as a forward-thinking partnership whose main interest lies firmly with the client.

Leo Abse & Cohen

Lester Aldridge

23 OLD CHRISTCHURCH ROAD
BOURNEMOUTH
DORSET
BH1 1BE
Phone: 0202 23663

Fax: 0202 298510
DX: 7623 BOURNEMOUTH
Telex: 417196 **Other offices:** 6
Senior Partner: John Russell
Number of Partners: 26
Total Staff: 194

This newly merged Bournemouth firm incorporates two of the area's longest established and largest practices.

The firm: Lester Aldridge was formed in October 1988 as the result of the merger of Lester & Russell, which was established in 1913, and Mooring Aldridge, which dates from 1884. The aim of the new firm is to provide a practical and comprehensive service on all aspects of the law to the business community and to private clients. The firm is organised into departments.

There is an acute need for good qualified staff, and the firm expects to recruit at least four assistant solicitors in 1989 for commercial litigation, general litigation and company/commercial. Enquiries to Mr AC Roberts (Westover Chambers, Hinton Road, Bournemouth, Dorset BH1 2EQ).

In addition four articled clerks are recruited annually. There are no minimum academic requirements. Apply by letter (with CV) to Raymond G Brown (Westover Chambers, as above).

Other offices: Bournemouth (2), Poole, Parkstone, Christchurch, Westbourne.

Agency work: The firm accepts work from other solicitors: contact John Ainsworth (general litigation); Martin Kilner (property); David Bollington (company/commercial).

Types of work undertaken: Since the merger the new firm has set up experienced teams which handle commercial litigation, insolvency, banking, insurance and finance, in addition to the longstanding company/commercial, property, and tax, probate and trusts departments.

The firm is well known locally for its commercial expertise; indeed, it is one of the few firms in the region with a separate commercial department of three partners and two assistant solicitors. One of the partners has wide experience in the fields of credit finance and equipment leasing.

Over recent years the firm has undertaken (very successfully) heavyweight commercial litigation in foreign jurisdictions, particularly in the EEC (Belgium and the Netherlands), Switzerland, the United States and Belize. In addition it has the largest general litigation practice in the area.

The property department is highly regarded and acts for a number of local developers as well as handling domestic conveyancing. The full range of private client services is offered, including tax and financial planning, wills and trusts, family matters, matrimonial, and crime. Legal aid work is undertaken.

Overall, Lester Aldridge sees itself as capable, approachable, and behaving with absolute integrity.

A brochure describing the range of services offered is available on request.

LESTER ALDRIDGE

Lewis Silkin

1 BUTLER PLACE
BUCKINGHAM GATE
LONDON
SW1H 0PT
Phone: 01 222 8191

Fax: 01 222 4633
DX: 2321 VICTORIA SW1
Telex: 269577 **Other offices:** 1
Senior Partner: John Fraser MP
Number of Partners: 20
Total Staff: 110

Lewis Silkin has offices in Westminster and Peckham, combining commercial and 'high street' practices and offering a 'one stop' legal service for both commercial and private clients.

The firm: Lewis Silkin, father of John and Sam, first practised in the 1920s but his Parliamentary and Ministerial career delayed the firm's real development until the 1950s when the Westminster office was opened. The Parliamentary connection continues today. Senior partner John Fraser is the Member of Parliament for Norwood and Shadow Solicitor General.

The last four years have seen rapid growth, with a doubling of the number of partners, but the expansion has been carefully controlled in order to preserve a consistently high quality of service.

In 1989 the firm expects to recruit eight assistant solicitors for all areas of the practice. Enquiries to Andrew Thomas.

In addition, Lewis Silkin recruits 12 to 15 articled clerks every year. The minimum educational requirement is a 2(2) degree, not necessarily in law. Long-term prospects are excellent: 70 per cent of the present partners served articles with the firm. Apply by handwritten letter (with CV) two years in advance to Andrew Thomas.

Other offices: South London.

Types of work undertaken: Having offices in Westminster and south London, the firm has a diverse practice and a wide client base, which includes PLCs, individuals, advertising agencies, estate developers, housing associations, insolvency practitioners, publishers, and institutional lenders.

On the commercial side, the firm's work includes acquisitions, mergers, flotations, management buy-outs, start-ups, BES work, taxation planning, commercial contracts and licensing.

The service to private clients includes advice on tax, probate, matrimonial matters and trusts, while anti-trust and competition law is an area of particular experience. The firm is also well known for its 'media law' work, which covers intellectual property, consumer protection, trading and advertising law, breach of confidence and libel.

The property department deals with commercial and residential conveyancing, planning, institutional and domestic mortgaging, right-to-buy, estate disposal and, notably, housing association work.

The work of the litigation department ranges from heavy commercial, building and construction, insolvency and intellectual property, through to matrimonial, immigration, crime and personal injury.

Lewis Silkin feels its character lies in combining a refusal to be pigeon-holed with a commitment to broad experience.

LEWIS SILKIN

Linklaters & Paines

BARRINGTON HOUSE
59-67 GRESHAM STREET
LONDON
EC2V 7JA

Phone: 01 606 7080

Fax: 01 606 5113
DX: 10 LONDON CITY EC3
Telex: 884349 **Other offices:** 5
Senior Partner: Mark Sheldon
Number of Partners: 103
Total Staff: 1,250

This large City-based firm is well known for its financial, commercial and international work.

The firm: The result of a 1920 merger of two firms that had then been in existence for nearly 100 years, Linklaters & Paines has expanded steadily over the past three decades and remains one of the largest practices in the country. Today Linklaters has a strong international and European bias and provides a round-the-clock legal service from its six strategically located offices.

Continued strong growth means that Linklaters is always looking for qualified staff, particularly newly qualified lawyers or those with two to three years experience in areas such as property, mainstream corporate and international finance. In 1989, 40 vacancies for assistant solicitors are expected. Enquiries should be addressed to the head of personnel.

In addition, 100 articled clerks are recruited annually. The preferred educational qualification is at least a 2(1) degree, though not necessarily in law. Long-term prospects are excellent: the majority of the partners served articles with the firm. Apply by letter (with CV and names of referees) or application form to Robert Williams.

Other offices: Brussels, Hong Kong, New York, Paris, Tokyo.

Types of work undertaken: With offices in the world's main financial centres, Linklaters is well placed to advise businesses on a wide range of domestic and international matters. Active property, litigation, tax, trusts, pensions and intellectual property departments, together with the firm's substantial corporate department, provide a full business law service.

As is to be expected of such a large and thriving firm, it is well known in a number of fields: mergers and acquisitions (both domestic and – of increasing importance with the approach of 1992 – cross-frontier); equity and debt financing in the domestic market, the international securities markets, and by way of bank finance; regulatory compliance; UK and offshore investment funds; anti-trust and EEC law matters; domestic and international projects; property investment and development; litigation; tax planning; intellectual property, trusts and pension funds work.

Overall, Linklaters sees itself as a leading international firm providing high quality, practical advice on a broad range of major transactions and situations. It is a firm with the experience, staff and technical resources necessary to undertake large and complex projects at short notice and to complete them with speed and efficiency. Linklaters prides itself on maintaining close working relationships with all of its clients. Brochures are available upon request.

LINKLATERS & PAINES

Lupton Fawcett

YORKSHIRE HOUSE
GREEK STREET
LEEDS
LS1 5SX
Phone: 0532 469696

Fax: 0532 456782
DX: 12035 LEEDS-1
Telex: 557538 **Other offices:** 2
Managing Partner: Mr JM Norris
Number of Partners: 10
Total Staff: 76

Lyon Clark

DAVIOT HOUSE
LOMBARD STREET WEST
WEST BROMWICH
WEST MIDLANDS B70 8EL
Phone: 021 553 3211

Fax: 021 553 2079
DX: 14603 WEST BROMWICH
Telex: none **Other offices:** 2
Senior Partner: Mr IGW Whyte
Number of Partners: 10
Total Staff: 51

Mackrell Turner Garrett

INIGO PLACE
31 BEDFORD STREET
LONDON
WC2E 9EH
Phone: 01 240 0521

Fax: 01 240 9457
DX: 40037 COVENT GARDEN-1 WC2
Telex: 27979 **Other offices:** 8
Senior Partner: Mr KE Turner
Number of Partners: 20
Total Staff: 111

Malcolm Wilson & Cobby

3 LIVERPOOL TERRACE
WORTHING
WEST SUSSEX
BN11 1TA
Phone: 0903 37581

Fax: 0903 200624
DX: 3720 WORTHING
Telex: none **Other offices:** 3
Senior Partner: Mr AJ Viner
Number of Partners: 8
Total Staff: 62

Lovell White Durrant *see full-page profile*
Lyons Davidson *see full-page profile*
M5 Group *see full-page profile*
MacRoberts *see full-page profile*

Mace & Jones *see full-page profile*
Macfarlanes *see full-page profile*
Maclay Murray & Spens *see full-page profile*

Lovell White Durrant

21 HOLBORN VIADUCT
LONDON
EC1A 2DY

Phone: 01 236 0066

Fax: 01 248 4212
DX: 57 LONDON CHANCERY LANE WC2
Telex: 887122 **Other offices:** 4
Senior Partner: Mr PN Gerrard
Number of Partners: 110
Total Staff: 1,076

A commercial firm with a major international practice, Lovell White Durrant is one of the largest firms in the world.

The firm: Lovell White Durrant came into being in May 1988 as the result of the merger of two firms, Lovell, White & King and Durrant Piesse, both leading City firms which trace their origins back to the nineteenth century.

The merger of these two prestigious firms now makes available, from a single source, a wider range of skills and expertise, with stronger technical support, than either firm could have provided on its own. The ever-increasing demands on the legal profession, the greater complexity of the law, the competitiveness of the commercial environment in which clients are conducting their businesses, and the revolutionary state of communications and information technology are all issues which prompted the merger and which the new firm feels confident that it is well placed to deal with.

Lovell White Durrant serves commercial, financial and industrial clients in the United Kingdom and overseas from its base in the City of London and through offices in Brussels, New York and Hong Kong and using its facilties in Beijing.

The firm is particularly well known for banking and corporate finance, commercial law, including venture capital and management buy-outs, insolvency, commercial litigation and arbitration, property, including planning and rating, intellectual property, EEC and competitive law, construction and taxation.

The new firm remains committed to an approach to practice which led to the successful development of the two predecessor firms over many years. The characteristics of that approach are clear practical advice based on knowledge and awareness of the business context; ready access to partners; a balance between specialisation and broader legal knowledge; and friendliness and approachability at all levels within the firm and towards clients.

The firm places great importance on its international outlook. It has had an office in Brussels from the time of the UK's entry into the EEC, it was among the first of the British firms to open in New York, it is among the few British firms in China, and it has one of the larger expatriate offices in Hong Kong. As 1992 and the single European market approach, Lovell White Durrant is more than ever committed to thinking not just in European but in global terms.

Lovell White Durrant has a continuing need to recruit high-calibre assistant solicitors and in 1989 expects to recruit approximately 60 qualified staff in virtually all areas of the practice. There are opportunities for experience and eventual specialisation in a wide variety of areas. Apply to Hilton Wallace, the personnel manager.

Lovell White Durrant sees itself in the top ten leading law firms, and in order to maintain that position it seeks to recruit the best graduates. The firm seeks to recruit around 75 articled clerks annually. At least a 2(2) law degree, or a 2(1) non-law degree, is preferred. Personal qualities are also carefully assessed. The firm seeks candidates who have wide-ranging or special interests, those who are enthusiastic about life and who have made intelligent use of their time at university or in a previous job. Long-term prospects are excellent: the firm expects that the majority will stay once qualified. The firm believes that, for those who combine a practical, businesslike approach with the highest professional and technical standards, opportunities within the law are excellent and continually increasing. Applications should be made by the end of the second year at university on the firm's own form to Mrs Lynda Neal, the graduate recruitment officer.

Other offices: London, Brussels, New York, Hong Kong.

Types of work undertaken: The firm is organised into four main activity sectors, namely financial, commercial, property, and litigation.

The financial and corporate sector handles a wide range of matters including: flotations and new issues; retail banking; corporate and property taxation; Inland Revenue investigations; takeovers and mergers of listed and unlisted public companies; company and securities law and establishing unit trusts and other UK and offshore investment vehicles.

In the commercial sector activities include advising on the formation, acquisition and winding up of private companies, joint ventures and partnerships; the purchase, sale and financing of companies and businesses; corporate insolvencies; commercial agreements; exploitation of inventions and intellectual property rights; European Community law; competition legislation; employment and pensions law; industrial relations; computer and telecommunications law; agreements relating to construction and engineering projects; shipping matters; oil, gas, and mineral development projects; and insurance and reinsurance matters.

In the property sector Lovell White Durrant advises on transactions for corporate clients, pension funds, banks and other investing institutions relating to land ownership and development including: acquisitions; site assembly, funding and sale of property developments; banks and other loans secured on land or buildings; business leases; rating law; planning law and some residential sales and purchases.

Lovell White Durrant deals with all aspects of civil litigation in the High Court, county court and appellate courts. The work is mainly concerned with substantial commercial claims and disputes for corporate and institutional clients. The firm also handles arbitrations both domestic and international and cases referred to industrial tribunals and the Employment Appeal Tribunal.

Through the Brussels office the firm maintains close contacts with the EC Commission and other related matters.

Lovell White Durrant perceives itself as a significant leader operating in the forefront of a changing profession. A brochure describing the firm's services is available on request.

LOVELL
WHITE
DURRANT

Lyons Davidson

BRIDGE HOUSE
48-52 BALDWIN STREET
BRISTOL
BS1 1QD
Phone: 0272 297151

Fax: 0272 272679
DX: 7834 BRISTOL
Telex: 449467 **Other offices:** 1
Senior Partner: Mr PJM Lyons
Number of Partners: 12
Total Staff: 80

One of the leading Bristol firms, Lyons Davidson has a broadly based commercial law practice.

The firm: Formed in 1972 by the amalgamation of several well-established Bristol firms whose histories date back well into the last century, Lyons Davidson is now among the larger Bristol practices. The firm has developed from its substantial commercial property client base. It is organised into departments.

This expanding firm has a continuing need for specialist qualified staff at all levels and in all disciplines. Enquiries to Mr TJ Davidson.

In addition Lyons Davidson recruits three or four articled clerks every year. The minimum educational requirement is a 2(2) degree in any discipline, although a law degree is preferred. Prospects after qualification are good. Apply by handwritten letter (with CV and names of referees) to Mr BV Rowe in September two years in advance.

Other offices: Chew Magna.

Agency work: The firm accepts litigation work from other solicitors; contact Mr BV Rowe.
Types of work undertaken: Lyons Davidson provides a very wide range of commercial law services. The client base includes both public and private companies, local authorities and insurance companies.

Particular areas of expertise are commercial property and property development work, personal injury, building and commercial litigation and corporate and commercial work.

The property department's clients range from major national developers and local authorities to medium sized developers and individuals. The work includes investment and funding transactions, purchases, sales, commercial letting and development agreements. On the residential side, the firm specialises in estate and flat scheme documentation.

The corporate/commercial department advises on the full range of business activities, which includes purchases and sales of companies and businesses, flotations, management buy-outs, partnerships, intellectual property and security and insolvency related matters.

Lyons Davidson has a large and comprehensive litigation department which acts for building contractors, engineering companies, insurance companies, retailers, building societies and other financial and trading clients.

The firm also has a well-established private client practice.

Overall, the firm sees itself as an expanding and broad-based commercial practice.

Lyons Davidson

The M5 Group

A GROUP OF INDEPENDENT
LEGAL PRACTICES BASED IN
BIRMINGHAM, BRISTOL, EXETER,
CAMBRIDGE, LEEDS, MANCHESTER,
NORWICH, AND PLYMOUTH

Offices: 8
Managing Director: Peter F Smith
Number of Partners: 164
Total Staff: 1,455

The firms: M5 is a group of independent legal practices, and consists of six of the largest solicitors' firms outside London. They are Addleshaw, Sons & Latham of Manchester; Bond Pearce of Plymouth and Exeter; Booth & Co of Leeds; Bristol-based Burges Salmon; Mills & Reeve Francis of Norwich and Cambridge; and Wragge & Co of Birmingham. Together they have a combined total of 164 partners and 1,455 staff, of whom 256 are assistant solicitors and 86 are articled clerks.

The nature of the group: The M5 Group was formed in the mid-1970s. For a time the activities of the group were confined to business comparisons at partner level, but in the early 1980s members started to produce client publications and to hold training conferences. The group is now well known for the professional education it offers to lawyers.

Main activities of the group: Joint activities of the group are organised by M5 Limited — a company offering services to the member firms and based in Birmingham.

M5 training offers a number of joint training conferences and seminars to lawyers in the group throughout the year and also co-ordinates the separate training programmes of each member firm. M5 conferences cover both the practical and academic skills required of solicitors and bring practitioners up to date on topics of interest.

The group has developed recruitment initiatives to encourage staff to join M5 firms. In November 1988 the group announced a marked increase in the number of applications for articles and a similar improvement in the general quality of applicants.

The interchange of legal and business information remains a major reason for participation in the M5 Group. The group has also established its own database of legal information which is available to lawyers throughout the member firms.

The future: It is expected that M5 will become an increasingly important aspect of each member practice but there are no plans to change the current structure of independent member firms. Specialist groups control the main areas of group activity. Recently a European Group was formed to ensure that member firms are in the best possible position to capitalise on the advantages offered by the Single European Market.

M5 has long been regarded by its member firms as offering the best of both worlds. M5 firms enjoy the traditional independence of well-established regional practices but are also part of one of the largest legal organisations in the UK. Details of all member firms appear in this publication.

MacRoberts

152 BATH STREET
GLASGOW
G2 4TB

Phone: 041 332 9988

Fax: 041 332 8886
Rutland Exchange: 70 GLASGOW
Telex: 778134 **Other offices:** 2
Senior Partner: James C Osborne
Number of Partners: 16
Total Staff: 120

This Glasgow and Edinburgh-based firm has a predominantly commercial practice, acting for corporate and commercial clients.

The firm: Founded in Paisley in 1850, MacRoberts moved to Glasgow in 1905. The original practice grew up around the area's thread producers and heavy engineering companies. Today the firm has a substantial commercial practice, serving a wide spectrum of businesses and commerce as well as individual clients.

This expanding firm is always seeking to recruit high-calibre qualified staff, and in 1989 expects to have vacancies for six assistant solicitors in the commercial and commercial property departments. Enquiries should be addressed to the staff partner.

Four trainee solicitors are usually recruited every year. The minimum educational requirements are a Scottish law degree and a Diploma in Legal Practice. Apply on form (available on request) to the staff partner.

Other offices: 27 Melville Street, Edinburgh EH3 7JF (phone: 031 226 2552); London.

Agency work: The firm accepts work from other solicitors in most aspects of company/commercial, litigation, arbitration, property and family work.

Types of work undertaken: MacRoberts handles commercial work for corporate and commercial clients, and offers a complete private client service. The four main departments are corporate and commercial, litigation, commercial property and personal.

The litigation department deals with all aspects of civil litigation, and is particularly well known for commercial litigation (including building and engineering disputes, employment law matters, and product liability), as well as personal injury and reparation claims and matrimonial disputes.

The commercial property department handles the full range of commercial property and security work, and has particular experience and expertise in leasing, timeshares and leisure developments.

The substantial corporate and commercial department, with its extensive knowledge and practical experience of corporate and institutional business, advises on all aspects of corporate and commercial law, including incorporations, reorganisations, takeovers and mergers, loan and equity finance, banking flotations, management buy-outs, employee share and incentive schemes, and pension schemes. It has also developed specialist expertise in EEC law, intellectual property, computer contracts, franchising, entertainment and corporate insolvency.

MacRoberts sees itself as a firm that is go-ahead, skilled and efficient. A brochure for clients is available on request.

Mace & Jones

DRURY HOUSE
19 WATER STREET
LIVERPOOL
L2 ORP
Phone: 051 236 8989

Fax: 051 227 5010
DX: 14166 LIVERPOOL
Telex: 629660 **Other offices:** 4
Senior Partner: Mr GB Marsh
Number of Partners: 13
Total Staff: 100

This broadly based Liverpool firm has a considerable reputation in employment law and industrial relations.

The firm: Mace & Jones, which dates back to 1927, has its origins in a small general practice which in recent years merged with the long-established practices of Oliver Jones & Co and Latin & Masheder. This busy firm has expanded rapidly and now has four other offices around Liverpool and Manchester.

There is a continuing need for assistant solicitors, and in 1989 four vacancies are expected. Enquiries to Mr S Kerruish.

In addition, the firm normally recruits four articled clerks every year. The preferred educational qualification is a 2(1) law degree; non-law graduate applicants are welcome. Apply by handwritten letter (with CV and names of referees) at commencement of degree course to Carole Atkinson.

Other offices: Manchester, Huyton, St Helens, Walton.

Agency work: All types of work from other solicitors is accepted; contact Craig Blakemore.

Types of work undertaken: Mace & Jones is an expanding general practice capable of meeting the most demanding legal problems. It is organised into departments.

The commercial department has particular expertise in franchising, insolvency and computer law, as well as company formations and takeovers, mergers and partnerships, intellectual property, EEC law, media and entertainment.

Other departments handle all aspects of employment law; conveyancing and property; wills, probate and trust; divorce and matrimonial; tax and investment planning; personal injury litigation, and commercial litigation.

The firm is probably best known for its expertise in employment law and industrial relations; the senior partner, Mr GB Marsh, has written a leading work on the subject, and another partner, Martin Edwards, is well known for his books and articles on the same subject.

The client base is very wide, encompassing several major PLC clients and many small to medium sized businesses, as well as a substantial private client base. Legal aid work is undertaken at the Huyton, St Helens and Walton branches.

Mace & Jones feels that speed and efficiency have been its watchwords for many years. It is probably best regarded as a very go-ahead, dynamic and expanding firm which has achieved considerable growth and expertise while maintaining traditional values and complete integrity. A brochure describing the work of the firm is available on request.

M A C E & J O N E S

Macfarlanes

10 NORWICH STREET
LONDON
EC4A 1BD

Phone: 01 831 9222

Fax: 01 831 9607
DX: 138 LONDON CHANCERY LANE WC2
Telex: 296381
Senior Partner: Vanni E Treves
Number of Partners: 36
Total Staff: 332

Now predominantly a commercial practice representing many substantial corporate and institutional clients, Macfarlanes is one of the leading firms in the City.

The firm: Founded in 1875, Macfarlanes has seen a shift of emphasis from the trust and private client work with which it was mostly concerned in the 1950s and 1960s to the prominence of its commercial work today. Macfarlanes has enjoyed substantial expansion in the last five years and is best known for its work in such areas as the Stock Exchange and USM, venture capital, offshore fund work, international.trade finance, international commercial litigation, property development and financing together with a private client department which is virtually unique among City firms.

Many of the firm's clients are based overseas or have international operations and interests. To meet their needs, Macfarlanes has established very close working relationships with many top lawyers in other jurisdictions.

Macfarlanes has maintained a continuous presence in the City of London since 1875, and in 1983 the firm moved into purpose-built premises in Norwich Street. This move has allowed the strong personal identity of the firm to be developed. Professional excellence and personal commitment are two of the key characteristics of this identity.

Macfarlanes takes pride in establishing close contacts with clients whether they be business or private to make sure that advice is given only after a clear understanding of the client's overall objectives has been achieved.

Together with this emphasis on traditional values, Macfarlanes offers an up-to-date and businesslike service through its continuing investment in the latest communications technology and in high-calibre personnel.

In 1989 the firm expects to recruit about twelve additional assistant solicitors for all departments but especially for banking, intellectual property, and corporate and commercial property. Enquiries should be addressed to John G Rhodes.

In addition, approximately 25 articled clerks are recruited annually. The firm looks for candidates with sound academic ability, initiative, a sense of humour and a record of past achievement in some area of interest. Long-term prospects are excellent. The sole purpose of the articled clerk programme is to recruit and train top quality lawyers to work with the firm after qualification — more than two-thirds of the present partners served articles with the firm. Apply by form (available on request) or by CV with names of referees two years in advance to Mrs Tricia Brett.

Agency work: Large-scale High and Appellate Court proceedings, including Privy Council and House of Lords work, are undertaken for other solicitors; for details contact David JC Wyld.

Types of work undertaken: Macfarlanes is divided into four main departments, namely corporate, commercial and banking; litigation; property; and tax and financial planning

The corporate, commercial and banking department deals with the whole area of corporate and commercial law, from public company takeovers and mergers to business start-ups, with clients ranging from individual entrepreneurs to multinational corporations. The department advises on such matters as competition, patent, trademark and copyright law, joint ventures, distributorship agreements and terms and conditions of trading. The firm has particular knowledge of the procedures of the Stock Exchange and the Panel on Takeovers and Mergers and it is well known for its venture capital, management buy-out and USM work.

The litigation department has a very broad practice undertaking almost all the contentious matters in the firm. It does not, however, undertake matrimonial or criminal work.

The international scope of the practice has grown considerably in recent years: the firm represents foreign governments and clients of overseas law firms in proceedings in the Privy Council and UK courts. There is particular expertise in disputes involving international trade and commodities, sovereign immunity, building and civil engineering, intellectual property, insurance and employment.

The property department deals with all transactions involving the ownership and development of land, with commercial property being the most rapidly expanding area. Both institutional and developer clients are represented, and advice is given on all aspects of acquisition, building contracts and planning.

This department advises private and institutional investors, farmers, landlords and tenants on their agricultural investments or businesses, while the residential property practice advises on the purchase, sale and leasing of houses, flats and country estates both in the UK and abroad.

The well-known tax and financial planning department acts for individuals with substantial businesses and for wealthy families in all their business affairs. Tax advice is based on efficiency and mitigation through expert advance planning, but tax litigation and appeals are also handled. The department advises on the tax-efficient use of foreign companies and trusts for international trading and investment.

Some 600 trusts are administered by this department which has a specially developed computerised accounting system. The department is frequently called upon to advise on trust problems in other jurisdictions. In addition the pension and immigration work of the firm are handled here. A specialised service for the pension schemes of corporate clients is offered by the department.

Overall, Macfarlanes sees itself as a forward-looking and businesslike practice which offers professional excellence and personal commitment to both commercial and private clients.

The firm intends to continue its recent growth to meet the demands of its clients without any sacrifice of its standards or identity. Brochures detailing the services offered by the firm are available on request.

MACFARLANES

Maclay Murray & Spens

151 ST VINCENT STREET
GLASGOW
G2 5NJ

Phone: 041 248 5011

Fax: 041 248 5819
Rutland Exchange: 67 GLASGOW
Telex: 77474 **Other offices:** 1
Managing Partner: J Anthony S Murray
Number of Partners: 25
Total Staff: 182

One of the largest legal firms in Scotland, Maclay Murray & Spens offers the full range of services to commercial and private clients in Edinburgh and Glasgow.

The firm: Founded in 1871, the original practice was linked to the commercial and industrial life of Glasgow and its international shipping, whisky and manufacturing trade. From this base the firm has expanded into Edinburgh and developed a broad client base, national and international, corporate and private.

This thriving firm is always seeking to recruit able assistant solicitors, and in 1989 expects to have ten vacancies, in corporate, commercial property, litigation, and private client work. Enquiries to Mr JAS Murray.

The firm also recruits eight trainee solicitors every year. There are no minimum educational requirements; the firm prefers to judge applicants on individual merits. Prospects after qualification are good; many of the present partners were trained with the firm. Apply by letter (with CV) to Jane Garvie.

Other offices: Edinburgh.

Types of work undertaken: There are four main departments, namely company/commercial, commercial property, litigation, and private client. The wide-ranging client base includes companies, banks and other financial institutions, professionals, developers, timesharers, retailers, as well as individuals, resident in the UK and abroad.

Public company work (including flotations and Stock Exchange practice), EEC law and institutional funding are areas where the company/commercial department has a great deal of expertise. The department also handles public company takeovers, pensions, insolvency, and private company work.

The commercial property department deals with all aspects of buying, selling and leasing commercial property in Scotland. In addition, the department advises on property development, funding agreements and secured lending over commercial property.

There is a strong litigation department which is well known for the high quality of its shipping, aircraft, intellectual property and employment work. The department covers all aspects of the settlement of commercial disputes, and conducts litigation in the Court of Session in Edinburgh and the sheriff courts.

The firm retains its traditional private client base; the work covers wills, executries, trusts, tax planning, general financial advice, and the transfer of property, including farms and estates. The firm also advises small businesses in the early stages of their development.

In short, Maclay Murray & Spens sees itself as professional and reliable, with renowned expertise, and able to respond quickly and efficiently. A brochure is available on request.

Maclay Murray & Spens

Malkin Cullis & Sumption

INIGO HOUSE
29 BEDFORD STREET
LONDON
WC2E 9RT
Phone: 01 379 3385

Fax: 01 379 3137
DX: 40034 COVENT GARDEN-2
Telex: 263604
Senior Partner: Michael Simmons
Number of Partners: 20
Total Staff: 127

This long-established, medium sized firm, based in Covent Garden, mixes commercial and private client work, with the emphasis now on corporate work.

The firm: Malkin Cullis & Sumption celebrates its centenary in 1989. It was a small mixed City practice until after the Second World War, when a tax and corporate practice developed and then it merged with one or two small firms. The business/private client mix has been retained although, as the firm has expanded, the quality of the clientele has improved. Over the next five years the firm foresees general growth with a greater emphasis on corporate work.

The firm is keen to interview experienced solicitors. Apply to Mr M Simmons.

Three articled clerks are generally recruited annually. Mature candidates, including those making a career change, are sought. Apply by handwritten letter (plus CV and referees) to Linda Humphreys.

Agency work: The firm undertakes work for overseas lawyers and for UK practices with whom it already has a relationship.

Types of work undertaken: The firm is organised into four departments, namely company/commercial, litigation, property, and private client. The client base is extremely mixed and consists of large public companies

and institutions, including insurers and underwriters; lenders; landlords and tenants; smaller companies, particularly those with an entrepreneurial flavour, both public and private; and individuals. The firm has a considerable overseas clientele.

This is a broadly based general practice with particular emphasis on conveyancing, litigation, divorce and company/commercial work. In recent years, the firm has developed expertise in immigration law and management consultancy to the professions.

Conveyancing and litigation are strongly commercially based, but the firm also undertakes private work in both these fields. The property department acts for established UK and overseas property investors and is involved in security work for banks, building societies and other financial institutions. The litigation department handles a considerable amount of heavyweight commercial work and, in conjunction with associates abroad, is involved in numerous international matters. The work of the company/commercial department includes handling all aspects of company structure and finance, taxation and investment matters, commercial agreements, employment law and intellectual property.

Overall, Malkin Cullis & Sumption perceives itself as a firm operating to the highest professional standards which, at the same time, is businesslike and always does the best possible for its clients. A brochure is available.

Malkin Cullis & Sumption

Manby & Steward

MANDER HOUSE
MANDER CENTRE
WOLVERHAMPTON
WV1 3NE
Phone: 0902 772711

Fax: 0902 24321
DX: 10403 WOLVERHAMPTON-1
Telex: 265451 **Other offices:** 3
Senior Partner: Robert King
Number of Partners: 16
Total Staff: 106

The firm is based in the West Midlands and offers comprehensive legal services for both private and commercial clients.

The firm: Manby & Steward has over 150 years' experience as solicitors. Established in 1826 by William Manby, it has expanded rapidly over the last two decades, maintaining its strong identity as family solicitors and, at the same time, developing a vigorous commercial practice. It is organised into departments.

This expanding practice sees a continuing need for qualified solicitors over the next few years; enquiries to the partnership secretary.

Three articled clerks are recruited annually. Prospects are very good: nine of the present partners served articles with the firm. Applications by handwritten letter (plus CV and referees) should be addressed to the partnership secretary in September for the following year.

Other offices: Dudley, Bridgnorth, Telford. The firm also has associated offices in Brussels, Paris and Munster.

Agency work: The firm undertakes litigation work for other solicitors. For details contact Clive Williams.

Types of work undertaken: This expanding West Midlands practice retains its family solicitor character, while expanding its commercial work. As would be expected of such a long-established firm there are a substantial number of private clients as well as local industrial and commercial concerns. It offers wide-ranging company and commercial services and handles commercial litigation and employment law matters.

The firm is particularly well known for commercial leasing, employment, town planning, and child care and family law. Its strong private client department deals with all aspects of family law, including separation and divorce together with the problems of finance and custody. It also handles employment matters such as unfair dismissal, redundancy and sex or racial discrimination.

The commercial property department deals with leasing, buying and selling, and has considerable experience in the field of planning, handling negotiations with planning authorities and landowners and acts for developers, builders and housing associations.

The firm offers substantial advice in the specialist area of agriculture, including representing clients before agricultural land tribunal hearings.

This rapidly expanding provincial firm is looking forward to 1992 by creating associations with European law offices. Overall, it sees itself as helpful and pleasant to deal with. A brochure is available for clients.

Manches & Co

10 DUKE STREET
LONDON
W1M 6BH

Phone: 01 486 6050

Fax: 01 935 1276
DX: 76 LONDON CHANCERY LANE WC2
Telex: 266174 **Other offices:** 1
Senior Partner: Alasdair John Simpson
Number of Partners: 16
Total Staff: 112

Manches & Co is a medium sized and principally commercial London practice with an active private client department.

The firm: Founded in the City in 1937, the firm moved 20 years ago to its present offices in the West End. Its five main departments have grown considerably in recent years and the partners are committed to a programme of continued expansion.

Manches & Co require several assistant solicitors in 1989, in the company/commercial, commercial property, commercial tax and intellectual property departments. Enquiries to the senior partner, Mr AJ Simpson.

Five articled clerks are recruited annually. Those with a good degree, not necessarily in law, should apply (with CV and two referees) to Mr JS Foster two years in advance.

Other offices: Oxford.

Agency work: The Litigation Department acts in substantial commercial cases.

Types of work undertaken: The firm is primarily concerned with commercial transactions, but has a very active private client department handling matrimonial, probate and residential conveyancing. Clients range from major public companies to individuals setting up new businesses.

Particular expertise include corporate finance work, management buy-outs, commercial work in the Lloyd's insurance market, tax and trusts, family law, property development and investment, residential estate development, substantial litigation, employment and intellectual property.

The Company/Commercial Department handles company acquisitions and disposals, joint ventures and partnerships, takeovers, mergers, service agreements, share options and other executive incentive schemes, competition law, computer contracts, commercial trading agreements and intellectual property.

The Commercial Property Department deals with development and funding work for major property companies; acquisition, development and management work for multiple retailers; secured lending; and the general property requirements of businesses.

The work of the Litigation Department is essentially commercial and includes breach of contract, professional negligence, personal injury, property disputes and actions between employers and employees.

The Tax Department specialises in commercial tax, trusts and personal tax.

Manches & Co is regarded as having a courteous, fair, efficient and firm approach, in the best interests of its clients. It has an ever-increasing City presence based on a depth of expertise in commercial and corporate matters, and maintains its strong traditional links with property and tax work.

MANCHES & CO

March Pearson & Skelton

41 SPRING GARDENS
MANCHESTER
M2 2BB

Phone: 061 832 7290

Fax: 061 832 2655
DX: 14349 MANCHESTER-1
Telex: 669489
Senior Partner: Mr SP Green
Number of Partners: 11
Total Staff: 70

Martin Tolhurst Partnership

7 WROTHAM ROAD
GRAVESEND
KENT
DA11 0PD
Phone: 0474 325531

Fax: 0474 560771
DX: 6801 GRAVESEND
Telex: none **Other offices:** 4
Senior Partner: Mr AL Martin
Number of Partners: 11
Total Staff: 90

Maxwell Batley

27 CHANCERY LANE
LONDON
WC2A 1PA

Phone: 01 405 7888

Fax: 01 242 7133
DX: 190 LONDON CHANCERY LANE WC2
Telex: 28717 **Other offices:** 1
Senior Partner: Mr DJ Jefferson
Number of Partners: 10
Total Staff: 68

Maxwell Entwistle & Byrne

14 CASTLE STREET
LIVERPOOL
L2 0SG

Phone: 051 227 4545

Fax: 051 227 5468
DX: 14192 SOLIHULL-2
Telex: none **Other offices:** 8
Senior Partner: Mr TFJ Costigan
Number of Partners: 12
Total Staff: 81

Marshalls *see full-page profile*
Martineau Johnson *see full-page profile*
Masons *see full-page profile*

Marshalls
(formerly Day Whately & Co)

102 HIGH STREET
GODALMING
SURREY
GU7 1DS
Phone: 04868 6101

Fax: 04868 27265
DX: 58354 GODALMING
Telex: 859909
Other offices: 1
Number of Partners: 5
Total Staff: 56

This small but thriving Surrey firm offers a full legal service to a wide range of business and private clients.

The firm: Founded in Godalming in 1831 by Henry Marshall, the firm subsequently changed its name to Day Whately & Co, but has recently reverted to Marshalls. The emphasis in the original practice was on conveyancing and probate, areas which continue to be strong. During recent years, however, the commercial and litigation departments have expanded considerably. Indeed, all areas of the firm have expanded rapidly in the last five years. The firm is organised into departments.

In 1989, the firm expects to have two vacancies for assistant solicitors. Enquiries to Sara Coate.

In addition, six articled clerks are recruited annually. Prospects after qualification are excellent, given the expansion rate of the firm. Applications should be made one year in advance by letter (with CV) to Sara Coate.

Other offices: Woking.

Agency work: The firm accepts work from other solicitors. For litigation work, contact Marc Lazarus; for property, contact Anne-Marie Kitson.

Types of work undertaken: As is to be expected of a long-established provincial firm, this is a broadly based practice. The mixed business and private client base is largely local in nature, although the number of regional and national clients is growing rapidly.

The firm has four main departments, namely company/commercial; property; litigation; and tax, probate and trusts.

The company/commercial department is the largest in the firm, and handles all aspects of commercial work for a wide range of clients, from local businesses (incorporated and unincorporated), to large private companies (situated in London and throughout the UK), and PLCs. The firm is particularly well known for its commercial joint venture work and growing intellectual property practice, as well as commercial property work.

The work of the litigation department encompasses commercial, general civil and some criminal work. There is a strong conveyancing department handling both commercial and domestic work, as well as time-share agreements. Other private client work covers advice on all aspects of probate, trusts and taxation.

Overall, Marshalls sees itself as a young, energetic and ambitious partnership, which upholds the profession's traditional standards of integrity but also embraces the modern management and marketing concepts.

Marshalls

Martineau Johnson

ST PHILIPS HOUSE
ST PHILIPS PLACE
BIRMINGHAM
B3 2PP
Phone: 021 200 3300

Fax: 021 200 3330
DX: 13031 BIRMINGHAM-1
Telex: 339793
Senior Partner: Theo Christophers
Number of Partners: 22
Total Staff: 130

One of the largest firms of solicitors in Birmingham, Martineau Johnson is a broadly based practice serving a wide range of commercial and private clients.

The firm: Martineau Johnson was formed in 1987 with the merger of Ryland Martineau and Johnson & Co, which were established in 1828 and 1876 respectively. Both firms were city-centre practices with strong commercial and financial links combined with substantial traditions of private client service. The new firm is expanding its commercial practice while maintaining its private client base.

There is a need for qualified staff, and in 1989 the firm expects to recruit at least ten solicitors. Enquiries to Simon Arrowsmith.

There are normally ten or 12 vacancies for articled clerks each year. Prospects after qualification are excellent: most of the present partners served articles with the firm. Apply by letter (with CV) or by form two years in advance to Michael Fea.

Agency work: Local civil litigation work is accepted; contact Brian Aikman.

Types of work undertaken: Martineau Johnson's practice is broadly based across commercial, property, civil litigation, private client and institutional work. The firm's clients include major corporations, small local businesses, banks and other financial institutions, universities and polytechnics, churches, charities and very substantial private clients.

On the commercial side, the firm has a high reputation for its USM, venture capital, buy-out and 'City' work, including acquisitions, project finance, technology transfer and international business arrangements.

The particular strength of the litigation department is in civil cases, with the emphasis on commercial and employment matters (including intellectual property, planning appeals, insolvency, landlord and tenant, building contracts, partnership disputes and personal injury claims). Domestic and personal disputes are also handled by the department.

The private client department has considerable experience in personal financial and tax planning, ecclesiastical law and charity matters. Clients include a number of educational establishments, landed estates and wealthy individuals. The work involves the writing of wills and settlements, administering trusts and estates, estate management, related tax matters and probate.

Overall, Martineau Johnson sees itself as a high quality, soundly based provincial practice, combining a traditional approach to client-partner relations with the modern drive for expansion and expertise. Brochures describing the work of the firm are available.

MARTINEAU JOHNSON

Masons

10 FLEET STREET
LONDON
EC4Y 1BA

Phone: 01 583 9990

Fax: 01 353 8810
DX: 63 LONDON CHANCERY LANE WC2
Telex: 8811117 **Other offices:** 4
Senior Partner: Bill Heys
Number of Partners: 32
Total Staff: 245

This City firm has a long-established practice in building and engineering law and has increasing strengths in other fields.

The firm: Masons has experienced a period of sustained growth in the last 15 years. It has opened two additional UK offices as well as one overseas and is opening an office in Manchester this year. It also has three associate international offices (Cairo, Grand Cayman, Beijing). From its original strengths in the litigation and construction fields the firm has expanded into many other commercial and property-related areas of practice, both in the UK and abroad.

There is a continuing need for qualified staff, and in 1989 the firm expects to recruit assistant solicitors for commercial litigation, construction and engineering, private client, company/commercial and property. Enquiries to John Bishop, managing partner.

In addition, 10 articled clerks are recruited annually. A 2(2) degree or above, not necessarily in law, is preferred. Long-term prospects are good: a third of the present partners were articled with the firm. Apply by letter (with CV) to Martin Roberts.

Other offices: Bristol, Leatherhead, Manchester, Hong Kong.

Agency work: The firm accepts Privy Council work from other solicitors and will also act as London agents in certain cases.

Types of work undertaken: One of the leading firms in building and civil engineering law, Masons offers clients a thorough and comprehensive service covering the whole construction process. The emphasis is on prevention rather than cure whenever possible, and the service includes contract drafting and detailed advice during the contract period. When disputes arise, Masons has wide experience of negotiation, litigation and arbitration in the UK and in numerous overseas jurisdictions.

Litigation experience beyond construction-related matters includes commercial, contractual and tortious liability disputes, labour law, insolvency, insurance, and intellectual property.

The company/commercial practice centres on mergers and acquisitions, but also includes corporate finance, joint ventures, business start-ups and general corporate and commercial work. There is a vigorous property division advising developers, banks and others in connection with all aspects of the acquisition, development and sale of property, with planning law as a particular strength. The firm is at the forefront of the development of environmental law.

Masons sees itself as one of the foremost law firms in construction and engineering and is expanding fast in these and other areas.

Mayo & Perkins

CLARENDON HOUSE
20 GILDREDGE ROAD
EASTBOURNE
EAST SUSSEX BN21 4RP
Phone: 0323 30543

Fax: 0323 37214
DX: 6900 EASTBOURNE
Telex: none **Other offices:** 3
Senior Partner: Mr HA Riddick
Number of Partners: 11
Total Staff: 86

McClure Naismith Anderson & Gardiner

292 ST VINCENT STREET
GLASGOW
G2 5TQ

Phone: 041 204 2700

Fax: 041 248 3998
Rutland Exchange: 64 GLASGOW
Telex: 779233 **Other offices:** 1
Senior Partner: Mr WM Millar
Number of Partners: 18
Total Staff: 120

McGrigor Donald

PACIFIC HOUSE
70 WELLINGTON STREET
GLASGOW
G2 6SB
Phone: 041 248 6677

Fax: 041 204 1351
Rutland Exchange: 135 GLASGOW
Telex: 778744 **Other offices:** 2
Senior Partner: Mr F Shedden
Number of Partners: 36
Total Staff: 214

Merrils Ede

PRINCIPALITY BUILDINGS
QUEEN STREET
CARDIFF
CF1 4LR
Phone: 0222 371111

Fax: 0222 383469
DX: 33003 CARDIFF
Telex: none **Other offices:** 5
Senior Partner: Mr Sidney Isaacs
Number of Partners: 13
Total Staff: 60

McKenna & Co *see full-page profile*
Memery Crystal *see full-page profile*

McKenna & Co

INVERESK HOUSE
1 ALDWYCH
LONDON
WC2R 0HF
Phone: 01 836 2442

Fax: 01 379 3059
DX: 724 LONDON CITY EC3
Telex: 27251 **Other offices:** 7
Senior Partner: Mr RH Malthouse
Number of Partners: 60
Total Staff: 554

One of the major City firms, McKenna & Co has a substantial broadly based commercial practice, both domestic and international.

The firm: McKenna & Co was founded in 1882 and has experienced its greatest period of growth since the mid-1970s. The firm's reputation has been built on its thriving corporate and commercial law, construction, litigation and property practices. The firm is organised into departments.

McKenna & Co has a continuing need for assistant solicitors for all areas of the practice. Languages, particularly Mandarin and Japanese, as well as the principal European languages, are an advantage. In addition, the firm employs specialists (such as engineers and chemists) to assist in technical work, and encourages them to train as solicitors. Apply to Bernadette Willoughby.

The firm recruits about 35 articled clerks every year. A degree is the minimum academic requirement, and the firm judges applicants on individual merit. Applications should be by form (available on request) two years in advance (late applications considered) and addressed to Sally Hinton.

Other offices: London (City and Lloyd's), Bahrain, Brussels, Hong Kong, Singapore, Tokyo.

Types of work undertaken: The firm is well known for its corporate practice including corporate finance (Stock Exchange, financial services, privatisation); banking, rescheduling and recoveries, project and development finance; asset leasing; insolvency; mergers, acquisitions and disposals; corporate reorganisations, management and leveraged buy-outs; corporate tax; employment and pensions; and EEC and UK competition law.

The firm is a leader in the field of construction law and also for major projects often, but not always, in the construction field. The firm has developed a reputation for commercial property work including development work and planning.

The firm handles litigation and dispute resolution particularly in corporate affairs, financial services, insurance, environmental law and product liability and has expertise in intellectual property, acting for traditional and high-technology industries including bio-technology and information technology, and also advises on business in China.

McKenna & Co offers a broadly based international service, accommodating the demands of particular transactions, projects or problems.

This is one of the major London firms, with recognised expertise in a number of fields and a strong international presence. Brochures describing the services the firm offers to clients are available on request.

McKENNA & Co

Memery Crystal

31 SOUTHAMPTON ROW
LONDON
WC1B 5HT

Phone: 01 242 5905

Fax: 01 242 2058
DX: 156 LONDON CHANCERY LANE WC2
Telex: 298957
Senior Partner: Peter M Crystal
Number of Partners: 7
Total Staff: 56

The emphasis in this small but thriving central London firm is on commercial business and corporate matters.

The firm: John Memery and Peter Crystal, both of whom had been with large London practices, founded Memery Crystal in 1978 in response to what they saw as the commercial community's need for a closer relationship and a faster response from solicitors who knew and understood the way the City operates.

Expansion in the 1980s has been rapid and there is a continuing need for good qualified staff. In 1989 the firm expects to recruit four assistant solicitors, one for each department. Enquiries to Sue Cooke.

In addition, the firm normally recruits one or two articled clerks every year. The educational requirement is a law degree. Apply by handwritten letter (with CV and names of referees) two years in advance to Mr JP Davies.

Agency work: Work is accepted from other solicitors.

Types of work undertaken: Memery Crystal sees itself as a young and growing firm of the 1980s, which is forward looking and possesses the expertise and capacity to act quickly for corporate clients.

The work undertaken by the firm breaks down into three main areas: company/commercial, litigation and property. Clients range from public to private companies and partnerships. Much of the work is of an international nature, and the firm has established links with lawyers in Hong Kong, Singapore, Malaysia, Australia, EEC capitals and the USA.

The work of the company/commercial department covers the full range of commercial business. It is well known for advising medium sized companies on entry to USM and the Third Market, on capital raising and on acquisitions. Employment matters are also handled by the department, and there is an increasing intellectual property and entertainment law practice covering copyright, licensing, and 'know-how' agreements, particularly for film production companies, and the high-profile electronics and high-tech related industries.

The litigation work undertaken by the firm is primarily in commercial matters in the High Court and other tribunals. Litigation is often conducted in close collaboration with other departments, particularly when a swift and incisive judicial remedy is needed.

The property department acts for investment institutions involved in the purchase or sale of industrial estates, shops or offices, property development companies, listed companies with investment property, and individuals buying domestic property.

MEMERY CRYSTAL

Metcalfe, Copeman & Pettefar

6 YORK ROW
WISBECH
CAMBRIDGESHIRE
PE13 1EF
Phone: 0945 64331

Fax: 0945 584767
DX: 41350 WISBECH
Telex: 32719 **Other offices:** 4
Senior Partner: Mr JR Bostock
Number of Partners: 12
Total Staff: 78

A medium sized firm with five offices, Metcalfe, Copeman & Pettefar has a traditional provincial practice with a commercial bias.

The firm: Founded some 200 years ago in Wisbech, the firm has expanded since the Second World War, establishing offices in nearby King's Lynn and Downham Market, and more recently in Peterborough and Thetford. Over the years, the firm has retained its traditional private client base and, although it has always done a certain amount of commercial work, this area of the practice has expanded rapidly in the last ten years.

The firm describes its recruitment needs for qualified staff as 'continuous'. In 1989 it expects to have vacancies for four assistant solicitors: for property (two) and litigation (two). Enquiries should be addressed to the recruitment partner.

In addition, the firm recruits two or three articled clerks every year. There are no set educational requirements; the firm judges applicants on individual merits. Prospects after qualification are good; most articled clerks stay with the firm. Applications should be made by handwritten letter at anytime addressed to the recruitment partner.

Other offices: Downham Market, King's Lynn, Peterborough, Thetford.

Types of work undertaken: This is a traditional, but increasingly commercially orientated, provincial practice operating from five offices of a similar size. The client base is wide and includes national and local companies and substantial farming companies, as well as private individuals.

Metcalfe, Copeman & Pettefar is well known for its commercial and residential property development work, including related planning aspects.

There is a particularly strong litigation practice, handling personal injury claims (usually on behalf of plaintiffs) and criminal cases, as well as general litigation work. The firm has several experienced advocates and their expertise has attracted a substantial amount of work from large retail companies defending actions concerning consumer protection, Sunday trading and other matters.

Company/commercial is an expanding area of the practice, and includes company sales and purchases, reorganisations, commercial contracts, and partnership agreements.

Private client work continues to be important; the firm handles the full range of trust, probate, and family law. Legal aid work is also undertaken.

Metcalfe, Copeman & Pettefar considers itself to be a highly motivated traditional practice with the special expertise needed to meet the demands imposed by the rapid expansion of the East Anglian economy.

Metcalfe, Copeman & Pettefar

Michael Freeman & Co

ONE GREAT CUMBERLAND PLACE
LONDON
W1H 7AL

Phone: 01 258 3434

Fax: 01 724 6823
DX: 4 LONDON CHANCERY LANE WC2
Telex: 27526
Senior Partner: Michael D Freeman
Number of Partners: 9
Total Staff: 60

This central London firm is a predominantly commercial practice with a private client department.

The firm: Established in 1967 by the present senior partner, the firm has expanded organically from a one-person practice to a thriving, medium sized firm. The clientele has always consisted mainly of entrepreneurs involved in a wide variety of business.

Michael Freeman & Co expects to have two vacancies for assistant solicitors in 1989, one in company/commercial and one in property. Enquiries to Mr RM Roseman.

The firm normally has two vacancies for articled clerks every year. A 2(1) degree is preferred, not necessarily in law, although the firm assesses candidates on individual merits. Apply in writing (with CV and referees) to Mr RM Roseman two years in advance.

Agency work: The firm accepts litigation work from other solicitors; contact Mr RM Roseman.

Types of work undertaken: Michael Freeman & Co is predominantly a commercial practice with a very wide client base, ranging from individuals and private companies to public companies and multinationals. There are four main departments, commercial and residential property, company/commercial, litigation, and private client.

All the departments are well known for their expertise, and a 'team approach' is adopted when a matter calls for expertise in different fields. In recent years the firm has been involved in several highly complex and very substantial matters where the 'other side' has been represented by major City firms.

The property department has a high reputation for its work which covers the full range of transactions, from the acquisition, financing and development of large commercial sites, to agricultural property matters and residential conveyancing.

The company/commercial department handles a wide variety of work such as corporate formations, disposals and acquisitions, share issues and trading documentation.

The litigation department deals with all manner of cases including company/partnership, landlord and tenant, intellectual property, professional negligence, building disputes, libel and slander, and some matrimonial work is undertaken.

The private client department deals with tax, trusts, wills and probate.

Michael Freeman & Co sees itself as a firm of lawyers which is aware of the commercial realities of the business world, of the need to consider every problem in the round and not simply within the confines of one particular discipline, and of the importance of speed, acumen and common sense in all its dealings.

MICHAEL FREEMAN & CO.

Middleton Potts

3 CLOTH STREET
LONG LANE
LONDON
EC1A 7LD
Phone: 01 600 2333

Fax: 01 600 0108
DX: 46621 BARBICAN
Telex: 928357
Senior Partner: William Middleton
Number of Partners: 14
Total Staff: 70

This City firm offers the full range of company and commercial legal services to financial, commercial and industrial clients from all parts of the world.

The firm: Middleton Potts was founded in 1976 by William Middleton, Christopher Potts and four other partners, all of whom had been with a well-established City practice. The strong commercial nature of the firm has been retained and strengthened, and the firm has expanded sixfold since its conception.

Because of rapid expansion the firm requires between four to eight assistant solicitors in 1989 for all departments. Enquiries should be addressed to Mr CD Lucas.

Six to eight articled clerks are recruited each year. The minimum requirement is a 2(1) degree, not necessarily in law. Applications by handwritten letter (plus CV) should be made in August/September two years in advance to Mr CD Lucas.

Types of work undertaken: The firm is divided into three departments, namely company/commercial (non-contentious), commercial litigation, and property. The client base is strongly international, with long-standing Italian links and newer connections with clients in western Europe, North America, the Middle East, the Indian subcontinent and the Far East. Clients cover a

broad commercial and industrial spectrum and include banks, insurance companies, P and I Clubs, oil majors and traders, commodity traders, ship owners and other companies involved in all aspects of shipping and international trade.

As well as its prominence in the company and commercial field, the firm is especially renowned for its commercial litigation practice, and in particular shipping and commodities work. The degree of its success may be gauged by the frequency with which its name appears in law reports: Lexis records 148 reported cases between March 1977 and June 1988, more than one case a month. This takes no account, of course, of the very high percentage of major commercial disputes which are resolved by arbitration: the firm always aims to achieve the best commercial result for clients, which is often a negotiated settlement rather than full litigation.

Among the broad range of services offered by the company/commercial department are finance and banking, corporate and commercial matters, insurance, employment, tax and intellectual property.

In view of the very strong international element of its work the firm has developed close worldwide legal contacts.

Middleton Potts sees itself as a young, rapidly developing firm with a reputation for producing the highest calibre work with a high measure of integrity.

MIDDLETON POTTS

Mills & Reeve Francis

3-7 REDWELL STREET
NORWICH
NR2 4TJ

Phone: 0603 660155

Fax: 0603 633027
DX: 5210 NORWICH
Telex: 97375 **Other offices:** 2
Senior Partner: Michael M Orr
Number of Partners: 43
Total Staff: 300

One of the largest regional firms, Mills & Reeve Francis is a broadly based practice with a strong commercial emphasis.

The firm: Mills & Reeve Francis is the merger of two old-established firms in Norwich and Cambridge. The expansion of the firm, particularly within Cambridge, reflected the rapid growth of Cambridge and Norwich as commercial and technological centres, as well as the agricultural nature of the region. Mills & Reeve Francis is a member of the M5 group (see separate entry).

The firm is always interested in able and enthusiastic assistant solicitors, particularly for company/commercial work. Enquiries to the personnel manager, Charlotte Points at the Norwich address.

In addition, the firm recruits up to 15 articled clerks every year. The preferred academic qualification is a 2(1) degree. Prospects after qualification are good and many of the present partners served articles with the firm. Apply by letter (with CV and names of referees) by September to the personnel manager, as above.

Other offices: Cambridge, St Helier (Jersey).

Agency work: The firm accepts litigation work from other solicitors; contact Ed Callaghan, Norwich.

Types of work undertaken: As one would expect of a major regional practice, the firm offers the full range of legal services to a wide variety of clients, both private and commercial.

The litigation department has expanded greatly in the fields of professional indemnity, commercial work (including intellectual property work), employment law and agricultural matters.

There is a strong emphasis in the unusually large private client department on tax and estate planning, for landowners and farmers as well as for established and growing companies and businesses. The agricultural law unit is part of the private client department.

The usual range of general solicitors' work is undertaken (including family, personal injury and conveyancing). Legal aid work is accepted.

On the commercial side, the firm has earned a high reputation for all aspects of commercial and company law, corporate finance, partnerships and property.

In brief, Mills & Reeve Francis perceives itself as an efficient, progressive, commercial practice, which is committed to providing a wide range of legal services throughout the East Anglian region, as well as for national and overseas clients.

Brochures describing the work of the firm are available for clients and articled clerks.

MILLS & REEVE FRANCIS

Milne Mackinnon & Peterkins

BURGH HOUSE
7 KING STREET
ABERDEEN
AB2 3AA
Phone: 0224 645046

Fax: 0224 634256
Rutland Exchange: 40 ABERDEEN
Telex: 739342 **Other offices:** 5
Senior Partner: Mr Patrick Davies
Number of Partners: 18
Total Staff: 84

Mincoff Science & Gold

4-6 OSBORNE ROAD
JESMOND
NEWCASTLE UPON TYNE
NE2 2AA
Phone: 091 2816151

Fax: 091 2818069
DX: 61027 NEWCASTLE UPON TYNE
Telex: 537211
Senior Partner: Mr Austen SCIENCE
Number of Partners: 7
Total Staff: 61

Mitchells Robertson

GEORGE HOUSE
36 NORTH HANOVER STREET
GLASGOW
G1 2AD
Phone: 041 552 3422

Fax: 041 552 2935
Rutland Exchange: 77 GLASGOW
Telex: 777257
Senior Partner: Mr NW McMillan
Number of Partners: 14
Total Staff: 58

Moore & Blatch

48 HIGH STREET
LYMINGTON
HAMPSHIRE
SO41 9ZQ
Phone: 0590 72371

Fax: 0590 71224
DX: 34050 LYMINGTON
Telex: none **Other offices:** 7
Senior Partner: Mr PO Ziegler
Number of Partners: 17
Total Staff: 170

Mishcon de Reya *see full-page profile*

Mishcon de Reya

125 HIGH HOLBORN
LONDON
WC1V 6QP

Phone: 01 405 3711

Fax: 01 404 5982
DX: 65 LONDON CHANCERY LANE WC2
Telex: 21455
Senior Partner: Lord Mishcon
Number of Partners: 18
Total Staff: 120

Mischon de Reya is a medium sized City commercial practice offering a full range of legal services.

The firm: Victor Mischon & Co was founded 50 years ago. In 1988 the firm merged with seven partners of Bartletts de Reya, including its entire entertainment, arts and media department and solicitors from the property and commercial departments. The senior partner, Lord Mishcon, is vice-chairman of the Solicitors' All-party Parliamentary Committee of the Law Society and the Opposition spokesman in the House of Lords on both home and legal affairs.

This rapidly expanding firm has a continuing need for solicitors in all departments. It recruits five or six articled clerks annually. Candidates should have a good post-qualification degree, non-law graduates are encouraged. Prospects are excellent. Apply on the firm's form to Ms S Davis or Mr A Julius.

Types of work undertaken: Mishcon de Reya's practice is commercial in nature. It is divided into six departments, namely litigation, entertainment, property, company/commercial, matrimonial and private client. The client base encompasses both corporate and private clients. The firm is well known for its work in intellectual property, family, entertainment, commercial property and planning, defamation and employment.

The entertainment and media department advises on and negotiates agreements in all areas of the media including film, television and video, cable and satellite, theatre, music recording and management, book publishing, and computer and information technology.

The contentious legal work undertaken by the litigation department includes libel, media and entertainment, patents, contempt of court, UK and international disputes, employment and trade union law, company and shareholder litigation, landlord and tenant, building disputes, insurance and reinsurance, fraud and securities offences, personal injury and medical negligence.

The property department offers a comprehensive legal service covering all aspects of property work including planning. The company/commercial department's work ranges from company formations and shareholder agreements, mergers and acquisitions, to flotations, employment contracts and pensions. The matrimonial department provides advice relating to family matters, and the private client department handles all matters affecting personal status and property.

The firm perceives itself as one of the leading integrated media practices, as well as a top property practice, having combined a solid reputation with the complementary experience and vitality of young partners.

MISHCON DE REYA

Morton Fisher

CARLTON HOUSE
WORCESTER STREET
KIDDERMINSTER
WORCESTER DY10 1BA
Phone: 0562 820181

Fax: 0562 820066
DX: 16301 KIDDERMINSTER
Telex: none **Other offices:** 5
Senior Partner: Mr MF James
Number of Partners: 20
Total Staff: 140

Mounseys

19 CASTLE STREET
CARLISLE
CUMBRIA
CA3 8TW
Phone: 0228 25195

Fax: 0228 511051
DX: 63105 CARLISLE
Telex: none **Other offices:** 3
Senior Partner: Mr IS Sutcliffe
Number of Partners: 12
Total Staff: 75

Mullis & Peake

MARSHALLS CHAMBERS
80A SOUTH STREET
ROMFORD
ESSEX RM1 1QS
Phone: 0708 762326

Fax: 0708 47145
DX: 4604 ROMFORD
Telex: none **Other offices:** 3
Senior Partner: Mr C Mullis
Number of Partners: 8
Total Staff: 70

Mundays

THE BELLBOURNE
103 HIGH STREET
ESHER
SURREY KT10 9QE
Phone: 0372 67272

Fax: 0372 63782
DX: 36300 ESHER
Telex: 897742 **Other offices:** 3
Senior Partner: Mr P Munday
Number of Partners: 9
Total Staff: 51

Morgan Bruce & Hardwickes *see full-page profile*
Morton Fraser & Milligan WS *see full-page profile*

Morgan Bruce & Hardwickes

1 MUSEUM PLACE
CARDIFF
CF1 3TX

Phone: 0222 233677

Fax: 0222 399288
DX: 33014 CARDIFF
Telex: 497902 **Other offices:** 3
Senior Partner: Raymond Griffiths
Number of Partners: 27
Total Staff: 171

Morgan Bruce & Hardwickes is one of the leading independent law firms in Wales and offers the full range of legal services.

The firm: In 1987 two long-established South Wales practices — Morgan Bruce & Nicholas, which dates from 1876, and Hardwickes of Cardiff, founded in 1912 — merged to form Morgan Bruce & Hardwickes. The new firm's Swansea office derives from a further merger with the commercial practice of Geo L Thomas Nettleship & Co in 1988.

The firm has a continuing requirement for high-quality staff, and in 1989 expects to have up to ten vacancies for assistant solicitors in all departments. Enquiries to the partnership administrator, David Jones.

Six to 12 articled clerks are recruited annually. A 2(2) degree, not necessarily in law, is required. Apply (with CV and name of referee) in September of final university year to the partnership administrator.

Other offices: Swansea, Pontypridd, Porth.

Agency work: All types of work are accepted from other solicitors; contact Philip Howell-Richardson (Cardiff) or Emyr Lewis (Swansea).

Types of work undertaken: The firm is divided into four main departments, namely company/commercial, commercial property, litigation and private client.

The company/commercial department has earned a formidable reputation through acting for a wide range of government agencies, local authorities and financial institutions, as well as public and private companies. The department has particular expertise in corporate investment by financial institutions, acquisitions and disposals, intellectual property and insolvency.

The litigation department is well known as a leading defendant insurance practice and for construction law work, professional negligence and NHS and other health related work. Clients also include private and public companies, financial institutions, statutory bodies and professional associations as well as the individual.

The commercial property department serves the requirements of a number of developers, breweries and public authorities, and increasingly is involved with major office, shop and factory developments. It also has particular expertise in housing association matters and Spanish property transactions. In the well-established private client department there is wide experience in major probate, trust and financial planning work.

The firm sees itself as a modern and expansive commercial practice upholding the traditional values of integrity and reliability. Brochures are available on request.

MORGAN BRUCE & HARDWICKES

Morton Fraser & Milligan WS

15 & 19 YORK PLACE
EDINBURGH
EH1 3EL

Phone: 031 556 8444

Fax: 031 557 3778
Rutland Exchange: 119 EDINBURGH
Telex: 727248
Senior Partner: John Wightman CBE
Number of Partners: 15
Total Staff: 99

The Edinburgh firm of Morton Fraser & Milligan offers a wide range of legal services to commercial and private clients.

The firm: Morton Fraser & Milligan was formed by the 1968 amalgamation of three Edinburgh firms, all of which had roots in the eighteenth century. Initially, each partner followed the Scottish tradition of acting as the 'man of business' for clients. More recently, as the firm grew and the need for specialisation became more important, the firm reorganised into departments.

This expanding firm has a continuing need for high-calibre assistant solicitors, especially in residential property and company/commercial. Apply to the staff partner.

Currently, four trainees are recruited every year. The minimum educational requirements are a law degree and a DipLP. Prospects after qualification are excellent; almost all of the present partners were apprenticed to the firm. Apply by handwritten letter (with CV and names of referees) one year in advance to the staff partner.

Agency work: The firm accepts work from other solicitors, including all aspects of company/commercial, employment, family and personal injury matters, or any work where expertise in Scottish law is required.

Types of work undertaken: The work of the firm is divided into four departments. The company/commercial department deals with both national and international business for clients ranging from the largest corporate entities to small family businesses. The department is well known for its expertise in licensing law, equipment leasing, pension schemes and commercial property. The department handles all forms of commercial work, from banking to employment and computer law.

The litigation department deals with commercial and private client litigation, covering commercial disputes, arbitration and industrial tribunals, contractual disputes, matrimonial matters, civil legal aid work and debt collection.

The personal services department offers everything required by the private client, including wills, tax, investment and financial planning, and farm and estate work. In addition, the firm does a significant amount of charitable trust work, for which it has gained a high reputation.

There is a strong residential property department, and through Morton Fraser Relocation Ltd the firm provides employers with employee relocation packages.

Morton Fraser & Milligan sees itself as a modern expert practice with a tradition of academic excellence. While there is a strong emphasis on commercial work, the firm offers a personal service for the private client.

Murray Beith & Murray WS

39 CASTLE STREET
EDINBURGH
EH2 3BH

Phone: 031 225 1200

Fax: 031 225 4412
Rutland Exchange: 40 EDINBURGH
Telex: 727429
Senior Partner: Mr GW Burnet
Number of Partners: 10
Total Staff: 62

Nabarro Nathanson

50 STRATTON STREET
LONDON
W1X 5FL

Phone: 01 493 9933

Fax: 01 629 7900
DX: 77 LONDON CHANCERY LANE WC2
Telex: 8813144
Senior Partner: Mr J Greenwood
Number of Partners: 70
Total Staff: 550

Nalder & Son

FARLEY HOUSE
FALMOUTH ROAD
TRURO
CORNWALL TR1 2AT
Phone: 0872 41414

Fax: 0872 42424
DX: none
Telex: none **Other offices:** 3
Senior Partner: Mr JB Pollock
Number of Partners: 9
Total Staff: 60

Nelsons

SCARBOROUGH HOUSE
30-32 BRIDLESMITH GATE
NOTTINGHAM
NG1 2GQ
Phone: 0602 586262

Fax: 0602 584702
DX: 10096 NOTTINGHAM
Telex: none **Other offices:** 2
Senior Partner: Mr RW Nelson
Number of Partners: 9
Total Staff: 60

Needham & James *see full-page profile*

Needham & James

WINDSOR HOUSE
TEMPLE ROW
BIRMINGHAM
B2 5LF
Phone: 021 200 1188

Fax: 021 236 9228
DX: 13022 BIRMINGHAM·1
Telex: 338460 **Other offices:** 3
Senior Partner: Keith R James
Number of Partners: 28
Total Staff: 250

Although Needham & James was originally a general practice, the firm is now almost exclusively a commercial practice.

The firm: Needham & James was founded as a general practice in Birmingham in 1930. A period of steady growth followed and in 1961 the firm moved to its present city centre offices. In the mid-1970s an office was opened in Stratford upon Avon and in 1988 the firm merged with the London practice of Byatt Michau & Smart. Over the past decade, Needham & James has expanded at least fourfold, and concentrates almost exclusively on commercial law work. The firm is organised into departments.

This expanding firm has an increasing need for qualified staff, and expects to recruit 12 to 15 assistant solicitors for all areas of the practice. Enquiries to the partnership secretary.

In addition, 15 articled clerks are recruited annually. The minimum educational qualification is an honours degree. Apply by letter (with CV) in September/October two years in advance to Jeremy Roper.

Other offices: London, Stratford upon Avon, Warwick.

Agency work: Occasionally litigation work is accepted from other solicitors; contact Andrew Booth.

Types of work undertaken: Virtually all of the firm's work is commercial in orientation (whether it be company, litigation or conveyancing work), although some private client work is carried out at the Stratford upon Avon office.

Clients range from large quoted companies to sole traders and business start-ups. With its principal office in Birmingham, Needham & James acts for many large corporate clients in the Midlands, as well as large company clients who have traditionally used London solicitors but who have now opted for the more cost-effective and personal service of a specialist provincial commercial practice.

Having recently merged with a central London commercial practice experienced in flotations, the firm's capacity and flexibility to deal with corporate and City work as well as High Court litigation is considerably enhanced. The asset of a London office is being utilised to assist in the expansion of the firm's international practice.

The firm is particularly well known for its work in management buy-outs, flotations, franchising, banking, share option schemes, commercial conveyancing, construction litigation, intellectual property, entertainment law, competition and EEC law, and employment matters.

Needham & James aims to provide a highly efficient commercial service, and sees itself as dynamic, friendly and rapidly expanding.

NEEDHAM & JAMES
SOLICITORS

Neves

8 GEORGE STREET WEST
LUTON
BEDFORDSHIRE
LU1 2DA
Phone: 0582 25311

Fax: 0582 400972
DX: 5900 LUTON
Telex: none **Other offices:** 4
Senior Partner: Mr WJ Edwards
Number of Partners: 9
Total Staff: 67

Nicholson Graham & Jones

19-21 MOORGATE
LONDON
EC2R 6AU

Phone: 01 628 9151

Fax: 01 638 3102
DX: 58 LONDON CHANCERY LANE WC2
Telex: 8811848 **Other offices:** 1
Senior Partner: Mr PL Morgenstern
Number of Partners: 18
Total Staff: 118

Norton Peskett & Forward

148 LONDON ROAD NORTH
LOWESTOFT
SUFFOLK
NR32 1HF
Phone: 0502 565146

Fax: 0502 515941
DX: 41200 LOWESTOFT
Telex: none **Other offices:** 5
Senior Partner: Mr DL Adkinson
Number of Partners: 6
Total Staff: 58

Overbury Steward & Eaton

3 UPPER KING STREET
NORWICH
NORFOLK
NR3 1RL
Phone: 0603 610481

Fax: 0603 632460
DX: 5208 NORWICH
Telex: 957751
Senior Partner: Mr TC Eaton
Number of Partners: 12
Total Staff: 85

Nicholson Cadge & Gilbert *see full-page profile*
Norton Rose *see full-page profile*
Osborne Clarke *see full-page profile*
Oswald Hickson, Collier & Co *see full-page profile*

Nicholson Cadge & Gilbert

23 ALEXANDRA ROAD
LOWESTOFT
SUFFOLK
NR32 1PP
Phone: 0502 562140

Fax: 0502 568814
DX: 41204 LOWESTOFT
Telex: 97377 **Other offices:** 4
Managing Partner: Mr RJ Nicholson
Number of Partners: 11
Total Staff: 64

This provincial firm offers the full range of legal services and has a strong litigation practice.

The firm: In 1972 Johnson & Nicholson (of Lowestoft) and Cadge & Gilbert (of Loddon and Beccles), both old-established practices that date back to the latter half of the nineteenth century, merged to form the present partnership. The office in Lowestoft has grown rapidly, and Cadge & Gilbert's client base has been retained in Loddon, Beccles and the surrounding agricultural areas. The Harleston office was opened recently and Bungay at the time of merging.

All departments of the firm are expanding and applications from qualified solicitors are welcome at any time. Two solicitors are needed in the company/commercial conveyancing, and family and criminal litigation areas. Enquiries to Mr RJ Nicholson.

Normally there are two vacancies a year for articled clerks in Lowestoft. All graduates considered. Handwritten applications (plus CV and references) to Mr RJ Nicholson.

Other offices: Loddon, Beccles, Bungay, Harleston.

Agency work: All types of work from other solicitors are accepted, especially commercial/civil litigation (contact Mr MJ Nicholson or Mr D Evered) and criminal litigation (contact Mr WM Clarke).

Types of work undertaken: The firm acts for mostly private (and a few public) company clients involved in agriculture, property development, brewing, shipping and the oil service and holiday industries, and for its substantial private client base.

The Lowestoft office offers all the services which a large provincial town practice would provide, particularly in company/commercial work, civil litigation and insolvency. The office is broadly divided into five departments covering company and commercial work, including commercial conveyancing, partnership, corporate taxation and finance, mergers, acquisitions and reconstructions; commercial civil litigation and insolvency work, including all High Court and county court claims, industrial tribunals, personal injury and debt collection; domestic conveyancing; family and criminal litigation; and trust and probate, including personal tax planning.

The branches offer a full range of services in the fields of conveyancing, probate and trust work, and family and criminal litigation.

In short, Nicholson Cadge & Gilbert aims to give a full service to all private and commercial clients within its area, and likes to work closely with accountants, architects, surveyors and other professional advisers to ensure that clients are given the best possible service.

NICHOLSON CADGE & GILBERT

Norton Rose

KEMPSON HOUSE
CAMOMILE STREET
LONDON
EC3A 7AN

Phone: 01 283 2434

Fax: 01 588 1181
DX: 1064 LONDON CITY EC3
Telex: 883652 **Other offices:** 3
Senior Partner: Mr DO Hamilton
Number of Partners: 77
Total Staff: 660

The City firm of Norton Rose has developed a powerful international practice handling all types of commercial work.

The firm: Norton Rose's origins lie in the amalgamation in 1960 of the two long-established firms of Norton Rose & Co (founded in 1794) and Botterell & Roche (founded 1830), combining substantial practices in the fields of banking, corporate law and shipping. These traditional interests are still to be found today and have developed into a strong domestic and international practice in all areas of commercial law practice.

The firm is continually looking for bright and enthusiastic lawyers of the right calibre. Enquiries to Gillian Smith.

About 60 articled clerks are recruited annually. Candidates of all academic disciplines are welcomed. Apply by letter (with form, and names of referees) to Gillian Smith two years in advance.

Other offices: Hong Kong, Singapore, Bahrain.

Types of work undertaken: Norton Rose is one of the leading City firms, with an extensive UK and international practice offering advice on all aspects of company, commercial, banking and capital markets, shipping and aviation finance, property, marine, aviation, litigation, energy, competition and EEC, taxation and personal finance matters.

The firm specialises in corporate and financial work, taxation, litigation, property and personal finance. In fact, much of the firm's work is international. Clients include sovereign states, merchant banks, PLCs, insurers, professional institutions, regulatory bodies, multinationals, developers, and a diverse range of industrial concerns.

Norton Rose is particularly well known for its work in asset finance; aviation; banking; commercial property and property development; planning; corporate finance; energy; insurance; intellectual property; litigation (commercial and marine); management buy-outs; mergers, acquisitions and takeovers; shipping, and taxation. It offers the full range of both commercial and non-commercial services, including pensions, employment, personal injury, and private client work.

Overall, Norton Rose sees itself as a large City firm with a well-established UK and international practice offering a comprehensive range of services through highly professional and innovative teams of specialists. The firm is flexible to clients' needs, as well as being aggressive and effective. Norton Rose believes it is the only major City firm combining a corporate practice with a substantial marine and aviation practice. Brochures describing the work of the firm are available on request.

Norton Rose

Osborne Clarke

30 QUEEN CHARLOTTE STREET
BRISTOL
BS99 7QQ

Phone: 0272 230220

Fax: 0272 279209
DX: 7818 BRISTOL
Telex: 44734 **Other offices:** 1
Senior Partner: Charles N Clarke, CBE
Number of Partners: 27
Total Staff: 201

This leading provincial firm, based in Bristol, has a broadly based practice acting for commercial, institutional and private clients.

The firm: Formed in 1969, Osborne Clarke is the result of the merger of Osborne Ward and Clarke Gwynn & Press, both established in approximately 1720. Today, the firm acts for a wide range of local, regional and national companies and commercial organisations (many of which operate on an international basis), as well as many of the institutions and families whom the firm represented in the eighteenth century. The firm is a member of the Legal Resources Group (see separate entry).

Osborne Clarke expects to recruit about 15 assistant solicitors in 1989. The firm prefers candidates with up to three years' qualified experience. Enquiries to the senior partner.

In addition, eight articled clerks are recruited annually. A 2(2) degree or above is preferred. Apply by handwritten letter (with CV) two years in advance to Mr ARG James.

Other offices: London.

Agency work: Work is accepted from other solicitors; contact Mr JG Orme.

Types of work undertaken: This well-established provincial firm offers the full range of legal services and has five main departments, namely property, litigation, company/commercial, private client and banking/finance. There is an unusually large and highly regarded practice in USM work.

The company/commercial department has particular experience in Stock Exchange admissions, takeovers and mergers, BES start-ups and re-financing, venture capital, partnerships, and general commercial agreements. There are also well developed intellectual property, insolvency and company secretary/registrar services.

The work of the property department includes advice on planning law and appeals, landlord and tenant matters, project finance and tax. The department also has extensive experience in the acquisition of property abroad, particularly in France.

The litigation department handles building, commercial and employment disputes, media law, and negligence and related claims, and represents clients before all courts, tribunals, arbitrations and planning inquiries.

For many years the firm has worked closely with banks and banking institutions involved in both the retail and corporate banking sectors. In addition, the firm operates a debt collection service, and there is a strong private client department which includes estate managing and investment services.

Overall, Osborne Clarke perceives itself as a firm of highly skilled professionals providing a first-class service for its clients.

OSBORNE : CLARKE

SOLICITORS & NOTARIES

Oswald Hickson, Collier & Co

ESSEX HOUSE
ESSEX STREET
LONDON
WC2R 3AQ
Phone: 01 836 8333

Fax: 01 240 2236
DX: 200 LONDON CHANCERY LANE WC2
Telex: 22533
Senior Partner: Paul Davies
Number of Partners: 14
Total Staff: 53

Oswald Hickson, Collier & Co is a central London firm with an international reputation for libel, slander and copyright work.

The firm: Founded in 1903 by Oswald Squire Hickson, the firm provides a wide range of legal services for commercial clients, most particularly in publishing law (including libel), property, company and shipping law.

Oswald Hickson is always seeking to recruit suitably qualified assistant solicitors. Enquiries to Richard Shillito.

In addition, the firm usually recruits three articled clerks each year. Candidates with a 2(1) degree, not necessarily in law, are preferred. Apply by handwritten letter (with CV) to Michael Hudson.

Agency work: The firm undertakes general company and commercial work including corporate financing and flotations in London for solicitors based elsewhere.

Types of work undertaken: The firm is organised into four main departments, namely litigation, property, company/commercial, and shipping.

The litigation department deals with the high-profile side of this internationally known practice, offering advice on libel, slander, copyright, passing off, contempt of court, reporting restrictions, pre-publication and pre-broadcasting advice, and breach of confidence, as well as advice on libel insurance and publishing agreements. The department also handles work (either in the courts or before arbitrators) in a variety of other fields, such as building disputes; claims under professional indemnity, errors and omissions, and public liability insurance policies; Lloyd's insurance and reinsurance disputes; and employment law.

The property department handles commercial conveyancing work including residential and office site development and provides a full residential conveyancing service for private clients.

The work of the company/commercial department covers all the day-to-day advice required by the firm's corporate clients in connection with their business operations, including formation of companies and partnerships, joint ventures, takeovers, company reorganisations and amalgamations, corporate finance, flotations, commercial agreements, advice on restrictive trade practice legislation, liquidations and receiverships, pension share option and profit sharing schemes, and taxation advice.

The shipping department handles marine disputes, the conduct of marine arbitrations, ship sale, vessel registration, and finance.

Oswald Hickson, Collier & Co is a small but personable commercial firm which is prominent in publishing law and has a reputation for being firm but fair.

OSWALD HICKSON, COLLIER & CO.

Owston & Co

23 FRIAR LANE
LEICESTER
LE1 5QQ

Phone: 0533 530851

Fax: 0533 532690
DX: 10832 LEICESTER-1
Telex: 342734 **Other offices:** 1
Senior Partner: Mr RH Bloor
Number of Partners: 7
Total Staff: 66

Oxley & Coward

34 MOORGATE STREET
ROTHERHAM
SOUTH YORKSHIRE
S60 2HB

Phone: 0709 374091

Fax: 0709 377163
DX: 12600 ROTHERHAM-1
Telex: none **Other offices:** 5
Senior Partner: Mr AH Pickles
Number of Partners: 12
Total Staff: 125

Paisner & Co

BOUVERIE HOUSE
154 FLEET STREET
LONDON
EC4A 2DQ

Phone: 01 353 0299

Fax: 01 583 8621
DX: 198 LONDON CHANCERY LANE WC2
Telex: 263189
Senior Partner: Mr HM Paisner
Number of Partners: 24
Total Staff: 190

Palmers

19 TOWN SQUARE
BASILDON
ESSEX
SS14 1BD

Phone: 0268 22122

Fax: +0268 530799
DX: 53002 BASILDON
Telex: none **Other offices:** 4
Senior Partner:
Number of Partners: 4
Total Staff: 70

Pannone Blackburn

123 DEANSGATE
MANCHESTER
M3 2BU

Phone: 061 832 3000

Fax: 061 834 2067
DX: 14314 MANCHESTER-1
Telex: 668172 **Other offices:** 5
Senior Partner: Mr RJ Pannone
Number of Partners: 18
Total Staff: 144

Paris Smith & Randall

LANSDOWNE HOUSE
CASTLE LANE
SOUTHAMPTON
HAMPSHIRE SO9 4FD

Phone: 0703 635191

Fax: 0703 631835
DX: 2008 SOUTHAMPTON
Telex: 47389 **Other offices:** 1
Senior Partner: Mr PT Ely
Number of Partners: 9
Total Staff: 84

Park Nelson

1 BELL YARD
LONDON
WC2A 2JP

Phone: 01 404 4191

Fax: 01 405 4266
DX: 186 LONDON CHANCERY LANE WC2
Telex: 894760
Senior Partner: Mr EA O'Keeffe
Number of Partners: 8
Total Staff: 70

Park Woodfine & Co

1 LURKE STREET
BEDFORD
MK40 3TN

Phone: 0234 64321

Fax: 0234 211973
DX: 5603 BEDFORD
Telex: 826747 **Other offices:** 3
Senior Partner: Mr WG Park
Number of Partners: 8
Total Staff: 75

Pardoes *see full-page profile*

Pardoes

6-9 KING SQUARE
BRIDGWATER
SOMERSET
TA6 3DG
Phone: 0278 457891

Fax: 0278 429249
DX: 80602 BRIDGWATER
Telex: 46377 **Other offices:** 1
Senior Partner: Mr PJF Synge
Number of Partners: 8
Total Staff: 74

A general practice based in Somerset, Pardoes has a long-established private client base and an expanding commercial law practice.

The firm: Founded approximately 100 years ago as a general country practice, the firm has seen rapid expansion within the last 20 years. In that time the office space in Bridgwater has had to be increased fivefold, and in 1983 a Taunton office was opened. The firm is organised into departments.

Up to six solicitors are required next year, in the areas of agricultural property, upper market domestic conveyancing, commercial property, probate and tax, insolvency, and commercial contracts. Contact the staff partner Mr SR Morley.

In addition, four articled clerks are normally recruited every year. The minimum educational qualification is a 2(2) degree. Applications (with CV and the names of two referees) should be made two years in advance to Mr SR Morley.

Other offices: Taunton.

Agency work: The firm accepts all types of agency work for other solicitors, except criminal work. Contact Mr CJ Spencer.

Types of work undertaken: Pardoes undertakes all forms of work, private and commercial, contentious and non-contentious, with the exception of legally aided criminal work. Work is allocated to increasingly specialist departments and is of a quality not normally associated with a country-based practice.

The firm is particularly well known for employment law, commercial property, agricultural law, civil litigation, commercial contracts and litigation, personal injury work, general commercial, taxation, insolvency, probate, and matrimonial litigation. The firm's residential property department continues to expand, as does its agricultural work.

The work of the commercial department includes intellectual property, competition law, company law, employment, computer law and planning work. Pardoes also has a very busy matrimonial practice.

The client base ranges from the individual private client to public companies, and includes nationally known companies. Although based in Somerset, Pardoes has clients all over the UK.

The firm likes to feel that it is regarded as a worthy adversary, and as a young, energetic general practice very much with an eye to the future. Pardoes has a substantial and increasing proportion of high-quality commercial and litigation work of a type normally associated with large city-centre practices. In short, this is a firm which offers clients the best of both worlds.

Brochures are available upon request.

PARDOES

Parker Bullen

45 CASTLE STREET
SALISBURY
WILTSHIRE
SP1 3SS
Phone: 0722 412000

Fax: 0722 411822
DX: 58001 SALISBURY
Telex: 47152 **Other offices:** 2
Managing Partner: Mr NA BOURNE
Number of Partners: 14
Total Staff: 79

Patterson Glenton & Stracey

LAW COURT CHAMBERS
WATERLOO SQ
SOUTH SHIELDS
TYNE AND WEAR NE33 1AW
Phone: 091 456 0281

Fax: 091 455 7380
DX: 60750 SOUTH SHIELDS-1
Telex: none **Other offices:** 2
Senior Partner: Mr AG Brown
Number of Partners: 10
Total Staff: 57

Pattinson & Brewer

30 GREAT JAMES STREET
LONDON
WC1N 3HA

Phone: 01 404 0282

Fax: 01 405 7239
DX: 394 LONDON CHANCERY LANE WC2
Telex: 268913 **Other offices:** 1
Senior Partner: Mr JAI Warren
Number of Partners: 15
Total Staff: 58

Paull & Williamsons

INVESTMENT HOUSE
6 UNION ROW
ABERDEEN
AB9 8DQ
Phone: 0224 631414

Fax: 0224 640446
Rutland Exchange: 35 ABERDEEN
Telex: 73183
Senior Partner: Mr IMS Park
Number of Partners: 16
Total Staff: 120

Payne Hicks Beach

10 NEW SQUARE
LINCOLN'S INN
LONDON
WC2A 3QG
Phone: 01 242 6041

Fax: 01 405 0434
DX: 40 LONDON CHANCERY LANE WC2
Telex: 24437
Senior Partner: Mr ABV Hughes
Number of Partners: 29
Total Staff: 155

This well-known City firm has a strong private client base combined with a substantial corporate practice.

The firm: Payne Hicks Beach was founded in 1730, but its present character is the result of successive amalgamations, the most recent being with Francis & Crookenden and Roper Piesse in 1988 and the acquisition of the private client department of Cameron Markby. Over the last 20 years the practice has expanded rapidly to include a wide range of individual and corporate clients, with a strong international emphasis.

The firm usually recruits about five assistant solicitors each year. Address enquiries to the managing partner.

In addition, there are five to six vacancies for articled clerks every year. The minimum educational requirement is a 2(2) degree. Long-term prospects are good; many of the present partners served articles with the firm or joined shortly after qualifying. Applications should be made by letter (with CV and references) and addressed to the recruitment partner.

Types of work undertaken: The firm's traditional private client base of landowners, trusts and a wide cross-section of individuals has been retained, and a substantial business clientele, including both public and private companies, has been added over the last two decades. Many clients are foreign based, and the firm has extensive international legal contacts, particularly in Europe. The firm is organised into six main departments, namely company/commercial, litigation, family law, property, planning, and tax and trusts (including probate).

There is considerable expertise in tax planning and the formation and administration of trusts. Other private client areas in which the firm has a high reputation include all aspects of family law, especially matrimonial.

The commercial conveyancing practice is expanding rapidly, particularly property development work. Residential conveyancing, agricultural law matters and estate management are also handled.

There is an expanding commercial litigation department, which is noted for its intellectual property, commercial disputes, arbitration and planning work.

The full range of corporate legal work is dealt with by the company/commercial department which has particular expertise in sales and purchases of companies, USM, and international work of all types.

Overall, Payne Hicks Beach sees itself as a well-respected firm with a strong private client base and an expanding commercial practice both in the UK and internationally. Brochures for clients detailing the services that the firm offers are available on request.

Penningtons
(Inc Penningtons, Ward Bowie, Cardales & Barry Lewis)

CLEMENT HOUSE
99 ALDWYCH
LONDON
WC2B 4LJ

Phone: 01 242 4422

Fax: 01 430 2210
DX: 33 LONDON CHANCERY LANE WC2
Telex: 22509 **Other offices:** 8
Joint Chairmen: Mr DG Stedman & Mr JSNJ Horsey
Number of Partners: 44 **Total Staff:** 305

A broadly based practice, Penningtons has expanding corporate, commercial property, litigation, licensing, private client and matrimonial departments in its offices in and outside London.

The firm: Penningtons was formed in 1986 as the result of a merger of Penningtons and Ward Bowie, whose origins can be traced back to the eighteenth century. Both firms have always maintained strong London offices, but have recognised increasingly the value of thriving offices in significant locations outside London. In October 1986 the newly merged firm acquired the London practice of Cardales, which led to the opening of a City office, housing the corporate department, and in October 1988 the firm merged with Barry Lewis, who deals exclusively with insurance related litigation.

Penningtons requires 15 to 20 assistant solicitors in 1989 for offices in and outside London, particularly in the corporate, property and litigation fields. Solicitors up to two years qualified are preferred. Enquiries for London appointments should be sent to Mr DG Stedman and outside London to Mr JSNJ Horsey.

In addition the firm recruits ten to 12 articled clerks annually. Candidates with a 2(1) degree, not necessarily in law, are preferred. Apply by handwritten letter (plus CV and names of referees) during autumn two years in advance to Mrs Lesley Lintott, at the Aldwych office.

Other offices: Basingstoke, Bournemouth, Godalming, Guildford, Newbury, Poole, Thatcham, London (EC2).

Agency work: The firm accepts work from other solicitors as well as acting as UK agents for many overseas firms. Contact the head of the litigation department, Paul Hadow.

Types of work undertaken: This practice serves business and private clients and is well placed through its international connections to offer assistance in the UK and abroad.

Penningtons is particularly strong in corporate work, including new issues, USM flotations, company mergers, acquisitions and corporate finance generally; property development matters; private client work; litigation (including insurance claims); liquor licensing; and matrimonial law.

Overall, this is a fast-growing firm with an ever-expanding commercial property and corporate practice, which takes advantage of its multiple office locations. It has a definite commitment to expanding its European network (the firm is a member of two European Law Associations, giving it contacts in 12 countries), yet is able to offer a personal service to both business and private clients, covering a broad spread of legal expertise.

Penningtons

Percy Hughes & Roberts

19 HAMILTON SQUARE
BIRKENHEAD
MERSEYSIDE
L41 6AY

Phone: 051 647 6081

Fax: 051 666 1080
DX: 17862 BIRKENHEAD-1
Telex: none **Other offices:** 2
Senior Partner: Mr DJS Roberts
Number of Partners: 12
Total Staff: 70

Pickering & Butters

19 GREENGATE STREET
STAFFORD
ST16 2LU

Phone: 0785 56361

Fax: 0785 211115
DX: 14551 STAFFORD-1
Telex: none **Other offices:** 2
Senior Partner: Mr R Thomas
Number of Partners: 17
Total Staff: 77

Pickering Kenyon

23-24 GREAT JAMES STREET
LONDON
WC1N 3EL

Phone: 01 404 5522

Fax: 01 404 0070
DX: 218 LONDON CHANCERY LANE WC2
Telex: 22863
Senior Partner: Mr RG Bellenger
Number of Partners: 9
Total Staff: 54

Porter Bartlett & Mayo

CENTRAL HOUSE
CHURCH STREET
YEOVIL
SOMERSET BA20 1HD

Phone: 0935 23245

Fax: 0935 706063
DX: 100501 YEOVIL
Telex: 46645 **Other offices:** 6
Senior Partner: Mr PF Moule
Number of Partners: 13
Total Staff: 122

Peter Peter & Wright *see full-page profile*
Phillips & Buck *see full-page profile*
Pictons *see full-page profile*
Pinsent & Co *see full-page profile*
Pitmans *see full-page profile*

Peter Peter & Wright

8 FORE STREET
HOLSWORTHY
DEVON
EX22 6ED
Phone: 0409 253262

Fax: 0409 254091
DX: none
Telex: none **Other offices:** 3
Senior Partner: James Rowland
Number of Partners: 9
Total Staff: 61

Peter Peter & Wright is a long-established Devonshire firm with three branch offices and a thriving general practice.

The firm: The original firm was founded over 200 years ago in Holsworthy. The present firm is the result of a series of mergers in 1985-86, between Peter Peter & Sons of Holsworthy and Goaman & Wright of Bideford, and then with Peter Peter & Sons (unrelated to the original Holsworthy firm) of Bude and Okehampton.

Over the next ten years the firm is seeking to recruit up to six young assistant solicitors; in 1989 it expects one vacancy, for general private client work. Enquiries to Mr JM Rowland.

In addition, one or two articled clerks are recruited every year. The minimum educational requirement is an honours degree, not necessarily in law. Prospects after qualification are good; the firm aims to recruit trainees who have the potential to contribute to its long-term development. Apply by letter to Mr JA Spiers.

Other offices: Bideford, Bude, Okehampton.

Agency work: The firm accepts work from other solicitors; contact Mrs P Edwards (county court work) or Mr NJR Clark (financial services).

Types of work undertaken: This is a typical provincial practice offering a broad range of legal services to a client base that includes commercial clients such as hoteliers and retailers, individuals, and farmers; indeed the firm is particularly well known for its private client work for farmers and landowners.

There is a substantial property practice handling all types of work for agricultural, commercial and private clients, including sale and purchase, conveyancing, insurance matters, taxation work and financing.

On the commercial side, the firm handles the full range of work, including company formations, partnership agreements, service contracts and financial planning.

The firm has a thriving litigation practice, which handles civil cases, such as personal injury claims, landlord and tenant disputes, debt collection, property damage claims and employment disputes. Criminal cases are also undertaken, as are divorce and family law proceedings.

The firm acts as executors and trustees for a large number of family trusts, advises on tax matters and financial investments, and arranges insurance cover. Legal aid work is undertaken.

Overall, Peter Peter & Wright sees itself as a substantial, established and reliable firm of high-quality lawyers, and has a reputation as a 'good firm to do business with'.

PETER PETER & WRIGHT

Phillips & Buck

FITZALAN HOUSE
FITZALAN ROAD
CARDIFF
CF2 1XZ
Phone: 0222 471147

Fax: 0222 464347
DX: 33016 CARDIFF
Telex: 497625 **Other offices:** 3
Senior Partners: Roger G Thomas & D Keith James
Number of Partners: 20 **Total Staff:** 240

Phillips & Buck is the largest firm of solicitors in Wales and serves commercial and private clients in the region.

The firm: Formed in 1947 by the amalgamation of two firms, Phillips & Buck was originally a private practice firm. Over the last 25 years commercial work has become dominant and the firm has grown greatly. In September 1988 Phillips & Buck joined with other major legal firms in initiating moves to establish the UK's first national commercial law firm.

There is a constant requirement for bright, enthusiastic lawyers who wish to specialise in all types of company and commercial work. The firm expects to recruit at least ten solicitors over the next year. All enquiries to be addressed to the Personnel Manager, Ms JS Buckley.

The firm recruits 12 articled clerks annually. At least a 2(2) degree is required, not necessarily in law. Long-term prospects are excellent: nearly half the present partners served articles with the firm. Candidates should send a completed application form (available on request) to Ms JS Buckley.

Other offices: Cardiff (2), London.

Agency work: The firm does agency work for other solicitors; contact the relevant department's senior partner. For court agency work contact the senior litigation partner.

Types of work undertaken: The firm undertakes all types of legal work required by its commercial clients and offers a private client service both in support of the commercial practice and independently. The client base is a broad commercial connection, including listed companies, large private companies and the public sector, as well as younger businesses and private clients.

The firm is known for company purchase, sale and finance, commercial advice, banking and finance, house advice and document-ation, commercial property, employment law, commercial litigation, debt collection, insurance and intellectual property.

The commercial work also includes pensions, general and building litigation, European Community Law, and planning, and the private client service includes matrimonial, personal injury and financial planning units. The firm will work closely with the client's other advisers — accountants, bankers and stockbrokers — to ensure an effective and efficient service. Brochures are available for clients on request.

This major regional practice has a young and energetic team experienced in respond-ing to problems very quickly. The firm prides itself on offering clients a professional and progressive legal service combined with commercially sensible advice.

Pictons

'KEYSTONE'
60 LONDON ROAD
ST ALBANS
HERTFORDSHIRE AL1 1NG
Phone: 0727 40431

Fax: 0727 38066
DX: 6103 ST ALBANS
Telex: 23285 **Other offices:** 7
Senior Partner: David Picton
Number of Partners: 20
Total Staff: 171

Pictons is a general practice offering the full range of legal services to private and commercial clients.

The firm: Established in 1967 as a general practice, it has grown rapidly with eight offices throughout Hertfordshire, Bedfordshire and Buckinghamshire. The direction of the firm has shifted to more specialised areas coupled with rapid expansion of the commercial practice.

Because of the firm's continuing growth, it is always seeking to recruit assistant solicitors; in 1989 it expects six to eight vacancies, especially in the commercial and personal injury fields. Enquiries to David Picton.

In addition, the firm generally recruits ten articled clerks every year. Reasonable academic qualifications are expected but applicants are judged on individual merits. Apply by letter (with CV) as early as possible to David Picton.

Other offices: Watford, Hemel Hempstead, Luton, Bedford, Bletchley, Central Milton Keynes, Stevenage.

Agency work: All offices accept magistrates or county court work from other solicitors.

Types of work undertaken: This is a general practice with particular strengths in conveyancing, family law, general civil liti-gation, crime, general commercial work and wills. There are special units in all main areas of private client and commercial work, as well as expertise within the firm in narrower fields. The private client base is primarily regional, and commercially the emphasis is on small to medium sized companies.

On the commercial side, the firm feels it has a trader's instinct and a complete under-standing of the need to find commercially acceptable solutions to problems. It is becoming well known for company acqui-sitions and business structure requirements, and is developing a computer-based credit control and debt collection service. Other commercial work undertaken includes tax planning, pensions, employment law, estate development and town planning, landlord and tenant, and intellectual property, as well as all aspects of finance.

On the private client side, the firm handles the usual trust, probate and wills work, conveyancing, matrimonial and family law matters. There is a strong personal injury department, and two offices have particular expertise in criminal law. In addition, there is a more unusual expertise in sporting contracts and negotiations.

Overall, the firm feels it has a very broad and sound base in all major areas of the law. Pictons sees itself as practical and constructive in its approach to legal matters, and progressive in its attitudes.

Pictons

Pinsent & Co

POST & MAIL HOUSE
26 COLMORE CIRCUS
BIRMINGHAM
B4 6BH

Phone: 021 200 1050

Fax: 021 200 1040
DX: 24903 BIRMINGHAM-4
Telex: 335102 **Other offices:** 1
Senior Partner: David C Cooke
Number of Partners: 27
Total Staff: 194

Pinsent & Co is a major commercial practice with nationwide interests based on its substantial list of quality corporate clients.

The firm: Pinsent & Co has been established for over a hundred years and is situated in the heart of the commercial district of Birmingham. As the regions industrial base has expanded and developed over generations, so the firm has grown, adapting and increasing its services until it is now one of the country's largest firms outside the City of London, with a substantial portfolio of listed company clients.

This constantly expanding firm needs about ten solicitors of first-rate ability at all levels; the firm is particularly interested in lawyers with City experience. Contact the staff partner.

In addition, 18 articled clerks are recruited annually. Candidates are expected to have a 2(1) degree, not necessarily in law. Knowledge of French or German is an advantage. Apply two years in advance on an application form (available on request) to Mr JB Hopkinson or Mr AJ Paton.

Other offices: London

Types of work undertaken: This is a substantial corporate and commercial practice, which is well known for the depth and breadth of its services to corporate clients. The client base is principally listed companies combined with a substantial number of private companies.

Pinsent & Co has probably the largest taxation department outside the City, and has notable expertise in flotations, Stock Exchange Yellow Book work, management buy-outs, banking, intellectual property, corporate pension schemes, property development, and town and country planning.

Professional indemnity insurance litigation is another major field of work, and there are also specialist partners in computer contracts, overseas trusts, product liability, historic houses and employee share schemes, as well as the more traditional areas of corporate, commercial, property and tax law.

The firm is a member of the Legal Resources Group which comprises five leading English provincial legal practices. While each firm retains its complete independence, a central resource company provides helpful services to all group members, with particular emphasis on training at all levels.

Pinsent & Co perceives itself as a major public company practice, serving the whole of the UK whilst retaining its involvement in the City of Birmingham, through its work on many of the major public projects, and provides high standards of professional expertise and integrity.

PINSENT & CO.

Pitmans

47 CASTLE STREET
READING
BERKSHIRE
RG1 7SR
Phone: 0734 580224

Fax: 0734 585097
DX: 40102 CASTLE STREET READING
Telex: 849723
Senior Partner: Michael Hatch
Number of Partners: 6
Total Staff: 62

The emphasis in this old-established Reading firm is on commercial law, but there is also a strong private client practice.

The firm: The origins of the firm can be traced back to the mid-nineteenth century. The present firm was formed in 1974 when the Reading office of the old-established firm Pitman & Bazett merged with another well-known local firm, Kent Thomas & Jones. At that time the firm increased its concentration on commercial work. The firm has expanded more than threefold in the last decade.

The firm is always seeking to recruit high-calibre qualified staff, and in 1989 expects to have three vacancies for assistant solicitors. Enquiries to Michael Hatch.

Three to four articled clerks are normally recruited every year. A 2(1) degree is preferred and applications from non-law graduates are welcome. Apply with a full CV in the autumn to Neil Bucknell.

Types of work undertaken: The firm is commercially orientated with a wide range of clients including a number of substantial quoted companies (where Pitmans usually works with one of the major City firms on Yellow Book work). There are four main departments, namely commercial conveyancing, company/commercial, litigation and planning, and private client.

The firm is best known for its commercial property work, particularly the acquisition of land (whether by option or otherwise) for residential development, and joint venture arrangements between developers for the long-term acquisition and development of substantial acreages. The commercial conveyancing department handles work spread over much of the country.

The thriving company/commercial department handles a wide variety of general commercial matters, including company formations, purchases and sales of companies and businesses, management buy-outs, institutional investment agreements, trading agreements, employment matters, intellectual property work, and financial services.

The firm offers a comprehensive litigation service for business and private clients for any legal disputes in which they may become involved, other than matrimonial or criminal matters. The firm is very well known for its public enquiry planning work.

The firm also undertakes a substantial amount of non-contentious work for private clients: residential conveyancing, and trusts and probate work dealing with wills, family settlements and personal tax planning.

Pitmans sees itself as a serious commercial organisation with a commercial approach, which never loses sight of important legal concepts and principles. The firm operates with a personal touch but aims at a quality of work expected from a top City practice.

Pitmans

Powell Magrath & Spencer

290 KILBURN HIGH ROAD
LONDON
NW6 2DB

Phone: 01 624 8888

Fax: 01 328 1221
DX: 37700 KILBURN
Telex: none
Senior Partner: Greg Powell
Number of Partners: 7
Total Staff: 54

Powell Magrath & Spencer is predominantly a litigation and legal aid practice providing a high quality of legal services.

The firm: Powell Magrath & Spencer was established in 1977 with the aim of providing a legal aid practice to a deprived inner city area. The practice has continued to expand and is now one of London's leading legal aid practices.

The firm is always looking for assistant solicitors for all departments, especially applicants who are ambitious and have the ability to work hard. There is a particular need for magistrates court advocates. Enquiries should be addressed to Greg Powell.

There are approximately two vacancies each year for articled clerks. Applicants should have passed the Finals exam and preferably have some experience of working in a lawyer's office. Apply (with CV) to Greg Powell one year in advance.

Agency work: The firm undertakes criminal work for other solicitors in north-west and central London magistrates courts. For details contact Richard Spencer. For USA immigration, visa and commercial work, contact Chris Magrath.

Types of work undertaken: Legal aid work predominates: 60 per cent is criminal and 40 per cent civil, with considerable

criminal law experience (including major fraud, corporate, and white-collar crime).

The civil work is made up of family law (dealing mainly with care, wardship, domestic violence and divorce), which often necessitates applying for emergency injunctions. The firm is experienced in all aspects of personal injury claims and handles many medical negligence actions; indeed, this is an area of the practice that is expanding rapidly. The firm also acts in landlord and tenant disputes (for tenants only). There are also departments dealing with employment work (unfair dismissal and tribunals) and domestic conveyancing.

Powell Magrath & Spencer is closely involved in civil liberties work (and acts for various refugee and charitable bodies).

The firm also undertakes a considerable amount of commercial litigation (mainly, but not exclusively, for clients in the entertainment and music world), as well as intellectual property and commercial conveyancing matters. A particular area of expertise is in USA visa and immigration matters, mainly on behalf of business and entertainment clients. The firm will act on an agency basis for other firms in this regard.

Powell Magrath & Spencer's reputation has grown rapidly over the years. The firm is generally regarded as providing a high-quality service – particularly for clients who might not otherwise have access to a good lawyer.

POWELL   MAGRATH   +   SPENCER

Prettys

ELM HOUSE
25 ELM STREET
IPSWICH
SUFFOLK IP1 2AD
Phone: 0473 232121

Fax: 0473 230002
DX: 3218 IPSWICH
Telex: 987764 **Other offices:** 3
Senior Partner: Mr Paul Butters
Number of Partners: 13
Total Staff: 105

Prince Evans

77 UXBRIDGE ROAD
EALING
LONDON
W5 5ST
Phone: 01 567 3477

Fax: 01 840 7757
DX: 5100 EALING
Telex: none **Other offices:** 1
Senior Partner: Mr LJ Robert
Number of Partners: 8
Total Staff: 59

Pritchard Englefield & Tobin

23 GREAT CASTLE STREET
LONDON
W1N 8NQ

Phone: 01 629 8883

Fax: 01 493 1891
DX: 88 LONDON CHANCERY LANE WC2
Telex: 23836 **Other offices:** 3
Senior Partner: Mr JJ Tobin
Number of Partners: 17
Total Staff: 71

Punch Robson Gilchrist Smith

35 ALBERT ROAD
MIDDLESBROUGH
CLEVELAND
TS1 1NU
Phone: 0642 230700

Fax: 0642 218923
DX: 60501 MIDDLESBROUGH
Telex: none **Other offices:** 2
Managing Partner: Mr Alan Mottram
Number of Partners: 10
Total Staff: 60

R Gwynne & Sons

EDGBASTON HOUSE
WALKER STREET
WELLINGTON
SHROPSHIRE TF1 1HF

Phone: 0952 641651

Fax: 0952 47441
DX: 23107 TELFORD
Telex: none **Other offices:** 5
Senior Partner: Mr MT Gwynne
Number of Partners: 10
Total Staff: 81

R L Edwards & Partners

20 NOLTON STREET
BRIDGEND
MID GLAMORGAN
CF31 1DU

Phone: 0656 56861

Fax: 0656 68190
DX: 38008 BRIDGEND
Telex: none **Other offices:** 5
Managing Partner: Mr Hywel P Huws
Number of Partners: 10
Total Staff: 80

Radcliffes & Co

10 LITTLE COLLEGE STREET
WESTMINSTER
LONDON
SW1P 3SJ

Phone: 01 222 7040

Fax: 01 222 6208
DX: 113 LONDON CHANCERY LANE WC2
Telex: 919302
Managing Partner: Mr PRH Dixon
Number of Partners: 26
Total Staff: 165

Rawlison and Butler

GRIFFIN HOUSE
135 HIGH STREET
CRAWLEY
WEST SUSSEX RH12 1DY

Phone: 0293 27744

Fax: 0293 20202
DX: 57112 CRAWLEY
Telex: 877751 **Other offices:** 3
Senior Partner: Mr RCO SKINNER
Number of Partners: 11
Total Staff: 90

Rapers *see full-page profile*

Rapers

55 WEST STREET
CHICHESTER
WEST SUSSEX
PO19 1RU
Phone: 0243 788155

Fax: 0243 775290
DX: 30302 CHICHESTER
Telex: none **Other offices:** 2
Senior Partner: Richard Hugh Mosse
Number of Partners: 9
Total Staff: 60

Rapers is a long-established general practice which has expanded particularly its commercial and litigation work in recent years.

The firm: One of the oldest firms of solicitors in England, in 1945 a branch office was established at Selsey and in 1981 the firm became partners in the established practice of Albery & Lucas in Midhurst; the firms merged in 1986. Until recently, the practice was typically market-town and the nature of its work remains general, but the firm has substantially built up the commercial and litigation side of its practice and further growth is anticipated. In 1988 a managing partner and executive were appointed and the firm is now well into a complete reorganisation.

Because of its continuing expansion, the firm is planning to recruit a number of people, particularly in the company and commercial area. Enquiries to the managing partner, Mr R Deighton.

One or two articled clerks will be recruited in 1990. Candidates should have a 2(1) degree (not necessarily in law). Prospects are good: no articled clerks have ever left without a job to go to. Apply during the last year at university to the managing partner.

Other offices: Selsey, Midhurst (all offices have close links).

Agency work: The Chichester office is prepared to undertake agency work of all types for other solicitors.

Types of work undertaken: As well as its substantial general practice, in recent years this traditional market-town firm has built up a strong property business, working for developers in both private residential and commercial property. It holds the office of Clerk to the Commissioners and partners take an active interest in local Chambers of Commerce, the local Health Authority etc.

The work of the rapidly expanding litigation department includes representing national insurance companies in personal injury and other litigation. A partner is on the Law Society's Child Care Panel and it has close links with insolvency practitioners.

Rapers is known locally as one of the leading firms in licensing and employment law, both of which are the direct responsibility of the managing partner. In addition, the senior partner, Richard Mosse, is an acknowledged expert on taxation, particularly capital and inheritance tax.

Overall this firm sees itself continuing to expand under its present management from a solid traditional base into what it perceives to be the fields of the future, particularly company/commercial and litigation.

A brochure describing the services the firm offers is available on request.

Read Hind Stewart

IVEBRIDGE HOUSE
59 MARKET STREET
BRADFORD
WEST YORKSHIRE BD1 1SL
Phone: 0274 723858

Fax: 0274 728493
DX: 11705 BRADFORD
Telex: none **Other offices:** 4
Senior Partner: Mr JG Read
Number of Partners: 14
Total Staff: 107

Robert Gore and Company

17 GROSVENOR STREET
LONDON
W1X 9FD

Phone: 01 491 2020

Fax: 01 499 6123
DX: 44624 MAYFAIR W1
Telex: 264656 **Other offices:** 1
Senior Partner: Mr Robert Gore
Number of Partners: 7
Total Staff: 66

Robin Thompson & Partners

BAINBRIDGE HOUSE
BAINBRIDGE STREET
LONDON
WC1A 1HT
Phone: 01 637 9761

Fax: 01 631 5249
DX: 35722 BLOOMSBURY WC1
Telex: none **Other offices:** 5
Senior Partner: Mr Robin Thompson
Number of Partners: 34
Total Staff: 380

Robinson & Allfree

17-25 CAVENDISH STREET
RAMSGATE
KENT
CT11 9AL
Phone: 0843 592361

Fax: 0843 582774
DX: 30604 RAMSGATE
Telex: none **Other offices:** 4
Senior Partner: Mr JP Robinson
Number of Partners: 10
Total Staff: 88

Redfern & Stigant *see full-page profile*
Reynolds Porter Chamberlain *see full-page profile*
Richards Butler *see full-page profile*

Redfern & Stigant

57 BALMORAL ROAD
GILLINGHAM
KENT
ME7 4PA
Phone: 0634 575511

Fax: 0634 55152
DX: 6607 GILLINGHAM-1
Telex: none **Other offices:** 4
Senior Partner: Anthony Redfern
Number of Partners: 10
Total Staff: 73

This expanding firm, which serves the Medway Towns, has a general practice with a significant commercial law element.

The firm: Redfern & Stigant was formed in 1976 as a result of the merger of Kenneth Redfern & Co and Stigant, Son & Taylor, which between them had some 160 years' experience providing professional services both within and outside Kent. The new firm is better placed to serve the changing needs of the population of the Medway Towns, which are undergoing a commercial transformation. While the commercial side has expanded, the firm remains committed to general practice including the legal aid scheme.

Three vacancies for assistant solicitors are expected in the next 12 months, in estate development and planning law, commercial conveyancing, and civil litigation. Enquiries to Patrick Bligh.

Three articled clerks are recruited annually. A 2(2) degree is required, not necessarily in law. Applications should be made by handwritten letter (plus CV) two years in advance to Andrew Pearson.

Other offices: Chatham (2), Rainham, Strood.

Agency work: Redfern & Stigant undertakes work for other solicitors: in the district registry and county court (contact Charles Fuchter); crime work in the magistrates court (Patrick Bligh); and licensing in the magistrates court (Andrew Pearson).

Types of work undertaken: To serve the needs of the expanding Medway Towns, specialist departments have been established for domestic and commercial conveyancing, company and commercial work, and civil, matrimonial and criminal litigation.

The firm is committed to assisting commercial clients to grasp the opportunities offered by the development of the Medway Towns, and in particular the Chatham Dockyard. While the practice serves corporate clients, commitment to individual clients is not forgotten, and a large volume of legal aid work is carried out.

Redfern & Stigant is particularly well known for its work in the areas of estate development, commercial property, trust and probate, civil and commercial litigation, licensing law, child care, mobile home and houseboat law, and volume debt collection, as well as for its specialised criminal defence department.

Overall, Redfern & Stigant perceives itself as the largest and best established firm in the Medway Towns that has matched its expansion with that of the area. It is a firm that can offer continuity and a good all-round service to the private and corporate client.

REDFERN & STIGANT

Reynolds Porter Chamberlain

CHICHESTER HOUSE
278-282 HIGH HOLBORN
LONDON
WC1V 7HA
Phone: 01 242 2877

Fax: 01 242 1431
DX: 81 LONDON CHANCERY LANE WC2
Telex: 265092
Senior Partner: Mr EM Garston
Number of Partners: 25
Total Staff: 162

This old-established Holborn practice is one of the country's leading insurance firms with extensive commercial and private client bases.

The firm: Reynolds Porter Chamberlain is the result of the merger of Reynolds Porter, which was founded about a century ago, and Chamberlain & Co, which dates from the 1920s. The firm has enjoyed steady expansion since the merger and is now regarded as a major insurance and commercial practice. The firm is organised into departments.

The firm is always seeking to employ good qualified staff, and in 1989 expects to have six vacancies for assistant solicitors, mainly for commercial and litigation work. Enquiries to the partnership secretary, Ms V Bowles.

In addition, 8 to 11 articled clerks are recruited annually. A good honours degree, not necessarily in law, is required. Prospects after qualification are good: a number of the present partners served articles with the firm. Apply in writing (with CV and names of referees) from 1 September two years in advance to Charles Gardner.

Agency work: The firm accepts all kinds of litigation work from other solicitors; contact Charles Gardner or Elisabeth Mahn.

Types of work undertaken: Much of the work undertaken by the firm's large litigation department is non-marine insurance related. It is especially noted for its professional indemnity and personal injury claim work. The firm also acts in an enormous variety of civil litigation matters, mainly in the commercial field but also for private clients, and is well known for its expertise in construction law and intellectual property matters. Indeed, non-contentious work in these latter two fields is also expanding rapidly.

There is a thriving commercial department acting for multinational corporations, private companies and professional and trade associations. The work includes acquisitions and mergers, competition law, debt recovery, trade union law, employment law, pensions and all aspects of the law of education and school management, including in particular representation of leading head teachers' and teachers' associations.

The conveyancing department is concerned mainly with commercial property transactions, although a certain amount of residential conveyancing is also handled.

The work of the private client department includes advising on matters varying from the formation of trusts, and probate matters, to adoption and wardship for local authorites, divorce work and personal injury claims. Other notable areas of expertise – for both corporate and private clients – are immigration and international tax. This is a professional firm with a personal touch.

Reynolds Porter Chamberlain

Richards Butler

5 CLIFTON STREET
LONDON
EC2A 4DQ

Phone: 01 247 6555

Fax: 01 247 5091
DX: 1066 LONDON CITY EC3
Telex: 949494 **Other offices:** 5
Senior Partner: Mr SN Beare
Number of Partners: 64
Total Staff: 461

Richards Butler combines an important shipping, insurance and aviation practice with substantial company and commercial work.

The firm: Founded in 1920 the growth of this major City firm has been especially rapid in the last decade with offices opened in Abu Dhabi (1978), Hong Kong (1980) and Tokyo (1987). Recently, existing areas of work in the aviation, banking, corporate finance and financial services industries have been strengthened by partners and their assistants joining from other firms.

Such has been this growth that there are opportunities and vacancies at most levels for able and ambitious lawyers in many departments with opportunities for overseas secondment. Enquires and applications to the personnel officer, Miss Elspeth Pye.

The firm recruits about 35 articled clerks per year. Academic requirements are not rigid but a 2(1) degree is usual. Non-law graduates are encouraged. Training and prospects are excellent with the vast majority remaining with the firm on qualification. Those accepted for articles are paid during their time at Law School. Apply by handwritten letter (plus typed CV) to Mr JMM Johnson.

Other offices: London, Abu Dhabi, Hong Kong and Tokyo. The firm has a truly international practice and maintains close links with law firms in most major centres throughout the world.

Types of work undertaken: Richards Butler has a broadly based, international practice, strong in shipping and insurance and with substantial aviation, banking and finance, company and commercial, entertainment, litigation, pensions, private client, commercial property and taxation departments. The clientele embraces a wide cross-section of commerce and industry and includes governments, banks and corporations of national and international repute.

The firm is particularly well known for its work in shipping, international trade and arbitration; in Hong Kong it has established one of the leading corporate finance and banking practices. The recently enlarged aviation department, whose members have extensive experience in the industry, is a natural extension of the firm's practice in transport and asset financing and leasing which is a particular strength in the Tokyo office. Richards Butler has represented companies and individuals in the entertainment and media industries worldwide for over 50 years. In addition, the firm has particular experience in pharmaceuticals, EEC and UK competition law, international joint ventures and intellectual property.

This thriving City firm offers a wide range of national and international expertise and is well regarded for its professionalism.

RICHARDS BUTLER

Robinson Jarvis & Rolf

PORTLAND HOUSE
18 MELVILLE STREET
RYDE
ISLE OF WIGHT PO33 2AP
Phone: 0983 62201

Fax: 0983 616602
DX: none
Telex: 86178 **Other offices:** 4
Senior Partner: Mr Clive Rolf
Number of Partners: 10
Total Staff: 95

Rollit Farrell & Bladon

KING WILLIAM HOUSE
MARKET PLACE
HULL
HUMBERSIDE HU1 1YJ
Phone: 0482 23239

Fax: 0482 26239
DX: 11901 HULL 1
Telex: 592412 **Other offices:** 1
Senior Partner: Mr THF Farrell
Number of Partners: 17
Total Staff: 94

Rootes & Alliott

27 CHERITON GARDENS
FOLKSTONE
KENT
CT20 2AR
Phone: 0303 851100

Fax: 0303 851150
DX: 4903 FOLKESTONE
Telex: 965345 **Other offices:** 2
Senior Partner: Mr PA Alliott
Number of Partners: 11
Total Staff: 54

Rotheras

24 FRIAR LANE
NOTTINGHAM
NG1 6DW

Phone: 0602 470831

Fax: 0602 410105
DX: 10028 NOTTINGHAM
Telex: 377958
Senior Partner: Mr PH Mellors
Number of Partners: 12
Total Staff: 60

Rooks Rider *see full-page profile*
Ross Harper & Murphy *see full-page profile*

Rooks Rider

8 & 9 NEW SQUARE
LINCOLN'S INN
LONDON
WC2A 3QJ
Phone: 01 831 7767

Fax: 01 242 7149
DX: 78 LONDON CHANCERY LANE WC2
Telex: 261302
Senior Partner: Mr BJ Prichard
Number of Partners: 11
Total Staff: 64

This Lincoln's Inn firm has a general practice serving both corporate and private clients.

The firm: Rooks Rider was formed in 1977 as the result of the amalgamation of the City firm of Rooks and the Lincoln's Inn firm of Riders, both of which date back some 200 years and had built strong reputations in private client work. Since the amalgamation Rooks Rider has expanded rapidly and a thriving commercial practice has been developed. The firm is organised into departments.

This expanding firm is always seeking to recruit high-calibre qualified staff, and in 1989 expects to have four to five vacancies for assistant solicitors for company/commercial and commercial conveyancing. Enquiries to the partnership secretary.

In addition, Rooks Rider usually recruits four articled clerks annually. The minimum educational requirement is a 2(1) degree, not necessarily in law. Prospects after qualification are good; the firm regards articled clerks as the prime source of future assistant solicitors and partners. Applications should be made by handwritten letter (with CV and names of referees) two years in advance and addressed to the partnership secretary.

Agency work: The firm accepts litigation work from other solicitors.

Types of work undertaken: Rooks Rider is a general practice which concentrates on providing good personal service to clients, whether individual or corporate. There are four main departments, namely company/commercial, conveyancing, litigation, and private client.

The company/commercial department has a broad range of work with a client base that varies from large PLCs and substantial private companies to sole traders and partnerships. There is a strong emphasis on tax work.

There is particular strength in conveyancing, with the emphasis on commercial transactions, although a considerable amount of residential conveyancing is undertaken.

From its traditional private client base the firm has maintained a thriving client list to whom it offers the full range of services. It is well known for the high quality of its taxation work, and especially the establishment and administration of off-shore trusts. Other work covered includes probate and wills, matrimonial and family law matters, crime and legal aid work.

There is a substantial commercial litigation practice, and the firm also acts in personal injury litigation, matrimonial disputes, employment law matters and intellectual property disputes.

In short, Rooks Rider perceives itself as a firm that is competent, reliable and efficient, with a friendly approach.

ROOKS RIDER

Ross Harper & Murphy

232 ST VINCENT STREET
GLASGOW
G2 5RH

Phone: 041 248 3611

Fax: 041 226 4198
Rutland Exchange: none
Telex: 777967 **Other offices:** 19
Senior Partner: Prof J Ross Harper CBE
Number of Partners: 25
Total Staff: 225

This young vigorous Glasgow-based general practice has the largest branch office network of any firm in Britain.

The firm: Founded by the present senior partner in the early 1960s, this is a general practice with the emphasis on the private client, with an increasingly important company and commercial workload. The firm has grown dramatically since its inception: there is a substantial departmentalised head office and 19 branches.

The firm is always seeking assistant solicitors for all departments; 12 vacancies are expected in 1989. Enquiries (with CV) to the staff partner, Rod McKenzie.

Ross Harper & Murphy normally recruits 12 trainee solicitors every year. The minimum educational qualifications are a law degree plus a DipLP. Long-term prospects are good, the firm regards trainees as its future. Apply on form (with CV and names of referees) one year in advance to the staff partner, Rod McKenzie.

Other offices: Glasgow (2), Edinburgh (2), Shawlands (2), Airdrie, Bellshill, Castlemilk, Easterhouse, East Kilbride, Cumbernauld, Hamilton, Kirkintilloch, Paisley, Pollok, Rutherglen, Shotts, Uddingston.

Agency work: The firm accepts work from other solicitors; contact Linda Smith (criminal); Rod McKenzie (civil and commercial litigation and employment); Gordon Stoddart (domestic conveyancing); Lorne Crerar (leasing and securities); or Robert Hynd (corporate business).

Types of work undertaken: With such a large number of branch offices the firm has a very general practice, but there are four specialist departments. Most branches handle criminal work, while there is a specialist office at Ingram Street, Glasgow.

The fastest growing department is that handling company and commercial work; this department has developed particular expertise in licensing, management buy-outs and company acquisitions and flotations, as well as offering the full range of company/commercial work.

The bulk of the work dealt with by the conveyancing department is domestic; commercial conveyancing is generally done by the company/commercial department.

Civil work is dealt with throughout the branches, with a special department at St Vincent Street, Glasgow. A large amount of divorce work is handled, together with personal injury matters, employment law, and the whole range of civil litigation. All kinds of legal aid work are undertaken.

Overall, Ross Harper & Murphy sees itself as large, efficient, forward-thinking in management, and able to cope with any area of law.

Rowe & Maw

20 BLACK FRIARS LANE
LONDON
EC4V 6HD

Phone: 01 248 4282

Fax: 01 248 2009
DX: 93 LONDON CHANCERY LANE WC2
Telex: 262787 **Other offices:** 1
Senior Partner: Nigel Graham Maw
Number of Partners: 40
Total Staff: 302

Rowe & Maw, a medium sized City firm, has a commercially orientated practice with a wide range and diversity of work.

The firm: Rowe & Maw is a thriving firm, founded in 1895. The firm moved to its present attractive City offices in 1985. Work ranges from aviation and banking law to unit trusts and wills. In the last 20 years the firm has expanded steadily, and recently opened an office at Lloyd's handling insurance work. The firm is organised into partner-led teams.

Rowe & Maw generally requires up to 20 assistant solicitors every year. Whilst most vacancies for assistant solicitors are filled by the articled clerks qualifying in the firm, there are likely to be, each year, vacancies in corporate finance and commercial property. Enquiries to Mrs Diane Austin, Personnel Manager.

The firm recruits 20 articled clerks annually. A 2(1) degree is preferred. Apply to Diane Austin by handwritten letter (plus CV and names of referees) during the summer term of second year.

Other offices: London (Lloyd's).

Types of work undertaken: Rowe & Maw aims to offer a total legal service to its clients. The clientele ranges from large institutions and multinational corporations to small privately owned businesses and partnerships.

There is a particular interest in entrepreneurs starting new businesses or investing in the UK for the first time. Services include the full range of corporate and financial work, tax, employment, property, litigation, information technology and intellectual property.

The firm is particularly strong in construction law and, indeed, is recognised as one of the leading construction practices. It is also well known for its expertise in pensions and related financial services and insurance.

Other areas of activity include commercial property for both retail and development company clients. The firm has considerable experience in most areas of commercial law, including mergers and acquisitions, flotations, and insurance. At Rowe & Maw there is always a varied mix in litigation.

For a medium sized firm, there is a particularly large litigation department. In addition, the private client department specialises in tax planning, wills and probate.

Although the firm has a wide range of specialisations, it is organised so that partners are responsible for the clients. This ensures maximum continuity and contact with clients. The firm is developing a series of guides and memoranda for the benefit of clients; in addition, brochures giving details of services are available on request.

Overall, the firm is perceived as being sound, professional and knowledgeable.

Rowe & Maw

Rowlands

35 FOUNTAIN STREET
MANCHESTER
M2 2AF

Phone: 061 228 1561

Fax: 061 228 0984
DX: 14371 MANCHESTER-1
Telex: 668818 **Other offices:** 8
Senior Partner: Mr S Mocton
Number of Partners: 12
Total Staff: 102

Rowley Ashworth

KENNEDY TOWER
ST CHAD'S QUEENSWAY
BIRMINGHAM
B4 6JG

Phone: 021 233 1831

Fax: 021 200 1205
DX: none
Telex: 335812 **Other offices:** 3
Senior Partner: Mr Roger Goodier
Number of Partners: 9
Total Staff: 127

Rowleys & Blewitts

HALIFAX HOUSE
93-101 BRIDGE STREET
MANCHESTER
M3 2GX

Phone: 061 834 4215

Fax: 061 834 5153
DX: 14332 MANCHESTER 1
Telex: 668780 **Other offices:** 1
Senior Partner: Mr GN Gibbons
Number of Partners: 11
Total Staff: 52

Russell & Russell

9-13 WOOD STREET
BOLTON
LANCASHIRE
BL1 1EE

Phone: 0204 34051

Fax: 0204 389223
DX: 24146 BOLTON-1
Telex: 635454 **Other offices:** 8
Senior Partner: Mr T T Bennett
Number of Partners: 11
Total Staff: 85

Roythorne & Co *see full-page profile*
Rubinstein Callingham Polden Gale *see full-page profile*
Russell Jones & Walker *see full-page profile*

Roythorne & Co

10 PINCHBECK ROAD
SPALDING
LINCOLNSHIRE
PE11 1PZ
Phone: 0775 4141

Fax: 0775 5736
DX: 26701 SPALDING
Telex: 32823 **Other offices:** 1
Senior Partner: Mr TW Harbage
Number of Partners: 15
Total Staff: 110

The wide range of commercial services offered to its clients by Roythorne & Co reflects the firm's status as a major provincial practice.

The firm: Established in Spalding for over 50 years, Roythorne & Co has expanded into a leading firm in the east of England with close connections to the City of London and other provincial centres. Based in a predominantly farming area, it has strong links in the agricultural community.

The firm is set to expand further and it is likely that it will recruit ten assistant solicitors in 1989, in all areas of civil and commercial work.

At least two articled clerks are recruited annually. A 2(2) degree in law is required. Apply by handwritten letter (plus CV, photograph and the names of two referees) to Mr AD McCrindle. A brochure for articled clerks is available upon request.

Other offices: Boston, Lincolnshire.

Agency work: Work for other solicitors is undertaken in all fields in which Roythorne & Co specialises.

Types of work undertaken: Roythorne & Co undertakes a wide range of agricultural law work, and combines this with a strong commercial practice for industrial and professional clients. The firm has been organised into four main departments, namely litigation, tax and probate, conveyancing, and commercial.

The work of the litigation department extends from debt collection to more complex civil litigation and includes criminal cases and family law matters. The department is particularly strong in the fields of employment law and the contentious side of agricultural law.

The conveyancing department deals with a wide range of agricultural, commercial and industrial property matters, as well as residential conveyancing.

The work of the tax and probate department encompasses the administration of estates and trusts, tax planning schemes and general taxation advice, as well as the preparation of wills and the establishment of settlements.

The company and commercial department typically handles such matters as the acquisition and disposal of businesses and companies, the financing and organisation of companies, public subscriptions for shares, commercial agreements and business terms and conditions.

Overall, this leading provincial firm perceives itself as progressive and forward-looking, and foresees strong and continued growth in all areas, particularly in aspects of its civil and commercial practice.

ROYTHORNE & CO.

Rubinstein Callingham Polden Gale

2 RAYMOND BUILDINGS
GRAY'S INN
LONDON
WC1R 5BZ

Phone: 01 242 8404

Fax: 01 831 7413
DX: 125 LONDON CHANCERY LANE WC2
Telex: 894100
Senior Partner: Anthony Rubinstein
Number of Partners: 16
Total Staff: 91

Rubinstein Callingham, which has recently merged with Polden Bishop & Gale, has a long-established reputation in intellectual property, publishing and entertainment law.

The firm: The original firm, Rubinstein Nash, was founded in Gray's Inn around 1826. It merged with Callingham Tucker in 1976. The merger in 1987, with Polden Bishop & Gale, has brought a strong commercial law and property bias to the firm.

The firm is actively recruiting qualified staff, and in 1989 expects six vacancies for assistant solicitors, for property, intellectual property, commercial and litigation. Enquiries to Richard Sax.

In addition four articled clerks are recruited annually. A 2(1) degree, not necessarily in law is preferred. Apply by handwritten letter (with CV and names of referees) to Richard Sax two years in advance.

Agency work: The firm accepts substantial commercial litigation work from other solicitors; contact Stephen Creed.

Types of work undertaken: The firm has developed a broad base of legal expertise to serve the needs of its traditional private and expanding corporate clientele. The firm is divided into six main departments, namely company/commercial; property; intellectual property; litigation; matrimonial/family; and trusts, probate and estate planning. The firm has practitioners experienced in tax law planning, insurance, pensions and employment law.

The large property department undertakes, in addition to standard commercial and general work, direct involvement in project management combined work, corporate funding and banking. The company department has expanded, taking in acquisitions, management buy-outs, share option schemes, pensions, flotations and associated taxation issues. The litigation department has emphasis on commercial issues, building, and landlord and tenant disputes.

Rubinstein Callingham has traditionally been prominent in copyright, publishing law, defamation, entertainment and other related branches of intellectual property law. Now it has senior expertise in heavy commercial patent and trademark work.

The family law side of the practice has been expanded; the present family law partner is president of the Solicitors Family Law Association. The firm has many international associations, with one of the partners entitled to practise at the New York Bar.

Rubinstein Callingham with Polden Bishop & Gale sees itself as combining the very best of the traditional virtues maintaining high professional standards, commercial skills with innovative and imaginative approaches in providing solutions to clients' needs.

RUBINSTEIN CALLINGHAM POLDEN GALE

Russell Jones & Walker

SWINTON HOUSE
324 GRAY'S INN ROAD
LONDON
WC1X 8DH
Phone: 01 837 2808

Fax: 01 837 2941
DX: 202 LONDON CHANCERY LANE WC2
Telex: 23616 **Other offices:** 5
Senior Partner: John M Webber
Number of Partners: 20
Total Staff: 165

A leading national firm of solicitors with a network of regional offices, Russell Jones & Walker provides a wide range of legal services and specialises in litigation.

The firm: Originally the in-house legal team of a trade union, the firm established itself as an independent legal practice in 1926, acting principally for trade unions and undertaking personal injury and employment law work. Over the last 20 years the practice has also built up a substantial business in other spheres, including administrative and constitutional law, libel law, criminal work, commercial property, and commercial insurance, as well as expanding its established reputation as one of the leading firms of solicitors representing institutions and their members. In recent years the firm has opened a number of regional offices, firmly establishing itself as a nationally based practice.

Russell Jones & Walker will require a minimum of eight solicitors in 1989 for new positions, particularly for contentious work. All applications should be addressed to Mr JM Webber.

In addition the firm recruits three or four articled clerks annually. Apply by handwritten letter (plus CV, photograph and two referees) to Edward Cooper.

Other offices: Leeds, Birmingham, Bristol, Bath, Manchester.

Agency work: Most types of High Court contentious work are undertaken on behalf of other solicitors.

Types of work undertaken: The firm is one of the main litigation practices acting in the fields of personal injury and disaster work. It also has an established reputation in the areas of industrial relations and employment law, quality insurance work and libel law, as well as a growing reputation in the field of white-collar investigative work. The firm offers a fully integrated legal service to its institutional, clients, and their members through its regional office network.

The firm frequently undertakes high-profile work, ranging from 'front-page issues' to national political questions, for its institutional clients. As well as its traditional institution-orientated litigation work, the firm undertakes commercial litigation including professional negligence and major insurance claims.

The firm aims to offer all its clients a fully integrated legal service, including criminal and investigations, commercial and residential property transactions in the UK amd abroad, matrimonial, libel, and general commercial services. An associated practice – Townleys with Russell Jones & Walker – undertakes corporate and non-contentious work. A brochure is available for clients.

RUSSELL JONES & WALKER

Russell-Cooke Potter & Chapman

2 PUTNEY HILL
LONDON
SW15 6AB

Phone: 01 789 9111

Fax: 01 788 1289
DX: 59456 PUTNEY
Telex: 295042 **Other offices:** 2
Senior Partner: Mr LH Chapman
Number of Partners: 13
Total Staff: 90

Rutherfords

6-9 LADY BANK
TAMWORTH
STAFFORDSHIRE
B79 7NF
Phone: 0827 311411

Fax: 0827 311666
DX: 12654 TAMWORTH
Telex: none
Senior Partner: Mr RJ Whitehead
Number of Partners: 13
Total Staff: 80

Sacker & Partners

43 GREAT MARLBOROUGH ST
LONDON
W1V 2NX

Phone: 01 437 5633

Fax: 01 494 0086
DX: 44633 MAYFAIR W1
Telex: 263647
Senior Partner: Mr HB Sacker
Number of Partners: 17
Total Staff: 54

Seifert Sedley Williams

1 & 3 DYERS BUILDINGS
LONDON
EC1N 2JL

Phone: 01 831 3030

Fax: 01 831 7197
DX: 425 LONDON CHANCERY LANE WC2
Telex: 8953097
Senior Partner: Mr JL Williams
Number of Partners: 8
Total Staff: 67

S J Berwin & Co *see full-page profile*
Saunders Sobell Leigh & Dobin *see full-page profile*

SJ Berwin & Co

236 GRAYS INN ROAD
LONDON
WC1X 8HB

Phone: 01 278 0444

Fax: 01 833 2860
DX: 255 LONDON CHANCERY LANE WC2
Telex: 8814928
Senior Partner: Christopher Haan
Number of Partners: 37
Total Staff: 215

This is one of the major City firms, with a substantial national and international practice, and a particular emphasis on EEC law.

The firm: SJ Berwin & Co was founded in 1982 by Stanley Berwin, formerly senior director of NM Rothschild & Sons, the merchant bankers; he died suddenly in July 1988. Expansion has been remarkable and has been achieved largely by recruiting leading lawyers in varying fields.

There is a continuing need for well qualified assistant solicitors in this rapidly expanding firm; in 1989 up to 20 vacancies are expected. Enquiries should be addressed to Robert Missig.

Between 12 and 15 articled clerks are recruited annually. The firm expects candidates to have a good degree, not necessarily in law. Apply by handwritten letter (with CV and names of referees) in September two years in advance to the personnel manager.

Types of work undertaken: As is to be expected of a high-flying City firm, SJ Berwin & Co is committed to providing the full range of legal services to financial, industrial and commercial clients, both national and international. The firm also advises private clients on trusts, tax planning and asset protection. There are four main departments (corporate finance, commercial and EEC, property and taxation) with expert teams working in particular areas.

The corporate finance department is the largest in the firm, and is particularly well known for its work in mergers and acquisitions, listings and banking. International tax planning is another area of expertise within SJ Berwin.

The firm has a strong bias towards EEC law; and indeed is one of the founder members of the CBI 1992 Initiative. Litigation and non-contentious work are combined in the commercial department; the firm feels this provides continuity if relationships become contentious. Other expert groups within the department include intellectual property, pharmaceuticals, and the recently established media and communications group.

The property department handles all aspects of commercial property work for large property companies, developers, banks, financial institutions, local authorities and major retail and hotel chains. A planning and development group has recently been formed within the property department.

The aim is to provide speedy and positive legal advice that is both commercial and practical, enabling clients to make decisions with full knowledge of their consequences. The firm regards a creative approach as essential. The partnership sees itself in the front rank of City firms, although it is still smaller than many of the longer established firms.

SJ Berwin & Co

Saunders Sobell Leigh & Dobin

20 RED LION STREET
HOLBORN
LONDON
WC1R 4PB

Phone: 01 242 2525

Fax: 01 405 4202
DX: 86 LONDON CHANCERY LANE WC2
Telex: 21762
Managing Partner: Brian L Sobell
Number of Partners: 23
Total Staff: 140

A medium sized Holborn firm, Saunders Sobell Leigh & Dobin offers a wide range of legal services to commercial clients.

The firm: Founded in 1913, the practice initially serviced the needs of private clients, although there was always a certain amount of commercial work. Over the last 15 to 20 years, however, the emphasis of the practice has changed radically and is now predominantly commercially orientated. In February 1989 the firm moved into new offices in Holborn to provide room for further expansion to meet the firm's growth requirements. The building provides the firm with up-to-date facilities including a restaurant where members can meet informally. The firm is organised into departments and has a management structure based on corporate lines. The firm's managing partner spends most of the time in a 'MD' role supported by three functional partners responsible for business development, IT and staff respectively. In turn, they are supported by professional managers.

There is a continuing need for qualified staff, and those who have had experience with a City or West End commercial practice are preferred; in 1989 the firm expects ten vacancies for assistant solicitors. Enquiries to Michael Robin, staff partner.

In addition, five articled clerks are recruited every year. A law degree is preferred, although non-law graduates are considered. Long-term prospects are good: nearly half of the present partners served articles with the firm. Apply on form (available on request) two years in advance to the personnel manager.

Types of work undertaken: The firm's clients are predominantly businesses, ranging from fully listed to substantial private companies as well as young, growing enterprises.

The firm undertakes a wide range of work in the area of business law, and is divided into seven main departments, namely commercial property, town planning, corporate tax, company/commercial, litigation, residential estates, and private client.

The firm has expertise in all aspects of commercial property work, including town planning, rating and building construction law and town centre redevelopment work (acting for local authorities and developers), and 'edge-of-town' retail developments.

In the company/commercial field, the firm offers experience in dealing with acquisitions and disposals, USM flotations, setting up distribution and joint venture arrangements as well as advising the growing company.

Overall, Saunders Sobell Leigh & Dobin is a medium sized but expanding firm with high professional standards, having the ability to understand clients' commercial goals and to help translate them into reality. The firm has a solid base in property and a growing reputation in other areas of business law.

Saunders
Sobell
Leigh & Dobin

Seymour Major Barnes

60 FORE STREET
EDMONTON
LONDON
N18 2TT
Phone: 01 884 2277

Fax: 01 807 0614
DX: 36200 EDMONTON-1
Telex: none **Other offices:** 8
Senior Partner: Mr Nigel G Barnes
Number of Partners: 7
Total Staff: 75

Shacklocks

19-21 THE ROPEWALK
NOTTINGHAM
NG1 5DU

Phone: 0602 410789

Fax: 0602 475561
DX: 10076 NOTTINGHAM
Telex: none **Other offices:** 3
Senior Partner: Mr AE Shepperson
Number of Partners: 13
Total Staff: 88

Shakespeare Duggan Lea & Co

10 BENNETTS HILL
BIRMINGHAM
B2 5RS

Phone: 021 632 4199

Fax: 021 643 2257
DX: 13015 BIRMINGHAM-1
Telex: 339019
Senior Partner: Mr Michael Hayes
Number of Partners: 15
Total Staff: 103

Sharman & Trethewy

1 HARPUR STREET
BEDFORD
MK40 1PF

Phone: 0234 41171

Fax: 0234 52114
DX: 5604 BEDFORD
Telex: 265871 **Other offices:** 2
Senior Partner: Mr WS Northey
Number of Partners: 9
Total Staff: 71

Sharman Sykes

WEST END HOUSE
60 OXFORD STREET
WELLINGBOROUGH
NORTHAMPTONSHIRE NN8 4JW
Phone: 0933 79000

Fax: 0933 227350
DX: 12855 WELLINGBOROUGH
Telex: none **Other offices:** 6
Managing Partner: Mr JA Read
Number of Partners: 8
Total Staff: 65

Sheridans

14 RED LION SQUARE
LONDON
WC1R 4QL

Phone: 01 404 0444

Fax: 01 831 1982
DX: 270 LONDON CHANCERY LANE WC2
Telex: 21297
Senior Partner: Mr B Sheridan
Number of Partners: 12
Total Staff: 63

Sherwins

THE OLD MANOR HOUSE
WICKHAM ROAD
FAREHAM
HAMPSHIRE PO16 7AR
Phone: 0329 822611

Fax: 0329 822612
DX: 40816 FAREHAM
Telex: none **Other offices:** 5
Senior Partner: Mr Nigel Steward
Number of Partners: 10
Total Staff: 85

Simmonds Church Smiles & Co

13 BEDFORD ROW
LONDON
WC1R 4BU

Phone: 01 242 9971

Fax: 01 405 0874
DX: 101 LONDON CHANCERY LANE WC2
Telex: 295573 **Other offices:** 2
Senior Partner: Mr AJ Quinton
Number of Partners: 13
Total Staff: 66

Shepherd & Wedderburn WS *see full-page profile*
Shoosmiths & Harrison *see full-page profile*

Shepherd & Wedderburn WS

16 CHARLOTTE SQUARE
EDINBURGH
EH2 4YS

Phone: 031 225 8585

Fax: 031 225 1110
Rutland Exchange: 49 EDINBURGH
Telex: 727251
Senior Partner: Ivor R Guild
Number of Partners: 25
Total Staff: 205

One of the largest and oldest Scottish law firms, Shepherd & Wedderburn is a general practice serving a very wide range of clients, both private and commercial.

The firm: Shepherd & Wedderburn traces its origins back to 1768, and was established in its present name and premises in 1922 on the amalgamation of Guild & Shepherd and Carment, Wedderburn & Watson. For well over 65 years the firm has maintained its position in the forefront of commercial practice, having particularly strong links with the Edinburgh financial community.

This thriving firm is always seeking to recruit high-calibre qualified staff, and in 1989 expects to have up to ten vacancies for assistant solicitors in all areas (especially corporate, commercial property and private client work). Enquiries to the staff partner.

Shepherd & Wedderburn recruits six or more trainee solicitors every year. The minimum requirement is a Scottish law degree; applications from English lawyers wishing to requalify are welcome. Prospects are excellent; the majority of the present partners served articles with the firm. Apply by handwritten letter (with CV) one year in advance to the staff partner.

Agency work: The firm accepts all types of work from other solicitors; contact the head of the appropriate department.

Types of work undertaken: There are five main departments, namely corporate, commercial property, residential property and estate agency, private client, and litigation.

The firm's reputation for corporate and commercial work was established through its work in the investment and investment management fields, connections which it still enjoys and values, and over the last two decades it has established a wide client base in the financial sector generally. It is acknowledged for its expertise in PLC and Stock Exchange (especially listings) work.

In the commercial property field the firm handles the full range of transactions for financial institutions, developers, lenders, retailers and others. The residential property department includes an estate agency.

All forms of litigation and arbitration are dealt with by the large litigation department, with particular emphasis on commercial and professional indemnity litigation and arbitration.

In common with the other leading Scottish commercial practices the firm also has a thriving private client practice, which is well known for its work in trust law, personal tax and executries.

Shepherd & Wedderburn perceives itself as having a City-type practice with an unusually strong private client side. A brochure for clients is available on request.

SHEPHERD & WEDDERBURN WS

Shoosmiths & Harrison

COMPTON HOUSE
ABINGTON STREET
NORTHAMPTON
NN1 2LR
Phone: 0604 29977

Fax: 0604 20229
DX: 12404 NORTHAMPTON-1
Telex: 312167 **Other offices:** 10
Senior Partner: George Pollard
Number of Partners: 43
Total Staff: 340

Northampton-based Shoosmiths & Harrison is one of the largest provincial firms, and provides a full range of legal services from its 11 offices.

The firm: Founded by William Shoosmith in 1845, there has been continual expansion since the 1960s when the first two branch offices were opened. Since then eight more local offices have been opened. The firm has recently announced a merger with the long-established practice of Warmingtons & Hasties, strengthening its London office.

Solicitors are in continuous demand. In 1989 there will be 10 vacancies. Those with experience in commercial litigation, commercial property and company law are most needed. Address enquiries to Richard Black.

In addition, generally 10 to 15 articled clerks are recruited annually. A 2(2) degree, not necessarily in law, is required. Apply by letter (with CV and referees) in September/October of final year to Richard Black.

Other offices: Northampton (2), Banbury, Bedford, Daventry, London, Nottingham, Reading, Rugby, Towcester.

Agency work: All offices accept all types of work from other solicitors.

Types of work undertaken: In this broadly based firm there is a strong commercial bias combined with a substantial private client practice. The client list includes many of the leading companies and commercial organisations in the Midlands and beyond. The firm's six departments (agricultural, company/commercial, local authority and planning, litigation, probate and trusts and property) draw together experts from across the firm, facilitating training, referral of work between offices where appropriate and the fostering of the practice's strong 'one firm' culture. Thus each office can offer the full range of legal services.

The individual offices have their own particular areas of expertise: Northampton, the largest office, is well known for commercial property, planning, building society, all types of litigation, company and general commercial and employment work; Nottingham for company work; Banbury for property, general commercial (including commercial litigation) and family work; Rugby for property, general commercial and family work; Towcester for agricultural law; London for property and general commercial work; and Reading for insurance litigation. Civil legal aid work is undertaken at all offices.

Overall, Shoosmiths & Harrison sees itself as expert, progressive and vigorous, retaining the traditional values of integrity, reliability and friendliness. Its geographical spread is a particular strength, enabling the firm to offer clients a personal and convenient service.

SHOOSMITHS&HARRISON

Simmons & Simmons

14 DOMINION STREET
LONDON
EC2M 2RJ

Phone: 01 628 2020

Fax: 01 588 4129
DX: 12 LONDON CHANCERY LANE WC2
Telex: 888562 **Other offices:** 3
Senior Partner: Stephen James
Number of Partners: 91
Total Staff: 756

Simmons & Simmons is one of the largest City firms. Its practice covers all aspects of the law except criminal and matrimonial and the firm has strong international connections. Company/commercial and banking are the fastest growing areas of work.

The firm: Founded in 1896 by the twin brothers, Percy and Edward Simmons, as a general commercial practice, the firm has seen uninterrupted growth, especially in the last 20 years, and it continues to expand rapidly. It looks to the financial and business community, both in the UK and overseas, for the majority of its work, but also maintains a substantial private client practice. Clients range from governments and multinational companies, through publicly and privately owned companies and commercial entities, to private individuals.

In addition to the articled clerks who remain with the firm on qualification, Simmons & Simmons will need to recruit approximately 15 assistant solicitors in all its departments in 1989. Enquiries should be addressed to John Bradshaw, the recruitment partner.

Forty-five to 50 articled clerks are recruited by the firm every year. At least a 2(1) degree is preferred, not necessarily in law. Apply (with CV and names of two referees – one academic and one personal) to John Bradshaw two years in advance.

Other offices: Brussels, Hong Kong, and (in co-operation with Maître Francis Meyrier) Paris.

Types of work undertaken: Simmons & Simmons is a broadly based commercial practice with a strong emphasis on corporate and international work.

The firm is particularly well known for its expertise in corporate finance, mergers and acquisitions, banking, intellectual property, commercial property and planning, international litigation and arbitrations.

Simmons & Simmons deals with all types of corporate finance and company transactions, banking and international finance, commercial and trade law, including UK and EEC competition law, employment and pensions. Other areas of expertise are taxation (including corporate, commercial and private client), litigation (encompassing virtually every field of contentious business), and property and planning law for UK and overseas clients.

The firm's offices in Paris, Brussels and Hong Kong and its close links with law firms throughout the world enable clients to receive legal assistance on a worldwide basis.

Overall, Simmons & Simmons sees itself as a progressive, broadly based practice that is securely placed within the Top Ten City law firms. A brochure describing the full range of services is available on request.

SIMMONS & SIMMONS

Simon Olswang & Co

1 GREAT CUMBERLAND PLACE
LONDON
W1H 7AL

Phone: 01 723 9393

Fax: 01 723 6992
DX: 44407 MARBLE ARCH W1
Telex: 296909 **Other offices:** 1
Senior Partner: Simon Olswang
Number of Partners: 9
Total Staff: 63

This progressive London firm has developed a substantial entertainment law practice with strong international connections and has a growing reputation in all sectors of corporate and commercial law.

The firm: Simon Olswang & Co was founded in March 1981, and soon developed a reputation as a leading practitioner of commercial law for the entertainment industry. The firm has grown rapidly throughout its existence (particularly in the last few years) and has diversified, retaining its core business base but developing equivalent strengths in other aspects of corporate business law. The firm is organised into four key groups.

The firm expects to recruit 12 assistant solicitors in 1989. Enquiries to Julia Palca or Julia Dickens.

In addition, four to six articled clerks are needed annually. A 2(1) degree is preferred, not necessarily in law. Applications (with CV, plus resume of how applicant would like to develop career in law) to Julia Palca.

Other offices: Los Angeles.

Agency work: Work referred by European and American law firms is often undertaken.

Types of work undertaken: The firm has a growing reputation for practising a high standard of commercial law in each of its four key groups. Simon Olswang & Co acts for an unusually high number of public companies.

The client base reflects the firm's particular areas of expertise in corporate finance (mergers, acquisitions, management buy-outs and venture capital), media and communications law, industrial relations, intellectual property, litigation and commercial property (for many 'blue-chip' retail property clients).

The entertainment division handles film and television production, distribution and finance; cable, satellite and other communications media; recording and other music industry contracts, and sponsorship. In line with the firm's pre eminence in the entertainment field it has a Los Angeles office.

Company/commercial work includes corporate finance, venture capital, company acquisitions and joint ventures (national and international), management buy-outs, advertising law, computer law and franchising.

The commercial property group handles retail leases, commercial developments, and security for lending. Litigation work includes media, copyright, industrial relations, defamation and contract disputes.

This young and vital practice is now a serious alternative source of the top quality legal service normally associated with larger City firms. It has no wish to become a giant, but sees itself as innovative, efficient and competitive; dedicated to the pursuit of excellence and the highest professional standards.

SIMON
OLSWANG
AND Co

Simpson Curtis

41 PARK SQUARE
LEEDS
LS1 2NS

Phone: 0532 433433

Fax: 0532 445598
DX: 26440 LEEDS PARK SQUARE
Telex: 55376
Senior Partner: Anthony Blackmore
Number of Partners: 19
Total Staff: 210

This Leeds-based practice, one of the leading law firms outside London, offers a full range of legal services with particular emphasis on corporate matters. It is a member of the Legal Resources Group (see separate entry).

The firm: Founded in 1850, and based in the commercial heart of Yorkshire, Simpson Curtis is a corporate law practice, representing a wide variety of industrial, financial and commercial enterprises, many operating on a national and international basis. The firm is organised into four main departments.

This expanding firm expects to recruit 30 assistant solicitors in the next year in the fields of company, litigation, property and taxation. Applicants with experience in City or major provincial firms are preferred. Enquiries to Nigel Binks.

Up to 12 articled clerks are recruited annually. The firm assesses candidates on experience and interview. Prospects are excellent; half the existing partners were articled with the firm. Apply (on form or with CV and photo) to Jonathan Jeffries two years in advance.

Types of work undertaken: This is a full service law firm, specialising in the representation of commercial, industrial and financial enterprises.

Simpson Curtis acts for over 20 leading financial institutions, as well as many substantial public and private corporate clients, and a number of prestigious private clients and estates. Increasingly, much of the work is becoming international and the firm has developed informal links with lawyers in all leading jurisdictions.

The work is divided into four departments, company/commercial, litigation and insolvency, property and taxation. Each department has a number of specialist units which include banking and financial services, competition, intellectual property, debt collection, building contracts, and professional negligence, planning and licensing, employment, agricultural land, property development, trusts, personal and corporate tax, and tax investigation.

Particular areas in which the firm is well regarded include corporate finance; takeovers and mergers; management buy-outs; flotations; general company law; banking and insolvency; commercial property development; building litigation; commercial leases; competition; intellectual property; employment law; planning and licensing; corporate tax and personal tax planning, and franchising.

Overall, this Leeds-based firm perceives itself as a very experienced and efficient large commercial practice, with an enviable reputation nationally and a commitment to providing the highest quality service to its clients. A brochure is available on request.

Sinclair Roche & Temperley

STONE HOUSE
128-140 BISHOPSGATE
LONDON
EC2M 4JP
Phone: 01 377 9044

Fax: 01 377 1528
DX: 1075 LONDON CITY EC3
Telex: 889281 **Other offices:** 2
Senior Partner: John Morris
Number of Partners: 30
Total Staff: 210

This is a medium sized international City firm with overseas offices in Hong Kong and Singapore, and a presence in Tokyo.

The firm: The origins of Sinclair Roche & Temperley can be traced back to the late nineteenth century. The firm adopted its present name in 1934. Initially, the firm specialised in shipping and maritime law; this has grown into a practice concentrating on international trade and transportation and also offering general commercial services. The firm is organised into departments.

The firm has a continuing requirement for high-quality qualified staff, and in the next 12 months expects to appoint ten new assistant solicitors. Enquiries to the controller of administration.

In addition, seven articled clerks are normally recruited every year. The minimum educational requirement is an above-average degree. Prospects after qualification are good: most articled clerks stay on with the firm. Apply by handwritten letter (with CV and names of referees) by May to the controller of administration.

Other offices: Hong Kong, Singapore.

Types of work undertaken: Shipping and maritime law remains the largest part of the practice, but it has expanded to encompass shipping, aircraft and project

finance, commercial and shipping litigation and arbitration, company and commercial, general banking, taxation and commercial property.

In Singapore the firm handles primarily financial and commercial English law matters with a particular expertise in the offshore field.

The litigation department deals with disputes arising from a comprehensive range of commercial and shipping transactions. The Admiralty department handles all problems arising from major marine casualties throughout the world. The main shipping finance clients are international banks, in particular those based in the major world shipping centres, as well as many of the world's leading shipowners and shipyards.

The company/commercial department specialises in assisting both British and overseas companies in expanding their UK operations and extending their business elsewhere in Europe. It is also active in relation to buy-outs and major operations. Taxation is one of the newer departments, formed to provide clients with a comprehensive service in corporate matters. The aviation department advises banks, leasing companies, manufacturers and airlines on all aspects of the law and practice relating to the purchase, financing and leasing of aircraft worldwide.

Sinclair Roche & Temperley sees itself as highly skilled, competent and efficient.

Sinclair Roche & Temperley

Slater Heelis

LLOYDS BANK BLDGS
1 TATTON ROAD
SALE
CHESHIRE M33 1XR
Phone: 061 969 3131

Fax: 061 973 1018
DX: 19261 SALE-1
Telex: none **Other offices:** 1
Senior Partner: Mr RC Curl
Number of Partners: 18
Total Staff: 120

Slee Blackwell

2/6 SOUTH STREET
BRAUNTON
DEVON
EX33 2AA
Phone: 0271 812019

Fax: 0271 816805
DX: 50452 BRAUNTON
Telex: none **Other offices:** 6
Senior Partner: Mr JAG Pearn
Number of Partners: 5
Total Staff: 75

Smith & Harrison

126 CROSSBROOK STREET
CHESHUNT
WALTHAM CROSS
HERTFORDSHIRE EN8 8JS
Phone: 0992 24232

Fax: 0992 32193
DX: 80800 WALTHAM CROSS
Telex: none **Other offices:** 1
Senior Partner: Mr WDV Pegg
Number of Partners: 9
Total Staff: 70

Sparling Benham & Brough

3 WEST STOCKWELL STREET
COLCHESTER
ESSEX
CO1 1HQ
Phone: 0206 577767

Fax: 0206 564551
DX: 3607 COLCHESTER
Telex: none **Other offices:** 3
Senior Partner: Mr RA Jacklin
Number of Partners: 14
Total Staff: 66

Slaughter and May *see full-page profile*
Smith Morton & Long *see full-page profile*

Slaughter and May

35 BASINGHALL STREET
LONDON
EC2V 5DB

Phone: 01 600 1200

Fax: 01 726 0038
DX: 11 LONDON CITY EC3
Telex: 883486 **Other offices:** 4
Senior Partner: Mr GB Inglis
Number of Partners: 77
Total Staff: 972

To many people, Slaughter and May is 'the' City firm. It is one of the leading law firms in the world, offering an international service to a wide range of clients.

The firm: Slaughter and May was established in 1889. From its earliest days its clients have been drawn from the banking, mercantile and industrial sections of the community who have valued the firm's ability to grasp the commercial rationale of any transaction and, in applying the law, to achieve the client's objectives. From the outset the firm has operated internationally. The firm has grown steadily since its foundation; in terms of numbers, the growth has been more pronounced since the Second World War but has not been confined to the most recent period.

About 35 vacancies for assistant solicitors are anticipated in 1989. There are some particularly interesting opportunities in the EEC and pensions departments. Enquiries to Peter Morley-Jacob.

Fifty to 55 articled clerks are recruited annually. The usual academic requirement is a 2(1) degree, not necessarily in law. Apply by handwritten letter (with CV and names of referees) to Peter Morley-Jacob as early as possible.

Other offices: Hong Kong, Paris, New York, Tokyo.

Types of work undertaken: This is a major international practice. The firm does mainly commercial work (both industrial and financial) for corporate clients, both domestic and international, ranging from small jobs to mega-mergers, for 'one-man bands', multinationals and governments. Through the commercial and the specialist departments (property, litigation, tax, EEC, competition, pensions, employment, and private client) Slaughter and May meets all its clients' needs throughout the world.

The commercial department is the heart of the firm and is divided into groups. The firm has a high reputation across the whole spectrum of corporate and financial work, but is genuinely proud of its expertise in all areas. It is particularly well known for its work in mergers and acquistions, privatisations, flotations and new issues, international finance and venture capital work.

As well as its own offices in Europe, the USA and the Far East, the firm has long-standing relationships with lawyers abroad.

In short, the firm believes that there is no commercial matter (however large or small) in which it cannot provide a very high quality of service. Slaughter and May would like its clients and the profession to see it as providing not just well-thought-out legal views but practical advice based on good judgement — that is, 'value added' to the normal legal role. Brochures are available.

SLAUGHTER AND MAY

Smith Morton & Long

ESSEX HOUSE
22 CROUCH STREET
COLCHESTER
ESSEX CO3 3ES
Phone: 0206 562296

Fax: 0206 572393
DX: 3603 COLCHESTER
Telex: none **Other offices:** 2
Senior Partner: Anthony H Frost
Number of Partners: 11
Total Staff: 90

This is a medium sized Essex firm which offers a very wide service to corporate and private clients.

The firm: This old-established firm has grown and developed areas of expertise considerably in recent years. From its original base in Halstead it opened an office in Colchester in 1973, and on a recent merger acquired a practice in Clacton on Sea. While retaining a general practice, the firm is constantly extending to specialist services to meet demand. Its staff of 90 includes five assistant solicitors, four articled clerks and twelve legal executives in addition to a university-based consultant.

This expanding firm is always seeking to recruit qualified staff, and in the next 12 months it expects to have at least four vacancies for assistant solicitors for company/commercial, private client, and commercial conveyancing. Enquiries to Anthony H Frost.

In addition, the firm usually recruits two articled clerks every year. The minimum academic requirement is a good degree (not necessarily in law), but personality and ability to communicate are considered relevant. Great importance is applied to the training of articled clerks. Prospects after qualification are good; nearly half the present partners served articles with the firm. Apply by handwritten letter (with CV and referees) to Mr CJ Holmes.

Other offices: Halstead, Clacton on Sea.

Agency work: The three offices accept general litigation work from other solicitors.

Types of work undertaken: This is a broadly based provincial practice offering a wide range of legal services to a varied base of private and corporate clients. In addition to the usual range of private client work, the firm is strong in the areas of trusts, tax planning, divorce and employment law. The firm has particular expertise in agricultural work, commercial property (including town and country planning and landlord and tenant), and has an expanding commercial practice handling a variety of work including formations, acquisitions and disposals, reorganisations, partnership and related matters.

The firm is well known for its litigation practice, and in particular for personal injury, divorce, building, and employment matters (employee and employer).

The firm also undertakes conveyancing (both commercial and residential), crime, and legal aid work.

Overall, Smith Morton & Long sees itself as an efficient and effective mixed practice, with a highly professional standard of work and commitment, providing a complete range of services to all its clients. A brochure for clients detailing the services that the firm offers is available on request.

Smith Morton & Long

Speechly Bircham

BOUVERIE HOUSE
154 FLEET STREET
LONDON
EC4A 2HX
Phone: 01 353 3290

Fax: 01 353 4825
DX: 54 LONDON CHANCERY LANE WC2
Telex: 22655
Senior Partner: John Avery Jones
Number of Partners: 33
Total Staff: 181

Speechly Bircham is a broad-based City practice, whose principal reputation is in the fields of property, tax, and commercial law, as well as in private client work. The firm also has a developing intellectual property and information technology practice.

The firm: The firm expects to recruit ten to 20 assistant solicitors during the next year, particularly property lawyers with commercial flair and company lawyers. Enquiries to the Personnel Partner, Mark J Musgrave.

Additionally the firm expects to recruit six articled clerks annually. Candidates are required to have a 2(1) degree in any discipline. Greater emphasis is placed on the ability to accept responsibility and communicate at all levels. Prospects are good. Apply by letter and application form two years in advance to Richard M Schmidt.

Types of work undertaken: True to its origins in the property and commercial fields, this City practice remains solid in these areas. In addition, it is well known for its revenue law work and taxation work, both in the UK and internationally.

Commercial property is the largest area of activity at Speechly Bircham. The team advise a wide range of corporate clients on all aspects of landlord and tenant law, and on planning and construction, as well as dealing with property litigation and building disputes.

The company and commercial team works closely with the taxation, employment and information technology teams to provide a complete legal package. They advise all manner of corporate clients, including several large multinational companies, banks and financial institutions. The internationally renowned taxation team works for both private and corporate clients and has expertise in corporate planning and acquisition, VAT, inheritance tax and international trusts.

The service provided by Speechly Bircham covers litigation arising from property, financial and contractual transactions, as well as employment law. While much of the firm's work is in the High Court, it extends to all courts, as well as arbitration, enquiries and tribunals.

Speechly Bircham also has a strong private client practice. Work is undertaken both in the UK and internationally, and covers the whole spectrum of an individual's legal requirements, from wills and personal taxation, to trusts and family law, and includes matrimonial and family litigation. The firm also has experience in immigration work.

Overall, Speechly Bircham offers clients a wide range of services, but with particular emphasis on property, taxation, commercial and private client work and providing a partner-orientated service to every client.

SPEECHLY
BIRCHAM

Stafford Young Jones

2 SUFFOLK LANE
CANNON STREET
LONDON
EC4R OAU
Phone: 01 623 3501

Fax: 01 929 5704
DX: 128 LONDON CHANCERY LANE WC2
Telex: 924076 **Other offices:** 1
Senior Partner: Mr DG FISHER
Number of Partners: 18
Total Staff: 80

Staffurth & Bray

YORK ROAD CHAMBERS
BOGNOR REGIS
WEST SUSSEX
PO21 1LT
Phone: 0243 864 001

Fax: 0243 860 708
DX: 31212 BOGNOR REGIS
Telex: none **Other offices:** 2
Senior Partner: Mr Roger Turner
Number of Partners: 9
Total Staff: 63

Stamp Jackson & Procter

5 PARLIAMENT STREET
KINGSTON UPON HULL
NORTH HUMBERSIDE
HUMBERSIDE HU1 2AZ
Phone: 0482 24591

Fax: 0482 224048
DX: 11927 HULL-1
Telex: 597001 **Other offices:** 4
Senior Partner: Mr HG Procter
Number of Partners: 15
Total Staff: 104

Steedman Ramage & Co WS

6 ALVA STREET
EDINBURGH
EH2 4QQ

Phone: 031 226 3781

Fax: 031 225 8329
Rutland Exchange: 95 EDINBURGH
Telex: none
Senior Partner: Mr ED Buchanan
Number of Partners: 10
Total Staff: 65

Stanley Tee & Co *see full-page profile*

Steele & Co

7 MERE STREET
DISS
NORFOLK
IP22 3AD
Phone: 0379 652175

Fax: 0379 652960
DX: 42507 DISS
Telex: 97445 **Other offices:** 6
Senior Partner: Mr CGA Steele
Number of Partners: 10
Total Staff: 82

Stevens & Bolton

5 CASTLE STREET
FARNHAM
SURREY
GU9 7HT
Phone: 0252 725040

Fax: 0252 723501
DX: 32800 FARNHAM
Telex: 265871 **Other offices:** 3
Senior Partner: Mr JN Hand
Number of Partners: 13
Total Staff: 98

Stevens Drake & Pope

MIDLAND HOUSE
117-119 HIGH STREET
CRAWLEY
WEST SUSSEX RH10 1YN
Phone: 0293 544071

Fax: 0293 560553
DX: 57104 CRAWLEY
Telex: 8950511 **Other offices:** 3
Managing Partner: Mr JE Drake
Number of Partners: 9
Total Staff: 150

Stokes

108 VICTORIA ROAD NORTH
PORTSMOUTH
HAMPSHIRE
PO5 1QQ
Phone: 0705 828131

Fax: 0705 811339
DX: 2220 PORTSMOUTH
Telex: none **Other offices:** 3
Senior Partner: Mr C Wood
Number of Partners: 9
Total Staff: 60

Steggles Palmer *see full-page profile*
Stephens & Scown *see full-page profile*
Stephenson Harwood *see full-page profile*
Stephensons *see full-page profile*

Stanley Tee & Co

6 HIGH STREET
BISHOP'S STORTFORD
HERTFORDSHIRE
CM23 2LU
Phone: 0279 755200

Fax: 0279 758400
DX: 50404 BISHOP'S STORTFORD
Telex: none **Other offices:** 2
Senior Partner: John N Turner
Number of Partners: 9
Total Staff: 85

A large provincial firm with strong departmental areas of special skill, Stanley Tee & Co is based in Bishop's Stortford.

The firm: Founded approximately 75 years ago by H Stanley Tee as a sole practitioner serving a traditional market town, he was subsequently joined by his two sons after the Second World War, both of whom retired in 1981. By that time the practice had grown to a six-partner firm with an established and strong client base. Since that time rapid expansion has taken place under the senior partnership of Mr JN Turner. Work is organised mainly in four departments.

The firm expects three vacancies for assistant solicitors in the next year if suitable high-quality applicants are forthcoming. Enquiries to Rodney Stock.

In addition, there are vacancies for three to five articled clerks annually. The preferred educational qualification is a 2(1) degree, but a good 2(2) law degree is accepted. Apply by handwritten letter (with CV and names of referees) 12 to 24 months in advance to the recruitment partner, David Redfern.

Other offices: Braintree, Dunmow.

Agency work: Work of a local nature is accepted from other solicitors.

Types of work undertaken: Stanley Tee & Co's client base has remained strong, with clients ranging from public to private companies through agricultural, insurance and commercial concerns, and also a large private clientele.

There is still a sizeable conveyancing service within the firm but this now includes specialist commercial areas such as agricultural law and major development work. The company/commercial department deals with continuing advice to existing clients as well as handling large mergers and acquisitions. The well-regarded and strong tax/trust/probate department has a substantial client base. The litigation department undertakes commercial litigation, especially in the agricultural and personal injury fields. There is also a large expert matrimonial practice.

The firm's particular areas of specialisation are commercial conveyancing (development and agricultural work); company mergers and acquisitions; personal advice on tax and trust matters; insurance company litigation (including agricultural insurers); matrimonial, and general advocacy.

This established professional firm sees itself as operating with complete integrity. Its acknowledged skill and expertise is combined with an entirely modern outlook. Stanley Tee & Co is one of a growing number of provincial firms offering a quality service which can challenge London advice.

STANLEY TEE & CO.

Steggles Palmer

2 BEDFORD ROW
LONDON
WC1R 4BU

Phone: 01 404 4477

Fax: 01 430 1300
DX: 114 LONDON CHANCERY LANE WC2
Telex: 24258
Senior Partner: Peter E Steggles
Number of Partners: 8
Total Staff: 52

This medium sized central London firm has a general practice, with the emphasis on commercial law work.

The firm: Established in 1971 as the London office of a country firm, Steggles Palmer has now developed into an independent London practice, while retaining strong associations with the provinces. In recent years the firm has expanded rapidly. Steggles Palmer is organised into departments.

This expanding firm is constantly seeking to recruit good-quality qualified staff, and in 1989 expects to have vacancies for six assistant solicitors; two each for the company/commercial, property and litigation departments. Enquiries should be addressed to Mr GE Morris.

In addition, three articled clerks are normally recruited every year. The minimum educational requirement is a 2(2) degree, not necessarily in law. Prospects after qualification are excellent; it is the firm's policy to appoint young partners. Apply by handwritten letter (with CV) two years in advance to Mr GE Morris.

Agency work: The firm accepts civil litigation work from other solicitors; contact Mr GE Morris. City-type work from provincial firms is also accepted; contact Mr CAM Henniker.

Types of work undertaken: This is a general practice with a commercial bias. There are three main departments, namely company/commercial, property and litigation. As well as significant corporate and private client bases, the firm acts for institutional clients in personal injury litigation and in the trade union, labour and employment law fields.

Litigation has always been a particularly strong area of practice and, besides trade union and disaster work, the firm handles a considerable amount of general commercial litigation as well as substantial personal injury work for institutions and insurance companies as well as individuals.

The company/commmercial department has particular expertise in flotations, management buy outs, securities law (acting for companies rather than issuing houses), company acquisitions and hotel and leisure industry matters, and insolvency, as well as offshore company work and overseas investment in the United Kingdom (including incorporations, tax work, property investments and other corporate work).

There is a strong property department, handling the full range of commercial transactions, notably development work.

Steggles Palmer sees itself as an expanding and effective commercial firm handling a wide variety of high-quality work and committed to close partner/client involvement.

STEGGLES PALMER

Stephens & Scown

3 CROSS LANE
ST AUSTELL
CORNWALL
PL25 4AX
Phone: 0726 74433

Fax: 0726 68623
DX: none
Telex: 45726 **Other offices:** 7
Senior Partner: Ian C Waite
Number of Partners: 22
Total Staff: 167

One of the major law firms in the West Country, Stephens & Scown provides a comprehensive legal service for both commercial and private clients.

The firm: Founded at St Austell in its present form some 50 years ago, the firm expanded into Devon in the 1960s. Throughout the last two decades it has continued to expand in both counties to become one of the largest practices in the region. In 1988 it opened an office in Swindon.

The firm seeks to recruit four assistant solicitors, for commercial, civil litigation and conveyancing. Enquiries should be addressed to the partnership administrator.

There are normally four vacancies for articled clerks. The firm encourages mature applicants. Long-term prospects are excellent: the majority of the present partners served articles with the firm. Applications should be made by handwritten letter (plus CV) 12 to 18 months in advance and addressed to the partnership administrator.

Other offices: Exeter, Looe, Torquay, Truro, Liskeard, Swindon, Lostwithiel.

Agency work: The firm undertakes all types of agency work for other solicitors.

Types of work undertaken: This is one of the major firms in Devon and Cornwall. As is appropriate in this region, the firm is well known in the areas of mining and agricultural law (including the establishment and exploitation of mines and quarries and milk quotas). It is also particularly experienced in employment and industrial law, estate development, town and country planning, personal injury and medical negligence.

The larger offices, in St Austell and Exeter, are organised into departments specialising in civil litigation, family and matrimonial law, criminal litigation, commercial, conveyancing, and wills, probate and trusts. The offices at Torquay, Looe, Liskeard and Truro are typical high street general practices; the Swindon office specialises in property matters.

The firm's client base is wide and includes listed companies, private companies of many descriptions, property developers, insurers and insurance brokers, merchant banks and clearing banks, liquidators and receivers, investment trusts and unit trusts, architects and surveyors, chartered accountants, advertising agencies and private individuals.

Through its network of offices the firm provides a personal service supported by specialist expertise on the full range of legal topics. Legal aid work is accepted.

Overall, Stephens & Scown sees itself as an efficient modern firm which offers a specialised, first-class service, while retaining a personal friendly approach.

STEPHENS & SCOWN

Stephenson Harwood

ONE ST PAUL'S CHURCHYARD
LONDON
EC4M 8SH

Phone: 01 329 4422

Fax: 01 606 0822
DX: 64 LONDON CHANCERY LANE WC2
Telex: 886789 **Other offices:** 2
Senior Partner: Anthony Isaacs
Number of Partners: 53
Total Staff: 380

One of the major City practices, Stephenson Harwood is particularly well known for its corporate, banking and commercial work, as well as for shipping.

The firm: In 1828 William Tatham established the practice which was to become Tatham & Lousada. From small beginnings the firm, which amalgamated with Stephenson Harwood in 1920, has become one of the largest corporate/commercial practices, with a national and international client base. Currently, the firm is undergoing a prolonged period of growth.

There is a continuing need for qualified staff, especially for young assistant solicitors with City commercial experience. Enquiries to Denis Reed.

In addition, 20 to 25 articled clerks are recruited annually. A 2(1) degree is required, not necessarily in law. Prospects after qualification are good: about half the present partners served articles with the firm. Apply on form (available on request) with hand-written letter before the end of second university year to Colin MacKenzie-Grieve.

Other offices: Hong Kong, Madrid.

Types of work undertaken: This major City firm is organised into departments, including: company/commercial, banking and finance, litigation, shipping, property, private client and taxation. Clients include major PLCs, international banks, multinationals and foreign companies, statutory authorities, private companies, partnerships and individuals.

Stephenson Harwood is well known for its corporate, commercial and banking work, particularly corporate finance (including issues, mergers and acquisitions, corporate reorganisations, management buy-outs), banking and finance (asset finance, trade and project finance, money market transactions, security, off-shore funds, investment trusts and unit trusts), and insolvency. International taxation is another area of expertise. The emphasis in the property department is on development, planning and rating. The litigation department has a high reputation in the fields of insurance and reinsurance and international arbitration, as well as for its work in business crime. There are separate groups dealing with information technology, construction and engineering, and media and entertainment. The shipping department also forms a significant part of the practice, with clients including shipowners, shipyards, salvage companies and P & I clubs. The private client department is unusually large for a City practice.

The firm sees itself as low profile, but with a high reputation for quality. It regards its City commercial and financial practice as greater than would be expected for a firm of its size.

Stephenson Harwood

Stoneham Langton & Passmore

8 BOLTON STREET
PICCADILLY
LONDON
W1Y 8AU
Phone: 01 499 8000

Fax: 01 629 4460
DX: 37223 PICCADILLY-1
Telex: 21640 **Other offices:** 2
Senior Partner: Mr JG Middleton
Number of Partners: 19
Total Staff: 108

Stones

NORTHERNHAY PLACE
EXETER
DEVON
EX4 3QQ
Phone: 0392 51501

Fax: 0392 57007
DX: 8306 EXETER
Telex: 42588
Senior Partner: Mr RH Trafford
Number of Partners: 12
Total Staff: 95

Stronach & Company

12 CARDEN PLACE
ABERDEEN
AB9 1FW

Phone: 0224 643573

Fax: 0224 648217
Rutland Exchange: none
Telex: 739393 **Other offices:** 2
Senior Partner: Mr JEF Thomson
Number of Partners: 18
Total Staff: 76

Sydney Mitchell & Co

CAVENDISH HOUSE
39 WATERLOO STREET
BIRMINGHAM
B2 5PU
Phone: 021 233 1711

Fax: 021 200 1513
DX: 13054 BIRMINGHAM-1
Telex: none **Other offices:** 7
Senior Partner: Mr PJ Hill
Number of Partners: 10
Total Staff: 110

Stones Porter *see full-page profile*

Stephensons

26 UNION STREET
LEIGH
GREATER MANCHESTER
WN7 1AT
Phone: 0942 608942

Fax: 0942 679778
DX: 22504 LEIGH
Telex: none **Other offices:** 9
Senior Partner: Chris Stephenson
Number of Partners: 10
Total Staff: 120

This long-established Lancashire firm has a broadly based practice, serving the needs of both commercial and private clients.

The firm: Stephensons traces its roots back to Leigh in 1831, when Richard Marsh started a business, later to become Marsh Son & Calvert. A partner of that firm, Chris Stephenson, set up a separate firm in the 1970s which, in 1987, merged with Marsh Son & Calvert. Recent expansion has been rapid. The firm is organised into departments.

This expanding firm is continually seeking to recruit good qualified staff, and in 1989 expects to have vacancies for five or six assistant solicitors, for general litigation (including personal injury), commercial and residential conveyancing. Three or four para-legals are also required for litigation work. Enquiries to Chris Stephenson.

In addition, four or five articled clerks are recruited every year. A degree is required, not necessarily in law, and personality is of major importance. Apply by letter (with CV) at any time to Zep Bellavia.

Other offices: Leigh (2), Bolton, Wigan (2), St Helens, Golborne, Platt Bridge, Hindley, Newton le Willows.

Agency work: The firm accepts all general legal work from other solicitors, particularly litigation, in the firm's geographical area.

Types of work undertaken: This is a general law practice covering all types of work. A large amount of legal aid work is undertaken, and there is a fast-developing commercial office. The client base is wide and includes 22,000 clients.

The firm has a number of departments, namely commercial conveyancing, residential conveyancing, accident/personal injury, medical negligence, probate, welfare rights, and financial services.

Stephensons is particularly well known for handling emergency actions – especially matrimonial – and offers clients a 24-hour service. It also has a great deal of expertise and experience in divorce and criminal cases, as well as in civil and commercial litigation matters in the county court and High Court (including landlord and tenant and employment). There is a substantial residential conveyancing practice. The firm was the first to establish a solicitor-run and privately financed welfare rights office. The accident/personal injury department is expanding rapidly, and deals with all accident claims, whether at work, on the road or elsewhere. The commercial and financial services department is known for its independent advice.

Stephensons describes itself as an approachable firm, which, first and foremost, is a service organisation handling a wide variety of clients and matters.

Stones Porter

26 FARRINGDON STREET
LONDON
EC4A 4AQ

Phone: 01 248 9991

Fax: 01 236 4025
DX: 1056 LONDON CHANCERY LANE WC2
Telex: 884810
Senior Partner: Mr JH Purves
Number of Partners: 12
Total Staff: 60

Stones Porter is a medium sized City firm with a broad commercial base and clients ranging from private individuals to public companies.

The firm: Stones Porter was formed in the 1960s and 1970s through an amalgamation of a number of small City firms, the earliest of which dates back to the early nineteenth century. The firm has increased its commercial client base substantially over the last ten years and is now primarily a commercial practice with selective private client departments.

The firm has grown rapidly in recent years and has a need for high-calibre assistant solicitors. It expects to recruit six in 1989 — four in commercial property, one in litigation and one in company/commercial. Enquiries to Roger Hanson.

Two articled clerks are recruited annually. The minimum requirement is a 2(2) degree, preferably in law. Apply by handwritten letter (plus CV and referees) to Jonathan Morshead.

Types of work undertaken: At least 90 per cent of the firm's work is commercial, encompassing property development and investment work for major institutions and developers, and property advice to retailers, clearing banks and businesses; banking work for clearing and other banks; commercial advice to public and private companies and partnerships, including share flotations, management buy-outs, mergers and pension schemes; and litigation services for a wide range of commercial clients, including arbitrations. Selected private client work is also undertaken.

The firm enjoys a client base of outstanding quality, considered comparable with the largest practices, including insurance companies, pension funds, clearing banks, public company developers and retailers, professional partnerships, and service and manufacturing companies. The firm attributes this to its policy of providing a high standard of personal service at partner level and by demonstrating a commercial understanding of the clients' objectives.

Stones Porter's leading area of specialisation is commercial property, covering purchase for investment and the development and management of all types of retail, industrial, office, leisure and residential property. It advises on town and country planning, planning and highway agreements, appointments of professionals, building contracts and sub-contractors' warranties.

Overall, Stones Porter sees itself as a firm which provides a high standard of service to a prestigious commercial clientele with a personal approach and which is able to compete successfully with the largest practices in its chosen areas of specialisation.

Stones Porter

TG Baynes & Sons

27 UPPER WICKHAM LANE
WELLING
KENT
DA16 3AB
Phone: 01 304 4717

Fax: 01 304 4012
DX: 50203 WELLING
Telex: none **Other offices:** 5
Senior Partner: Mr JR Symonds
Number of Partners: 14
Total Staff: 112

Tallents Godfrey & Co

3 MIDDLEGATE
NEWARK
NOTTINGHAMSHIRE
NG24 1AQ
Phone: 0636 71881

Fax: 0636 700148
DX: 11801 NEWARK
Telex: none **Other offices:** 9
Senior Partner: Mr RJ Godfrey
Number of Partners: 12
Total Staff: 91

Tarlo Lyons Randall Rose

HIGH HOLBORN HOUSE
52-54 HIGH HOLBORN
LONDON
WC1V 6RU
Phone: 01 405 2000

Fax: 01 405 3976
DX: 82 LONDON CHANCERY LANE WC2
Telex: 267572
Senior Partner: Mr S Ford
Number of Partners: 18
Total Staff: 65

Thatcher & Hallam

ISLAND HOUSE, THE ISLAND
MIDSOMER NORTON
BATH
AVON BA3 2HJ
Phone: 0761 414646

Fax: 0761 413754
DX: 45203 MIDSOMER NORTON
Telex: 265871 **Other offices:** 3
Senior Partner: Mr EWL Hallam
Number of Partners: 5
Total Staff: 53

Taylor Garrett *see full-page profile*
Taylor Vinters *see full-page profile*
Taylor Walker *see full-page profile*

Taylor Garrett

180 FLEET STREET
LONDON
EC4A 2NT

Phone: 01 430 1122

Fax: 01 528 7145
DX: 149 LONDON CHANCERY LANE WC2
Telex: 25516 **Other offices:** 1
Joint Senior Partners: Murray Sears and Michael Morrison
Number of Partners: 34 **Total Staff:** 184

This long-established City commercial law firm has a fast-growing practice and strong international connections.

The firm: Taylor Garrett traces its origins back to 1782. The present firm is the result of the 1982 merger of Taylor & Humbert and Parker Garrett & Co. Since then, the firm has doubled in size and has a policy of continuing expansion. Taylor Garrett has a strong international bias with an office in Brussels and close links with the US and Japan. It is a founder member of Interlex, an international association of lawyers in 15 countries. Taylor Garrett is organised into five main departments.

There is a continuing need for first-class qualified staff, and in 1989 the firm expects to have 10 to 15 vacancies for assistant solicitors. Address enquiries to Margaret Mannell.

The firm normally has 8 to 12 vacancies for articled clerks every year. A 2(1) degree, not necessarily in law, is preferred. Applications should be made on form (available on request, with CV and names of referees) in August/September and sent to John Bridge.

Other offices: Brussels.

Agency work: The firm will accept work from other solicitors on request.

Types of work undertaken: Taylor Garrett is a broadly based commercial practice, which is well known for its particular expertise in banking and corporate finance, commercial property (including planning) and shipping. Insurance and reinsurance, medical negligence, construction law, taxation, EEC competition and trade law, and private client work (including divorce) are other areas where the firm has considerable expertise and experience. Clients range from national and multinational public companies and banks through to private companies and individuals.

The firm's departments are company/commercial, commercial property, commercial litigation, shipping and private client. Taylor Garrett pioneered the concept of multi-disciplinary groups of lawyers drawn from different departments to specialise in particular areas of the law or industry sectors. Existing groups handle finance (debt and equity finance), employment law, international matters, EEC competition and trade law, computer law, construction law, town planning and development, and taxation.

Overall, Taylor Garrett perceives itself as a progressive, forward-moving commercial practice which, despite its rapid growth, has not forgotten the importance of the personal touch. This is a well-respected firm which offers in-depth legal knowledge and experience, combined with a full understanding of the commercial world.

TAYLOR GARRETT

LAWYERS   WHO   MEAN   BUSINESS

Taylor Vinters

MERLIN PLACE
MILTON ROAD
CAMBRIDGE
CB4 4DP
Phone: 0223 423444

Fax: 0223 423486
DX: 5801 CAMBRIDGE
Telex: 81237 **Other offices:** 2
Senior Partner: John Horwood Smart
Number of Partners: 21
Total Staff: 165

This substantial East Anglian firm offers particular expertise in company/commercial, commercial property and litigation work, as well as having a successful and growing agricultural and bloodstock practice.

The firm: Taylor Vinters is the result of the 1988 amalgamation of two well-established East Anglian firms: Vinters of Cambridge, which had a substantial litigation practice and an increasing reputation in commercial work; and Taylors of Newmarket, which was well known for commercial property, agricultural and bloodstock work. Since the 1960s both firms have been growing in size and in the range of expertise they offer, and the merger brings together complementary skills and client bases. Taylor Vinters is organised into departments.

There is a continuing need for qualified staff, and in 1989 the firm expects to recruit at least four assistant solicitors for commercial property, litigation and company/commercial. Enquiries should be addressed to Michael Womack.

In addition six articled clerks are recruited annually. The minimum academic requirement is a 2(2) degree, not necessarily in law. Apply by handwritten letter (with CV, passport photograph and names of referees) two years in advance to Michael Womack.

Other offices: Newmarket, Cambridge.

Agency work: The firm accepts litigation work from other solicitors; contact John Walsh or Claire Pick.

Types of work undertaken: Taylor Vinters has five departments, namely company/commercial; conveyancing; litigation; agricultural and bloodstock; and wills, trusts and probate. Clients range from private individuals through professional partnerships to charities and substantial companies.

The firm is particularly well known for its expertise in commercial property work, insolvency, business start-ups, commercial litigation and personal injury litigation, as well as its work in the areas of agricultural property and bloodstock.

Taylor Vinters is very much involved in the well-publicised Cambridge phenomenon, an entrepreneurial spirit among academics working in the scientific field. This involves the firm's lawyers in designing documents to exploit and safeguard state-of-the-art technology and ideas, as well as setting up often complex funding and investment packages for start-ups, management buy-outs and development work. In addition the firm offers advice on what are often complicated taxation planning problems.

Overall, Taylor Vinters perceives itself as a go-ahead, efficient and approachable practice. A brochure detailing the services of the firm is available on request.

The Simkins Partnership

45-51 WHITFIELD STREET
LONDON
W1P 5RJ

Phone: 01 631 1050

Fax: 01 436 2744
DX: 7 LONDON CHANCERY LANE WC2
Telex: 28329
Senior Partner: Mr M Simkins
Number of Partners: 13
Total Staff: 54

Thomson Snell & Passmore

3 LONSDALE GARDENS
TUNBRIDGE WELLS
KENT
TN1 1NX
Phone: 0892 510000

Fax: 0892 49884
DX: 3914 TUNBRIDGE WELLS
Telex: 95194 **Other offices:** 6
Senior Partner: Mr HM Aspinall
Number of Partners: 48
Total Staff: 260

Thornton Oliver WS

WHITEHALL CHAMBERS
11 WHITEHALL STREET
DUNDEE
DD1 4AE
Phone: 0382 29111

Fax: 0382 21779
Rutland Exchange: 0382 DUNDEE
Telex: 76527 **Other offices:** 6
Senior Partner: Mr JS Fair
Number of Partners: 19
Total Staff: 110

Thorpe & Co

17 VALLEY BRIDGE PARADE
SCARBOROUGH
NORTH YORKSHIRE
YO11 2JX
Phone: 0723 364321

Fax: 500459
DX: 61811 SCARBOROUGH
Telex: none **Other offices:** 3
Senior Partner: Mr CM Thorpe
Number of Partners: 12
Total Staff: 61

Theodore Goddard *see full-page profile*
Thomas Eggar Verrall Bowles *see full-page profile*

Taylor Walker

65 HIGH STREET
HARPENDEN
HERTFORDSHIRE
AL5 2SW
Phone: 05827 65111

Fax: 05827 69089
DX: 80450 HARPENDEN
Telex: 826957 **Other offices:** 3
Senior Partner: David Wilson
Number of Partners: 13
Total Staff: 80

Taylor Walker is a Hertfordshire firm that combines a traditional provincial practice with a growing commercial practice.

The firm: Founded in 1907 in The Strand, London, during World War II the firm moved to Harpenden, where it already had a part-time office. The practice was a typical local one until the early 1970s, when a decision was made to build up the commercial side of the practice – a policy which has since proven to be very successful.

This expanding firm has a continuing need for high-calibre qualified staff, and expects to have five vacancies in the next year, two in company/commercial, two in commercial property, and one in litigation. All enquiries should be addressed to Colin Reavell.

The firm normally recruits three articled clerks every year. Candidates are considered on their merits and mature applicants are welcomed. Applications should be in writing (with CV) and addressed to Mr TJ Thomson two years in advance.

Other offices: Luton, St Albans, Welwyn Garden City.

Agency work: The firm undertakes selected work for other solicitors.

Types of work undertaken: As is to be expected of a broadly based local practice, there is a very wide-ranging client base, from local retailers, professionals and small businesses to individuals. In addition, in recent years the firm has vastly expanded the commercial side of the practice, with a corresponding expansion of its commercial client base.

The firm undertakes a wide range of commercial work, including commercial leases, USM work, takeovers and mergers, debt collection, town and country planning, and estate development.

There is a strong conveyancing practice, handling both commercial work – particularly shops and offices – and a substantial amount of residential conveyancing.

A considerable amount of litigation work is undertaken, and the firm is particularly well known for its expertise in civil litigation and employment law matters, as well as criminal cases, divorce work and personal injury claims.

On the private client side, the firm undertakes the full range of work, including family law matters, wills, trusts and probate, personal injury claims and defamation. Legal aid work is accepted.

Taylor Walker perceives itself as a client-driven commercial practice whose low profile masks quiet efficiency and rapid expansion.

A brochure for clients is available on request.

TAYLOR
WALKER

Theodore Goddard

16 ST MARTIN'S-LE-GRAND
LONDON
EC1A 4EJ

Phone: 01 606 8855

Fax: 01 606 4390
DX: 47 LONDON CHANCERY LANE WC2
Telex: 884678 **Other offices:** 3
Senior Partner: Stuart May
Number of Partners: 42
Total Staff: 377

Theodore Goddard, a City-based firm, is one of the major names in the world of corporate and commercial law.

The firm: Founded in 1902, the firm was initially litigation-orientated and earned a considerable reputation in defamation cases. This remains an important part of the firm's work, although the corporate and commercial side of the practice now constitutes the principal part of Theodore Goddard's work.

In 1989 the firm expects vacancies for 30 additional assistant solicitors, particularly for corporate and commercial property lawyers. Enquiries to Elizabeth Toner.

In addition, the firm recruits 20 to 22 articled clerks annually. A 2(1) degree is preferred, not necessarily in law. Apply by form (available on request) with names of referees to John Kelleher.

Other offices: Paris, Jersey, St Albans.

Types of work undertaken: Theodore Goddard has six departments, namely corporate, commercial, corporate tax, property, litigation and private client. However, the approach is integrated: teams with members from several departments will work together whenever necessary. Clients range from the largest financial institutions to smaller private companies and individuals of substance.

The volume and scope of the firm's corporate and commercial work is impressive. It is very well known in the field of corporate finance, where it has worked on prestigious acquisitions, sales and management buy-outs (including the TSB's acquisition of Hill Samuel and the Target Group – value £1 billion; the sale of British Caledonian to British Airways and Ratners' acquisition of Zales and Salisburys from Next). Its expertise in flotation, banking, venture capital, corporate tax and employee incentive option work is also well known.

The firm is skilled in all aspects of EEC law and competition policy, and is well placed to advise clients on 1992 opportunities and Europe-wide anti-trust legislation. The firm also offers expertise in East/West trade.

As well as the firm's long experience of defamation and commercial litigation work, other areas of expertise include product liability, employment and pensions, property (including commercial leases, town and country planning and estate development), entertainment and media, and intellectual property (including copyright, designs and patents), as well as all aspects of the law relating to technology, computers and bio-technology. Unusually for a City firm, there is a strong private client department.

Theodore Goddard sees itself as responsive and commercially minded, with a wide range of experience and expertise in focussed areas of company and commercial work.

Thrings & Long

MIDLAND BRIDGE ROAD
BATH
AVON
BA1 2HQ
Phone: 0225 448494

Fax: 0225 319735
DX: 8002 BATH
Telex: 444712
Senior Partner: Mr JJ Thring
Number of Partners: 12
Total Staff: 74

Thursfield Adams & Westons

14 CHURCH STREET
KIDDERMINSTER
HEREFORD AND WORCESTER
DY10 2AJ
Phone: 0562 820575

Fax: 0562 66783
DX: 16304 KIDDERMINSTER
Telex: 337837 **Other offices:** 3
Senior Partner: Mr HM Thursfield
Number of Partners: 15
Total Staff: 85

Timms

EMPIRE BUILDINGS
23 WEST STREET
SWADLINCOTE
DERBYSHIRE DE11 9DQ
Phone: 0283 214231

Fax: 0283 222272
DX: 23903 SWADLINCOTE
Telex: none **Other offices:** 2
Senior Partner: Mr CW Farrow
Number of Partners: 9
Total Staff: 59

Tinsdill Hollinshead & Moody

CHICHESTER HOUSE
BROAD STREET, HANLEY
STOKE ON TRENT
STAFFORDSHIRE ST1 4EU
Phone: 0782 262031

Fax: 0782 287571
DX: 20710 HANLEY
Telex: none **Other offices:** 2
Senior Partner: Mr JM Hand
Number of Partners: 13
Total Staff: 69

Tilly, Bailey & Irvine *see full-page profile*

Thomas Eggar Verrall Bowles

EAST PALLANT
CHICHESTER
WEST SUSSEX
PO19 1TS
Phone: 0243 786111

Fax: 0243 775640
DX: 30300 CHICHESTER
Telex: 86593 **Other offices:** 6
Senior Partner: Clifford Hodgetts
Number of Partners: 35
Total Staff: 290

This large provincial, but City-style, firm, built upon an extensive private client base, earns increasing respect for its growing company, commercial and property departments and, more recently, for its European work.

The firm: Established this year (1989) by the merger of Thomas Eggar & Son (founded 1881) and the Worthing firm of Verral Bowles & Stevens (founded 1875/1884), TEVB is one of the largest South Coast firms.

The firm expects to recruit about four assistant solicitors in 1989, for tax and trust planning and commercial related work; European languages are an advantage. Applications should be sent to the partnership secretary, Mr WA Evershed.

Seven articled clerks are generally recruited each year. Candidates with 2(1) degree, not necessarily in law, are preferred. Apply to the partnership secretary (at the Chichester office) for an application form.

Other offices: Horsham, Worthing, Littlehampton, Lancing, Goring by Sea, Paris. The firm opened its Paris office in 1973 and is able to deal with all aspects of French and EEC law (for commerce and industry, as well as for private clients).

Agency work: The firm undertakes work for other solicitors. For details, contact Mr CW Doman (Chichester), Mr JA Stapleton (Worthing), or Mr RJD Allan (Horsham).

Types of work undertaken: This firm's size and its departmentalisation in its three principal towns enables it to provide an exceptionally wide range of services for a provincial firm. There are 12 main departments, namely company/commercial; commercial property; residential property; town and country planning and estate development; probate; tax (including Estate Tax Planning); trust (including Offshore Trusts), insurance; criminal and civil litigation (including employment law); family law; European law; and ecclesiastical law (in which the firm is particularly experienced). The company and commercial workload has expanded rapidly in recent years.

The firm is particularly strong in taxation and trust planning for private clients, and in commercial property work for business clients. It has created a new and growing department for European work and the firm employs French, German, Spanish, Portuguese and Dutch language speakers.

The partnership owns an investment management company (THESIS) to deal with the investments of its clients. Brochures outlining the firm's services are available.

Overall, Thomas Eggar Verral Bowles sees itself as a modern firm offering the traditional values of sound service and advice, and the highest professional standards.

Tilly, Bailey & Irvine

YORK CHAMBERS
YORK ROAD
HARTLEPOOL
CLEVELAND TS26 9DP
Phone: 0429 264101

Fax: 0429 274796
DX: 60650 HARTLEPOOL
Telex: 58349 **Other offices:** 1
Senior Partner: John Tilly
Number of Partners: 9
Total Staff: 52

This commercially orientated Teeside firm has a long association with Hartlepool's business and professional community, and a substantial private client base.

The firm: Tilly, Bailey & Irvine dates back to 1841, when one of the founders of West Hartlepool, Edward Turnbull, opened a practice there. The firm had its roots in shipping and shipbuilding, traditional industries of the region, and has built up experience and expertise in commercial law work. Expansion has been steady, and there has been a series of amalgamations with other local firms; the latest, in 1985, with Watsons, a Barnard Castle practice established in 1756 with wide experience in agricultural and land-owning matters.

There is a continuing need for qualified staff, and in 1989 the firm expects two vacancies for assistant solicitors, in matrimonial, probate and taxation; and civil litigation. Enquiries to John Hall.

In addition, one articled clerk is recruited every year. The minimum educational requirement is a law degree. Prospects after qualification are excellent: three-quarters of the present partners served articles with the firm. Apply by handwritten letter (with CV) at least one year in advance to John Hall.

Other offices: Barnard Castle (trading as 'Watsons').

Agency work: All types of work accepted from other solicitors; contact John Tilly.

Types of work undertaken: As is to be expected of a traditional provincial firm, this is a wide-ranging general practice with a varied client base, including public authorities, listed companies, private companies and individuals throughout the north of England. All types of work are undertaken, from representations in the magistrates' courts to public flotations.

Tilly, Bailey & Irvine is particularly well known for its strong commercial law practice (including company sales and purchases, and finance) and the substantial commercial property portfolio that it administers. Matrimonial work, as well as all aspects of family law (including divorce, maintenance and settlements, wardship, custody and foreign matters) is another field of expertise.

The firm still pursues aspects of one of its original areas of interest, shipping, a certain amount of Admiralty work being carried out. The firm is the local representative of several P & I clubs. In addition, since amalgamating with Watsons, agricultural law has become an important area.

Overall, Tilly, Bailey & Irvine perceives itself as progressive but with a traditional background, upholding traditional values and having a range of experience and expertise unusual in the immediate area.

TILLY, BAILEY & IRVINE

Titmuss Sainer & Webb

2 SERJEANTS' INN
LONDON
EC4Y 1LT

Phone: 01 583 5353

Fax: 01 353 3683
DX: 30 LONDON CITY EC3
Telex: 23823
Senior Partner: John Hamblett
Number of Partners: 39
Total Staff: 294

Titmuss Sainer & Webb is a leading medium sized commercial practice involved primarily in corporate, commercial and property work.

The firm: Established in the City of London in 1938, the firm has seen substantial expansion in all major work areas during the 1980s. In particular, there has been notable growth in specialist commercial areas and an increased demand from overseas-based corporate clients.

There is a continuing need for qualified staff; in 1989 there will be 35 vacancies for solicitors in all areas. In particular for corporate finance, commercial property, taxation and intellectual property. Enquiries to the managing partner, Dick Russell.

Some 15 to 20 articled clerks are recruited annually. A 2(2) degree is preferred, not necessarily in law. Apply by form to the articled clerk recruitment partner, Steven Fogel.

Types of work undertaken: This leading medium sized City commercial practice is involved primarily in corporate, commercial and property work and acts for nationally prominent public and private companies, particularly in the retail, publishing and printing sectors. There are four main departments (corporate, property, litigation, and private client) and six specialist units (construction law, planning, employment, commercial, taxation, and investigations).

The firm is particularly well known for its work in corporate finance (particularly acquisitions, mergers and buy-outs); commercial property (land development and investment for sophisticated property companies, and acquisitions, disposals and management of retail premises for national multiples and specialist traders); employment law; and intellectual property.

The corporate department provides the full range of commercial law services and includes specialist taxation, employment, competition law, and intellectual property units.

The property department has particular expertise in dealing with the sale, purchase and leasing of all types of commercial land and buildings and with property funding, development and mortgaging.

The litigation department covers a wide range of commercial disputes and its work touches upon most areas of civil law – in particular the contentious aspects of employment and intellectual property work. The private client department's specialisation is personal tax planning.

Overall, Titmuss Sainer & Webb sees itself as an extremely professional firm which is competitive, yet retains professional standards, is co-operative, innovative, forward looking, and generally good to do business with. General and specialist brochures regarding the firm are available on request.

Titmuss Sainer & Webb

Tods Murray WS

66 QUEEN STREET
EDINBURGH
EH2 4NE

Phone: 031 226 4771

Fax: 031 225 3676
Rutland Exchange: 58 EDINBURGH
Telex: 727258
Senior Partner: Robin Bell
Number of Partners: 18
Total Staff: 106

This well-established Edinburgh firm has a broadly based practice with a growing emphasis on corporate and commercial property work.

The firm: Tods Murray has occupied its present, recently refurbished, offices since 1856. Traditionally a broad general practice, in recent years there has been considerable expansion in corporate work, commercial property and commercial litigation. This growth is reflected in the departmental organisation of the firm.

Tods Murray is always looking for well-qualified, highly motivated assistant solicitors, and in 1989 expects to have five vacancies in conveyancing, commercial property, tax and estate planning, and litigation. Enquiries to Graham M Burnside.

Four or five trainee solicitors are usually recruited every year. The minimum academic requirement is a law degree; English graduates will be expected to obtain Scottish qualifications. Prospects after qualification are good; around a quarter of the present partners served traineeships with the firm. Apply by letter (with CV and names of referees) in September one year in advance to Charles Abram.

Agency work: The firm accepts instructions from other solicitors; contact Robin Bell or Michael Simpson (litigation).

Types of work undertaken: The firm has a wide-ranging client base, including listed companies, institutional investors, landowners and farmers, small businesses and private individuals. There are four main departments, namely commercial property, corporate, litigation, and private client.

In the commercial property field, the firm has extensive experience and expertise in major developments and funding agreements, and acts for a number of major insurers and pension funds in relation to their property portfolios.

The corporate department is particularly well known for corporate finance (including public issues), banking, unit trusts and time-sharing, as well as acquisitions, private placings and buy-outs.

Commercial litigation (especially arbitration) is another notable area of expertise; the litigation department deals with all types of civil litigation for both commercial and private clients.

The private client department handles tax and estate planning work (for which is it is particularly well known), residential conveyancing, agricultural estate and forestry work, trusts and executries.

Tods Murray sees itself as a young and vigorous partnership – the average age is 36 – which predominantly acts for corporate and business clients, whilst maintaining a substantial private client practice.

TODS MURRAY WS

Townsend Livingston

6-9 LAWSON STREET
BARROW IN FURNESS
CUMBRIA
LA14 2LT
Phone: 0229 20585

Fax: 0229 37160
DX: none
Telex: none **Other offices:** 1
Senior Partner: Mr AD Langtree
Number of Partners: 7
Total Staff: 52

Townsends

42 CRICKLADE STREET
SWINDON
WILTSHIRE
SN1 3HD
Phone: 0793 35421

Fax: 0793 616294
DX: 6204 SWINDON-1
Telex: 265871 **Other offices:** 1
Senior Partner: Mr GCM Young
Number of Partners: 12
Total Staff: 108

Tozers

2-5 ORCHARD GARDENS
TEIGNMOUTH
DEVON
TQ14 8DR
Phone: 0626 772376

Fax: 0626 770317
DX: none
Telex: none **Other offices:** 3
Senior Partner: Mr MA Sutton
Number of Partners: 14
Total Staff: 90

Trethowans

COLLEGE CHAMBERS
NEW STREET
SALISBURY
WILTSHIRE SP1 2LY
Phone: 0722 412512

Fax: 0722 411300
DX: 58004 SALISBURY
Telex: 477668 **Other offices:** 3
Senior Partner: Mr DM Morris
Number of Partners: 15
Total Staff: 90

Toller Hales & Collcutt *see full-page profile*
Travers Smith Braithwaite *see full-page profile*

Toller Hales & Collcutt

CASTILIAN CHAMBERS
2 CASTILIAN STREET
NORTHAMPTON
NN1 1JX
Phone: 0604 232105

Fax: 0604 230285
DX: 12422 NORTHAMPTON-1
Telex: 312211 **Other offices:** 5
Senior Partner: Michael Francis Collcutt
Number of Partners: 21
Total Staff: 175

Toller Hales & Collcutt is a broadly based practice, serving the Northamptonshire and Peterborough areas.

The firm: Founded in 1877 in Kettering, the firm has expanded steadily since the late 1950s and has established five branch offices. The original practice was small and general and from its inception through to current times has always a good reputation for the abilities of its advocates and litigators. Toller Hales & Collcutt offers the full range of corporate, commercial, agricultural and domestic legal services that one would expect of a busy provincial practice.

The firm has vacancies for four qualified staff in 1989 in the commercial, family/matrimonial and commercial conveyancing departments. Enquiries to Andrew Rudkin.

Ten to 12 articled clerks are recruited annually. A first or second class degree is required, not necessarily in law. Apply by form (available on request) to Andrew Rudkin.

Other offices: Peterborough, Corby, Kettering, Wellingborough, Higham Ferrers.

Agency work: The firm accepts civil litigation work from other solicitors; contact John F Campbell.

Types of work undertaken: Toller Hales & Collcutt has a general practice with a wide client base, although commercial work is now expanding faster than other areas.

The company/commercial department acts mainly for private companies but also for several listed companies. Much of the work for private companies involves mergers, acquisitions and disposals.

The firm does a considerable amount of commercial conveyancing for PLCs and private companies, involving leasehold offices and industrial units, and for builders and developers. In addition, domestic conveyancing, agricultural law and domestic tenancies are handled. Civil litigation is another major area of work, including commercial and engineering disputes, employment, personal injury and general litigation for commercial, insurance companies and private clients. Among the private client services offered are family and matrimonial, crime, probate, trust and tax.

In particular the firm is well known for general corporate and commercial work (especially acquisitions and mergers of private companies), civil litigation, personal injury and insurance company work, and commercial and domestic conveyancing.

Overall, Toller Hales Collcutt sees itself as a firm with high professional standards undertaking a broad spectrum of work without discrimination (legal aid work is not refused), but nevertheless a firm that is progressive with modern attitudes to its work.

Travers Smith Braithwaite

6 SNOW HILL
LONDON
EC1A 2AL

Phone: 01 248 9133

Fax: 01 236 3728
DX: 79 LONDON CITY EC3
Telex: 887117 **Other offices:** 1
Senior Partner: Mr AC Humphries
Number of Partners: 29
Total Staff: 217

Travers Smith Braithwaite a medium sized City firm, is particularly well known for its corporate finance and Stock Exchange work.

The firm: From the time it was founded in the latter part of the eighteenth century, the firm has provided legal advice to major City firms, financial institutions and corporate and private clients. The firm has grown into one of the busiest law firms specialising in City work. It is organised into departments.

The firm is recruiting assistant solicitors in all areas of its activities, but principally for the company/commercial department. Enquiries to Mr CC Bell.

In addition, the firm recruits 12 to 15 articled clerks annually. Long-term prospects are excellent: about half the present partners were articled with the firm. Applications should be made in the autumn two years in advance (with CV and names of referees) and should be addressed to Mr CC Bell.

Other offices: Douglas, Isle of Man.

Types of work undertaken: Travers Smith Braithwaite provides its clients with a comprehensive legal service through its six main legal departments, namely corporate, corporate tax, litigation, property, trust, and pensions. The main client base comes from City institutions and corporate clients.

The firm is heavily involved in corporate transactions (including capital raising, takovers and mergers, and new issues on the Stock Exchange and the USM); indeed, the corporate department is the largest in the firm. It also engages in general company and commercial work, advising corporate and other clients, including merchant banks, securities firms and accountants.

The property department is involved in property finance and large-scale commercial developments. The litigation department handles commercial work as well as arbitration. There is a substantial private client base and services offered include trust and probate work, as well as all aspects of pensions.

The corporate tax department provides skilled tax planning for companies and also advises the other departments on the tax implications of proposed transactions they are carrying out.

Travers Smith Braithwaite is best known for its City work of capital raising; takeovers and mergers, and new issues, both on the Stock Exchange and the USM. It also has particular expertise in property finance, commercial property development, unit trusts, venture capital and general corporate work.

Overall, the firm perceives itself as a growing high-quality City practice with a distinguished list of clients. It is the smallest firm regularly involved in Stock Exchange-related transactions. A brochure is available.

TRAVERS SMITH
BRAITHWAITE

Truman Close Kendall & Appelby

22 PARK ROW
NOTTINGHAM
NG6 1GX

Phone: 0602 417275

Fax: 0602 484272
DX: 10023 NOTTINGHAM
Telex: none **Other offices:** 2
Senior Partner: Mr DH Close
Number of Partners: 9
Total Staff: 107

Tuck & Mann & Geffen

SWEECH HOUSE
4 & 6 GRAVEL HILL
LEATHERHEAD
SURREY KT22 7HF

Phone: 0372 374148

Fax: 0372 374748
DX: 7303 LEATHERHEAD
Telex: 8955319 **Other offices:** 3
Senior Partner: Mr SM Southgate
Number of Partners: 17
Total Staff: 91

Turberville Woodbridge

122 HIGH STREET
UXBRIDGE
MIDDLESEX
UB8 1JT

Phone: 0895 59871

Fax: 0895 73519
DX: 45116 UXBRIDGE
Telex: 23791 **Other offices:** 2
Senior Partner: Mr AR Woodbridge
Number of Partners: 7
Total Staff: 68

Turner & Debenhams

6 ST PETERS STREET
ST ALBANS
HERTFORDSHIRE
AL1 3LG

Phone: 0727 37161

Fax: 0727 30506
DX: 6105 ST ALBANS
Telex: 923531 **Other offices:** 4
Senior Partner: Mr BG McGuiness
Number of Partners: 12
Total Staff: 80

Trowers & Hamlins *see full-page profile*
Trump & Partners *see full-page profile*

Trowers & Hamlins

6 NEW SQUARE
LINCOLN'S INN
LONDON
WC2A 3RP
Phone: 01 831 6292

Fax: 01 831 8700
DX: 31 LONDON CHANCERY LANE WC2
Telex: 21422 **Other offices:** 3
Senior Partner: Mr AG Trower
Number of Partners: 38
Total Staff: 275

This is a large central London firm with a broadly based practice and a high reputation for housing law work.

The firm: First established as a private client practice in Lincoln's Inn in the eighteenth century, Trower, Still & Keeling absorbed Hamlins, Grammer & Hamlin to become Trowers & Hamlins in February 1987. The firm has expanded in all areas in recent years, and today the scope of the practice is wide and varied.

This expanding firm expects to have five or six vacancies for assistant solicitors over the next 12 months. Enquiries to Mr NH Hills.

In addition, the firm usually has between 9 and 11 vacancies for articled clerks every year. The preferred educational qualification is a 2(1) degree; applicants who have come from other professions and careers are welcome. Prospects after qualification are good; around half of the present partners served articles with the firm. Apply on form (available on request) to Mr EA Payne.

Other offices: Manchester, Exeter, Oman.

Types of work undertaken: Trowers & Hamlins handles the full range of contentious and non-contentious work expected of a sizeable central London firm. There are four main departments, namely property, company/commercial, litigation and private

client. Clients include banks, public and private companies, public institutions, insurance companies, housing associations, partnerships and individuals of every kind.

The firm is particularly well known for its housing law work, especially housing finance (acting on three of the public issues of loan stock intended to raise finance for housing associations); indeed, the firm acts for over 90 housing associations.

Commercial property is an increasingly important area of the practice. The work covers building construction, commercial conveyancing (including purchases, sales and lettings of offices, shops and factories), estate conveyancing, as well as agricultural property transactions, planning and landlord and tenant.

The company/commercial department handles the full range of company, commercial and business law. There is a strong international orientation to this work, and, as well as its office in Oman, the firm has a considerable Anglo-German practice and a firmly established network of relationships with lawyers throughout the world. The litigation department deals with all types of civil litigation and arbitration. In addition, the usual private client services – tax, trust and probate – are available.

Trowers & Hamlins sees itself as a broadly based, well-established and professional firm, with particular experience in housing law.

TROWERS & HAMLINS

Trump & Partners

34 ST NICHOLAS STREET
BRISTOL
BS1 1TS

Phone: 0272 299901

Fax: 0272 298232
DX: 7815 BRISTOL
Telex: 9312110674(TP)
Senior Partner: William F Trump
Number of Partners: 11
Total Staff: 49

This Bristol-based firm has a substantial private client practice, with a growing emphasis on company/commercial and commercial conveyancing work.

The firm: Trump & Partners was founded in 1903 by the present senior partner's grandfather. Over the years, the firm has grown steadily and expanded from a small family practice into one which numbers individuals, partnerships, public and private companies, banks and institutions among its clients.

The firm has a continuing need for assistant solicitors who are newly qualified or who have several years post-qualification experience. In 1989 two to four vacancies are expected. Enquiries to John Kane.

Two articled clerks are normally recruited each year. The minimum educational requirement is a 2(2) law degree. Apply by handwritten letter (with CV) two years in advance to Robert Lee or Robert Bourns.

Agency work: Work is accepted from other solicitors, principally litigation; contact Andrew Troup.

Types of work undertaken: Over the last 20 years, Trump & Partners has earned a high reputation in the commercial law field. On the company/commercial side, it has particular expertise in insolvency work (handled by licensed insolvency practitioners), and in professional partnerships (particularly in medical), as well as in employment law, service agreements, sole trading, financing, licensing agreements and intellectual property.

The firm is well known for its commercial conveyancing work, notably commercial property developments with emphasis on funding and disposal. In addition, the firm is experienced in all aspects of planning law.

Litigation is another area where Trump & Partners has wide experience, handling court proceedings and arbitrations, especially in personal injury claims, fatal accident litigation and professional and medical negligence cases.

This well-established Bristol firm has maintained its traditional private client base; indeed, it has a very high reputation for all aspects of its family law work, encompassing matrimonial, finance, property, taxation and adoption, landlord and tenant, as well as wills, probate and trusts. Clients include the self employed, the farmer, private company shareholders, those with inherited capital and state beneficiaries. In addition, it has a strong residential conveyancing department, for home owners and residential property developers.

In short, this is an established practice with a forward-looking approach, and a reputation for competence, promptness and integrity.

TRUMP
& PARTNERS

Turners

1 POOLE ROAD
BOURNEMOUTH
DORSET
BH2 5QQ
Phone: 0202 291291

Fax: 0202 23606
DX: 7637 BOURNEMOUTH
Telex: 41158 **Other offices:** 2
Senior Partner: Mr CC Wilson
Number of Partners: 12
Total Staff: 92

Varley Hibbs & Co

KIRBY HOUSE
LITTLE PARK STREET
COVENTRY
WEST MIDLANDS CV1 2JZ
Phone: 0203 631000

Fax: 0203 630808
DX: 11214 COVENTRY-1
Telex: none **Other offices:** 1
Senior Partner: Mr JP Varley
Number of Partners: 8
Total Staff: 63

Veale Wasbrough

17 BERKELEY SQUARE
BRISTOL
AVON
BS8 1HD
Phone: 0272 290221

Fax: 0272 279235
DX: 7832 BRISTOL
Telex: 444671 **Other offices:** 1
Managing Partner: Mr JM Westcott
Number of Partners: 27
Total Staff: 200

W & J Burness

16 HOPE STREET
CHARLOTTE SQUARE
EDINBURGH
EH2 4DD
Phone: 031 226 2561

Fax: 031 225 2964
Rutland Exchange: 73 EDINBURGH
Telex: 72405 **Other offices:** 2
Senior Partner: Mr C Baxter
Number of Partners: 22
Total Staff: 195

Turner Kenneth Brown *see full-page profile*
Vizards *see full-page profile*

Turner Kenneth Brown

100 FETTER LANE
LONDON
EC4A 1DD

Phone: 01 242 6006

Fax: 01 242 3003
DX: 150 LONDON CHANCERY LANE WC2
Telex: 297696 **Other offices:** 3
Senior Partner: David R Wightman
Number of Partners: 41
Total Staff: 302

This City firm serves a wide range of national and multinational corporations while maintaining a significant private client base.

The firm: Turner Kenneth Brown can trace its origins back to the last decade of the eighteenth century. It is one of the major corporate practices in the UK.

The firm needs a considerable number of well-qualified assistant solicitors annually at all levels and in all departments. Candidates who have worked in City or large provincial firms are preferred. Enquiries to Peter Williamson.

There are vacancies for 25 to 30 articled clerks annually. A 2(1) degree is preferred. Prospects after qualification are excellent: a significant number of the present partners served articles with the firm. Apply by form (available with recruitment brochure on request) to the personnel manager. Applications from non-law graduates, particularly scientists, are welcomed.

Other offices: Reading, Hong Kong, London.

Agency work: The firm accepts High Court litigation and general commercial and commercial property work from other solicitors; contact Stuart Benson.

Types of work undertaken: Turner Kenneth Brown has expanded rapidly in recent years, consolidating its position in the commercial area (particularly in USM, BES, and management buy-out work). The firm has gained an increasing reputation in litigation, especially in the field of commercial litigation (notably construction law). It is also well known for its commercial property work, as well as maintaining a very significant private client base.

The firm has four main departments, company/commercial, property, litigation, and private client. There are also smaller departments and groups which cover tax, banking, intellectual property and information technology, construction and employment.

The firm's 'M4' office was opened in Reading in 1988 in order to bring City-quality legal services closer to industrial and commercial clients in an area of economic growth. The firm is a member of OASIS, an international association of lawyers.

The firm aims to provide clients with a personal service which is comprehensive enough and of the quality required to cover all aspects of their business and private lives.

On 1 May 1989 the firm of Lawrance, Messer & Co will merge with Turner Kenneth Brown, which will remain the name of the combined firm. Overall, Turner Kenneth Brown is regarded as a highly efficient company and commercial practice which also deals with substantial private client work. Brochures are available on request.

TURNER
KENNETH
BROWN

Vizards

42-43 BEDFORD ROW
LONDON
WC1R 4LL

Phone: 01 405 6302

Fax: 01 405 6248
DX: 189 LONDON CHANCERY LANE WC2
Telex: 261045 **Other offices:** 2
Senior Partner: Christopher DF Oldham
Number of Partners: 14
Total Staff: 52

Vizards, a medium sized central London firm, is commercially orientated with a substantial international practice.

The firm: Founded in 1797 by William Vizard, who was later appointed solicitor to Queen Caroline and acted in the Prince Regent's divorce proceedings against her, the firm has developed, by amalgamation and association, into a substantial, modern international commercial practice, and has links with lawyers throughout the world.

The firm is continually seeking to recruit quality qualified staff, and in the next 12 months expects to have vacancies for four assistant solicitors in litigation (personal injury and insurance), commercial and conveyancing. Enquiries should be addressed to Mark R Newman.

In addition, the firm usually recruits three articled clerks every year. The minimum educational requirement is a 2(2) degree, not necessarily in law. Prospects after qualification are excellent; most of the present partners served articles with the firm. Apply by handwritten letter (with CV) two years in advance to Mark R Newman.

Other offices: Paris, Milan.

Agency work: The firm accepts only international work from other solicitors; contact Michael PD Ellman.

Types of work undertaken: The firm represents a number of insurance companies, charities and voluntary associations, as well as international companies and individuals based in the UK and overseas.

The firm's work is wide ranging, covering commercial litigation and arbitration matters, as well as the full range of general company/commercial work, the establishment and administration of trusts (particularly offshore), and a significant conveyancing practice, handling both commercial and domestic work.

Vizards is particularly well known for its work in the fields of insurance law (most notably personal injury claims, professional negligence work, policy construction matters, products liability disputes, and fire and material loss claims); building disputes; all types of arbitration work; Parliamentary and Privy Council agency work; and charity law matters.

As well as its Paris and Milan offices, the firm has close links with an established network of associated law firms throughout the world. Correspondence at the London office is conducted in French, Italian and German, as well as English.

Overall, Vizards sees itself as a well-established traditional firm which has managed to develop in particular fields and specialities on an international scale as well as in the UK. A brochure is available on request.

VIZARDS

Wade Gery Farr

30-32 BROMHAM ROAD
BEDFORD
MK40 2QD

Phone: 0234 273273

Fax: 0234 53110
DX: 5614 BEDFORD
Telex: 265871 **Other offices:** 2
Senior Partner: Mr A Abrahams
Number of Partners: 6
Total Staff: 80

Wake Smith & Co

TELEGRAPH HOUSE
HIGH STREET
SHEFFIELD
S1 1SF

Phone: 0742 730088

Fax: 0742 731956
DX: 10534 SHEFFIELD
Telex: 54317 **Other offices:** 4
Senior Partner: Mr JCV Hunt
Number of Partners: 8
Total Staff: 84

Walter Gray & Co

4 ST THOMAS STREET
RYDE
ISLE OF WIGHT
PO33 2ND

Phone: 0983 63765

Fax: 0983 617102
DX: none
Telex: none **Other offices:** 5
Senior Partner: Mrs PM Saul
Number of Partners: 10
Total Staff: 60

Wannop & Falconer

SOUTH PALLANT HOUSE
8 SOUTH PALLANT
CHICHESTER
WEST SUSSEX PO19 1TH

Phone: 0243 782688

Fax: 0243 788349
DX: 30305 CHICHESTER
Telex: none **Other offices:** 1
Senior Partner: Mr BJ Bird
Number of Partners: 7
Total Staff: 58

Walker Martineau *see full-page profile*
Walker Morris Scott Turnbull *see full-page profile*
Walker Smith & Way *see full-page profile*
Waltons & Morse *see full-page profile*

Walker Martineau

64 QUEEN STREET
LONDON
EC4R 1AD

Phone: 01 236 4232

Fax: 01 236 2525
DX: 74 LONDON CHANCERY LANE WC2
Telex: 28843 **Other offices:** 2
Senior Partner: John Wynter Bee
Number of Partners: 19
Total Staff: 110

The emphasis in this medium sized City firm is on commercial law matters for corporate and institutional clients, but Walker Martineau also has a substantial private client base.

The firm: Founded in 1826, the firm was based in Gray's Inn until recently. An office was established in the Thames Valley in 1972. Over the last seven years Walker Martineau has shown rapid growth and it opened an office in the City in August 1987.

Because of continuing expansion the firm is always looking for good qualified staff, particularly in the company/commercial and commercial property departments. Enquiries to Andrew Dixon.

Six to eight articled clerks are recruited each year. A 2(2) law, or a 2(1) non-law, degree is required. Apply by handwritten letter (plus CV and references) by August two years in advance to Richard Ham.

Other offices: London, Reading.

Agency work: Litigation work is accepted from other solicitors. Contact PF Wynter Bee.

Types of work undertaken: The firm is divided into four groups, namely property, company/commercial, litigation and financial services. The firm is particularly well known for its work in banking, inward investment, medico-legal tribunals, estate planning, and international commercial contracts.

Corporate and institutional clients account for the majority of the firm's client base by the instructions to the company/commercial, property and litigation groups. Walker Martineau also retains substantial and long-standing private clients and family groups, some of whom the firm has represented for generations.

The work of the company/commercial group includes flotations, acquisitions, formation of companies, commercial and banking documentation, taxation, intellectual property, partnership and employment law.

The conveyancing department handles a considerable volume of work for banks, developers of commercial and residential property, institutions, and individuals.

The firm handles all aspects of litigation (except criminal work) and specialises in disciplinary tribunal work.

The financial services group deals with probate and estate planning work, trusts and settlements for substantial private clients, and tax matters. The reputation of the firm in the area of estate planning also attracts clients with significant agricultural interests.

Overall, this youthful and dynamic practice perceives itself as a firm that is providing sound legal advice and balanced commercial judgement to the business community in London and the Thames Valley.

Walker Martineau

Walker Morris Scott Turnbull

ST ANDREW HOUSE
119-121 THE HEADROW
LEEDS
LS1 5NP
Phone: 0532 469686

Fax: 0532 435483
DX: 12060 LEEDS
Telex: 557455 **Other offices:** 4
Senior Partner: Leslie Morris
Number of Partners: 21
Total Staff: 250

This firm prides itself on being a true 'full-service' law firm able to give positive and relevant legal advice in virtually all areas to both corporate and private clients.

The firm: Walker Morris Scott Turnbull is the result of the merger, in 1988, of the well-known and established practices of Walker Morris & Coles and Scott Turnbull & Kendall. The new firm is one of the largest in the north of England. The firm is organised into six departments.

Because of continuing expansion the firm invariably has vacancies at any one time for well qualified assistant solicitors.

In addition the firm recruits up to ten articled clerks annually. The firm looks for bright commercially minded individuals with pleasant outgoing personalties. All applications to the training partner.

Other offices: Leeds (2), Bradford, London.

Agency work: The firm undertakes agency work (mainly litigation) for other solicitors.

Types of work undertaken: Clients include banks, building societies, financial institutions, public and private companies, businesses of all sizes, and private individuals.

The work is divided into six major departments. The company/commercial and taxation department's work includes corporate finance, public company takeovers and mergers, flotations, intellectual property, acquisitions and disposals of companies, management buy-outs, insolvency, and general corporate advice for major commercial clients and smaller businesses.

The commercial property department deals with all the legal aspects of the acquisition of sites for development including major town centre redevelopments, town and country planning, property portfolios for institutions and large companies, and commercial lettings and joint ventures.

The work done by the civil litigation department is broad in its scope. The firm has one of the largest computerised debt collection services in the country, and a road accident department that deals with over 20,000 cases a year.

Areas covered by the criminal and matrimonial department include all aspects of criminal work; matrimonial disputes and related issues, injunctions, and care cases; and, unusually, prosecution work on behalf of government and local authorities. There are also substantial domestic conveyancing and probate departments.

The firm sees itself as a dynamic, energetic, and expanding firm which has become a major force within the north of England. A brochure is available on request.

WALKER
MORRIS
SCOTT
TURNBULL
—SOLICITORS—

Walker Smith & Way

26 NICHOLAS STREET
CHESTER
CH1 2PQ

Phone: 0244 321111

Fax: 0244 327080
DX: 19982 CHESTER
Telex: 61150 **Other offices:** 3
Senior Partner: Mr JB Makinson
Number of Partners: 18
Total Staff: 125

This medium sized firm has a long-established private client base and an ever-expanding commercial law practice.

The firm: Founded in 1837 as a one-person practice, the firm grew steadily until the 1950s. Since then, the rate of expansion has been dramatic, making Walker Smith & Way the largest firm in Chester; this has been achieved through natural growth rather than through amalgamations. The firm is organised into departments.

There is a continuing need for good qualified staff, and in 1989 the firm expects to have two or three vacancies for assistant solicitors, for company/commercial work. Enquiries to Mr RA Dawson.

In addition, the firm usually recruits four or five articled clerks every year. The minimum educational requirement is a 2(2) law degree. Prospects after qualification are excellent; most of the present partners served articles with the firm. Apply by handwritten letter (with CV and names of referees) two years in advance to Mr G Prett.

Other offices: Chester, Ellesmere Port, Wrexham.

Agency work: The firm accepts all types of work from other solicitors; contact Mr JHD Heath (litigation) or Mr RA Dawson for company/commercial and tax/probate.

Types of work undertaken: This is a broadly based practice with a large regional client base in the North West and in North Wales. Likewise, the range of clients is wide, from individuals and small companies to trade unions, substantial companies and insurance companies.

In line with the commercial revitalisation of the Chester area, the firm's commercial practice has grown rapidly. The full range of legal services is offered, and the firm has particular expertise in takeovers, company formations and management buy-outs.

There is a strong litigation department undertaking all types of litigation for private and institutional clients. The firm is well known for its personal injury work, employment law claims, and divorce work.

As is to be expected of a long-established family-type firm, there is a strong emphasis on private client work. As well as litigation work, Walker Smith & Way has considerable experience in probate and wills, the setting up and administration of trusts, and all aspects of family law work. Domestic conveyancing is also undertaken, along with a substantial amount of commercial property work. All types of legal aid work are accepted.

Overall, Walker Smith & Way perceives itself as a dynamic yet reliable firm, one that is enjoying steady but controlled expansion while maintaining the traditional values of integrity and efficiency.

WALKER, SMITH & WAY

Waltons & Morse

PLANTATION HOUSE
31-35 FENCHURCH STREET
LONDON
EC3M 3NN
Phone: 01 623 4255

Fax: 01 626 4153
DX: 243 LONDON CHANCERY LANE WC2
Telex: 884209 **Other offices:** 1
Senior Partner: Ian Hattrick
Number of Partners: 21
Total Staff: 112

Waltons & Morse is a long-established City firm with a broadly based commercial law practice having a variety of specialisations.

The firm: Charles Walton began practising as a solicitor in 1835. His business was mainly concerned with marine insurance and shipping. Some 42 years later, Sydney Morse & Co was founded as a predominantly commercial practice, acting for large public companies and having a particular interest in the electricity supply and road passenger transport industries. These two practices amalgamated in 1975, and the new firm has developed considerably since then.

This growing firm is constantly looking for able assistant solicitors and anticipates a minimum of three vacancies in property, two each in corporate and litigation, and one in private client by the end of June 1989. Enquiries and applications to Christopher Parker, Director of Finance/Administration.

The firm offers four positions for articled clerks per year. The minimum academic requirement is a 2(2) degree, not necessarily in law. Apply (with CV and names of referees) to David Webster two years in advance.

Other offices: Lloyd's Building, Suite 642, Sixth Floor, Lime Street, London EC3M 7DQ.

Agency work: The firm is ready to accept litigation work from other solicitors; contact Martin Tovell for details.

Types of work undertaken: The firm's main activities are in company matters, insurance and reinsurance, shipping and transportation, property financing and development, and banking and insolvency. The firm is client led, calling on the relevant skills of its specialists within the company/commercial, litigation, property and private client departments to service its clients in the relevant business sectors.

In the corporate law area Waltons & Morse is particularly well known for industrial holdings group acquisitions and disposals; banking and insolvency; passenger transport; and electricity supply.

The property department deals with all aspects of land and buildings. Specialisations include major out-of-town shopping centres; city centre refurbishment projects; major office projects; and private estates.

The firm's shipping and insurance practice is broadly based and can involve anything from collision and salvage to carriage of goods by sea, road and air, and insurance and reinsurance disputes. In addition, the firm deals with a wide variety of commercial litigation actions.

This small to medium sized City firm sees itself as having several acknowledged market niches and feels it is organised and prepared for sustained growth in its chosen sectors.

WALTONS & MORSE

Ward, Gethin & Co

11-12 TUESDAY MARKET PLACE
KING'S LYNN
NORFOLK
PE30 1JT
Phone: 0553 773456

Fax: 0553 766857
DX: 57183 EDGWARE
Telex: none **Other offices:** 2
Senior Partner: Mr MRW Ward
Number of Partners: 12
Total Staff: 80

Warner Goodman & Streat

PORTLAND CHAMBERS
66 WEST STREET
FAREHAM
HAMPSHIRE PO16 0JR
Phone: 0329 288121

Fax: 0329 822714
DX: 40804 FAREHAM
Telex: none **Other offices:** 6
Senior Partner: Mr M Meggeson
Number of Partners: 16
Total Staff: 130

Wellingtons

57 WESTGATE STREET
GLOUCESTER
GL1 2NY

Phone: 0452 25164

Fax: none
DX: 7503 GLOUCESTER
Telex: none **Other offices:** 5
Senior Partner: Mr JC Cairns Terry
Number of Partners: 10
Total Staff: 60

Wells & Hind

14 FLETCHER GATE
NOTTINGHAM
NG1 2FX

Phone: 0602 506201

Fax: 0602 506501
DX: 10031 NOTTINGHAM
Telex: 377380 **Other offices:** 1
Senior Partner: Mr RB Stringfellow
Number of Partners: 17
Total Staff: 135

Wansbroughs *see full-page profile*
Warner Cranston *see full-page profile*
Watson Burton *see full-page profile*
Watson, Farley & Williams *see full-page profile*

Wedlake Bell *see full-page profile*
Wedlake Saint *see full-page profile*
Weightman Rutherfords *see full-page profile*

Wansbroughs

8 BROAD QUAY
THE CENTRE
BRISTOL
BS99 7UD
Phone: 0272 268981

Fax: 0272 291582
DX: 7846 BRISTOL
Telex: none **Other offices:** 2
Senior Partner: Mr KCR Gibson
Number of Partners: 21
Total Staff: 121

This medium sized Bristol-based firm has a strong reputation in commercial law work, and a substantial private client base.

The firm: Founded in 1882, the firm now has offices in Bristol, Devizes and Weston super Mare. The original commercial and corporate bias is as strong as ever, with continuing expansion in the litigation field since the 1960s.

In 1989 the firm expects to have vacancies for six assistant solicitors in the fields of corporate, commercial property, commercial litigation, and professional indemnity litigation. Candidates with up to two years' post-qualification experience are preferred. Apply to Mr CA Charles.

In addition, three articled clerks are recruited every year. The minimum educational requirement is a 2(2) degree. Apply by handwritten letter (with CV and names of referees) in September two years in advance to Mr CA Charles.

Other offices: Devizes, Weston super Mare.

Agency work: Civil litigation work from other solicitors is accepted; for details, contact Jane Weston.

Types of work undertaken: The firm acts for commercial clients in both a corporate and litigious capacity, with other departments concentrating on all areas of property, probate, tax and trust, and family law.

Litigation is the largest department in the firm. There is a strong insurance base to the work in both professional indemnity and liability insurance litigation – an area in which the firm is well known and in which its advice is sought nationally. The firm has an excellent reputation for commercial litigation.

On the non-contentious side, there is wide experience in commercial property (including agricultural), and the firm continues to increase its considerable reputation for corporate work, especially acting for sunrise industry clients, fast-growing companies and the high-tech sector, as well as for USM flotations work.

The client base is centred in the South West, where the firm has long-established connections with the local business community, as well as with an extensive network of private clients.

Wansbroughs has always prided itself on working to the highest standards and believes this is reflected in its longstanding and successful track record. The firm is also recognised for its modern and open-minded approach, a result of the partners' dedication to providing a first-rate service for commercial clients. A brochure detailing the firm's services is available on request.

Warner Cranston

PICKFORD'S WHARF
CLINK STREET
LONDON
SE1 9DG
Phone: 01 403 2900

Fax: 01 403 4221
DX: 39904 LONDON BRIDGE SOUTH
Telex: 8956033 **Other offices:** 1
Senior Partner: David C Warner
Number of Partners: 9
Total Staff: 67

This London firm, which has enjoyed rapid expansion in the decade since it was founded, has a thriving commercial practice.

The firm: The present senior partner, working as a sole practitioner, founded the firm in 1979 concentrating on employment law. The firm has since grown into a medium sized firm. This rapid expansion has been achieved by applying the technique of excelling within specific fields. The firm acquired the entire in-house litigation department of Courtaulds PLC in 1987.

The firm expects to have vacancies for three assistant solicitors in 1989. Enquiries to Mr PR Alfandary.

In addition, one or two articled clerks are recruited annually. The minimum educational requirements are a 2(1) law degree and the passing of all heads of the Law Society examinations at the first attempt. Apply by handwritten letter (with CV and names of referees) between January and April to Mr PR Alfandary.

Other offices: Coventry.

Types of work undertaken: The client base is predominantly corporate. The firm has strong international connections, particularly with the USA and France, and some members of the firm are bilingual. The firm is divided into departments: company/commercial, employment, commercial litigation, insurance, construction law, and debt collection.

The work of the commercial/finance department encompasses a wide variety of financial, corporate and commercial transactions as well as advising on legal and regulatory aspects of commercial life.

Employment law is still a particular strength. The department advises on service agreements, tax planning, remuneration packages, share options and pensions, as well as statutory matters including unfair dismissal, redundancy, anti-discrimination and trade union laws. Claims in the High Court and before industrial tribunals are also handled.

The litigation department handles substantial disputes arising out of a variety of transactions, including commercial and trading contracts, banking and financial operations, corporate and partnership matters, intellectual property and insolvency.

Much of the work of the insurance department is contentious, in particular employers' and public liability, motor risks and professional indemnity, while the construction law department receives instructions on both contentious and non-contentious matters. The firm's computerised debt collection department handles debt recovery nationally and worldwide.

In short, the firm perceives itself as specialist, excellent, serious and top quality. Brochures are available on request.

WARNER CRANSTON
S O L I C I T O R S

Watson Burton

20 COLLINGWOOD STREET
NEWCASTLE UPON TYNE
NE99 1YQ

Phone: 091 232 3101

Fax: 091 232 0532
DX: 61009 NEWCASTLE UPON TYNE
Telex: 53529 **Other offices:** 5
Senior Partner: David Carrick Foster
Number of Partners: 15
Total Staff: 158

This broadly based Newcastle practice, one of the best-known firms in the north of England, places a special emphasis on company and commercial work.

The firm: Watson Burton is an old-established practice, founded prior to 1820. Since Victorian times the firm has been associated with the electrical industry and business and commerce as a whole in the north of England. In the post-war period the firm expanded rapidly, and there has been a 50 per cent increase in staff and workload in the last 12 months alone. In addition to contentious and non-contentious business law, there is a good deal of private client work, especially in the branch offices.

Watson Burton continually seeks to recruit assistant solicitors; it expects to have about 12 vacancies in 1989. Enquiries should be addressed to David Foster.

In addition, the firm recruits at least five articled clerks per year. At least a 2(2) degree is required, preferably but not necessarily in law, engineers and linguists being particularly welcome. Apply to Rob Langley for the firm's own application form.

Other offices: Blyth, Cramlington, Newcastle, Whickham, Whitley Bay.

Agency work: The firm accepts all work from other solicitors. Contact Donald Todd.

Types of work undertaken: This is a broad-based practice. In the corporate and business sectors the firm's clients range from very substantial companies, institutions and statutory bodies to the smallest companies and individuals.

The firm is particularly well known for handling all types of public and private company work, including acquisitions and disposals, restructuring and venture capital; commercial property, especially business landlord and tenant work for industrial, commercial and retail clients, and property development; its broad general commercial service to business and industry; and 'one-off' work where lateral thinking, problem solving and original drafting are required for business clients. It also handles very high-volume personal injury work, including accidents in the mining industry; industrial and provident society law; electricity law; employment law; building and construction law, including drafting of contracts and conduct of litigation and arbitration; and heavy civil litigation.

Unlike many commercial firms, Watson Burton handles a full range of private client work, much of which is dealt with in the branches. All types of legal aid work are undertaken.

The firm sees itself as a provincial practice conforming to the standards expected of major London firms, but with greater flexibility and a less aggressive approach.

Watson Burton

Watson, Farley & Williams

MINORIES HOUSE
2-5 MINORIES
LONDON
EC3N 1BJ
Phone: 01 481 1000

Fax: 01 488 1586
DX: 530 LONDON CITY EC3
Telex: 8955707 **Other offices:** 1
Senior Partner: Mr AH Farley
Number of Partners: 19
Total Staff: 115

This commercial law firm, based in the City, has very strong overseas connections, particularly in Europe, with partners resident in Greece and Norway.

The firm: Watson, Farley & Williams was founded in 1982 by six partners, four of whom were previously partners in one of the largest City law practices. The practice is a commercial one with a strong marine bias and a substantial involvement in tax, banking and corporate activities. The average age of all qualified staff is 32, making the firm one of the youngest law practices in the City.

Between five and ten assistant solicitors are likely to be recruited by the firm in the next year in all areas in which it operates. All enquiries should be addressed to Geoffrey Williams.

In addition, five articled clerks are recruited annually. Candidates are expected to have a good academic background. Apply by form (available on request) or by letter (with CV and names of referees) to Geoffrey Williams.

Other offices: Oslo. The firm also has an associated office in Athens.

Types of work undertaken: Watson, Farley & Williams is a specialist commercial law practice with a strong base of banking and financial clients and, increasingly, corporate clients, including numerous prominent American and European banks and financial institutions, publicly quoted UK companies, foreign shipowners and shipyards, insurance brokers and underwriters, aircraft operators and manufacturers, equipment leasing companies and groups engaged in mining and oil exploration, production and trading.

The firm has deliberately avoided the establishment of a formal departmental structure, believing that departmental boundaries discourage the exchange of skills and experience between the firm's lawyers and inhibit the effective handling of clients' affairs. Instead the work is organised into more flexible specialist groups, namely banking and finance (both shipping and non-shipping, encompassing asset and project financing and raising finance through flotations); company/commercial (including oil and gas development work); taxation; property; and litigation (including marine litigation).

Areas for which the firm is particularly well known are banking and finance, marine and general commercial litigation, and taxation.

Overall, Watson, Farley & Williams perceives itself as a small but efficient firm producing good quality work in specialist areas. It is a 'niche' firm, founded on the belief that the commercial client's need for legal services is more effectively met by a smaller, more flexible firm concentrating on a number of interrelated fields.

WATSON, FARLEY & WILLIAMS

Wedlake Bell

16 BEDFORD STREET
COVENT GARDEN
LONDON
WC2E 9HF

Phone: 01 379 7266

Fax: 01 836 6117
DX: 40009 COVENT GARDEN-1 WC2
Telex: 25256 **Other offices:** 3
Senior Partner: Barry Weatherill
Number of Partners: 30
Total Staff: 180

Wedlake Bell is a progressive medium sized London firm which has an expanding and varied commercial, property and international practice, together with an established private client base.

The firm: The original practice dates back to 1780 when it was established in the Temple. Two hundred years later the firm moved from Lincoln's Inn to its present offices in Covent Garden. Wedlake Bell, which is organised into seven main departments, has considerable overseas connections with associated offices in Switzerland and Guernsey.

The firm recruits solicitors in the areas of commercial property, commercial litigation, pensions, corporate, EEC and banking.

In addition four or five articled clerks are recruited each year. Enquiries should be sent (with CV) to the recruitment partner.

Other offices: Thames Ditton, Guernsey, Geneva.

Types of work undertaken: The practice covers the broad range of corporate, banking, property, tax, intellectual property, litigation and private client work in which the major City firms are active. Being smaller than these firms, Wedlake Bell believes it is able to offer a more personal and flexible service with partner involvement to its clients.

Clients range from public companies, banks and major international concerns to smaller businesses and those running them.

The firm is particularly well known for its expertise in commercial property, USM and Stock Exchange, mergers and acquisitions and intellectual property, as well as wealth protection for private clients.

The corporate department advises on all aspects of business activity including management buy-outs, USM or Stock Exchange flotations, acquisitions and mergers, distribution agreements and joint ventures, while the banking department acts for the banking community in most types of lending transactions and includes insolvency and liquidation skills. The firm has a fund of experience in all types of commercial property transactions including joint developments and planning work.

The intellectual property department advises on the protection and commercial exploitation of patents, trademarks, copyrights and competition law within the EEC.

Additionally, the firm's clients can draw on the expertise of strong litigation, tax and pensions departments which serve both commercial and private clients.

Wedlake Bell perceives itself as a tough but fair, reliable and efficient practice.

A brochure for clients describing the work of the firm is available upon request.

WEDLAKE BELL

Wedlake Saint

14 JOHN STREET
LONDON
WC1N 2EB

Phone: 01 405 9446

Fax: 01 242 9877
DX: 407 LONDON CHANCERY LANE WC2
Telex: 263632 **Other offices:** 1
Senior Partner: Keith Perryman
Number of Partners: 11
Total Staff: 80

Wedlake Saint is a general commercial firm, with offices in central and north London, dealing with the whole spectrum of commercial and private client work.

The firm: Wedlake Saint dates from 1911. The firm started to expand in 1924 when it opened an office in Holborn and began to diversify. In the intervening years, the firm has grown into a vigorous medium sized firm offering a very wide range of legal services to a broad client base. The firm is organised into departments.

Because of its continued expansion, the firm is always seeking to recruit qualified staff, and in 1989 expects to have six vacancies for assistant solicitors. Enquiries to John Woodhead.

In addition, the firm has between two and five vacancies for articled clerks every year. Applicants are judged on individual merits rather than on academic results. Prospects after qualification are excellent: over half the partners served articles with the firm. Apply by handwritten letter (with CV and names of referees) as early as possible to John Woodhead.

Other offices: London.

Agency work: The firm accepts agency work from other solicitors; contact Tony Usher or Nicola Tomlins.

Types of work undertaken: This is a broadly based practice with four main departments, namely property, litigation, commercial, and tax and probate. Clients range from individuals and small family businesses to large companies.

The firm has a great deal of experience in commerical property work, including acting for property companies engaged in large-scale residential projects. The large residential property practice is also well known for Rent Act and compulsory purchase work.

The firm's litigation department has built up a high reputation. It handles disputes for large commercial clients and all types of civil cases, from commercial disputes to copyright, personal injury to probate, aviation, and divorce to defamation. Road transport work is a particular area of expertise.

The firm has extensive experience in all aspects of business law, including the full range of commercial transactions, company law, employment law, pensions and intellectual property rights.

Throughout its history, Wedlake Saint has handled the tax problems of many families with particular emphasis on estate planning and trusts. Wills and probate is another area where the firm is well known.

In short, Wedlake Saint sees itself as a well-established, progressive firm with a thriving commercial practice. A brochure for clients is available on request.

SOLICITORS
WEDLAKE SAINT

Weightman Rutherfords

RICHMOND HOUSE
1 RUMFORD PLACE
LIVERPOOL
L3 9QW
Phone: 051 227 2601

Fax: 051 227 3223
DX: 14201 LIVERPOOL
Telex: 627538
Senior Partner: Mr RS Bradshaw
Number of Partners: 22
Total Staff: 155

Two of Liverpool's long-established firms, both dating from the nineteenth century, have recently amalgamated to offer a unique strength in both commercial and private client work, with particular expertise in the field of litigation.

The firm: The practices of Weightmans and Rutherfords merged on 1 May 1988. Weightmans traces its origins back to the formation in 1860 of Field & Co in Liverpool; the firm developed its strength through amalgamations and natural growth. Rutherfords dates back to 1826 and was a general commercial and family practice, particularly well known for its work in liquor licensing. Weightman Rutherfords is the largest partnership based solely in Liverpool.

The firm is always looking for qualified staff of the right calibre. Enquiries should be addressed to Mr IR Evans.

Six articled clerks are recruited annually. The preferred educational qualification is a 2(1) degree (not necessarily in law), although this is not essential. Applications (by letter plus CV) should be made two years in advance to Mr IR Evans.

Types of work undertaken: The complementary nature of the merged practices gives Weightman Rutherfords considerable in-depth expertise, providing a full range of legal services to both business and private clients on a personal, national and international basis. The firm has a unique strength in both commercial and private client work, as well as considerable expertise in a number of specialities, namely defendant personal injury and professional indemnity litigation, licensing, shipping, arbitration, and planning.

Weightman Rutherfords is particularly well known in the field of defendants' litigation. It acts for many of the major insurance companies in connection with claims covering a wide area of the north of England, the Isle of Man and North Wales, as well as overseas. The firm also has a substantial Admiralty shipping and commercial litigation practice, including employment law, as well as family work.

Licensing work is conducted on behalf of many of the major breweries and wine and spirit merchants all over the country. In addition there is a strong entertainment law practice.

On the non-contentious side the firm handles all aspects of commercial and family practice, including probate, trusts, landlord and tenant, and conveyancing.

Weightman Rutherfords is a balanced practice with a traditional but progressive approach, seeking to give their clients a prompt and comprehensive service with a high degree of partner attention in all areas. A brochure describing the services offered by the firm is available on request.

WEIGHTMAN RUTHERFORDS

Westhorp Ward & Catchpole

32 MUSEUM STREET
IPSWICH
SUFFOLK
IP1 1JB
Phone: 0473 50191

Fax: 0473 52527
DX: 3251 IPSWICH
Telex: 987742 **Other offices:** 3
Senior Partner: Mr AH Catchpole
Number of Partners: 14
Total Staff: 78

White Brooks & Gilman

19 ST PETER STREET
WINCHESTER
HAMPSHIRE
SO23 8BU
Phone: 0962 844440

Fax: 0962 842300
DX: 2506 WINCHESTER
Telex: 47396 **Other offices:** 3
Senior Partner: Mr WMC Prideaux
Number of Partners: 10
Total Staff: 77

Wilkin & Chapman

NEW OXFORD HOUSE
OSBORNE STREET
GRIMSBY
HUMBERSIDE DN31 1HE
Phone: 0472 358234

Fax: 0472 360198
DX: 13511 GRIMSBY-1
Telex: 934999 **Other offices:** 6
Senior Partner: Mr DH Emmitt
Number of Partners: 19
Total Staff: 121

Wilkinson Maughan

SUN ALLIANCE HOUSE
35 MOSLEY STREET
NEWCASTLE UPON TYNE
NE1 1XX
Phone: 091 261 1841

Fax: 091 261 8267
DX: 61184 NEWCASTLE UPON TYNE
Telex: 537477
Senior Partner: Mr STL Harbottle
Number of Partners: 21
Total Staff: 82

Whitehead Monckton *see full-page profile*
Wild Hewitson & Shaw *see full-page profile*
Wilde Sapte *see full-page profile*

Whitehead Monckton

72 KING STREET
MAIDSTONE
KENT
ME14 1BL
Phone: 0622 690077

Fax: 0622 690050
DX: 4807 MAIDSTONE
Telex: 966417 **Other offices:** 2
Senior Partner: Mr PG Monckton
Number of Partners: 14
Total Staff: 85

Whitehead Monckton is a major provincial practice based in Maidstone, Kent. The firm acts for a wide range of commercial clients throughout the county and also undertakes substantial private client work.

The firm: Founded more than 200 years ago, the firm took on its present name when Whitehead, Thomas & Urmston merged with Monckton Son & Collis in 1968. The present senior partner is the fifth generation of his family in the practice. A partner serves as the main point of contact for each client and this individual relationship is seen as important: stress is laid on obtaining an overview of each client's legal requirements and on offering broad-based advice.

Whitehead Monckton is planning to recruit assistant solicitors in line with the continued expansion of the practice. Enquiries to the staff partner, Mr R Sykes.

Two articled clerks are needed each year. A substantially higher salary than the minimum rate is paid; the academic requirement is a 2(2) law or 2(1) non-law degree. Applications (with CV) to Mr R Sykes between September and November two years in advance.

Other offices: Tenterden, West Malling.

Agency work: The firm is prepared to act for other solicitors in all its areas of expertise.

Types of work undertaken: The emphasis is on commercial matters, including a significant element of agricultural work, although the practice also has a strong private client base.

The firm is seen as being strong in the fields of copyright, intellectual property and defamation; insolvency and credit control, with a linked computerised debt-collection service. The firm's long tradition of handling land matters is reflected in its substantial agricultural and commercial portfolios.

Sustained economic growth in Kent has led the practice to develop the areas of company law, commercial agreements, company purchases, sales and restructuring, commercial conveyancing, and business start-ups. The firm has a special interest in young businesses set on growth.

Employment and industrial relations law work is undertaken and a full company secretarial service is available. Goods vehicle operation law is also covered. In addition, a full range of private client services is offered, including property, family, wills, trust, probate and litigation. Legal aid work is accepted.

Overall, the firm sees itself as combining the experience of a long-established regional practice with the most modern business methods. Stress is laid on providing a rapid service with high standards for regional business and private clients. Brochures for clients are available on request.

Wild Hewitson & Shaw

SHAKESPEARE HOUSE
42 NEWMARKET ROAD
CAMBRIDGE
CB5 8EP

Phone: 0223 461155

Fax: 0223 316511
DX: 5805 CAMBRIDGE
Telex: 818302 **Other offices:** 3
Senior Partner: Peter G Shaw
Number of Partners: 27
Total Staff: 170

This medium sized Cambridge firm is a broadly based practice which has an increasing emphasis on commercial law work.

The firm: Established in 1934, Wild Hewitson & Shaw has grown from a sole practice to become one of the largest firms in East Anglia with branch offices in Saffron Walden and Bishop's Stortford. Recently it amalgamated with Ennions of Newmarket. By means of controlled expansion the firm continues to meet the increasingly complex demands of modern legal practice while striving to provide the personal service its clients require.

At least ten assistant solicitors will be recruited in the next 12 months, mainly in company/commercial and probate and trust. Enquiries to Mr DE Hollest.

The firm recruits six to ten articled clerks every year. A 2(1) degree is preferred (2(2) degree considered). Apply by letter (with CV and names of referees) to Lewis Isaacs two years in advance.

Other offices: Saffron Walden, Bishop's Stortford, Newmarket.

Agency work: Litigation work is accepted from other firms; contact Mr ERW Temple.

Types of work undertaken: The work is widely based with an increasing emphasis upon commercial property, corporate work, intellectual property and commercial litigation.

Particular fields of expertise are commercial and other property planning and development work, high-tech intellectual property matters, company and EEC law, and commercial litigation.

The work of the company/commercial department involves everything required by businesses, partnerships or companies, from their formation through their development to a full listing.

The commercial property department handles the acquisition of sites, funding work, leases, landlord and tenant, building and construction law and planning law. In addition, this provincial firm has a strong agricultural department dealing with such matters as share farming and partnerships, quotas and crop damage.

There is a busy private client practice covering the whole range of personal tax planning, will drafting, trust formation and administration, as well as conveyancing and other property matters.

The litigation department is particularly well known for intellectual property and general commercial litigation work.

Overall, Wild Hewitson & Shaw perceives itself as a major provincial practice with a strong emphasis on commercial work. A brochure is available on request.

WILD HEWITSON & SHAW *solicitors*

Wilde Sapte

QUEENSBRIDGE HOUSE
60 UPPER THAMES STREET
LONDON
EC4V 3BD
Phone: 01 236 3050

Fax: 01 236 9624
DX: 145 LONDON CITY EC3
Telex: 887793 **Other offices:** 1
Senior Partner: Charles Leeming
Number of Partners: 38
Total Staff: 395

Wilde Sapte is a corporate/commercial firm handling work for the banking and business communities that is wide-ranging and frequently international in scope.

The firm: This respected City practice was founded in 1785, and a number of important clients have used the firm since the nineteenth century. The firm's expansion from its established base started in the 1960s and has accelerated over the last ten years. As well as maintaining a New York office, Wilde Sapte has extensive connections with lawyers in other jurisdictions throughout the world.

All departments recruit a considerable number of newly qualified solicitors annually. The firm is always interested in first-class experienced people. Contact Malcolm Glover.

Twenty to 25 articled clerks are recruited annually. A good honours degree is required, not necessarily in law. Apply (with CV and referees) two years in advance to James Curtis.

Other offices: New York.

Types of work undertaken: Generally regarded as a firm with a practical and sensible approach, Wilde Sapte handles most types of company and commercial work, both UK and international and is especially strong in the banking and financial sector. It also concentrates on corporate and personal taxation and tax planning. The firm is well known for its insolvency work. The firm is organised into five principal departments, namely company/commercial, litigation, property, corporate tax and private client.

The company/commercial department deals with the full range of company and corporate work. Asset finance specialists deal with the finance of ships and aircraft, oil rigs, industrial complexes and satellites. Insolvency work is handled for receivers, administrators and liquidators. Work for leading UK and international banks covers the full range of banking services, and the department also specialises in monopolies, merger and competition work, consumer credit matters, pensions and insurance.

The corporate tax department is one of the fastest growing divisions in the firm.

The firm's large litigation department deals with all types of commercial disputes. Its long-standing position in banking, finance, and insolvency work is now supplemented by a growing involvement in other areas such as shipping, aviation, trade, insurance and employment. The property department covers all aspects of property work for substantial private estates, institutions, property developers, as well as the firm's corporate clients.

The firm has a strong private client department. A brochure is available.

WILDE SAPTE

Wilkinsons

14 CHURCH STREET
KINGSTON UPON THAMES
SURREY
KT1 1RN
Phone: 01 546 6223

Fax: 01 546 5838
DX: 31503 KINGSTON UPON THAMES
Telex: 8812239 **Other offices:** 3
Senior Partner: Mr Gordon Robinson
Number of Partners: 12
Total Staff: 70

Williams Hatch & Co and AE Wyeth & Co

BRIDGE HOUSE
HIGH STREET
DARTFORD
KENT DA1 1JR
Phone: 0322 76514

Fax: 0322 92632
DX: 31904 DARTFORD
Telex: none **Other offices:** 3
Senior Partner: Mr B Williams
Number of Partners: 9
Total Staff: 70

Williamson & Co

WILLIAMSON HOUSE
63 HIGH BRIDGE
NEWCASTLE UPON TYNE
NE1 1DU
Phone: 091 261 1431

Fax: 091 261 7099
DX: 61143 NEWCASTLE UPON TYNE
Telex: 53440 **Other offices:** 5
Senior Partner: Mr JH Thompson
Number of Partners: 13
Total Staff: 60

Willmett & Co

27 SHEET STREET
WINDSOR
BERKSHIRE
SL4 1BX
Phone: 0753 861381

Fax: 842172
DX: 3807 WINDSOR
Telex: none **Other offices:** 7
Senior Partner: Mr KJ LAWTON
Number of Partners: 7
Total Staff: 90

Willey Hargrave *see full-page profile*
William Prior & Company *see full-page profile*

Willey Hargrave

PARK LANE HOUSE
WESTGATE
LEEDS
LS1 2RD
Phone: 0532 441151

Fax: 0532 436050
DX: 12023 LEEDS-1
Telex: none **Other offices:** 2
Senior Partner: Mr LJ Hulme
Number of Partners: 14
Total Staff: 90

This specialist litigation practice (based in Leeds, London and Harrogate) has expertise in all areas of commercial and insurance litigation work, in addition to providing a general, principally commercial service.

The firm: Willey Hargrave was founded by Arthur Willey around 1910, and he was joined by WR Hargrave in 1925. Originally a general practice, the firm's forte now lies in its extensive litigation work.

This expanding firm needs to recruit three or four assistant solicitors (mainly in the litigation field), particularly for its London office. Enquiries should be addressed to Mr RA Heslett.

In addition, the firm generally recruits three articled clerks every year. The minimum educational qualification is a 2(2) degree, preferably in law. Long-term prospects are excellent: many of the present partners served articles with the firm. Articled clerks are encouraged to remain with the firm. Applications (with CV and names of referees) should be addressed two years in advance to Mr RA Heslett.

Other offices: Harrogate, London.

Agency work: The firm carries out all types of work for other solicitors. It has its own in-house investigative service which is available to others. For details contact Mr J Shepherd.

Types of work undertaken: This is a predominantly insurance based litigation practice. Clients include most major and minor insurance companies and Lloyd's. While it undertakes general litigation work, the firm has gained an excellent reputation for professional indemnity and personal injury work.

The firm is also well known for other areas of work which include public liability, fraud, and arson.

Willey Hargrave's investigation service is staffed by a highly skilled team with in-depth experience of all types of accidents and claims. All necessary documentation can be efficiently obtained.

The firm has an expanding company/commercial practice, providing a fully comprehensive legal service to both listed companies and small private businesses. In addition, the Leeds and London offices handle a considerable amount of commercial property work.

The firm also maintains an extensive private client network and undertakes all types of work in this field from domestic conveyancing, wills, probate and trusts to magistrates court work.

Overall, Willey Hargrave perceives itself as a specialist litigation firm with a growing company/commercial base. A brochure for clients detailing the services offered is available on request.

Willey Hargrave

William Prior & Company

TEMPLE BAR HOUSE
23-28 FLEET STREET
LONDON
EC4Y 1AA
Phone: 01 353 3571

Fax: 01 583 2295
DX: 37 LONDON CHANCERY LANE WC2
Telex: 263016 **Other offices:** 4
Senior Partner: Michael Prior
Number of Partners: 17
Total Staff: 124

William Prior & Company is a medium sized firm with its principal offices in the City and Manchester and an emphasis on commercial work.

The firm: Founded in 1950, the firm rapidly developed a reputation for insolvency work and for acting for many of the leading firms of accountants. During the 1960s, the scope of the practice was widened to encompass conveyancing and litigation, and since then a strong general commercial practice has been built up.

This expanding firm is always seeking to recruit qualified staff, and in 1989 expects to need up to eight assistant solicitors for company/commercial, commercial litigation, insolvency, banking and commercial conveyancing. Enquiries to Mr A Bugg (London) or Mr DR Haymes (Manchester).

At least six articled clerks are recruited annually. Long-term prospects are good, since the firm is expanding rapidly. Apply to Mr A Bugg (London) or Mr DR Haymes (Manchester).

Other offices: Bernard House, Piccadilly Plaza, Manchester M1 4DD (phone: 061 236 2646; fax: 061 236 3285). Also at Sidcup, Hove, Blackfen.

Agency work: Insolvency, banking and company/commercial matters are accepted from other solicitors; contact Mr DG Hill (London) or Mrs SM Spencer (Manchester).

Types of work undertaken: The vast majority of the firm's work is in the commercial field, much of it in the banking sector and the accountancy profession. There is a also a wide range of public and private company clients.

The firm is one of the leading insolvency practices, in particular corporate insolvency, and believes only one or two of the largest City firms are able to challenge it in terms of expertise and strength in depth. Moreover, the Manchester office has probably the largest insolvency department outside London.

The firm's involvement in the field of corporate insolvency brings it into close contact with the banking sector, and it advises banks on the whole range of substantial commercial matters.

Company/commercial is a growing area of work. The firm acts for all kinds of businesses on a broad range of corporate, commercial and financial issues. The strong litigation department deals with every type of dispute, from the most complex corporate and commercial dispute to private disagreements.

In short, William Prior & Company sees itself as a progressive and efficient practice dealing with a caseload of high-quality commercial work in a creative and innovative fashion. A brochure is available.

Wilson & Wilson
Inc Burgess & Jeffries

SHEERNESS HOUSE
41 MEADOW ROAD
KETTERING
NORTHAMPTONSHIRE NN16 8TN
Phone: 0536 410014

Fax: 0536 410444
DX: 12802 KETTERING
Telex: 341330 **Other offices:** 4
Senior Partner: Mr PJ Wilson
Number of Partners: 15
Total Staff: 94

Winter Wilkinson

114A HIGH STREET
HUNTINGDON
CAMBRIDGESHIRE
PE18 6NN
Phone: 0480 56331

Fax: 0480 411971
DX: 80900 HUNTINGDON
Telex: 32401 **Other offices:** 4
Senior Partner: Mr Newton
Number of Partners: 16
Total Staff: 130

Withy King & Lee

6 NORTHUMBERLAND BLDGS
QUEEN SQUARE
BATH
AVON BA1 2JE
Phone: 0225 25731

Fax: 0225 315562
DX: 8014 BATH
Telex: 265871 **Other offices:** 1
Senior Partner: Mr BBD Kain
Number of Partners: 6
Total Staff: 67

Woollcombe Watts

CHURCH HOUSE
QUEEN STREET
NEWTON ABBOT
DEVON TQ12 2QP
Phone: 0626 52661

Fax: 0626 61217
DX: 59100 NEWTON ABBOT
Telex: 42585 **Other offices:** 6
Senior Partner: Mr JS Scrivener
Number of Partners: 13
Total Staff: 95

Wilsons *see full-page profile*
Winckworth & Pemberton
  see full-page profile
Winter-Taylors *see full-page profile*
Wiseman Lee *see full-page profile*

Withers Crossman Block
  see full-page profile
Wolferstans *see full-page profile*
Woodham Smith *see full-page profile*

Wilsons

STEYNINGS HOUSE
FISHERTON STREET
SALISBURY
WILTSHIRE SP2 7RJ
Phone: 0722 412412

Fax: 0722 411500
DX: 58003 SALISBURY
Telex: 265871
Senior Partner: Mr AWC Edwards
Number of Partners: 9
Total Staff: 60

This Salisbury firm is a town and country practice offering a full legal service and specialist knowledge in the agricultural field.

The firm: The origins of the present firm lie in the eighteenth century, but most of its expansion and development have taken place during the last 15 years: in that period Wilsons has almost tripled in size. In 1987 the firm moved to modern purpose-built offices close to the station in Salisbury, but has retained its original offices to accommodate the domestic conveyancing department. The firm operates a departmentalised structure.

The firm is planning to recruit about four assistant solicitors in 1989: two in the private client department (particularly in the agricultural estates field) and one in each of the company/commercial and property departments. Enquiries to Rhoderick Voremberg.

Two to four articled clerks are recruited annually. Candidates should have a good honours degree (not necessarily in law). Apply by handwritten letter (with CV) to Rhoderick Voremberg two years in advance.

Agency work: The firm undertakes a variety of work for other solicitors. For details, contact: Mr M Hatt-Cook (residential conveyancing), Mrs J Beddow (commercial conveyancing), Mr AP Wiltshire (general litigation), Mr CDB Butler (matrimonial litigation), Mr RPG Voremberg (milk quota and agricultural advice) Mr TM Lea (tax planning advice) and Mr P Thomas (town and country planning).

Types of work undertaken: As befits a firm situated in the midst of a farming community, Wilsons has particular expertise in the agricultural field, dealing with all aspects of agricultural property and business as well as tax planning.

The commercial department also deals with substantial commercial property transactions, particularly development land, for both landowners and developers. It offers a Specialist Town & Country Planning section handling planning appeals and related problems. The litigation department acts for one of the clearing banks, as well as having considerable expertise in agricultural litigation and insolvency work.

The commercial department handles acquisition and disposal of businesses, joint venture agreements and partnerships. It also advises on the creation of a variety of different types of franchising operations.

The firm has a strong private client base and offers a comprehensive legal service, including all aspects of property law, taxation and estate planning, UK and overseas trusts, wills and probate, litigation and family law.

Overall, the firm sees itself as offering a high standard of service with an exceptional degree of professionalism.

WILSONS

Winckworth & Pemberton
(incorporating Knapp-Fishers)

35 GREAT PETER STREET
WESTMINSTER
LONDON
SW1P 3LR

Phone: 01 222 7811

Fax: 01 222 1614
DX: 2312 VICTORIA SW1
Telex: 8955719 **Other offices:** 2
Senior Partner: David Faull
Number of Partners: 15
Total Staff: 104

This long-established Westminster firm provides a comprehensive range of services to commercial, institutional and private clients.

The firm: Winckworth & Pemberton was established in 1967 by the merger of two well-known Westminster firms — Trollope & Winckworth, founded over 200 years ago, and Meynell & Pemberton. Since then, expansion has been rapid, and in 1987 a number of partners from Knapp-Fishers joined, enabling the firm to offer clients a broader base of services. The firm is run in departments.

Winckworth & Pemberton has a continuing need for qualified staff, and in 1989 expects to recruit seven assistant solicitors: four for property, and one each for company/commercial, private client and litigation. Enquiries to the partnership secretary.

In addition, three articled clerks are recruited annually. A 2(2) degree, not necessarily in law, is required. Apply by handwritten letter (with CV) by August to Mr K Miller.

Other offices: Chelmsford, Oxford.

Agency work: The firm accepts work from other solicitors.

Types of work undertaken: The original client list consisted mainly of individuals and landowners, but has grown to include state and church institutions, schools, and charities, as well as public and private companies. There are five main departments, namely property, litigation, private client, company/commercial and ecclesiastical.

The emphasis in the property department is on all kinds of commercial property work, notably for institutions and for clients in the licensed trade. There is also particular expertise in housing law, acting for housing associations and local authorities; indeed, Winckworth & Pemberton is one of the leading firms in this field.

The litigation department handles the full range of work, including liquor licensing, town and country planning, as well as personal injury claims, matrimonial matters and landlord and tenant disputes.

The company/commercial department is a particular growth area. The department acts for small and medium sized businesses, and is well known for its intellectual property work.

Winckworth & Pemberton has a long-established ecclesiastical practice, providing registries for several dioceses, and handling church property work, which includes major development sites in central London.

There is a substantial private client base, including a number of landed estate owners and substantial trusts, and a significant amount of personal tax and investment management work is undertaken.

WINCKWORTH
& PEMBERTON

Winter-Taylors

PARK HOUSE
LONDON ROAD
HIGH WYCOMBE
BUCKINGHAMSHIRE HP11 1BZ
Phone: 0494 450171

Fax: 0494 441815
DX: 4403 HIGH WYCOMBE
Telex: 837217 **Other offices:** 9
Managing Partner: Mr JHP Roberts
Number of Partners: 15
Total Staff: 137

This Buckinghamshire firm is a community-orientated practice, with a substantial small business and private client base.

The firm: Established in 1885, the firm has grown to its present size through amalgamations. An important stage in this development was in 1934 when the partnership of Winter-Taylor & Woodard was formed, and later extended, in 1943, to Winter-Taylor Woodward & Webb. The firm has flourished, acquiring three new offices since mid-1987.

The firm expects to recruit up to six assistant solicitors in 1989. Generally, solicitors qualified for four to five years are preferred. Enquiries to the director of services, Mr DJ Read.

In addition, there are usually six vacancies for articled clerks annually. The preferred educational qualification is a 2(1) degree, not necessarily in law; the minimum requirement is a 2(2) law degree. Long-term prospects are good: 40 per cent of the present partners served articles with the firm. Apply on form two years in advance to Mr RJ Gates.

Other offices: High Wycombe(2) Aylesbury, Haddenham, Hazlemere (Bucks), Lane End, Marlow, Princes Risborough.

Agency work: All types of work from other solicitors are accepted; contact Mr RA Hulett.

Types of work undertaken: The firm is divided into departments, namely company/commercial; residential conveyancing; family law; criminal law and general litigation; employment; licensing; wills, probate and trusts. The range of departments reflects the diversity of the firm's client base.

In line with Winter-Taylors' emphasis on serving community needs, the firm is well known for the quality of its advice and guidance to small and medium sized businesses.

The firm has particular expertise in all aspects of commercial and residential property development work, and the related field of commercial and residential conveyancing.

On the commercial side, there is a strong employment law practice, covering both employees and employers. Licensing is another area of law where the firm has particular expertise.

The family law department has wide experience in matrimonial work, and it also handles adoption, affiliation proceedings, financial matters, care proceedings and child matters.

Overall, Winter-Taylors perceives itself to be successfully bridging the gap between the traditional role of lawyers and the varied needs of the modern community.

WINTER - TAYLORS

Wiseman Lee

241 HIGH STREET NORTH
MANOR PARK
LONDON
E12 6SJ
Phone: 01 471 1114

Fax: 01 471 1645
DX: 4705 EAST HAM
Telex: none **Other offices:** 3
Senior Partner: Malcolm Lee
Number of Partners: 7
Total Staff: 57

Wiseman Lee is a strong London suburban firm with three branch offices and is a well-known common law practice.

The firm: Formed in the early 1950s, by the end of the decade Wiseman Lee had three branch offices. It expanded rapidly in the 1960s and, at the same time, built up its reputation for common law and in particular personal injury work. The firm is expanding steadily.

The firm expects to have two vacancies for assistant solicitors in the next 12 months: for contract law and common law litigation work. Enquiries to Malcolm Lee.

In addition, there are two vacancies for articled clerks. The firm prefers to judge applicants on individual merits rather than just on academic achievements. Prospects after qualification are good. Apply by letter (with CV) to Malcolm Lee.

Other offices: Wanstead, Walthamstow, East Ham.

Agency work: The firm accepts work from other solicitors; contact Paul Wershof (county court, High Court and common law) or Paul Kaufman (crime).

Types of work undertaken: This is a medium sized, wide-ranging practice. Clients include two London health authorities, public companies, insurance companies and syndicates; however, much of the work is for local working people and businesses.

Wiseman Lee is particularly well known for its civil litigation practice, especially in the fields of medical and other professional negligence work and personal injury claims. A considerable amount of heavy commercial litigation work is also undertaken, as well as employment law and landlord and tenant matters. Unusually for a non-central London firm there is an increasing amount of entertainment law work for clients who include a professional theatre company and musicians. Licensing matters are also handled.

A wide range of non-contentious commercial law work is dealt with, covering the full range of business activities, including business start ups, partnership agreements, management buy-outs and taxation advice and planning.

The firm is well known for its domestic and commercial conveyancing, and also handles finance and development work, notably for several medium sized developers.

Substantial private client work is undertaken – including divorce and family law matters, crime, trusts, probate and wills – some of it legally aided.

In short, Wiseman Lee is a broad-based firm that is very well known for its civil litigation practice and has the reputation of being tough but very positive. A brochure is available.

WISEMAN LEE

Withers Crossman Block

20 ESSEX STREET
LONDON
WC2R 3AL

Phone: 01 836 8400

Fax: 01 240 2278
DX: 160 LONDON CHANCERY LANE WC2
Telex: 24213 **Other offices:** 1
Senior Partner: John W Roome
Number of Partners: 34
Total Staff: 240

This central London firm has a substantial commercial base and is a leading private client and family practice.

The firm: In January 1988 Withers and Crossman Block & Keith, two of London's longest-established firms, merged to form Withers Crossman Block. There is a strong international emphasis in the new firm, which can draw on longstanding associations with lawyers worldwide. Through its Paris office and Spanish association the firm has a significant presence in Europe. The firm is organised into departments.

The firm is looking for eight assistant solicitors in all departments. Enquiries to Andrew Gerry.

In addition, nine or ten articled clerks are recruited annually. A 2(1) degree is usually required, not necessarily in law. Apply (on form available on request) by end of September to Stephen G Cooke.

Other offices: Paris.

Types of work undertaken: The firm acts for substantial companies and high net-worth individuals. Withers Crossman Block is well recognised in the areas of intellectual property; banking; employee incentive and share option schemes; trusts, probate and tax planning; matrimonial and family; shipping and insurance litigation, and aircraft financing

leasing.

The work of the company/commercial department includes corporate finance, particularly for management buy-outs and business start-ups, tax, insolvency, competition and trade practices, and computer and information technology.

The litigation department handles all aspects of contentious work in the commercial and banking fields, as well as in employment, property, shipping and aviation, insurance disputes, intellectual property and private client work.

The property department provides a full range of services, from agricultural and estate work to hotel, public houses and leisure, residential, shop, warehouse and office property. There is particular expertise in property-related banking work and development and development funding projects.

The private client department is one of the leading ones in London. As well as tax planning, trusts and wills, estate administration, charities and Court of Protection work, the department works with offshore trust companies and advises on international asset protection for a substantial number of foreign clients. There is also a large matrimonial and family department.

Withers Crosman Block is a growing and well-respected medium sized firm providing a wide range of services to corporate and private clients, both in the UK and abroad.

WITHERS CROSSMAN BLOCK

Wolferstans
(incorporating Broad & Spencer)

DEPTFORD CHAMBERS
62-64 NORTH HILL
PLYMOUTH
PL4 8EP

Phone: 0752 663295

Fax: 0752 672021
DX: 8206 PLYMOUTH-1
Telex: none **Other offices:** 4
Senior Partner: Mr DJL Gabbitass
Number of Partners: 13
Total Staff:73

This Plymouth-based firm is a general practice which prides itself on a modern approach with emphasis on the client/partner relationship.

The firm: Established in 1812 as a traditional family firm, Wolferstans has expanded rapidly following an amalgamation with the Devonport-based firm of Broad & Spencer in 1970 and now has four branch offices in the South West. The firm is organised into departments.

All departments in this firm are expanding, creating a continuing demand for solicitors in all areas. Enquiries should be addressed to the staff partner, Mr RAF Griggs.

Three or four articled clerks are recruited annually. The ability to get on with clients and a practical approach are more important than academic results. Applications by handwritten letter (plus CV and names of referees) should be sent to Mr RAF Griggs.

Other offices: Plymstock, Plympton, Crownhill (all Plymouth), Saltash (Cornwall).

Agency work: The firm undertakes all types of agency work for other solicitors.

Types of work undertaken: This wide-ranging general practice concentrates on residential and commercial conveyancing, general commercial work, criminal, family and welfare law, and all types of litigation. Clients include local companies, major insurance companies, legal expense insurers and government departments. In addition, the firm has a substantial private client base.

The firm has growing experience in management buy-outs, and for many years has handled a substantial amount of dock harbour work. It is particularly well known in the criminal law field, and has wide experience of courts martial. The senior partner, David JL Gabbitass, is a well-known advocate who has served on the Justice Committee on Fraud Trials.

There is a substantial personal injury department, both plaintiff and defendant, which includes a medical negligence unit and specialist inquest representation.

The firm has a separate family and welfare office specialising in all aspects of family law, including matrimonial, children, trusts and wills. In addition, there is a strong residential conveyancing department.

Through its network of offices the firm provides a personal service supported by specialist expertise on the full range of legal topics. All types of legal aid work are accepted. A brochure is available for clients on request.

Overall, this medium sized firm sees itself as large enough to give specialised advice but small enough to retain a personal approach.

Established 1812

WOLFERSTANS
SOLICITORS

Woodham Smith

12 GREAT JAMES STREET
LONDON
WC1N 3DR

Phone: 01 242 0801

Fax: 01 405 6767
DX: 188 LONDON CHANCERY LANE WC2
Telex: 22624 **Other offices:** 1
Senior Partner: Simon Barnes
Number of Partners: 14
Total Staff: 110

Woodham Smith's clients are primarily commercial and industrial, intellectual property is a major strength, and there is a strong international flavour to the practice.

The firm: Dating back to the 1890s, the firm has reached its current form through merger in the early 1970s. At that time it was a broadly based general practice, dealing mainly with private clients with a focus on medical matters and a specialisation in intellectual property. In recent years the firm has become more involved in the business sector.

There is a continuing need for assistant solicitors, particularly for intellectual property, commercial litigation, community law and commercial property. Enquiries to Peter Haigh-Lumby.

In addition, seven articled clerks are recruited annually. A 2(2) degree is required. Apply in writing (plus CV) to Isabel Davies.

Other offices: Ipswich.

Agency work: Intellectual property work is accepted from other solicitors; contact Richard Price.

Types of work undertaken: Woodham Smith is largely a commercial practice, with particular emphasis on all aspects of intellectual property and servicing growing entrepreneurial businesses. The client base is healthily varied comprising a number of household names in all sorts of industries and services, multinationals, one very large insurance company, and wealthy individuals.

The firm's particular specialities are intellectual property, trade and medical libel, medical partnerships, secured lending on commercial property, and planning.

The work of the firm is organised into four main departments, namely litigation and intellectual property, taxation and private client, company/commercial, and property.

Of these, the intellectual property department is well known and handles both contentious and non-contentious cases involving patents, trademarks, industrial and publishing copyright and confidential information. As regards other litigation, the firm has much international commercial litigation experience and, in particular, its US/UK and Anglo-German business is extensive. The taxation and company/commercial departments give a full range of services (including acquisitions, mergers, buy-outs, as well as USM and Stock Exchange transactions and related tax planning). The property department advises on planning and industrial and commercial transactions.

The firm has been described as the Aspreys of the intellectual property world. This the firm happily adopts as its maxim for all work it does; striving to give real personal service coupled with first class commercial advice.

WOODHAM SMITH

Wragge & Co

BANK HOUSE
8 CHERRY STREET
BIRMINGHAM
B2 5JY

Phone: 021 632 4131

Fax: 021 643 2417
DX: 13036 BIRMINGHAM-1
Telex: 338728
Senior Partner: Sir Patrick Lawrence CBE
Number of Partners: 26
Total Staff: 300

Wragge & Co is a major provincial firm with a thriving commercial and industrial practice.

The firm: Wragge & Co was founded in 1834 by George Wragge and Clement Ingleby. There has always been an emphasis on commercial law which started in the nineteenth century with the development of the canals and the banking system. Today, the international work is increasing. The firm is part of the M5 Group (see separate entry).

The firm is always looking for qualified staff and in 1989 it expects to have ten vacancies, for corporate finance, company/commercial, commercial property, intellectual property and EEC work. Enquiries to Mr CW Hughes.

About 20 articled clerks are recruited each year. The firm is big enough to provide an interesting and demanding spread of work, yet is structured to enable each articled clerk to feel part of an important team. Long-term prospects are excellent: three-quarters of the present partners served articles with the firm. Applications should be made either by letter (with CV) or by requesting an application form, in August two years in advance of the starting date. All correspondence should be addressed to the managing partner, Mr PM Wall.

Through the correspondent relationship with Smith, Gambrell & Russell, Attorneys, of Atlanta, USA, short-term secondments to their offices are arranged for qualified staff.

Types of work undertaken: There are six main departments, namely litigation; trusts, pensions and tax; property; company/commercial, corporate finance; and intellectual property and competition.

The firm undertakes all types of commercial and industrial law – notably flotations, business takeovers, intellectual property (particularly patent and copyright matters), corporate acquisitions, insolvency, venture capital, and corporate pensions – clients range from international public companies to small sole traders.

There is a substantial litigation department handling work which includes employment, insurance, professional negligence, construction, and insolvency related matters, as well as international arbitrations and EEC disputes.

On the private client side, the firm undertakes a significant amount of probate and trust work, domestic conveyancing, wills, tax planning, and some personal injury claims.

Wragge & Co perceives itself as a firm with a strong professional reputation and is regarded with respect for its traditional qualities of service and forward-thinking approach. The firm has a well-organised management structure and is commercially based.

Brochures describing the work of the firm are available upon request, together with booklets on a wide range of legal topics.

Wragge & Co

Wynne Baxter Godfree

DIAL HOUSE
221 HIGH STREET
LEWES
EAST SUSSEX BN7 2AE
Phone: 0273 477071

Fax: 0273 478515
DX: 3101 LEWES
Telex: 878216 **Other offices:** 9
Senior Partner: John C Lancaster
Number of Partners: 17
Total Staff: 107

This broadly based East Sussex practice offers a full legal service to both private and commercial clients.

The firm: Wynne Baxter Godfree has grown over the last 150 years from a sole practitioner in the county town of Lewes to a good sized firm with ten offices in the South East. The present firm is the result of the merger of Wynne Baxter Hillman & Carter and the Brighton firm of Neale Godfree. In 1988 Wintle & Co of Eastbourne joined. This has resulted in a substantial and progressive firm well placed geographically to meet the increasing demands of a commercially active and expanding area of the country.

This progressive firm welcomes applications from qualified staff and expects five vacancies for assistant solicitors throughout the firm's offices in the next 12 months. Enquiries to the partnership secretary.

In addition, two articled clerks are recruited annually. A 2(2) degree is required, not necessarily in law. Apply by handwritten letter (with CV and names of referees) two years in advance to Mr SJ Hall.

Other offices: Brighton (2), Seaford, Woodingdean, Peacehaven, Eastbourne, Newhaven, Hailsham, Lingfield (Surrey).

Agency work: The firm accepts work from other solicitors.

Types of work undertaken: The firm offers the full range of legal services to the private client (including trust and probate, civil and criminal litigation, personal injury claims, family law and conveyancing, and legal aid work) while retaining roots in the traditions of the trusted local family solicitor.

For the business community, the firm has a wide-ranging commercial practice, including company, corporate and commercial law, conveyancing, leases, licensing, debt collection, and franchising.

Wynne Baxter Godfree has a reputation for excellence as a sound, all-round practice with particular expertise in the fields of medical negligence and building society work. It continues to be well known for the scope and calibre of its wide range of court work. Specialist services are also provided in all aspects of property (including conveyancing), commercial and corporate work, employment legislation, and trustee and executorship.

Wynne Baxter Godfree, with its ten offices in the South East, is able to provide modern, technical support and is well prepared to give an enhanced service in an increasingly competitive profession. Close communication between offices enables specialist abilities to be available to all clients.

Overall, the firm perceives itself as being soundly based with a progressive approach to the challenges meeting the profession. A brochure for clients is available on request.

Yaffe Jackson & Ostrin

81 DALE STREET
LIVERPOOL
L2 2HZ

Phone: 051 236 5555

Fax: 051 236 2121
DX: 14205 LIVERPOOL
Telex: none **Other offices:** 4
Senior Partner: Anthony Rex Ostrin
Number of Partners: 7
Total Staff: 63

This Liverpool-based firm has a substantial private client base and an expanding commercial practice.

The firm: Founded in the mid-1940s by AJ Yaffe, the firm has a common law practice, as opposed to merely non-contentious work. In recent years expansion has been rapid, both in the firm's traditional family law areas and in the commercial sector (with particular reference to small business development). The firm is organised into teams.

This expanding firm is continually seeking to recruit good qualified staff, and in 1989 expects to recruit three assistant solicitors, two for general practice (with a broad litigation emphasis), and one advocate. Enquiries to Mr LJ Bennett.

In addition, the firm usually recruits between three and five articled clerks every year. Applicants are considered on individual merits. Prospects after qualification are excellent: over half of the present partners served articles with the firm. Apply by letter (with CV) to Mr LJ Bennett.

Other offices: Liverpool (2), Waterloo, Prescot.

Agency work: The firm accepts litigation and criminal work from other solicitors; contact Mr RJ Jones (litigation) or Mr D Lupton (crime).

Types of work undertaken: This is a broadly based practice with a traditional family firm profile. Combined with this is a vigorous commercial practice that is expanding very rapidly, in line with Liverpool's recent upturn. There is an old-established client base throughout the Merseyside area, including private clients, small businesses, trade unions, PLCs and insurance companies.

The firm's private client work includes crime (it is the largest crime practice on Merseyside), divorce, landlord and tenant, and plaintiff accident work, as well as child care and mental health reviews.

The firm acts for employees and trade unions in a wide variety of work, including labour relations, employment law matters, work-related accidents and negligence matters. A substantial amount of tribunal work is undertaken, representing both professionals and professional bodies in negligence cases.

The emphasis on the commercial side of the practice is on small, growing businesses, and there is an expanding financial services workload. In addition, the firm has its own real estate company based in Prescot.

In short, Yaffe Jackson & Ostrin sees itself as competent, solid, forward-looking, and prepared to consider opportunities. It perceives itself as a formidable, but fair and approachable, opponent.

Woolsey Morris & Kennedy

100 STATION ROAD
SIDCUP
KENT
DA15 7DT
Phone: 01 300 9321

Fax: 01 300 0443
DX: 31700 SIDCUP
Telex: none
Senior Partner: Mr CH Davidson
Number of Partners: 10
Total Staff: 61

Wright Johnson & MacKenzie

12 ST VINCENT PLACE
GLASGOW
G1 2FQ

Phone: 041 248 3434

Fax: 041 221 1226
Rutland Exchange: 129 GLASGOW
Telex: 778927 **Other offices:** 5
Senior Partner: Mr C White
Number of Partners: 18
Total Staff: 120

FOREIGN LAW FIRMS IN LONDON

Foreign law firms in London

In researching the 1989 edition of The Legal 500 we became increasingly aware of the growing role of foreign law firms in London. The world importance of London's financial markets, Lloyd's, and the oil industry – as well as language and a liberal regulatory structure – have all contributed to the presence of a broad array of overseas lawyers. Surprisingly, however, many British lawyers (and companies) are not familiar with the range of foreign legal services available in the UK; indeed, foreign lawyers have expressed astonishment at the willingness of some English solicitors to draft agreements for overseas jurisdictions without having consulted a local practitioner.

UK firms abroad: There are, of course, a number of British firms which have strong links abroad. They fall broadly into three categories. Firstly there are those who have overseas offices. This is a category which includes many of the major commercial firms; a browse through the A-Z section of this book will show how international the UK law scene has become.

Secondly, some UK firms have developed strong links with particular countries (and may well have foreign lawyers on the staff of their London offices). The reasons for such connections vary, but are often little more than historical accident. Here we would mention, for instance, **Pritchard Englefield & Tobin** (for its German work) and **Middleton Potts** (for Italy), both of which act for a number of household names from those countries. In addition, **Amhurst Brown Colombotti** is known, to a lesser extent, for its Spanish and Italian work.

In the third category are those firms that have developed formal or informal links with firms abroad, particularly within Europe. Generally, these UK firms prefer to rely upon established local contacts rather than opening foreign offices of their own. Going beyond correspondence arrangements, a number of UK firms are participating in European groups, paving the way for 1992. Indeed, some have been involved in such groups since as long ago as the 60s, although most joined after Britain's entry into the Common Market. They include **Pannone Blackburn**, which is part of a European Economic Interest Grouping called **Pannone De Backer**. (An EEIG, created under EC Regulation 2137/85, is a grouping which exists 'to facilitate or develop the economic activities of its members and to improve or increase the results of those activities', and is as close to a European-wide partnership as lawyers may currently go). On the other hand, **Herbert Smith** is part of a much looser arrangement called **Unilaw**, which also includes the Italian firm **Carnelutti**, which has a London office. Other groups (and their English link) include: **Club Oasis (Turner Kenneth Brown)**; Private Association of Lawyers, known as **Pals (Stoneham Langton and Passmore)**; **Interlex (Taylor Garrett)**; **Eurolaw (Penningtons)**; **Club de Abogados (Simmons & Simmons)**; and **The Club (Lovell White Durrant)**.

Distinct from such groupings is the firm of **Baker & McKenzie**. It claims to have a truly international partnership. This is, in fact, based around an Illinois partnership called **Baker & McKenzie International** (which is ranked third in the *American Lawyer's* America's One Hundred Highest

Grossing Firms). The partners of this Illinois firm are the partners of all the firms worldwide called **Baker & McKenzie**, or associated with **Baker & McKenzie** (but which, because of local bar association regulations, cannot use the same name). For instance, in Germany the partners of the Frankfurt firm **Doser Amereller Noack** are also members of the Illinois international firm. In England, the Law Society forbids profit-sharing with non-solicitors, and thus the London partners are members of a separate London partnership, and also members of the Illinois partnership. They can, however, receive a share of the Illinois profits without being in breach of Law Society rules; accordingly, if London is less profitable than the international firm, a residual profit-share can be passed to the London partners from the Illinois partnership. In total, **Baker & McKenzie** comprises some 45 offices in 33 jurisdictions.

Foyen of Sweden also has a number of offices around the world, linked by a form of partnership. In similar vein we would mention **Hartwig**, with offices in Germany, the USA and London.

Foreign firms: In our listing of foreign law firms in London we have included the London offices of foreign firms and London firms that are admitted in a foreign jurisdiction (even if there is no head office in that country). For instance, we include here both **Sullivan & Cromwell** (practitioners of US law based in the USA) and **The Law Offices of Gary M Ferman** (practitioners of US law based in London).

As a rule of thumb, foreign firms in London can be divided into three groups. A small number exist exclusively to service the needs of an expatriate community, as well as tackling some immigration questions (but usually this is integrated into a general commercial practice). The second group is of those who are, in practice, little more

than a 'post office' — providing office facilities and support for visitors from the home country, servicing one or two major clients, and providing the kudos of a London office. Similarly, there are those firms whose London office has little to do with business into or out of the UK, but is, rather, a staging post for the through-put of work — typically from the USA to Europe or the Middle East.

The final group (and the one with which we are principally concerned) is those firms who can genuinely hold themselves out as offering a full commercial service, very often (but not always) reflecting areas of expertise in the home practice. Whilst it might seem unlikely that a firm with fewer than, say, three to five lawyers would have the breadth of expertise to enable it to fall into this final category, many firms are taking full advantage of data, telecommunications and satellite links so that the London office may have full access to the expertise and databases of the home country. Thus a small office may be able to provide a surprising breadth of service, perhaps supporting visits from more specialised partners from the home country. Indeed, if it is true of UK firms that the skill in dealing with them is in identifying the particular work categories in which the firm excels, rather than relying upon the repute of the firm as a whole, then this applies even more to foreign firms. One should also have regard to how smoothly and readily further specialised advice is made available from the other offices.

There is an increase, not only in the number of foreign firms in London, but also in the amount of work being undertaken by them. This is a reflection of two trends. One is, of course, the 'internationalisation' of companies and corporate work; the other is the associated growth in the complexity of the transactions undertaken. A particular example of this, and an area in which the majority of overseas firms have developed a practice, is EEC Law (especially EEC competition law). The expansion is, however, facilitated by an important cultural development. As the City has become accustomed to dealing with overseas bankers, investors, and lenders, so it has become used to overcoming differences of approach and, we would suggest, national prejudices. Thus the resistance to using foreign law firms is decreasing. Additionally it has been suggested that as London commercial firms have brought their fees more into line with international norms, so the foreign – and particularly American – firms have become more competitive.

Jurisdictions: Some countries are more fully represented in London than others. There are few European firms, reflecting the tendency of firms in those countries to remain small; a fifteen-partner firm anywhere in Europe outside Britain would be exceptionally large. Moreover, European bars tend to be rather more restrictive than in the UK; for example, German firms are not permitted to open permanent overseas offices (and it is also worth noting that in Germany tax practitioners are members of a separate profession).

Interestingly the Scandinavian countries are somewhat better represented. No doubt this can be linked both to common interests in the North Sea and the relatively greater needs in those countries to raise money abroad (compared to, say, the facilities offered by the Frankfurt or Paris stock exchanges). It should not be forgotten that Norway, Sweden, Finland, and Denmark are linked by bodies of law covering core commercial areas. Since the turn of the century legislators in the four countries have attempted to draw up common statutes (and, in fact, Finnish law as a whole is based on the Swedish Code of 1834). However, there is a wide divergence of case law and, since their entry into the EEC, the Danes have given greater prominence to EEC laws. The degree of co-operation has tended to

diminish in recent years, so that, whereas contract and sales of goods laws are similar, that is no longer true of insolvency laws. Moreover, Finnish and Swedish case law resemble each other more closely than they do Norwegian case law.

For coverage of the Arab jurisdictions we would have to mention **SDF Associates**. In addition, the US firm **Bryan Cave McPheeters & McRoberts**, through its work in international real estate planning, has particular experience of the Middle East.

Currently only one Japanese firm, **Hamada and Matsumoto**, has opened a London office. Whilst it does offer its European clients advice on Japanese law, it is most widely known as being among the ten most active firms worldwide in Eurobonds.

Particularly well known for his practice throughout the Latin countries is **Eduardo Romero**. He has practised in London for many years, and is associated with practitioners in Spain and across Central and South America. We would also draw attention to the Panamanian lawyers comprising the unlikely sounding combination of **Arosemena Noriega & Castro**.

The USA, Canada, and Australia are all sufficiently well represented to offer a considerable degree of choice. Although these countries all operate federal legal systems, it is generally true that specialisations of practice will be more significant than state or provincial jurisdiction except, of course, where litigation is involved. Thus one might use **Simpson Thacher & Bartlett** *USA* in a merger transaction, but prefer **Morgan Lewis & Bockhius** *USA* if litigation in Philadelphia was entailed. In particular, in Australia matters of tax law, except stamp duties, are subject to federal not state law; and commercial law, whilst being enacted separately within each state, is, for the most part, in common form. An important exception to this is media law, which varies widely between the states and territories.

Specialisations: The reputations and specialisations of some firms are linked to the specialisation of their original base; for instance **Fulbright & Jaworski** *Texas USA*, **Vinson & Elkins** *Texas USA* and **Krefting Lochen Odegard & Sandven** *Norway* are known for their oil and gas exploration work, while **Mallesons Stephen Jaques** *Australia* has particular experience in mining. Panamanian firms in London tend to be associated with shipping work (as well as offshore incorporations).

Rather more often, however, a firm's presence in London will be because of London's position as a centre of commerce. Thus there are many firms reputed for their work in mergers and acquisitions; we would mention **Fried Frank Harris Shriver & Jacobson** *USA*, **Skadden Arps Slate Meagher & Flom** *USA*, **Simpson Thacher & Bartlett** *USA*, **Tory Tory DesLauriers & Binnington** *Canada* and **Gottesman Jones & Partners** (a London-based firm practising US law). A number of the largest US firms have traditionally had links with major banks (for instance **Davis Polk & Wardwell** with Morgan Guaranty, **Shearman & Sterling** with Citibank, **Sidley & Austin** with First Chicago). **Davis Polk & Wardwell** is also active in the Euromarket, while **Sidley & Austin** has a reputation for its work in swaps. In the area of insurance work we would mention **Osler Hoskin & Harcourt** *Canada* and **LeBoeuf Lamb Leiby & MacRae** *USA*. The latter is also known for its utilities work. **Stikeman Elliott** *Canada* is among firms known for their work in the field of tax, as is **Krefting Lochen Odegard & Sandven** *Norway*, which has advised the UK government on taxation reforms carried out in Norway.

In the entertainment field, our survey indicates that **Milbank Tweed Hadley & McCloy** *USA* has notable London contacts, while many firms represented in London have respected practices at home; for example the US firms of **Fried Frank Harris Shriver & Jacobson**, **Gibson Dunn & Crutcher**, **Jones Day Reavis & Pogue**, and **Morgan Lewis & Bockhius**.

Another well-known firm with an international reputation in a specific area of work is **Ladas & Parry** *USA:* it has a worldwide practice in patent, trademark and intellectual property law.

Lawyer to lawyer: In general terms, most foreign firms in London are willing to act as agents for UK solicitors; very often a relationship develops whereby the foreign firm will advise the client directly, but only on matters specifically relating to its jurisdiction. The firm will also act as counsel, examining documents and transactions.

An expanding and significant service is the advice given by foreign law firms in matters where there is no clear foreign legal content, but in which the structure and planning of the transaction are similar to matters in which the foreign firm has experience. An obvious example would be **LeBoeuf Lamb Leiby & MacRae** *USA* advising the British government on the electricity industry privatisation. A less obvious example would be the way in which **Cole Corette & Abrutyn** *USA* could be consulted for its knowledge of international silver markets. Other areas where this might be relevant are regulatory work and aspects of litigation (notably in pharmaceutical claims).

Similarly, foreign firms may have experience (and offices) in countries where British firms are sparsely represented. Thus, until January 1989, **Coudert Brothers** *USA* was the only Western law firm with an office in the Soviet Union (now **Baker & McKenzie** also has lawyers permanently staffing an office there). We would also mention that Robert Starr, the London resident partner of **Cole Corette & Abrutyn**

USA is generally known to be experienced in USSR joint ventures. The only English firm with any real experience in this area is **Theodore Goddard**.

East-West trade has been gradually expanding for a number of years. From 1 April 1989 opportunities will broaden further with the enactment in the USSR of legislation permitting a large variety of Soviet organisations to trade directly in foreign markets. Although the changes taking place in the Soviet Union may present new opportunities, they also present hazards. In particular, negotiators may find their Soviet counterparts unduly bureaucratic and inexperienced in making decisions. The capacity of Soviet lawyers to take a commercial view of matters is likewise limited. Moreover, it is now necessary to seek security in transactions where previously the Soviet government was considered a safe credit risk. One correlation of increased activity of British companies in this market will inevitably be more frequent recourse to foreign lawyers in London. Because of the undeveloped nature

of Soviet commercial law and the lack of international experience in the Soviet judiciary, it is generally necessary to agree arbitration in a third jurisdiction. Thus commodity contracts are commonly drawn up under Swedish law.

In conclusion, we would emphasise our earlier comments that, as the profession becomes increasingly international, the presence of foreign firms in London can only grow. This is something from which solicitors should be able to benefit considerably – and more than they do at present.

Foreign law firms in London: Overleaf we list 95 firms with their telephone numbers, grouped by home jurisdiction. These 95 firms are all the firms of which we are aware that have a presence in London (in the form of a separate office, rather than just an agency).

We welcome comments on the role of foreign law firms and on the experiences of UK solicitors in their dealings with them – in confidence, as always.

Foreign law firms in London

	Home jurisdiction	
ALLEN ALLEN & HEMSLEY	AUSTRALIA	01 606 2721
CORRS PAVEY WHITING & BYRNE	AUSTRALIA	01 929 4955
MALLESONS STEPHEN JAQUES	AUSTRALIA	01 982 0982
MINTER ELLISON	AUSTRALIA	01 831 7871
PINHEIRO NETO	BRAZIL	01 606 8261
BLAKE CASTLES & GRAYDON	CANADA	01 377 6800
FASKEN MARTINEAU WALKER	CANADA	01 929 2894
MCCARTHY & MCCARTHY	CANADA	01 588 1867
OSLER HOSKIN & HARCOURT	CANADA	01 283 3287
STIKEMAN ELLIOTT	CANADA	01 606 0811
TORY TORY DESLAURIERS & BINNINGTON	CANADA	01 831 8155
DRAGSTED LAW FIRM	DENMARK	01 236 4442
PLESNER & LUNOE	DENMARK	01 405 9586
SALTORP HALD & ANDERSEN	DENMARK	01 236 2023
PROCOPE & HORNBORG	FINLAND	01 831 0292
BERLIOZ & CO	FRANCE	01 831 4022
KYRIAKIDES & PARTNERS	GREECE	01 623 1357
LAW OFFICES GRAMATIDIS	GREECE	01 439 1251
DR AK ANVARI & ASSOCIATES	IRAN	01 724 9073
KENNY STEPHENSON & CHAPMAN	IRELAND	01 405 3331
CARNELUTTI	ITALY	01 242 2268
STUDIO LEGALE BISCONTI	ITALY	01 606 0416
HAMADA & MATSUMOTO	JAPAN	01 329 4438
EDUARDO ROMERO & ASSOCIATES	LATIN AMERICA	01 828 5247
SDF ASSOCIATES	MIDDLE EAST	01 221 5684
ADVOKATFIRMAET FOYEN & CO	NORWAY	01 839 7307
KREFTING LOCHEN ODEGARD & SANDVEN	NORWAY	01 242 2766
WIKBORG REIN & CO	NORWAY	01 236 4598
ARIAS FABREGA & FABREGA	PANAMA	01 839 7088
AROSEMENA NORIEGA & CASTRO	PANAMA	01 493 5139
MORGAN Y MORGAN	PANAMA	01 930 9221
QUIJANO & ASSOCIATES	PANAMA	01 499 4654
ANTONIO DE FORTUNY – ABOGADOS	SPAIN	01 629 2673
ADVOKATFIRMAN CARLER	SWEDEN	01 930 9877
ADVOKATFIRMAN LAGERLOF	SWEDEN	01 491 3424
ADVOKATFIRMAN RINDBORG	SWEDEN	01 938 5408
ADVOKATFIRMAN VINGE	SWEDEN	01 404 4825
FRORIEP RENGGLI & PARTNERS	SWITZERLAND	01 236 6000
SECRETAN TROYANOV TERRACINA & FIECHTER	SWITZERLAND	01 379 4020
HARTWIG	UK	01 681 8181
AKIN GUMP STRAUSS HAUER & FELD	USA	01 409 1093
BIGHAM ENGLAR JONES & HOUSTON	USA	01 283 9541
BINGHAM DANA & GOULD	USA	01 799 2646
BRACEWELL & PATTERSON	USA	01 355 3330
BRIGER & ASSOCIATES	USA	01 499 4822
BRYAN CAVE MCPHEETERS & MCROBERTS	USA	01 222 0511
CLEARY GOTTLIEB STEEN & HAMILTON	USA	01 638 5291
COLE CORETTE & ABRUTYN	USA	01 491 3735

	Home jurisdiction	
COUDERT BROTHERS	USA	01 236 5591
CRAVATH SWAIN & MOORE	USA	01 606 1421
CURTIS MALLET-PREVOST COLT & MOSLE	USA	01 489 9090
DAVIS HOCKENBERG WINE BROWN KOEHN & SHORS	USA	01 262 9022
DAVIS POLK & WARDWELL	USA	01 726 6250
DEBEVOISE & PLIMPTON	USA	01 329 0779
DECHERT PRICE & RHOADS	USA	01 631 3383
DORSEY & WHITNEY	USA	01 929 3334
FAEGRE & BENSON	USA	01 623 6163
FRIED FRANK HARRIS SHRIVER & JACOBSON	USA	01 600 1541
FULBRIGHT & JAWORSKI	USA	01 629 1207
GIBSON DUNN & CRUTCHER	USA	01 925 0440
GOTTESMAN JONES & PARTNERS	USA	01 242 8953
HANCOCK ROTHERT & BUNSHOFT	USA	01 220 7567
HAYTHE & CURLEY	USA	01 499 3112
JOEL Z ROBINSON	USA	01 638 0178
JONES DAY REAVIS & POGUE	USA	01 493 9361
KEVORKIAN & RAWLINGS	USA	01 734 9927
KILPATRICK & CODY	USA	01 321 0477
LADAS & PARRY	USA	01 242 5566
LANE & MITTENDORF	USA	01 491 4805
LAW OFFICES OF GARY M FERMAN	USA	01 499 5702
LEBOEUF LAMB LEIBY & MACRAE	USA	01 493 7331
LORD DAY & LORD BARRETT SMITH	USA	01 726 4451
MAYER BROWN & PLATT	USA	01 248 1465
MILBANK TWEED HADLEY & MCCLOY	USA	01 248 4205
MORGAN LEWIS & BOCKHIUS	USA	01 839 1677
MORRISON & FOERSTER	USA	01 408 1943
O'MELVENY & MYERS	USA	01 256 8451
PEPPER HAMILTON & SCHEETZ	USA	01 629 1076
PHELPS DUNBAR MARKS CLAVERIE & SIMS	USA	01 929 4765
PROSKAUER ROSE GOETZ & MENDELSOHN	USA	01 493 8913
ROGERS & WELLS	USA	01 628 0101
SATTERLEE BURKE & GURLAND	USA	01 409 1903
SHEARMAN & STERLING	USA	01 283 9100
SIDLEY & AUSTIN	USA	01 621 1616
SIMPSON THACHER & BARTLETT	USA	01 638 3851
SKADDEN ARPS SLATE MEAGHER & FLOM	USA	01 248 9929
STEVENSON & SHULMAN	USA	01 404 0456
SULLIVAN & CROMWELL	USA	01 606 8944
VINSON & ELKINS	USA	01 491 7236
WHITE & CASE	USA	01 726 6361
WHITMAN & RANSOM	USA	01 839 3226
WHYTE & HIRSCHBOECK SC	USA	01 405 0750
WILMER CUTLER & PICKERING	USA	01 839 4466
WINTHROP STIMSON PUTNAM & ROBERTS	USA	01 628 4931
YOUNGSTEIN & GOULD	USA	01 935 5372

Advokatfirmaet Foyen & Co

NORWAY HOUSE
21-24 COCKSPUR STREET
LONDON
SW1Y 5BN
Phone: 01 839 7307

Fax: 01 839 5995
Telex: 927840
Senior UK Partner: Michael SM Bell
Number of Resident Lawyers: 4
Total Number of Lawyers in Firm: 55
Head Office: Oslo

The Foyen group consists of ten law offices in five different countries offering commercial advice on a truly international scale.

The firm: The law firm of Stein A Foyen was founded in 1969 and remained a small but compact enterprise until 1980. From that time the firm enjoyed a period of substantial growth in Norway, and in 1982/3 the decision to expand internationally was taken. The decision was then put into operation with careful consideration given to the individuals to be involved.

The main purpose of this move was to improve assistance to international clients. The process of expansion started with offices in London and Stockholm. In 1986 two further offices were added, one in New York and one in New Jersey, and in the following year the group included an office in Rio de Janeiro.

By January 1989 the group consisted of ten law offices in five countries, employing a total of 104 people, including 55 lawyers.

In 1988 a close co-operation was established with Orlando Conseils Associés in Paris and the law firm of Peter Rud in Copenhagen. These firms now work in close co-operation with the Foyen group in matters relevant to these countries.

Because of this network, the Foyen group can offer unique assistance to international clients in matters related to the changing business environment created by the European 'open market' scheduled for 1992.

Other offices: Rio de Janeiro (Brazil); Copenhagen (Denmark); London, Crowborough (England); Paris (France); Oslo, Nesbru, Kristiansund, Gol (Norway); Stockholm (Sweden); New York, New Jersey (USA).

Agency work: The Foyen group is pleased to offer advice on an international scale in all commercial matters.

Types of work undertaken: The Foyen group advises in all commercial matters involving franchising, licensing, distribution, agency, acquisition and sale of companies. The firm can offer direct access to American, Brazilian, English, French and Scandinavian lawyers through its vast network of international offices.

The group's London office deals with a full range of commercial matters, including commercial litigation, while at present the Crowborough office deals mainly with conveyancing and other private client work. The Crowborough partner is, however, actively involved in building up a broad commercial client base, within the rapidly developing south east of England, the Channel Tunnel and 1992 deregulation with the EEC being of prime concern in this area. Brochures on the firm are available.

FOYEN

Advokatfirman Vinge

44-45 CHANCERY LANE
LONDON
WC2A 1JB

Phone: 01 404 4825

Fax: 01 831 6860
Telex: 25585
Senior UK Partner: Hans G Bagner
Number of Resident Lawyers: 7
Total Number of Lawyers in Firm: 81
Head Office: Stockholm

Vinge is the largest Scandinavian law firm, offering a full commercial service to corporate clients in Sweden and internationally.

The firm: Vinge traces its origins to three of the oldest law firms in Sweden, all founded around the turn of the century, based in Stockholm and Gothenburg. In 1983 one of Malmo's leading firms merged into Vinge. The firm also has offices in Helsingborg, Paris and Hong Kong.

The London office – Vinge's first outside Sweden – was opened in 1979. It was established to service the firm's Swedish commercial and corporate clients with interests in the UK, as well as to advise UK clients on matters of Swedish law. In recent years it has expanded rapidly to keep pace with demand in the financial markets.

The firm is deliberately structured to serve the needs of major corporate clients, who range from multinational corporations to private companies in many sectors including banking, insurance, real property, high-technology, manufacturing, engineering, construction, and shipping. Vinge also works closely with major accountancy practices.

The working languages of Vinge are Swedish and English. In addition, members of the firm work in French, German, Spanish, Italian and Russian.

Other offices: Stockholm (principal), Gothenburg, Malmo, Helsingborg, Paris, Hong Kong.

Agency work: Vinge is pleased to advise on all areas of Swedish law for UK solicitors, as well as providing arbitrators and litigating in Sweden.

Types of work undertaken: The firm's work in London is increasingly connected to the financial sectors. It practises in the areas of public offerings, venture capital, international finance, loan agreements and banking. The firm advises on mergers and acquisitions, engineering, construction, competition, incorporations, marketing, labour, real estate, insolvency, franchising and intellectual property (including trademark, copyright, licensing and technology law) In addition to litigation and judicial procedure, Vinge is experienced in alternative means of dispute settlement, such as arbitration.

Historically associated with its Gothenburg office is the firm's reputation in maritime and other transport law, including Admiralty, shipping and shipbuilding law. Vinge advises its clients on Swedish tax laws and relevant international treaties, as well as the tax aspects of business transactions.

Because of the relatively large size of the London office Vinge is able to offer a broad range of legal services backed by more specialist support from its other offices.

451

Allen Allen & Hemsley

BARTLETT HOUSE
9 BASINGHALL STREET
LONDON
EC2V 5BQ

Phone: 01 606 2721

Fax: 01 606 4669
Telex: 8952758
Senior UK Partner: Mr RI Barrett
Number of Resident Lawyers: 3
Total Number of Lawyers in Firm: 243
Head Office: Sydney

Allen Allen & Hemsley, the oldest law firm in Australia, is a major commercial practice well known to London's leading law firms and bankers.

The firm: Founded in 1822 by George Allen, the first solicitor to be trained in New South Wales, the firm's position was consolidated in the nineteenth century by successive generations of the Allen family and by Alfred Hemsley. After 1945 the firm grew into a major commercial practice.

Allen Allen & Hemsley is internationally based in terms of the clients it represents, the transactions in which it has been involved, the background of its lawyers and its links with law firms in the major financial and commercial centres of the world. Branch offices were opened in London and Singapore in 1981, and in New York in 1986.

Since establishment of the Australian Legal Group in 1987, Allen Allen & Hemsley is part of an Australia-wide federation of six major commercial law firms. Their joint purpose is to meet the demands of the rapidly changing corporate and commercial environment. Member firms continue to operate independently but with the facility to draw on the considerable resources of the group.

Other offices: Sydney (principal), New York, Singapore; and as part of the Australian Legal Group in Melbourne, Brisbane, Adelaide, Perth, Canberra, Hong Kong. Associated firm in Jakarta.

Agency work: A mutually exclusive agency agreement applies between the member firms of the Australian Legal Group. Allen Allen & Hemsley undertakes all commercial work relating to Australian law for London solicitors.

Types of work undertaken: Allen Allen & Hemsley has maintained a leading position in Australia for more than 165 years, providing legal services to Australian and international corporations and financial institutions. The firm deals mainly with the Australian law aspects of international financing, including Euro-bond issues and other raisings by Australian entities, and advice to UK and other EEC companies wishing to establish businesses in Australia. Main clients are other major London firms of solicitors and banks.

The firm has advised a number of governments in the Asia/Pacific region, particularly in relation to foreign investment legislation and the financing and structuring of major projects. Allen Allen & Hemsley's expertise falls into ten areas of specialisation, namely corporate and commercial; finance and banking; litigation; intellectual property; tax; resources; property; construction and arbitration; government liaison; and media and communications.

ALLENS

**ALLEN
ALLEN
&
HEMSLEY**

Carler

ALHAMBRA HOUSE
27-31 CHARING CROSS ROAD
LONDON
WC2H 0AU
Phone: 01 930 9877

Fax: 01 930 9269
Telex: 919771
Senior UK Partner: Sten Rystedt
Number of Resident Lawyers: 1
Total Number of Lawyers in Firm: 20
Head Office: Stockholm

Carler is an international firm handling all aspects of commercial law.

The firm: Carler was founded in Stockholm in 1960 by Gunnar Carler. The firm has offices in London, Paris, Stockholm, Gothenburg and Helsingborg, as well as representation in Milan. The firm has an international practice offering clients correspondence and negotiations in French, English, German, Spanish and Italian. In the Paris office, both Swedish and French lawyers are working together and Carler is the only Scandinavian firm to have acquired the status of Conseils Juridiques in France. In Italy Carler offers assistance by Italian as well as Swedish lawyers and in the UK close co-operation between Swedish lawyers and English solicitors has been established.

Carler prides itself on its commercial awareness and its forward-looking approach. The firm believes strongly that good lawyers need to be well informed not only about the present law of the countries concerned and the numerous changes thereof constantly taking place, but also of the business aspects of the operations of their clients. Carler, consequently, offers professional competence based on a combination of lawyers with traditional legal careers and company lawyers with experience of executive positions in publicly listed companies with education in economics,

taxes and business administration.

The firm keeps up to date by collaborating closely with its clients and with legal experts, and invests in systematic internal training to make sure that it stays ahead in this changing enviroment.

Other offices: Stockholm (principal), Gothenburg, Helsingborg, Paris; and also representation in Milan by reception offices and by close co-operation with local law firms.

Agency work: Carler is pleased to accept instructions to undertake international commercial matters for all UK solicitors.

Types of work undertaken: The firm's practice is predominantly commercial and includes the following areas of law: intellectual property law; licence agreements; distributor and agency agreements; establishment and acquisition of companies; construction work; competition and marketing; EEC; marine and transport; arbitration; product liability; labour law and labour market issues; taxation, financing and banking; real estate and contracted works.

The firm's ambition is to offer close collaboration with clients, to foresee legal and commercial opportunities and potential difficulties and to deal with these in a creative, knowledgeable and result-orientated manner.

ADVOKATFIRMAN

CARLER

Carnelutti

76 SHOE LANE
LONDON
EC4A 3BQ

Phone: 01 242 2268

Fax: 01 242 4190
Telex: 298389
Senior UK Partner: D Mills
Number of Resident Lawyers: 10
Total Number of Lawyers in Firm: 75
Head Office: Milan

This is a predominantly commercial practice with a substantial international client base.

The firm: Founded in Milan in 1900 by Professor Francesco Carnelutti, the leading Italian jurist of his generation, the firm has steadily expanded both in size and in reputation and now has offices in Rome, London and New York.

Carnelutti offers a full legal service to its clients, although the bias is mainly commercial. A large proportion of Carnelutti's clients are those with international interests. The London office was founded in 1978 for the dual purpose of providing Italian legal advice to British and other non-Italian clients, and providing services for Italian clients in the United Kingdom.

The practice is principally involved in company/commercial work with a bias towards cross-border transactions and acquisitions, particularly those coming into and going out of Italy. However, a significant part of the work involves advising non-Italian clients in multinational matters which have Italian ramifications.

Carnelutti has excellent relations with many leading UK solicitors and with firms in major European centres. Both of these associations facilitate an integrated transnational approach which is of particular assistance to firms with subsidiaries in several countries.

The firm also advises on Euroloan documentation, especially for Italians raising money outside Italy. The firm is instructed by corporates, solicitors and merchant banks. The London firm has a substantial practice in international corporate and private non-domiciliary tax planning.

Other offices: Milan (principal), Rome, New York.

Agency work: Carnelutti is pleased to advise both English businesses on Italian law and Italian clients on English law and accepts agency work from all UK solicitors.

Types of work undertaken: Primarily commercial, Carnelutti's practice includes banking, acquisitions, mergers, litigation, insolvency, general corporate work and company incorporation. The firm has been particularly active in managing acquisitions of Italian concerns by overseas companies and is now increasingly engaged in assisting foreign and domestic banks in Italy.

In London the practice is also mainly commercial, including cross-border acquisitions, banking and corporate services. It also assists with property transactions in Italy.

Carnelutti's clients are primarily firms of solicitors and their commercial clients. It advises many substantial UK and Italian corporations including the London branches of Italian banks.

CARNELUTTI

Corrs Pavey Whiting & Byrne

2ND FLOOR
103 CANNON STREET
LONDON
EC4N 6HH
Phone: 01 929 4955

Fax: 01 929 4164
Telex: none
Senior UK Partner: Michael J Owen
Number of Resident Lawyers: 2
Total Number of Lawyers in Firm: 132
Head Office: Melbourne

This old-established, leading Australian firm provides a full range of legal services to clients in all areas of commercial activity.

The firm: With origins dating back to 1848, the present-day firm is the result of two mergers involving three of Melbourne's major law firms: in 1982 Paveys merged with Whiting & Byrne and in 1984 that firm merged with Corr & Corr, and the firm's present structure was created.

In 1988 the London office was established to serve the firm's Australian clients in their business operations in Europe, in matters of Australian and international law. Both the Sydney and London offices are part of a comprehensive communications network which allows immediate access to the firm's combined legal expertise, and speedy delivery of written advice and documentation.

The strong growth of the firm in recent years has placed it at the forefront of the development of legal skills in Australia.

Other offices: Melbourne (principal), Sydney.

Agency work: Corrs Pavey Whiting & Byrne has close links with other firms in Australia's main cities. The firm is happy to assist English solicitors in all matters concerning businesses or investment in Australia.

Types of work undertaken: The firm's clients include many of Australia's largest companies, well-known entrepreneurs and international corporations.

The firm offers expertise in business law; banking and finance; foreign investment; trade law; commercial conveyancing and leasing; intellectual property; media law; tourism; computer law; mining and resouces; tax law; and litigation.

Corrs Pavey Whiting & Byrne sees its London office as providing the ideal location from which to support the operations of its clients in the UK and Europe in matters of Australian and international law.

For European clients seeking to conduct business in Australia, the London office gives access to the firm's extensive resources and expertise in Australia. For its Australian clients expanding their businesses in the UK and Europe, the firm acts in matters of trade law, international licensing agreements and financing, and as a referral centre for specialist advice in the laws of the UK and other European countries.

The firm uses the most up-to-date technology to support and enhance its professional skills, and this has been described as 'the most sophisticated legal system in Australia'. The firm is also committed to a high-quality programme of in-house training, and thereby maintains a leading position in its field.

CORRS

Corrs Pavey Whiting & Byrne

Coudert Brothers

4 DEAN'S COURT
LONDON
EC4V 5AA

Phone: 01 236 5591

Fax: 01 248 3153   **Telex:** 887071
Senior UK Partners: Barry Metzger and Christian Salbaing
Number of Resident Lawyers: 6
Total Number of Lawyers in Firm: 340
Head Office: New York City

Coudert Brothers is a major international law firm with a unique, worldwide network of offices providing legal services for international investment, trade and finance.

The firm: Founded in New York in 1854 and in Paris in 1879, Coudert Brothers is one of the oldest law firms in the United States and on the Continent. With the growth of world commerce following World War II, the firm expanded into Asia, South America and Australia.

The firm opened a Moscow office in 1988, the first Western law office to be opened in the Soviet Union. The move is part of Coudert's philosophy 'to be where internationally oriented corporate clients need us'.

The London office of the firm was established in 1960 to advise UK-based clients on their US, European and Asian investments and financing activities and to assist US, European and Japanese clients with their dealings in the UK. The resources and expertise of all the firm's offices are readily available.

The client base consists of United States, European, Japanese and other foreign corporations, joint ventures, public sector enterprises, government agencies and governments, individuals, trusts, partnerships and other law firms.

Other offices: North America: New York (principal), Washington DC, Los Angeles, San Francisco, San Jose; Europe: Paris, Brussels; Asia: Tokyo, Hong Kong, Beijing, Shanghai, Singapore; Australia: Sydney; South America: Rio de Janeiro, Sao Paolo; USSR: Moscow.

Agency work: Coudert Brothers welcomes the opportunity to advise English solicitors on matters of foreign and international law.

Types of work undertaken: Coudert Brothers offers experience and expertise in international and corporate law, banking, acquisitions, litigation, real estate, tax, estate planning, anti-trust and trade law. Specialities, such as EEC and high-technology law, are offered from certain offices.

The London office offers international tax planning, securities law advice and transactional and general corporate representation to British companies and institutions active in the United States, Europe and the Far East. In addition, the office has been involved for many years in international banking and finance transactions in the Euro-markets, including project finance and specialised, asset-based financings for aircraft, ships and real estate.

UK-based clients include those engaged in the financial services industry, publishing, manufacturing, property development and management, advertising and tele-communications.

COUDERT BROTHERS
INTERNATIONAL ATTORNEYS

Davis Polk & Wardwell

1 FREDERICK'S PLACE
LONDON
EC2R 8AB

Phone: 01 726 6250

Fax: 01 588 5048
Telex: 888238
Senior UK Partner: Joseph Chubb
Number of Resident Lawyers: 13
Total Number of Lawyers in Firm: 392
Head Office: New York City

This internationally orientated firm offers expertise and experience in complex financial matters in jurisdictions around the world.

The firm: Since its formation in 1849, Davis Polk & Wardwell has been involved in structuring and implementing the most sophisticated and innovative business transactions, both within the United States and internationally.

The London office was founded in 1973 for the primary purpose of making the firm's services more readily available to new and existing clients in industry, commerce, banking, insurance and other financial services.

The firm's London and Paris offices, which work closely together, advise US and European industrial clients and financial institutions on their European and US activities and their international interests. The European practice has increasingly come to involve advice to industrial clients and financial institutions on cross-border mergers, acquisitions and joint ventures, which complements this traditional financing transaction advice. The London office is an integral part of Davis Polk & Wardwell's worldwide practice and is linked by the most up-to-date technology to the firm's central data base in New York City and its offices outside New York.

Other offices: New York (principal), Washington DC, Paris, Tokyo.

Agency work: Davis Polk & Wardwell gives a broad range of US legal and regulatory advice to English solicitors, and works regularly with the top City firms and European law offices.

Types of work undertaken: Davis Polk & Wardwell advises US, UK and other European clients on a broad range of general corporate and tax matters including acquisitions, joint ventures, international restructurings, public and private offerings of debt and equity in the United States by foreign issuers and outside the United States by US and foreign issuers, swap transactions, and bank loans and credit arrangements.

In recent years a significant speciality has been advice on governmental privatisation transactions, in the UK, France and Spain. An important part of the practice involves keeping non-European clients abreast of developments in EEC law.

The firm's expertise in the corporate, tax and litigation areas, together with its international experience developed over many years in Europe, gives Davis Polk & Wardwell a unique ability to structure and co-ordinate international transactions spanning multiple jurisdictions while meeting complex tax and financial goals.

DAVIS POLK & WARDWELL

Dechert Price & Rhoads

52 BEDFORD SQUARE
LONDON
WC1B 3EX

Phone: 01 631 3383

Fax: 01 637 4250
Telex: 262658
Senior UK Partner: Edward L Kling
Number of Resident Lawyers: 7
Total Number of Lawyers in Firm: 356
Head Office: Philadelphia

One of the largest law firms in the United States, this firm has a diverse international client base.

The firm: Founded in the late nineteenth century, Dechert Price & Rhoads has grown to be one of the largest firms in the USA.

The London office was opened in 1973 to meet the needs of longstanding US multinational clients with European interests. Since its opening, the office has diversified to include a broad range of British and European clients, while still addressing the needs of its US clients in Europe.

The London office is staffed by both British and US trained lawyers who are active throughout Europe, specialising in a wide range of financial transactions, corporate acquisitions and dispositions, public and private securities offerings, licensing, distribution, and other intellectual property matters (particularly those related to companies specialising in high technology and data transmission), EEC anti-trust law, and international litigation.

Other offices: Philadelphia (principal), New York City, Washington DC, Boston, Princeton, Harrisburg, Brussels.

Agency work: Dechert Price & Rhoads is pleased to accept agency work for European clients with interests in the United States and for US clients with interests in Europe.

Types of work undertaken: Dechert Price & Rhoads advises many of the largest commercial, financial, industrial and service institutions both within the United States and abroad, as well as small and medium sized corporations and individuals.

The firm has four main areas of activity, namely business, litigation, taxation and personal planning. The firm's expertise in business matters includes the formation of business entities, financing arrangements (including private placements and public offerings), mergers and acquisitions, divestitures, tender offers, recapitalisations, employee relations and employee benefits, and regulatory and compliance matters.

The litigation practice is characterised by its diversity. Clients are also served in administrative proceedings, labour negotiations and trial and appellate work, and by preventative counselling.

Tax considerations come into almost all of the firm's legal work. Areas of expertise include the formation of business organisations, corporate reorganisations, liquidations, tax shelters, the taxation of international operations and the taxation of regulated investment companies.

Dechert Price & Rhoads also values its longstanding tradition of providing quality financial and business advice to individuals.

Fasken Martineau Walker

5TH FLOOR
10 ARTHUR STREET
LONDON
EC4R 9AY
Phone: 01 929 2894

Fax: 01 929 3634
Telex: none
Senior UK Partner: Roger D Wilson QC
Number of Resident Lawyers: 3
Total Number of Lawyers in Firm: 270
Head Office: Canada

Fasken Martineau Walker is a Canadian-based international law firm dedicated to helping its clients keep pace with the evolution of the modern commercial world.

The firm: Fasken Martineau Walker came into being in 1986 when Fasken & Calvin of Toronto (dating from 1863) and Martineau Walker (Quebec's largest law firm) created, not a merger, but a third partnership consisting of all the partners of each of the underlying firms. The purpose of this structure was to comply with interprovincial restrictions in Canada and to enable the new firm to provide national and international clients with co-ordinated legal services in Canada and abroad. The creation of this so-called 'super-partnership' immediately put the new firm at the top of the Canadian ranking system.

From the London office (opened in 1988), Fasken Martineau Walker provides UK and European clients with advice on Canada and Canadian law. From London also, Fasken Martineau Walker assists its Canadian and European clients with their international transactions, including financings, securities matters and acquisitions, often in consultation with local lawyers and other professional advisers.

Other offices: Montreal and Toronto (principal) and Quebec City.

Agency work: Fasken Martineau Walker's London office is pleased to advise on all matters relating to Canadian law.

Types of work undertaken: The firm offers experience and expertise in virtually every area of Canadian law and serves the complete legal needs of its national and international clients. The areas of expertise include international trade, finance, banking, securities, taxation, commercial and civil litigation, administrative and public law, intellectual property, high technology and computer law, communications and natural resources.

The London office offers a range of expertise in Canadian law, including business acquisitions, regulatory requirements and free trade matters. The office also offers experience in securities, banking, insurance, finance and Admiralty. In addition, the office handles Euro-financing deals and cross-border takeover work where Canada is involved.

Fasken Martineau Walker is one of the few firms qualified to provide bilingual advice on both Canadian common law and civil law matters.

The partners believe that the firm's growth and development have been based on dedicated service to clients and on the practical and innovative solutions it supplies for the most complex legal problems.

Fasken Martineau Walker

Fried, Frank, Harris, Shriver & Jacobson

3 KING'S ARMS YARD
LONDON
EC2R 7AD

Phone: 01 600 1541

Fax: 01 606 9416
Telex: 887606
Senior UK Partner: Jerry L Smith
Number of Resident Lawyers: 4
Total Number of Lawyers in Firm: 404
Head Office: New York City

One of the leading law firms in the United States, Fried, Frank, Harris, Shriver & Jacobson is best known for its work in sophisticated financial transactions.

The firm: With origins in the 1890s, the firm has acquired its present scope (and name) through the many talented lawyers who joined it in the 1950s.

Among law firms of similar size, Fried, Frank has been a leader in the trend away from dependency on general representation of regular clients. Most of its work involves matters that require specialised legal expertise. During the conglomerate boom of the 1960s, for example, Fried, Frank developed a major practice in the mergers and acquisitions field. The firm is now well known for its expertise in this area and has been involved in the majority of recent billion-dollar takeover bids.

Fried, Frank has roughly doubled in size in the last ten years and has been described as one of Wall Street's hottest firms. The partners attribute its success to the talent of its individual lawyers and their sometimes aggressively tenacious style of advocacy.

The London office was founded in 1970 principally to provide more convenient access to US legal advice for the firm's very important British clientele.

Other offices: New York (principal), Washington DC, Los Angeles.

Agency work: Fried, Frank regularly advises English solicitors on investments and transactions governed in whole or in part by United States law.

Types of work undertaken: Fried, Frank's lawyers deal with the most important legal issues of the day in such areas as mergers and acquisitions, securities, tax, litigation, government contracts and energy.

The London office primarily advises British and European clients on the United States legal aspects of their American investments. In addition, the office provides legal advice on the US aspects of European transactions. The London based lawyers specialise in company/commercial matters, but clients have the benefit of a general practice through the expertise of the US offices.

The office specialises in complex questions of United States corporate and tax law and their application to European clients and transactions. This work includes mergers and acquisitions, leveraged buy-outs, corporate restructuring, financing, securities regulation and the banking and thrift practice.

The firm does not itself advise on the laws of the UK or any European jurisdiction, but retains UK and European solicitors to do so when required. Fried, Frank works regularly with all the large firms of City solicitors.

FRIED, FRANK, HARRIS, SHRIVER & JACOBSON

Hartwig

15 WILLIAM MEWS
LONDON
SW1X 9HF

Phone: 01 235 1504

Fax: 01 681 8183
Telex: 946702
Senior UK Partner: Mr HJ Hartwig
Number of Resident Lawyers: 6
Associated Offices: 7
Head Office: London

Hartwig is an international firm which offers substantial experience and expertise in all matters of business law.

The firm: Hartwig has been in independent service since 1970 and has been licensed as English solicitors in New York State since 1976, and in West Germany since 1978. The emphasis of the firm is on successful commercial negotiation and litigation.

It remains a relatively small firm, one of the strengths of which is that it can be more involved than its larger counterparts, while at the same time providing sophisticated advice in three legal systems.

Where appropriate, Hartwig attends on clients in any part of the UK, Germany and adjacent countries, and North America, at no additional cost. Hartwig emphasises that its network is non-exclusive. The firm works with a wide range of specialist local counsel, and clients are referred to lawyers according to the size, location and specialism of the subject matter. The structure of the firm often allows it to recover all fees (when the client wins) in German litigation; to share fees with American lawyers; and to undertake conveyancing and litigation for foreign lawyers, in London or abroad, on terms which preserve both their client contact and much of the fees.

Associated offices: Croydon, New York State (2), Texas, Saarbrucken, Frankfurt, Dusseldorf.

Agency work: Hartwig is pleased to advise on both large and small commercial matters in the jurisdictions of the United States, West Germany and the UK.

Types of work undertaken: Hartwig offers a full range of legal services, though its specialism is business law. Work undertaken includes corporate, insurance, banking, tax, insolvency and intellectual property. There is a strong commercial litigation section and substantial private client, real estate, probate and European notarial departments. Instructions from professional clients are accepted on a 'counsel' basis and safeguard the client's relationship with existing advisers. Multi-currency client trust accounts are maintained to reduce exchange risks.

The firm's international practice has developed into three main areas, namely company/commercial; litigation, insolvency and banking; and the preparation of opinions on English and German law. Opinions on US federal and state laws and practice are procured from members of the appropriate bar. There is a strong real estate section. Child care and financial provision cases are handled. Much of the company/commercial practice is for longstanding clients, particularly in manufacturing industry.

HARTWIG

Krefting Lochen Odegard & Sandven

NORWAY HOUSE
21-24 COCKSPUR STREET
LONDON
SW1Y 5BN

Phone: 01 321 0330

Fax: 01 321 0845
Telex: 267506
Senior UK Partner: Per Sandven
Number of Resident Lawyers: 2
Total Number of Lawyers in Firm: 21
Head Office: Oslo

Initially known as a tax law practice, Krefting Lochen Odegard & Sandven has grown considerably in recent years to include most aspects of commercial law.

The firm: Krefting Lochen & Sandven has been established in its present form since 1975. Since then the firm has grown considerably and has developed other areas of legal expertise. The firm still retains a large tax department specialising in international taxation, taxation treatment of oil companies, splits, mergers and takeovers but in addition can now offer the services of a contract department dealing with most aspects of commercial law and, in particular, banking and shipping.

The London office was founded in 1984 to assist clients based in England or other European countries with commercial problems in Norway and, conversely, to provide the means of advising Norwegians wishing to set themselves up in business in England.

Krefting Lochen Odegard & Sandven has found its London presence to be of great value in major international transactions where a Norwegian party is involved but where the main contract is governed by English law. In these cases the offices in Norway have been able to assist by taking care of all matters needing direct attention in Norway.

Other offices: Oslo (principal), Hovik.

Agency work: Krefting Lochen Odegard & Sandven is pleased to advise European-based clients on their commercial legal problems in Norway and Norwegians already engaged in, or establishing, businesses in England.

Types of work undertaken: The firm has retained its involvement in taxation law while developing experience and expertise in the field of commercial law. Krefting Lochen Odegard & Sandven has a high reputation with all major Norwegian oil companies.

The firm has also enjoyed the privilege of advising the government on the subject of taxation reforms in Norway.

The London office undertakes general commercial and corporate work related to Norwegian law in England.

Particular areas of expertise are banking law, especially in the context of the shipping and oil industries. The firm is frequently asked to assist UK solicitors with matters in these fields and in the past this has included many of the major City firms. Krefting Lochen Odegard & Sandven has also acted for a number of large corporations investing in Norwegian companies.

In addition, the firm offers an expert service to non-commercial clients in the areas of Norwegian matrimonial, family, inheritance and taxation laws.

ADVOKATFIRMAET
KREFTING, LØCHEN, ØDEGÅRD & SANDVEN

Ladas & Parry

52-54 HIGH HOLBORN
LONDON
WC1V 6RR

Phone: 01 242 5566

Fax: 01 405 1908
Telex: 264255
Senior UK Partner: Iain C Baillie
Number of Resident Lawyers: 1
Total Number of Lawyers in Firm: 50
Head Office: New York City

This is an international firm specialising in all areas of intellectual property law.

The firm: Founded in 1912 by UK patent agent Lawrence Langner, the partners formed the firm Ladas Parry Von Gehr Goldsmith & Deschamps in 1971. In 1980 the present name was adopted. The firm is associated with the chartered patent and trademark agents Langner Parry, formed in 1969.

The London office is an integral part of a worldwide network of offices associated with three major patent jurisdictions: USA, UK, and Europe. In addition to practising directly or through Langner Parry before the British Patent Office and British Trade Marks Registry, the firm has an office in Munich for practice before the European Patent Office. The joint qualifications and experience of members of the firm enable it to co-ordinate applications in these three jurisdictions, and to assist in other countries, eg Japan.

Ladas & Parry has connections with counsel in most countries, facilitating multi-country programmes. Members are skilled in a broad range of technical matters, ranging from biotechnology to electronics. The client base is predominantly American, Japanese and British. The firm is retained by UK firms of solicitors, as well as acting as expert witness in litigation. The firm produces a periodic newsletter on intellectual property matters throughout the world.

Other offices: New York City (principal), Chicago, Los Angeles, Munich.

Agency work: The firm will act for UK firms in all intellectual property work, nationally and internationally; in particular, a trademark and company name surveillance service is offered.

Types of work undertaken: The firm covers the full range of intellectual property services: securing and registration of rights, advising on their maintenance and exploitation, licensing, franchising, character merchandising, and competition and anti-trust law. The firm advises on related issues, such as the intellectual property implications of mergers and acquisitions, and litigation.

The firm's specialisation has led to an involvement in contracts and litigation in the entertainment industry. The firm offers a worldwide trademark and company name surveillance service. Operated from New York, this brings together information from 130 countries in a multilingual and computerised department, advising promptly on marks published and on appropriate action. The firm's sophistication and close dealings with patent offices around the world allow it to service the maintenance of clients' registrations.

The London office will advise throughout its specialist field within British jurisdictions and internationally.

LADAS & PARRY

LeBoeuf, Lamb, Leiby & MacRae (UK)

SUITE 729
LLOYD'S 1986 BUILDING
ONE LIME STREET
LONDON EC3M 7DQ
Phone: 01 493 7331

Fax: 01 929 0042
Telex: 25955
Senior Resident Partner: Cynthia R Shoss
Number of UK Lawyers: 3
Total Number of Lawyers in Firm: 399
Head Office: New York City

One of the largest firms in the United States, LeBoeuf, Lamb, Leiby & MacRae leads in all aspects of insurance and insurance-related law.

The firm: Founded in 1929, LeBoeuf, Lamb, Leiby & MacRae initially specialised in regulated industries such as energy and natural resources, insurance, banking and telecommunications. Today the firm has a diverse national and international practice.

LeBoeuf, Lamb, Leiby & MacRae is one of the largest firms in New York and is among the largest in the whole of the United States. The firm is a recognised leader in all aspects of insurance and insurance-related law, including regulatory activities, corporate and tax advice, and litigation.

The London office was established in 1979 to extend (together with the other branch offices) the firm's general areas of expertise to national and international clients, and to enable the firm to offer specialised services to local clients. The firm's practice in London is a microcosm of its US practice.

The London office is utilised by practitioners in the areas of bankruptcy, real estate, insurance, utilities, employee benefits, immigration, corporate, litigation, banking, and tax-related matters. In particular, the London office serves as a liaison point for United States companies with operations in Europe, the Middle East and Scandinavia, and for foreign clients with investments in the United States.

In addition, the London office can provide English and EEC solicitors with the benefit of experience of legal practice in which the United States has taken the lead, for example in privatisations of certain industries and in new financial products.

Other offices: New York (principal), Washington DC, San Francisco, Salt Lake City, Jacksonville, Albany, Boston, Newark, Los Angeles, Raleigh, Brussels.

Agency work: LeBoeuf, Lamb, Leiby & MacRae provides United States legal advice to English solicitors whose clients are involved in the US insurance, banking, utilities, real estate and telecommunications markets.

Types of work undertaken: The firm has four broad practice areas, corporate and finance, insurance, litigation and utilities, and its clients are drawn from many industries. The firm concentrates chiefly on financial services, insurance and reinsurance, litigation, banking and investment banking, energy, natural resources, and communications.

During the expansion of recent years the firm has concentrated on broadening its expertise in existing areas of specialisation, as well as developing expertise in new areas of substantial concern to its clients.

LEBOEUF, LAMB, LEIBY & MACRAE

Mallesons Stephen Jaques

36-38 LEADENHALL STREET
LONDON
EC3A 1AP

Phone: 01 982 0982

Fax: 01 982 9820
Telex: 889206
Senior UK Partner: Richard A Ladbury
Number of Resident Lawyers: 5
Total Number of Lawyers in Firm: 507
Head Office: Australia

Mallesons Stephen Jaques is a large commercial firm which has been acting for international clients undertaking business in Australia for more than 150 years.

The firm: Mallesons Stephen Jaques is one of the largest law firms in Australia. It dates back to 1832 in Perth and to the 1840s and 50s in Sydney and Melbourne. The firm continues to regard itself as a pioneer and an innovator in the way in which it tackles the needs of modern business.

Mallesons Stephen Jaques has always been associated with banking, corporate and resources fields and is regarded as a leader in such specialisations as taxation, stamp duty, intellectual property, and real property.

The London office was opened by the Perth branch of the partnership in 1976. From 1987 the office became the responsibility of the national partnership and has expanded its scope considerably. The main focus of the London office is on Australian Euromarket borrowings and UK/EEC investment in Australia. There are two resident partners.

The office in London works in association with English solicitors or other advisers such as merchant banks and accountants to explain, draft or comment on Australia related and Australian law governed aspects of transactions. The firm frames and lodges applications for a wide range of government and other regulatory consents and exemptions.

Other offices: Sydney and Melbourne (principal), Perth, Canberra, New York, Hong Kong, Taipei.

Agency work: Mallesons Stephen Jaques undertakes all Australia related commercial work for UK solicitors and clients.

Types of work undertaken: The firm practises in all areas of commercial law, especially banking, finance, acquisitions, corporations and securities, mining and resources, taxation, intellectual property, commercial litigation, insurance, industrial relations, insolvency, international trade law, aviation and government and administrative law. The firm is also a licensed consultant under the Australian Government's Business Migration Programme.

The client base ranges from some of the world's leading banks and large public companies to private businesses and individuals.

Two particular values of the London office are its ability to advise on Australian law issues at the early, confidential planning phase of a transaction and its convenience for those in the UK and European time zones who are conducting business with Australia or seeking information and advice from it.

Mallesons Stephen Jaques enjoys a close and valued relationship with many leading City and other UK firms of solicitors.

MALLESONS STEPHEN JAQUES

Mayer, Brown & Platt

162 QUEEN VICTORIA STREET
LONDON
EC4V 4BS

Phone: 01 248 1465

Fax: 01 329 4465
Telex: 8811095
Senior UK Partners: R Cole and J Gordon
Number of Resident Lawyers: 8
Total Number of Lawyers in Firm: 470
Head Office: Chicago

Mayer, Brown & Platt is a large and long-established commercial practice which encompasses the full range of general corporate and financial matters.

The firm: Founded in 1881, Mayer, Brown & Platt is one of the oldest and largest law firms in the United States. The London office was opened in 1975 to advise the firm's UK and European clients on matters of United States law, and to assist the firm's non-UK and non-European clients in their dealings in the UK and in Europe.

The work of the London office includes representing clients in a wide variety of corporate and financial matters.

Other offices: Chicago (principal), New York, Los Angeles, Washington DC, Houston, Tokyo (liaison office).

Agency work: Mayer, Brown & Platt can advise UK solicitors directly, or through its network of United States offices, on all aspects of US law.

Types of work undertaken: The work of this commercial practice includes domestic and international financings, taxation, purchases and sales of businesses, joint ventures, securities transactions, corporate reorganisations, mergers and acquisitions, proxy contests, counselling of management, and a wide range of litigation.

The client base includes large multinational and smaller companies and financial institutions both in and outside the United States.

The London office advises UK and European clients on all aspects of acquisitions and securities offerings in the United States, setting up US operations on behalf of UK and European companies, reviewing, negotiating and advising on distributorship and sales agreements, joint ventures, partnerships and other corporate and international trade matters. The firm has represented a large number and variety of corporate clients, from leading public companies and merchant banks to relatively small businesses.

In addition, the London office represents financial institutions in capital markets and commercial banking matters, both on a continuing basis and in speciality matters, including, increasingly, buy-outs and other change of control transactions. The office has represented many US, English, Japanese, Belgian and Canadian financial institutions.

During the past four years the office has been heavily involved in ship financing workouts and enforcements and in advising in other problem credit situations throughout the world.

Mayer, Brown & Platt has worked closely with most of London's larger firms of solicitors in connection with these matters.

MAYER, BROWN & PLATT

Milbank, Tweed, Hadley & McCloy

1 COLLEGE HILL
LONDON
EC4R 2RA

Phone: 01 248 4205

Fax: 01 236 6958
Telex: (851) 887691
Senior UK Partner: David R Slade
Number of Resident Lawyers: 5
Total Number of Lawyers in Firm: 420
Head Office: New York City

Milbank, Tweed, Hadley & McCloy is a major commercial and financial law firm serving some of the world's most significant industrial, commercial and financial enterprises.

The firm: Founded more than 100 years ago, Milbank, Tweed, Hadley & McCloy has expanded its practice by establishing offices in the world's major financial and commercial centres. Clients are therefore assured of a global perspective in addition to local expertise.

Among the firm's banking clients are the Chase Manhattan Corporation, several major regional banks and more than 50 foreign banks and financial institutions.

Milbank, Tweed, Hadley & McCloy combines a longstanding reputation for excellence and dedication with expertise in the wide variety of issues faced by its clients.

The London office, which was established in 1979, offers expertise in general banking, financial and corporate law matters, including Euro-securities and credit transactions, US domestic securities issues, mergers and acquisitions, structured finance, project finance, leveraged and cross-border leasing, sovereign debt restructuring and debt-for-debt and debt-for-equity swaps, bankers acceptance, stand-by letter of credit and trade finance, and United States bank regulatory advice.

Other offices: New York City (principal), Los Angeles, Washington DC, Tokyo, Hong Kong, Singapore.

Agency work: Milbank, Tweed, Hadley & McCloy will advise UK lawyers on all US and international commercial law matters.

Types of work undertaken: The firm is organised into five major practice areas, namely banking, corporate, litigation, tax, and trusts and estates.

The Milbank banking practice is pre-eminent in both transactional and regulatory work, advising clients on regulatory barriers and tax implications and on structuring complex transactions. The firm maintains a leading position in domestic and international corporate finance matters, offering expertise in a wide range of complex transactions and financings, including institutional, asset-based and project financings, innovative capital markets products, securitised asset sales, mortgage-backed securities, interest rate swaps, structured receivables, secured and unsecured note and debenture issues, leveraged buy-outs, public offerings, commercial paper, leasings and restructurings, and business reorganisations.

In addition, the real estate, business reorganisation, and trusts and estates practices are unusually large for a major international law firm.

MILBANK, TWEED, HADLEY & McCLOY

Minter Ellison

20 LINCOLN'S INN FIELDS
LONDON
WC2A 3ED

Phone: 01 831 7871

Fax: 01 404 4610
Telex: 296710
Senior UK Partner: Michael D Whalley
Number of Resident Lawyers: 4
Total Number of Lawyers in Firm: 209
Head Office: Melbourne

Minter Ellison is one of Australia's leading national law firms, serving the Australian and international business community.

The firm: Minter Ellison's origins date back to 1827 in Sydney and to 1863 in Melbourne.

The London office was established in 1974, the first overseas office to be opened by an Australian law firm. Its client base now includes English, North American and European law firms, UK and European companies doing business in Australia, and banks and financial institutions.

Through its London office, Minter Ellison can advise on all aspects of Australian law (other than criminal and family law), and in particular on company/commercial transactions (including commercial agreements, takeovers and the offer and listing of securities), the establishment or purchase of Australian companies and businesses, joint venture, distributorship and licensing agreements, taxation, business migration, property investment and the Australian aspects of international banking transactions.

Private client advice is also given in the areas of taxation, business migration and probate and estate matters.

Other offices: Melbourne and Sydney (principal), Canberra, Singapore, Beijing, and associated firms in Adelaide, Brisbane and New Zealand.

Agency work: Minter Ellison's London office accepts instructions from UK solicitors to advise on all aspects of Australian law.

Types of work undertaken: Minter Ellison has a wide-ranging commercial practice. It is organised into specialist practice groups, namely company/commercial; banking and finance; commercial litigation; dispute resolution; insolvency; international trade law; labour law; media law; insurance; property; resources; taxation revenue and probate law; technology, licensing and trade protection; building, construction and planning law; public administration; and government relations. Many of the firm's clients have multinational operations, and the firm has extensive experience of international investment matters.

Minter Ellison is acknowledged to be a leading firm in areas relating to the securities industry, the regulation of public companies and takeovers, taxation and revenue law, insurance litigation and insolvency, commercial arbitration and dispute resolution, property investment and development, and the defence industry. The firm's strength is its reputation for providing timely, cost-effective and commercially innovative advice.

MINTER ELLISON
AUSTRALIAN SOLICITORS

O'Melveny & Myers

10 FINSBURY SQUARE
LONDON
EC2A 1LA

Phone: 01 256 8451

Fax: 01 638 8205
Telex: 918859
Senior UK Partner: Perry A Lerner
Number of Resident Lawyers: 3
Total Number of Lawyers in Firm: 455
Head Office: Los Angeles

This commercial firm operates on an international basis advising many large financial and industrial corporations in the United States, Europe and Asia.

The firm: O'Melveny & Myers was founded in 1885 in Los Angeles, California.

The growth of O'Melveny & Myers in its early years was closely linked to the growth of Los Angeles, but the firm later opened offices in major cities in the US and developed a national, and, in the last two decades, an increasingly international practice.

The firm's London office was opened in 1985 to serve the needs of US and Asian clients with interests and businesses in England and Europe, and to advise European clients on their dealings and investments in the United States.

As one of the larger and more experienced firms in the United States, O'Melveny & Myers is involved in virtually every area of the law, with extensive experience in negotiating, structuring and documenting mergers and acquisitions, leveraged buy-outs and corporate finance transactions. In addition the firm has an extensive litigation practice and is active in advising clients on matters of United States and international regulation, including trade regulation.

Other offices: Los Angeles (principal), New York, Washington DC, Tokyo, San Francisco, Century City (California), Newport Beach (California).

Agency work: O'Melveny & Myers provides UK solicitors with United States legal advice in all areas of law in which it practises.

Types of work undertaken: O'Melveny & Myers has a general US and international practice including corporate, commercial, banking, finance, tax, trade, securities, litigation, real estate, entertainment, creditors' rights, bankruptcy and labour law.

The clients of the London office are based in the United States, Europe and Asia, and include financial institutions, public and private corporations, individuals and partnerships. O'Melveny & Myers is a highly regarded firm whose advice is frequently sought by the leading UK firms of solicitors. The firm's practice is focussed on transactional work involving such areas as banking, finance, property development, mergers and acquisitions, international tax planning and entertainment.

The office has resident expertise in corporate and commercial transactions, including mergers and acquisitions, US and international taxation, international property development and joint ventures. The London office works closely with the firm's other offices and has ready access to the entire resources of the firm.

O'MELVENY & MYERS

Osler, Hoskin & Harcourt

CLEARY COURT
21-23 ST SWITHIN'S LANE
LONDON
EC4N 8AD
Phone: 01 283 3287

Fax: 01 283 1339
Telex: 928650
Senior UK Partner: David W Drinkwater
Number of Resident Lawyers: 3
Total Number of Lawyers in Firm: 242
Head Office: Toronto

One of Canada's largest law firms, Osler, Hoskin & Harcourt offers expertise in almost every area of Canadian and international law.

The firm: Osler, Hoskin & Harcourt has a tradition of service dating back through predecessor firms to 1862.

In 1985 the firm merged with a prominent law firm in Ottawa, and its strong corporate/commercial practice thereby expanded into important areas of federal regulation such as trade, communications, transportation, and food and drug regulation.

Osler, Hoskin & Harcourt's London office was founded early in 1987 in response to strong international trends in the firm's practice in Canada.

Other offices: Toronto (principal), Ottawa.

Agency work: Osler, Hoskin & Harcourt is pleased to advise UK solicitors in all commercial transactions which involve a Canadian aspect.

Types of work undertaken: Osler, Hoskin & Harcourt has solicitors specialising in most areas of Canadian law. Particular experience and expertise are offered in the following areas: banking; corporate finance and securities; corporate law; foreign investment; competition law; bankruptcy and insolvency; taxation; labour and employee matters; franchising; government affairs; energy, mining and resources; construction, architecture and engineering; insurance; estate planning and administration; family law; transportation; communications; anti-dumping, customs, excise and trade law; agriculture; intellectual property; civil litigation; and real property.

The professional staff of the London office are specialists in corporate and commercial law, but the office handles a much broader range of legal matters through consultation with experts based in the Canadian offices. For the UK client relatively unfamiliar with Canada, the firm can provide a comprehensive range of services, handling matters as diverse as complex international transactions, banking and other lending matters, trade law, tax planning and compliance, personal estate planning, real estate development and conveyancing, and civil litigation.

The London office's principal areas of expertise include international capital transactions (Euro-equity and Euro-debt financings, and financings for European clients in Canada) for both Canadian issuers and investment bankers handling international transactions involving Canada. The firm has also been actively involved in UK government privatisations.

OSLER,
HOSKIN &
HARCOURT

Pepper, Hamilton & Scheetz

CITY TOWER
40 BASINGHALL STREET
LONDON
EC2V 5DE

Phone: 01 629 1076

Fax: 01 493 5918   **Telex:** 886433
Senior UK Partners: JH McFadden,
GK Pilkington and BC Toms
Number of Resident Lawyers: 4
Total Number of Lawyers in Firm: 302
Head Office: Philadelphia PA

This is a general practice firm operating internationally in every aspect of financial, corporate tax, labour, environmental and administrative law, trusts and estates and litigation.

The firm: Founded in Philadelphia in 1890 by Senator George Wharton Pepper, the firm began opening offices in other US cities in the 1970s. At the outset, the firm's practice was built on general representation of large commercial and oil companies in the mid-Atlantic region of the United States, handling major litigation and creating and continuing several large and important trusts.

More recently, the firm has been involved in handling major acquisitions in the United States. Pepper, Hamilton & Scheetz was also responsible for the creation, privatisation and recent flotation of Conrail, now one of the largest US railroad companies.

With offices throughout the United States and in London, the firm today has an international practice in all areas of US law except most personal criminal law.

The London office was founded in the early 1980s to handle the firm's administrative practice for UK clients, and to assist US clients in their commercial ventures in England, the rest of Europe and the Middle East. In 1987, the London office was expanded to handle acquisitions, overseas securities offerings and

other matters. The London office has direct and easy access to all of the firm's offices in the United States.

Other offices: Philadelphia (principal), Washington DC, Detroit, Los Angeles, Wilmington, Berwyn, Harrisburg.

Agency work: Pepper, Hamilton & Scheetz is pleased to advise UK solicitors and their clients on all aspects of US law in which it practises.

Types of work undertaken: The firm has a general practice undertaking all aspects of financial, corporate tax, labour, environmental and administrative law, trusts and estates and litigation.

The London office deals with investments and acquisitions, US tax structuring, corporate finance and banking, including US securities and tax law for ADRs, offshore offerings, project financing and private placements, US construction law, US litigation and licensing and franchising law.

Pepper, Hamilton & Scheetz also provides advice to individuals on matters such as personal tax planning. Those seeking to establish residence in the United States can benefit from the firm's experience in limiting the extent of US taxation. The firm has available a general brochure and other publications covering specialised practice areas.

PEPPER, HAMILTON & SCHEETZ

RECRUITMENT AGENCIES

Recruitment agencies

Recruitment agencies are an established part of the legal scene. But 1988 has seen a bewildering increase in the number of agencies and, indeed, the choice of firms has widened dramatically.

Why have so many new agencies sprung up? The answer lies in two related trends. The major factor is the increasing number of individual consultants changing from one recruitment agency to another. In particular, many experienced consultants have left established firms and set up in business on their own. Indeed, all the largest and best known consultancies have spawned one or more 'new' firms over the last year; for example, **Graham Gill & Young** from **Chambers and Partners**, **Wilson Stephens** from **Badenoch & Clark** and **Quarry Dougall Recruitment** from **Reuter Simkin**. In addition, smaller agencies have also lost consultants – sometimes to established legal recruitment divisions within established management consultancy or chartered accountancy practices (for instance, both **Peat Marwick McLintock** and **Spicers & Oppenheim** are tentatively moving into the top end of the legal recruitment market).

The second factor has been the growing acceptance of new techniques, methods of behaviour, and areas of operation for recruitment consultants. For instance, there is increasing use of American-style 'retained search and selection' (ie headhunting by any other name), and there is also an increasing use of agencies for recruiting articled clerks. Only two or three years ago both these developments would have been regarded with some disfavour (both by firms of solicitors and individual recruitment agencies). Indeed, it is a reflection of the current recruitment crisis within the legal profession that this change of attitude – especially as regards using recruitment agencies to find articled clerks – has occurred so swiftly. As readers will know, the size and area of operation of the potential market for recruitment consultants has grown at the same time as the competition for job candidates has intensified. It may well be true that the largest three consultancies account for more than 60 per cent of all placements, yet the competitiveness and increasing size of the market mean that the number of recruitment agencies operating will continue to increase.

Legal recruitment survey: In recognition of the way the legal recruitment scene is changing, we have carried out a considerable amount of research into the way the agencies operate and their individual reputations. As part of this research we carried out a survey of some 11,000 young solicitors (together amounting to about one-fifth of all solicitors). We asked them for their comments on, and details of their experiences in, the use of recruitment agencies, and we also asked them to grade the agency they had used (on a scale ranging from very satisfactory through to very unsatisfactory). Needless to say, we received many interesting comments!

The detailed information that we received will be published separately in *The Legal Recruiters Guide 1989*. Solicitors qualified within the last five years can obtain a free copy by writing to us (please write on firm's headed notepaper stating date of qualification and own individual area of practice or expertise in the law). In addition, the full findings of the survey will be available as a specialist report, *The Legal Recruitment Survey 1989* (this publication is likely to be of interest only to recruitment consultancies themselves, or to recruitment partners.

Set out opposite are the basic findings — our ratings for the main agencies. It should be borne in mind, firstly, that these ratings assess agencies from the point of view of the job candidate (ie our survey was candidate rather than employer orientated). Secondly, we have excluded agencies for which we had a relatively low response rate (ie only a few votes), or which were founded in the last year or so. Thirdly, we should mention that we were surprised at the relatively high overall score achieved by most of the agencies. Although there were many individual horror stories (descibed in *The Legal Recruiters Guide 1989*), the overall rating of the agencies was higher than many cynics might have expected.

The new agencies: Many of the recently formed agencies did surprisingly well in our survey. Indeed, one of the initial conclusions would seem to be that the smaller the agency — and the more personal the service — the more likely it is that the young solicitor will be satisfied with its services.

However, we have excluded these agencies from our star-rating system, firstly because of the relatively low voting sample, and secondly because they have not been going long enough to have acquired a proper track record. Having said that, several of the newly created agencies did receive very strong recommendations, and particular mention must go to **Quarry Dougall Recruitment**, which had an excellent score and was on the verge of being eligible for inclusion (in which case it would have been one of the top agencies overall). Accordingly, we have no hesitation in selecting it as the outstanding new agency.

In addition, other newly created agencies that did particularly well include **Laurence Simons Associates** and **Graham Gill & Young**. Both were highly rated, although in each case the sample was relatively small.

Finally, one of the questions in our survey was designed to discover if The Legal 500 is indeed *the* guide to law firms. We asked solicitors (assuming that they were thinking of changing firms) if they would be likely to consult The Legal 500: even we were staggered to find that over 99.5 per cent said that they would consult The Legal 500!

How we rate the agencies

Daniels Bates

Charles Fellowes
Hughes-Castell
James Davis
Legal Opportunities
Meredith Scott

Able Man/Woman
Badenoch & Clark
Bee Professional
Chambers and Partners
Law Personnel
Law Placements
Michael Page
Reuter Simkin
Richard Owen & Harper
Wessex Consultants

Johnswood Farrer
Zarak Hay-at-Law

Top established agency
Daniels Bates

Top new agency
Quarry Dougall

Alexandra Gray

24 ROUNDHAY ROAD
LEEDS
LS7 1AB

Phone: 0532 422092
Fax: 0532 426690
Contact: Alexandra M Potts

Bee Professional

51 QUEENS ROAD
BRIGHTON
EAST SUSSEX
BN1 3XB

Phone: 0273 202828
Fax: 0273 205051
Contact: Rose Bell

Chambers and Partners

74 LONG LANE
LONDON
EC1A 9ET

Phone: 01 606 9371
Fax: 01 600 1793
Contact: Michael Chambers

Charles Fellowes Partnership

137 NEWHALL STREET
BIRMINGHAM
B3 1SF

Phone: 021 200 3363
Fax: 021 200 3341
Contact: Anthony Tomkins

Badenoch & Clark *see full-page profile*

Badenoch & Clark

16-18 NEW BRIDGE STREET
LONDON
EC4V 6AU

Phone: 01 583 0073
Fax: 01 353 3908
Contact: Judith Farmer 01 272 2837
(evenings and weekends)

The history: Established in 1980, Badenoch & Clark is the largest independent recruitment consultancy active in all areas of legal and financial recruitment. The legal division was founded in 1985 and at present has 18 consultants based throughout the UK. The London team operates from its Blackfriars and Oxford Street offices, whilst the regional network currently comprises Brighton, Birmingham, Milton Keynes and Reading, with plans to open several more offices in the spring and autumn of 1989.

The consultancy: The legal division provides a comprehensive service throughout private practice, commerce and industry and financial services.

A specialist service is offered in private practice throughout the UK across the variety of disciplines such as company and commercial, banking, corporate finance, litigation, tax, insolvency and property. Badenoch & Clark's clients range from small partnerships nationwide to major City firms.

Based upon the extensive contacts that Badenoch & Clark has built up over the last eight years in the financial sector, the legal division is also active in the recruiting of lawyers for domestic corporate finance, international capital markets and legal advisory positions. Similarly, Badenoch & Clark places lawyers at all levels in commercial organisations ranging from prestigious multi-nationals wishing to strengthen existing legal departments to smaller but expanding companies requiring an in-house specialist.

A full locum service was established during 1988 which caters for clients in all sectors.

The client base nationwide has been carefully cultivated, and all consultants have access to up-to-date records giving vital information about companies and firms for whom they recruit. 'We are confident that whatever candidates want to do, we can identify the appropriate clients. This, coupled with thorough interviewing means that they don't waste candidates' or clients' time.

'If we feel that candidates' career aspirations are unrealistic or not properly thought out, we will tell them,' says Judith Farmer. 'We actively encourage young solicitors to talk to us on an informal basis even if they have not decided to make a career move. Long-term planning generally eliminates bad career decisions.'

For details of the full range of vacancies available, refer to the *The Times* on Tuesdays and the *Law Society Gazette*.

Contact: one of the following:
Judith Farmer 01 583 0073 (London);
Helen Stockton 021 631 4211 (Birmingham);
Patrick Alford 0273 571490 (Brighton);
Sue Matheson 0734 393240 (Reading);
Miranda Whitamore 0908 690470 (Milton Keynes).

BADENOCH & CLARK

Daniels Bates Partnership Limited

JOSEPH'S WELL
HANOVER WALK
PARK LANE
LEEDS LS3 1AB

Phone: 0532 461671
Fax: 0532 456347
Contact: Ann Bates

The history: Daniels Bates Partnership was formed in 1983 by Brian Daniels and Ann Bates to provide a recruitment consultancy service to firms and individuals working in the professions. In 1985 a legal recruitment division was established, with Ann Bates becoming director of legal recruitment. Today four of the partnership's eight offices include specialist legal recruitment services. A ninth office will open in Cardiff by summer 1989 to cover the South West, and this, too, will have its own specialist legal division.

The four offices to offer this service are Leeds, Manchester, Nottingham and Aylesbury, while the remaining offices, all based close to major commercial centres, can call upon the experience and expertise of their colleagues whenever necessary.

In the last few years the Daniels Bates Partnership has risen in prominence to become one of the leading legal recruitment consultancies outside London, serving the whole of the UK from its well-situated offices.

The consultancy: Assignments are undertaken on behalf of clients and candidates at all levels, from junior clerk to senior partner, many of whom approach the partnership on the personal recommendation of colleagues or business associates. Equal care and attention is given to every assignment, whether a recruitment exercise or career and salary advice.

To enable Daniels Bates to provide a professional service many of its consultants are law graduates or solicitors, with specialist expertise and proven success in the profession. Before being appointed as a consultant they must also demonstrate the ability to fully understand the real needs of clients and candidates, an appreciation of the necessity for absolute confidentiality, and the ability to listen and learn.

It is care and attention to detail that have helped the Daniels Bates Partnership gain the respect and trust of the profession, and, in doing so, experience such substantial growth since the mid 1980s. As Ann Bates explains: 'Whether we have been asked to locate potential new partners for a private practice or suitable lawyers for industry, the identification stage is only the first step. The interview stage enables us to assess whether the two parties will actually complement each other in terms of style and personality. We have to be able to recognise when an appointment or career move, which on the surface looks satisfactory, will in practice prove unsuitable, and be prepared to say so.'

Contact: one of the following:
Ann Bates 0532 461671 – North East;
Peter Manners 061 835 3311 – North West;
Jan Collins 0602 483321 – Midlands;
Terry Rose 0296 393040 – South.

Daniels Bates Partnership
PROFESSIONAL RECRUITMENT

Gabriel Duffy

31 SOUTHAMPTON ROW
LONDON
WC1B 5HJ

Phone: 01 831 2288
Fax: 01 831 2009
Contact: Carl Batty

Graham Gill & Young

44-46 KINGSWAY
LONDON
WC2B 6EN

Phone: 01 430 1711
Fax: 01 831 4186
Contact: Dominique Graham

Hughes-Castell

11 BOLT COURT
FLEET STREET
LONDON
EC4A 3DU

Phone: 01 583 0232
Fax: 01 353 9637
Contact: Helen Castell

John Hamilton Associates

FRIARY COURT
13-14 HIGH STREET
GUILFORD SURREY
GU1 3DG

Phone: 0483 574814
Fax: 0483 300519
Contact: Helen Gould

James Davis & Partners *see full-page profile*

James Davis and Partners

160 NEW BOND STREET
LONDON
W1Y OHR

Phone: 01 493 8515
Fax: 01 495 0285
Contact: Alyson Lumsdon or
John G Grimwade

The history: James Davis and Partners is an established and successful specialist firm engaged in both national and international legal search and selection. The consultancy was established as an appropriate response to the market-driven needs of clients to recruit senior and partner level personnel. Based in London's Mayfair, James Davis has acted for selected clients across the whole spectrum of the law including private practice, banking, commerce and industry. The consultancy prides itself on its professional and individual service and pledges total confidentiality and absolute discretion.

The consultancy: Increasingly, search and selection has been identified as the most effective and secure method of making senior appointments. The degree of commitment required for a successful search and selection assignment makes this method best suited to appointments at senior or partner level. The candidate for such appointments can be confident in the quality of the appointment under discussion and can be given a detailed and accurate brief, both on the position itself and the nature of the firm.

James Davis and Partners therefore concentrates its expertise in the well-defined niche of selecting specialist, or high-profile lawyers for specific client appointments. The key to the consultancy's continued success lies with its ability to anticipate, understand and respond to its clients' needs. For example, the consultancy is now involved with the search for teams of senior lawyers and syndicates of partners for its clients. Similarly, it is able to offer informed and practical advice on the benefits and implementation of mergers and acquisitions.

A search assignment undertaken by James Davis and Partners begins with a detailed briefing from the client and the appointment of a consultant to conduct the exercise through to a successful conclusion. Advertising may be used to complement a particular assignment. When advertisements are used as an adjunct to the research process, they are written from the original instruction and produced in James Davis and Partners' house style. This corporate style is easily recognisable and has become known within the profession as representing professionalism and independence. The result of this systematic approach is that the client will meet only those lawyers who are both qualified for and interested in the position being offered.

In short, James Davis and Partners is confident that it is successful through professionalism and that it will foster long-term relationships with its clients. The consultancy has the energy, resources and commitment, not only to meet the challenges of today, but also the most exciting opportunities of the future.

Johnswood Farrer

26-29 ST CROSS STREET
HATTON GARDEN
LONDON
EC1V 8VH

Phone: 01 242 1140
Fax: 01 242 7600
Contact: Michael Farrer

Laurence Simons Associates

33 JOHN'S MEWS
LONDON
WC1N 2NS

Phone: 01 242 6644
Fax: 01 242 1522
Contact: Laurence Simons

Legal Opportunities

64 ABBEY ROAD
ENFIELD
MIDDLESEX
EN1 2QF

Phone: 01 360 0081
Fax: 01 242 1411
Contact: Jacqui Haworth

Link Legal Recruitment

PHOENIX HOUSE
1-3 NEWHALL STREET
BIRMINGHAM
B3 3NH

Phone: 021 233 3403
Fax: 021 233 2079
Contact: Susanne Dawson

Law Personnel *see full-page profile*
Law Placements *see full-page profile*

Law Personnel

95 ALDWYCH
LONDON
WC2B 4JF

Phone: 01 242 1281
Fax: 01 831 2901
Contact: Mack Dinshaw

The history: In 1977 the Managing Director, Mack Dinshaw — then a Company Secretary — formed Personnel Appointments with offices situated in Moorgate.

After a steady period of growth, the name changed to Law Personnel and the company now occupies considerably expanded modern offices in the Aldwych, just a few doors from the Law Courts.

When interviewed recently, Mack Dinshaw commented: 'It has never been our intention to be the largest consultancy, but always to be the best. Now that we have achieved this status, all of us enjoy being at the top, a position we guard with great jealousy.'

With a large team of consultants and an impressive support staff, Law Personnel now comprehensively covers the United Kingdom with strong connections worldwide.

The consultancy: 'People are the most important asset in any business.' Valid and much quoted, this statement is probably doubly true for the legal profession and this is fully recognised.

Law Personnel offers a totally professional, cost-effective and absolutely confidential selection and introduction service.

The company is often called upon to advise law practices on a variety of matters including salaries and interview technique and provides informed advice on possible mergers.

Planning the next step in a career is of vital importance. Because all consultants have law degrees themselves, they have the professional understanding that is necessary to build an efficient long-term relationship. Meetings conducted with applicants are designed to last at least an hour and seek to elicit more than just the appropriate qualifications and experience. Whether applicants exhibit a particular flair and wish to specialise or whether they are looking for a position as reliable technicians, their qualities are assessed and opportunities are discussed. The company does not believe in just pressing keys on a computer and the interpersonal aspect of this operation is a major factor. This well-proven formula is so successful that a high percentage of all applicants come to the company as a result of personal recommendation.

In short, Law Personnel makes sure that the right person is introduced for the position.

In just over ten years Law Personnel has built a wide client base consisting of firms in private practice, banks, insurance companies and other organisations in the commercial/industrial sector, selecting and introducing professional personnel at all levels worldwide.

Contact: either of the following:
Mack Dinshaw (Managing Director) or
Stephen Watkins (Director) on 01 242 1281
(answerphone after business hours).

Law Placements Limited

107 FLEET STREET
LONDON
EC4A 2AB

Phone: 01 353 5498
Fax: 01 353 9907
Contact: Suzanne Rose
or Kathi Hutchins

The history: Law Placements, established in the mid-1970s, was one of the first specialist legal recruitment consultancies, concentrating initially on the recruitment of lawyers for private practice. Building on this expertise, Law Placements has established a network of British offices and international associates to become one of the leading consultancies operating across all common law jurisdictions. In addition to its expertise in the home market, the consultancy's experience within the international legal market can provide invaluable guidance to candidates seeking to requalify in another jurisdiction.

The consultancy: As a legal recruitment consultancy, Law Placements is unashamedly candidate led. As Kathi Hutchins explains: 'We are in the business of providing counselling and guidance, as it is often the candidate who suffers most from an inappropriate career move.' By offering clear and informed advice to young solicitors contemplating a career move, it is not just the candidates but individual firms and the project as a whole that benefit.

Although based in London, Law Placements runs a large number of regional seminars to provide counselling locally. As sponsors of the Trainee Solicitors Group consultants also attend many regional social events.

For those people interested in advice on a move overseas, Law Placements believes that, with the development of the truly international law firm, lawyers should have access to counselling that is also international. Furthermore, this counselling should anticipate further trends that may shape the lawyer's career.

As with all professional services, continuity and personal service are vital elements in establishing a business relationship. Firms therefore deal with only one team of established consultants. Similarly, consultancy advice and services to individual candidates are based on interviews or individual contact. As Suzanne Rose comments: 'We try to sort out what is right for each candidate – even if they don't know themselves!'

To summarise, Law Placements is a leading national recruitment consultancy specialising in international placements. The consultancy's philosophy is that the influential role of the recruitment intermediary brings with it a responsibilty to individuals and the profession if successful working relationships are to be created and sustained.

Contact: one of the following
on 01 353 5498:
Suzanne Rose for London;
Kathi Hutchins for provinces;
David J Wilson for international;
Anne Niblock for articled clerks;
Geoff Allan for legal executives, cashiers and costs draftspersons.

Law Placements

Lipson Lloyd-Jones

SUITE 331
PREMIER HOUSE
10 GREYCOAT PLACE
LONDON SW1P 1SB

Phone: 01 222 4243
Fax: 01 976 7078
Contact: Simon Lipson

The history: Lipson Lloyd-Jones was founded in August 1987 by Simon Lipson, a solicitor with several years' experience in private practice in London and in industry, and Marian Lloyd-Jones, a recruitment specialist. The consultancy provides a highly efficient, professional and thorough service to candidates and clients alike. Since its inception, Lipson Lloyd-Jones has gained an enviable reputation within the profession for being dedicated to the recruitment of able lawyers at all levels, both within private practice and in commerce and industry.

The consultancy: The key to the company's success has been its insistence on complete integrity combined with an insider's view of the profession. The consultants are all lawyers with firsthand experience of the profession either, in the case of Lucy Boyd, as a barrister or, as with Simon Lipson and Michael Silver, as practising solicitors.

The consultants see it as a most important part of the recruitment process to interview all candidates personally or, if necessary, by way of a lengthy telephone discussion. Thereafter they will advise on, sift, and carefully select those positions most appropriate to each candidate and, most importantly, continue with the process of providing constructive advice and guidance until all avenues have been thoroughly investigated. Curriculum vitae are prepared to the highest standards and are noted within the profession for being clear, concise and straightforward. The consultants provide clients with full appraisals of each candidate based on the lawyer-to-lawyer interviews which will have been conducted as part of the consultancy's rigorous recruitment procedures.

Lipson Lloyd-Jones assists with the recruitment of top level personnel both nationwide and internationally. In this respect, the consultancy acts in association with Just Legal Pty in Australia. Additionally the consultancy provides a dedicated advertising service for clients with a particular recruitment requirement. Advice is given on copy, design and the most appropriate medium in which to advertise. Subsequently all respondents are interviewed and CVs prepared. Liaison is then maintained until the best candidate has been recruited.

Simon Lipson describes the consultancy in this way: 'As a former candidate myself, I am aware of the difficulties involved in making the right move, particularly early on in one's career. I founded Lipson Lloyd-Jones to provide a more comprehensive and informed service than I was offered at that crucial early stage.' At the forefront of Marian Lloyd-Jones's mind when founding the consultancy was 'the need to provide prompt, professional and informed advice to clients.'

Contact: Marion Lloyd-Jones

Meredith Scott

17 FLEET STREET
LONDON
EC4Y 1AA

Phone: 01 353 7085
Fax: 583 1850
Contact: Nicholas Rapaport

Michael Page Legal

39-41 PARKER STREET
LONDON
WC2B 5LH

Phone: 01 831 2000
Fax: 01 831 2612
Contact: Steven Grubb

Quarry Dougall Recruitment

46 BEDFORD ROW
LONDON
WC1N 2BL

Phone: 01 405 6062
Fax: 01 831 6394
Contact: Alistair Dougall

Wilson Stephens

20 COUSIN LANE
LONDON
EC4R 3TE

Phone: 01 236 7303
Fax: 01 489 1130
Contact: Lisa Wilson

Reuter Simkin *see full-page profile*
Richard Owen & Harper *see full-page profile*
Spicer & Oppenheim *see full-page profile*

Reuter Simkin

26-28 BEDFORD ROW
LONDON
WC1R 4HE

Phone: 01 405 6852
Fax: 01 405 3677
Contact: Paul Betterton

The history: Reuter Simkin opened its first office in central London in 1973. Today the company has a national network of offices located in major commercial centres throughout the country. A division for the placement of articled clerks was established in 1987 and the company's first overseas office was opened in Sydney, Australia in 1988.

The consultancy: Reuter Simkin believes its success to be dependent upon the quality of its service. The company offers a service which encompasses all aspects of recruitment: career counselling, CV writing, introduction to suitable employers, guidance on interview technique, interview follow-up and salary negotiation.

Piers Williams is the company's marketing director: 'Reuter Simkin is a recruitment consultancy with a difference. The high standards of practice we impose upon ourselves, coupled with substantial investment in sophisticated technology, ensure that all candidates receive a service tailored to their personal requirements.

'Being a people-oriented business we are aware that our own staff are our greatest asset. All our consultants are recruitment specialists; they spend a great deal of time to ascertain the requirements of both candidates and clients. Type of work is only one criterion to consider when matching employees and posts.

'Over the years we have built up a good client rapport across the breadth of private practice and industry and it is this in-depth knowledge of different firms that makes it easier for us to assess whether an applicant will 'fit' a particular department or practice. Factors such as size, culture, structure, etc are influential in determining the suitability of an applicant for a particular position.'

Reuter Simkin has the utmost regard for confidentiality and CVs are not presented to any employer without having first briefed the applicant in detail about the position available.

Career opportunities for young solicitors are greater now then ever before and candidates and clients owe it to themselves to be aware of the options on offer. Piers Williams defines Reuter Simkin's primary role as independent intermediary – 'to provide expert and unbiased information and advice to enable both clients and applicants to make the right choice.'

Contact: A consultant at one of their regional offices:
London: Paul Betterton 01 405 6852;
Leeds: Suzanne Hall 0532 446535;
Birmingham: Neal Parsons 021 200 2660;
Bristol: Jon Walsh 0272 226164;
Home Counties: Anita Amies 01 831 9211;
Sydney: Jane Martin 010 61 2 223 5766;
Manchester: Derath Nicklas-Carter 061 831 7127.

REUTER SIMKIN

Richard Owen & Harper

15 ST HELEN'S PLACE
LONDON
EC3A 6DE

Phone: 01 588 8373
Fax: 01 588 2283
Contact: Robert Thornhill

The history: The Richard Owen Group was established in 1969 by Richard Owen and started recruiting for the legal profession in 1973. Initially based in the City of London, the consultancy now has offices in all major regional centres, providing a truly national service to clients and applicants.

The consultancy: Richard Owen & Harper offers a personal and confidential service both to practices and companies offering career openings as well as to solicitors and legal executives looking for opportunities.

The consultancy interviews applicants with care in order to obtain an accurate assessment of their requirements. Time is devoted to their career history with a view to advising on their next career move or, sometimes, advising them to remain in their present employment; in this way a true career counselling service is offered. Great effort is also devoted to defining the requirements of a firm or company regarding the opportunity on offer and the experience and background preferred. The consultancy has built up an intricate and detailed knowledge of the legal profession from small firms to very large practices and companies, regularly visiting partners and directors to discuss their openings and opportunities offered.

At interview specific openings are discussed with applicants with the objective of meeting both their requirements and those of the firm or company. Generally, because of Richard Owen & Harper's extensive bank of vacancies, it can propose several specific and possible opportunities for each person. In some instances, where a person has a special need or experience, the consultancy can make direct approaches to the many clients with whom it is in regular contact. This often results in an opening being created to accommodate the talents of the person concerned. Of course, this is only done with the specific authority of the applicant as confidentiality is carefully protected. At no stage is a curriculum vitae ever disclosed without the prior approval of the person concerned.

The consultancy advertises regularly on behalf of its clients in the Law Society's Gazette. In addition, through its advertising subsidiary, it offers a full advertising service to aid major recruitment campaigns, relieving partners of the pressure of planning, implementing and processing the response of a media campaign. It is, therefore, most cost-effective.

Contact: Robert Thornhill (London); Robert Lee (Leeds); Alastair Seel (Birmingham); Judy Goffer (Bristol and Cardiff); Heather Walker (Bournemouth and Southampton); Max Siwicki (Croydon); Elizabeth Hockey (Colchester); Carol Newman (Manchester).

Richard Owen & Harper

Spicer & Oppenheim

13 BRUTON STREET
LONDON
W1X 7AH

Phone: 01 480 7766
Fax: 01 480 6947
Contacts: Clare Tattersall and
Belinda Worlock

The history: Spicer & Oppenheim is a leading firm of chartered accountants. Already well known and respected for its audit and tax advice to many legal practices, in 1981 the firm established a specialist recruitment service, Spicers Executive Selection (SES).

As a natural expansion of SES, a legal division was set up in 1988 primarily aimed at firms seeking to recruit senior legal members of staff.

This new legal specialism of SES provides a highly confidential recruitment and selection service which is predominantly, though not exclusively, London based.

The consultancy: The outstanding feature of SES is the close relationship maintained with senior and managing partners who deal directly with SES's specialist legal consultants. These consultants are therefore ideally placed to assist candidates seeking to move at partner or pre-partner level. In addition, at the start of each recruitment assignment, a detailed analysis is conducted of the client firm's structure and recruitment requirements. When appropriate, Spicers Consulting Group aids this analysis. The consultant therefore has a long-established, detailed and comprehensive understanding of the client's needs before interviewing commences. Based upon this detailed understanding candidates are only shortlisted if they match the client's specific requirements. Clearly, the greatest benefit of such an analysis is that it ensures the best fit between client and candidate as well as saving valuable time. Throughout each assignment the highest degree of confidentiality and discretion is assured to both client and candidate.

As SES is not a conventional recruitment 'agency', the consultancy's approach usually involves the placing of individual advertisements on behalf of specific clients. SES's advertising service offers advice on preparation of copy, choice of media and the analysis of response.

SES's distinctive logo has a particularly strong impact, combining as it does client anonymity and SES's reputation for representing senior level appointments. Although this approach is best suited to senior appointments, SES maintains a confidential register of candidates at all levels.

Both Belinda Worlock and Clare Tattersall, consultants in the legal division, have experience in private practice and legal recruitment. They describe SES in this way: 'We feel confident that this service, combining Spicer & Oppenheim's extensive knowledge of leading legal practices, our expertise in legal recruitment, and the focus on senior level appointments, is of enormous benefit to candidates and clients.'

Contact: Belinda Worlock
Clare Tattersall

**SPICERS EXECUTIVE
SELECTION**

Zarak Hay-at-Law

6 BROAD STREET PLACE
BLOMFIELD STREET
LONDON
EC2M 7JH

Phone: 01 588 9887
FAX: 01 588 1911
Contact: Nicholas Robbins

The history: Zarak Hay-at-Law was founded in 1981. Since then it has grown to become a highly efficient legal recruitment consultancy committed to personal service to both candidates and firms. It deals with vacancies across the breadth of private practice (nationally and abroad) and commerce and industry. The last year has seen a significant increase in the number of appointments to industry at a junior and senior level. The consultancy also has particular expertise in securing newly qualified solicitors their first qualified positions.

The consultancy: For the candidate, Nicholas Robbins (Director) considers the role of Zarak Hay-at-Law to be threefold: to advise a candidate on the firm's specialisation and the nature of the practice; to assess the candidate's own strengths and weaknesses; and to organise and follow up interviews with selected firms.

Nicholas Robbins LLB (Director), and Deborah Nicol LLB and other consultants, have built up a detailed knowledge of their fields and can therefore give pertinent advice on the style, atmosphere and type of work carried out by any major firm. Following an initial interview they are able to match candidates to a selection of vacancies. Alternatively, Zarak Hay-at-Law can directly recommend a candidate to a firm with whom it has a good working rapport. This method can be especially useful to candidates who wrongly feel they are not qualified for a particular position.

Making use of Zarak Hay-at-Law's accurate knowledge of the market rate for salaries helps candidates to achieve their full potential. Nicholas Robbins explains: 'As salary is considered an important factor in deciding a career move, our knowledge of the market rate is frequently put to good use in negotiating our candidate's salary and remuneration package. Similarly, salary advice to firms enables them to recruit the highest calibre staff at the optimum salary level.'

As a response to the needs of its candidates and its client firms, the consultancy has expanded its range of services during the course of the last year. For example, it now offers a comprehensive client advertising service in association with an international advertising agency. Zarak Hay-at-Law can therefore advise on all aspects of managing a successful recruitment drive, from choice of media through to pre-selection and interviewing of candidates. For the convenience of candidates it has opened a second office in the West End at 60 Marylebone Lane. Also, through a separate company, Zarak Hay-at-Law is able to offer a search and selection service for specific senior appointments.

Contact: Nicholas Robbins LLB (Director) on 01 588 9887 or Deborah Nicol LLB.

Your free copy of
The Legal Recruiters Guide 1989

As a companion to The Legal 500 we have produced The Legal Recruiters Guide 1989. It contains full details of all the major recruitment agencies and the services they offer. It also contains the major findings of our recruitment survey – the biggest survey ever undertaken on recruitment agencies. We recommend individual agencies – and we name names!

You can obtain a free copy of The Legal Recruiters Guide 1989 if you are a young solicitor. Write to us on your firm's notepaper, stating year of qualification (which must have been within the last five years) and your individual area of practice or expertise in the law. We shall then send you a free copy on publication.

The full statistical analysis of the survey is available separately in The Legal Recruitment Survey 1989. This contains extensive (anonymous) quotes on individual agencies, and gives regional ratings. It is available on a limited distribution basis only; enquiries to Legalease.

LEGALEASE

THE LEGAL 500
BY TOTAL STAFF

		Total staff	Partners	Assistant solicitors	Articled clerks
1	Clifford Chance	1649	144	424	151
2	Linklaters & Paines	1250	103	325	120
3	Lovell White Durrant	1076	110	225	94
4	Slaughter and May	972	77	267	102
5	Denton Hall Burgin & Warrens	854	91	124	53
6	Allen & Overy	787	80	203	94
7	Freshfields	762	72	240	66
8	Simmons & Simmons	756	91	142	82
9	Herbert Smith	729	74	176	64
10	Norton Rose	660	77	180	66
11	McKenna & Co	554	60	114	43
12	Nabarro Nathanson	550	70	90	40
13	Richards Butler	461	64	101	71
14	Dibb Lupton Broomhead	405	46	62	24
15	Wilde Sapte	395	38	78	34
16	Clyde & Co	384	62	63	27
17	Clarke Willmott & Clarke	384	36	31	14
18	Stephenson Harwood	380	53	93	32
19	Robin Thompson & Partners	380	34	10	5
20	Theodore Goddard	377	42	94	26
21	Ashurst Morris Crisp	369	35	84	27
22	Brian Thompson & Partners	369	30	31	10
23	Bevan Ashford	350	49	35	20
24	Cameron Markby	348	42	70	28
25	Shoosmiths & Harrison	340	43	23	14
26	Macfarlanes	332	36	65	27
27	DJ Freeman & Co	324	52	82	19
28	Evershed & Tomkinson	322	32	66	40
29	Edge & Ellison	320	30	50	16
30	Hammond Suddards	315	27	46	24
31	Berwin Leighton	310	45	42	15
32	Daynes Hill & Perks	304	46	29	15
33	Turner Kenneth Brown	302	41	61	28
34	Rowe & Maw	302	40	78	23
35	Mills & Reeve Francis	300	43	42	10
36	Wragge & Co	300	26	60	21
37	Titmuss Sainer & Webb	294	39	73	23
38	Booth & Co	291	25	46	15
39	Blake Lapthorn	291	22	27	13
40	Thomas Eggar Verrall Bowles	290	35	20	12
41	Penningtons	286	44	38	13
42	Alsop Wilkinson	285	51	57	30
43	Frere Cholmeley	283	33	66	28
44	Barlow Lyde & Gilbert	282	37	63	15
45	Lawrence Graham	282	32	60	12
46	Jaques & Lewis	279	46	43	13
47	Trowers & Hamlins	275	38	42	22
48	Holman, Fenwick & Willan	274	51	34	12
49	Baker & McKenzie	271	30	59	19
50	Thomson Snell & Passmore	260	48	14	4

		Total staff	Partners	Assistant solicitors	Articled clerks
51	Howes Percival	260	27	14	10
52	Needham & James	250	28	26	15
53	Walker Morris Scott Turnbull	250	21	24	14
54	Bond Pearce	247	31	41	15
55	Masons	245	32	42	17
56	Withers Crossman Block	240	34	37	20
57	Phillips & Buck	240	20	32	18
58	Donne Mileham & Haddock	235	35	13	9
59	Gouldens	230	22	41	23
60	Durnford Ford	220	23	4	4
61	Argles & Court	220	22	9	4
62	Boodle Hatfield	217	32	35	15
63	Travers Smith Braithwaite	217	29	46	16
64	SJ Berwin & Co	215	37	46	18
65	Hugh James Jones & Jenkins	215	24	17	15
66	Sinclair Roche & Temperley	210	30	50	16
67	Simpson Curtis	210	19	43	13
68	Hepworth & Chadwick	203	20	39	10
69	Osborne Clarke	201	27	40	11
70	Coffin Mew & Clover	201	18	8	3
71	Beachcroft Stanley	200	35	29	16
72	Farrer & Co	200	33	35	12
73	Veale Wasbrough	200	27	21	13
74	Dickinson Dees	195	23	20	12
75	Pinsent & Co	194	27	37	20
76	Lester Aldridge	194	26	15	10
77	Paisner & Co	190	24	30	11
78	Davies Arnold Cooper	190	19	33	13
79	Burges Salmon	190	17	42	14
80	Taylor Garrett	184	34	42	12
81	Leigh Williams	184	17	11	9
82	Ince & Co	181	34	27	11
83	Speechly Bircham	181	33	23	8
84	Charles Russell Williams & James	180	32	35	7
85	Wedlake Bell	180	30	27	8
86	Irwin Mitchell	180	23	17	11
87	Lace Mawer	175	29	22	12
88	Toller Hales & Collcutt	175	21	10	12
89	Cripps Harries Hall	173	19	17	4
90	Amery-Parkes & Co	172	21	5	3
91	Morgan Bruce & Hardwickes	171	27	31	13
92	Pictons	171	20	17	9
93	Wild Hewitson & Shaw	170	27	14	7
94	Moore & Blatch	170	17	17	8
95	Brecher & Co	168	30	23	9
96	Stephens & Scown	167	22	11	4
97	Radcliffes & Co	165	26	20	13
98	Taylor Vinters	165	21	18	9
99	Russell Jones & Walker	165	20	47	6
100	Edwards Geldard	164	22	27	15

		Total staff	Partners	Assistant solicitors	Articled clerks
101	Lees Lloyd Whitley	163	25	7	7
102	Reynolds Porter Chamberlain	162	25	32	11
103	Joynson-Hicks	161	27	30	14
104	Linnells	161	21	25	5
105	Cobbett Leak Almond	160	29	12	10
106	Brutton & Co	160	18	10	1
107	Hill Dickinson & Co	159	24	24	16
108	Watson Burton	158	15	15	8
109	Heald Nickinson	157	20	18	11
110	Payne Hicks Beach	155	29	15	10
111	Weightman Rutherfords	155	22	17	10
112	Deacon Goldrein Green	154	10	10	3
113	Bates & Partners	152	13	7	2
114	Cole and Cole	150	22	22	9
115	Bristows, Cooke & Carpmael	150	18	25	9
116	Stevens Drake & Pope	150	9	11	5
117	JW Ward & Son	149	18	17	8
118	Girlings	148	18	4	4
119	Kidd Rapinet	147	27	7	5
120	Blakemores	146	20	11	6
121	Cannons	145	16	14	5
122	Batten & Co	145	16	6	3
123	Pannone Blackburn	144	18	13	9
124	Saunders Sobell Leigh & Dobin	140	23	21	9
125	Morton Fisher	140	20	16	6
126	Glaisyers	140	20	13	8
127	Haden Stretton Slater Miller	138	13	10	3
128	Addleshaw, Sons & Latham	137	22	25	11
129	Lanyon Bowdler	137	17	6	4
130	Winter-Taylors	137	15	17	5
131	Cartwright & Lewis Vernon & Shakespeare	136	12	5	3
132	Cartwrights	135	20	18	7
133	Wells & Hind	135	17	24	6
134	Baileys Shaw & Gillett	130	23	20	8
135	Martineau Johnson	130	22	13	11
136	Hawkins Russell Jones	130	21	10	0
137	Grangewoods	130	19	14	5
138	Winter Wilkinson	130	16	8	4
139	Warner Goodman & Streat	130	16	4	1
140	Blythe Liggins	130	12	4	4
141	Malkin Cullis & Sumption	127	20	24	5
142	Hunt Dickins	127	18	11	9
143	Rowley Ashworth	127	9	5	2
144	Davies Wallis	126	22	31	4
145	Ironsides Ray & Vials	126	20	8	6
146	Blyth Dutton	125	18	23	10
147	Walker Smith & Way	125	18	14	6
148	Breeze and Wyles	125	14	10	11
149	Oxley & Coward	125	12	5	3
150	Fladgate Fielder	124	27	12	8

		Total staff	Partners	Assistant solicitors	Articled clerks
151	Bischoff & Co	124	20	21	9
152	William Prior & Company	124	17	19	6
153	Porter Bartlett & Mayo	122	13	6	4
154	Wansbroughs	121	21	24	6
155	Wilkin & Chapman	121	19	6	3
156	Mishcon de Reya	120	18	18	11
157	Slater Heelis	120	18	14	12
158	Bircham & Co	120	15	20	8
159	Stephensons	120	10	5	2
160	Bermans	120	8	11	3
161	Forsyte Kerman	119	20	16	11
162	Nicholson Graham & Jones	118	18	25	6
163	Leo Abse & Cohen	118	14	12	8
164	Cartwright Cunningham Haselgrove & Co	118	10	14	6
165	Loosemores	117	15	11	11
166	Watson, Farley & Williams	115	19	32	10
167	Amhurst Brown Colombotti	115	19	10	3
168	Ingham Clegg & Crowther and Laytons	115	16	15	6
169	Flint Bishop & Barnett	115	16	10	4
170	Hart Brown & Co	115	15	6	7
171	Greenwoods	114	13	6	6
172	Waltons & Morse	112	21	13	6
173	Manches & Co	112	16	26	6
174	TG Baynes & Sons	112	14	3	5
175	Mackrell Turner Garrett	111	20	3	4
176	Cuff Roberts North Kirk	111	10	13	12
177	Lewis Silkin	110	20	17	20
178	Harvey Ingram Stone & Simpson	110	20	6	6
179	Walker Martineau	110	19	18	10
180	Andrew M Jackson & Co	110	19	13	2
181	Foot & Bowden	110	19	12	8
182	Bird & Bird	110	18	18	8
183	Roythorne & Co	110	15	10	2
184	Bower & Bailey	110	14	18	6
185	Woodham Smith	110	14	16	11
186	Davis Campbell	110	14	8	8
187	Birketts	110	14	4	2
188	Boys & Maughan	110	13	1	4
189	Lawford & Co	110	10	7	4
190	Sydney Mitchell & Co	110	10	5	4
191	Glanvilles	109	14	9	4
192	Stoneham Langton & Passmore	108	19	10	5
193	Charles Lucas & Marshall	108	18	14	2
194	Townsends	108	12	13	4
195	Judge & Priestley	108	10	0	2
196	Wynne Baxter Godfree	107	17	8	4
197	Read Hind Stewart	107	14	12	3
198	Truman Close Kendall & Appelby	107	9	9	2
199	Manby & Steward	106	16	5	6
200	Hewitt Woollacott & Chown	105	15	14	11

		Total staff	Partners	Assistant solicitors	Articled clerks
201	Goodger Auden	105	15	7	3
202	Browne Jacobson	105	14	16	6
203	Prettys	105	13	8	5
204	Attey Bower & Jones	105	12	3	3
205	Laytons	105	10	10	4
206	Bray & Bray	104	17	5	1
207	Campbell Hooper	104	16	9	7
208	Winckworth & Pemberton	104	15	14	4
209	Stamp Jackson & Procter	104	15	4	4
210	Alsters Partnership	104	11	7	5
211	Ingledew Botterell	103	16	20	5
212	Birkbeck Montagu's	103	15	21	8
213	Shakespeare Duggan Lea & Co	103	15	8	8
214	Hextall Erskine & Co	103	15	3	3
215	Becke Phipps	103	13	12	4
216	Rowlands	102	12	7	4
217	Hill Bailey	102	11	4	1
218	Fennemores	102	9	12	8
219	Jeffrey Green & Russell	101	18	10	9
220	Elliott & Company	101	15	10	6
221	Fox Brooks Marshall	100	17	6	3
222	Hempsons	100	16	22	5
223	Kennedys	100	16	18	8
224	Jacksons	100	14	6	4
225	Castle Sanderson	100	14	5	3
226	Mace & Jones	100	13	13	7
227	Leeds Smith	100	7	6	2
228	Stevens & Bolton	98	13	9	3
229	Chattertons	98	7	7	3
230	Langleys	98	7	6	3
231	Constant & Constant	96	22	14	2
232	Fox & Gibbons	96	14	12	1
233	Lawrence Tucketts	96	11	18	4
234	Waterhouse & Co	95	15	9	5
235	Burstows	95	15	7	5
236	Woollcombe Watts	95	13	9	3
237	Brain & Brain	95	13	7	6
238	Buss Murton Partnership	95	13	6	3
239	Stones	95	12	13	4
240	Lamb Brooks Wills Chandler	95	12	5	5
241	Robinson Jarvis & Rolf	95	10	3	2
242	Eric Robinson & Co	95	9	4	4
243	Rollit Farrell & Bladon	94	17	10	7
244	Wilson & Wilson	94	15	5	4
245	Dawson & Co	93	24	6	7
246	Turners	92	12	2	1
247	Booth & Blackwell	92	10	3	5
248	Tuck & Mann & Geffen	91	17	9	7
249	Rubinstein Callingham Polden Gale	91	16	10	8
250	Harbottle & Lewis	91	13	17	2

		Total staff	Partners	Assistant solicitors	Articled clerks
251	Tallents Godfrey & Co	91	12	3	2
252	Alexander, Tatham & Co	90	17	11	11
253	Foster Baxter Cooksey	90	15	4	8
254	Trethowans	90	15	4	3
255	Willey Hargrave	90	14	13	3
256	Tozers	90	14	10	2
257	Crutes	90	14	7	1
258	Russell-Cooke Potter & Chapman	90	13	16	6
259	Lee Bolton & Lee	90	13	6	5
260	Elliot Mather Smith	90	12	5	1
261	Smith Morton & Long	90	11	6	4
262	Rawlison and Butler	90	11	4	2
263	Martin Tolhurst Partnership	90	11	3	2
264	Willmett & Co	90	7	10	2
265	Gosschalk Wheldon Chambers Thomas	89	15	3	2
266	Howard Kennedy	88	19	8	4
267	Shacklocks	88	13	3	3
268	Robinson & Allfree	88	10	2	0
269	Brachers	87	12	11	1
270	Hegarty & Co	87	9	4	5
271	Franklins	87	5	4	2
272	Braby & Waller	86	18	6	5
273	Burroughs Day Robert Smith	86	12	5	4
274	Mayo & Perkins	86	11	3	3
275	Gamlin Kelly & Beattie	86	5	13	3
276	Blackhurst Parker & Yates	85	16	4	2
277	Thursfield Adams & Westons	85	15	2	4
278	Whitehead Monckton	85	14	5	2
279	Bates Wells & Braithwaite	85	12	10	6
280	Overbury Steward & Eaton	85	12	8	3
281	Buckle Mellows	85	12	4	3
282	Furley Page Fielding & Barton	85	12	4	1
283	Russell & Russell	85	11	8	3
284	Sherwins	85	10	10	4
285	Stanley Tee & Co	85	9	5	6
286	Dale & Newbery	85	9	5	2
287	Keene Marsland	84	18	4	7
288	Heckford Norton	84	15	6	0
289	Higgs & Sons	84	14	6	4
290	Lawrance, Messer & Co	84	13	23	7
291	Curwen Carter & Evans	84	13	6	3
292	Paris Smith & Randall	84	9	9	3
293	Wake Smith & Co	84	8	8	6
294	Bunker & Co	84	7	5	3
295	Iliffes	83	15	3	4
296	Gamlens	83	14	8	7
297	Wilkinson Maughan	82	21	3	2
298	Kingsford Dorman & Routh Stacey	82	16	9	7
299	Carter Faber	82	14	5	6
300	Kingsley Napley	82	12	13	8

		Total staff	Partners	Assistant solicitors	Articled clerks
301	Darbey-Scott-Rees	82	12	2	7
302	Steele & Co`	82	10	0	0
303	Biddle & Co	81	19	13	8
304	Foysters	81	13	12	8
305	Maxwell Entwistle & Byrne	81	12	6	4
306	R Gwynne & Sons	81	10	5	2
307	Stafford Young Jones	80	18	4	4
308	Bankes Ashton	80	16	4	4
309	Halliwell Landau	80	15	13	10
310	Lee & Pembertons	80	15	10	5
311	Dodson Harding	80	14	3	1
312	Elborne Mitchell	80	13	18	8
313	Edwin Coe	80	13	6	3
314	Boyce Hatton	80	13	4	3
315	Rutherfords	80	13	2	2
316	Lyons Davidson	80	12	12	3
317	Turner & Debenhams	80	12	6	4
318	Ward, Gethin & Co	80	12	1	1
319	Clarks	80	11	8	8
320	Knight & Sons	80	11	5	7
321	Douglas-Jones & Mercer	80	10	6	5
322	RL Edwards & Partners	80	10	4	2
323	Gotelee & Goldsmith	80	9	6	0
324	Kirwan Nicholas Jones	80	9	2	2
325	Wade Gery Farr	80	6	5	4
326	Parker Bullen	79	14	7	3
327	Ford & Warren	79	12	8	4
328	Bury & Walkers	79	12	3	2
329	Westhorp Ward & Catchpole	78	14	2	2
330	Metcalfe, Copeman & Pettefar	78	12	6	2
331	Gordons and H M Dawson & Co	78	11	10	4
332	Grindeys	78	9	2	5
333	Greenland Houchen	78	5	7	0
334	Pickering & Butters	77	17	7	0
335	Burnetts	77	14	9	2
336	Bell Lamb & Joynson	77	12	4	2
337	White Brooks & Gilman	77	10	10	3
338	Ellison & Co	77	10	2	3
339	E Edwards Son & Noice	77	5	5	7
340	Hamlin Slowe	76	15	3	8
341	Gill Akaster	76	11	4	3
342	Hunt & Hunt	76	10	10	0
343	Lupton Fawcett	76	10	5	6
344	Gepp & Sons	76	8	4	6
345	Mounseys	75	12	4	3
346	Clintons	75	12	3	4
347	Wedlake Saint	75	11	8	5
348	Heringtons	75	11	4	1
349	George Green & Co	75	9	3	2
350	Park Woodfine & Co	75	8	4	2

		Total staff	Partners	Assistant solicitors	Articled clerks
351	Seymour Major Barnes	75	7	10	5
352	Gareth Woodfine and Partners	75	6	4	4
353	Slee Blackwell	75	5	9	2
354	Thrings & Long	74	12	10	2
355	Bishop Longbotham & Bagnall	74	11	3	0
356	Pardoes	74	8	9	6
357	Ingledew Brown Bennison & Garrett	73	16	8	6
358	Druces & Attlee	73	13	9	5
359	Wolferstans	73	13	3	3
360	Kenneth Bush & Co	73	12	1	1
361	Hepherd Winstanley & Pugh	73	11	5	4
362	Redfern & Stigant	73	10	2	1
363	Collyer-Bristow	73	9	8	5
364	Binks Stern and Partners	72	15	5	4
365	Challinor & Roberts	72	9	7	2
366	Abson Hall & Co	72	9	4	8
367	Lamport Bassitt	72	7	8	1
368	Larcomes	72	7	3	0
369	Dickinson Manser & Co	72	6	3	1
370	Pritchard Englefield & Tobin	71	17	7	8
371	Dutton Gregory & Williams	71	10	6	2
372	Lee & Priestley	71	10	2	1
373	Keogh Ritson	71	9	7	2
374	Sharman & Trethewy	71	9	6	2
375	Middleton Potts	70	14	6	10
376	Balderston Warren	70	13	5	2
377	Goodman Derrick & Co	70	12	12	6
378	Wilkinsons	70	12	5	2
379	Percy Hughes & Roberts	70	12	3	2
380	March Pearson & Skelton	70	11	10	6
381	Horwood & James	70	11	4	2
382	Brabner Holden & Co	70	10	11	1
383	Ford Simey & Ford	70	10	4	1
384	Lewis & Dick	70	10	0	0
385	Blaser Mills	70	9	9	2
386	Smith & Harrison	70	9	4	2
387	Williams Hatch & Co and AE Wyeth & Co	70	9	2	1
388	Park Nelson	70	8	9	2
389	Dibbens	70	8	2	0
390	Mullis & Peake	70	8	2	1
391	Palmers	70	4	1	0
392	Tinsdill Hollinshead & Moody	69	13	6	1
393	Church Adams Tatham & Co	68	13	8	4
394	Taylor Walker	68	12	6	3
395	Dolmans	68	12	5	6
396	Maxwell Batley	68	10	3	4
397	JM Rix and Kay	68	9	10	2
398	Turberville Woodbridge	68	7	12	5
399	Kidd & Spoor	68	7	6	4
400	Anthony Collins & Co	68	5	11	3

		Total staff	Partners	Assistant solicitors	Articled clerks
401	Hay & Kilner	67	13	8	5
402	Borneo Martell & Partners	67	12	2	2
403	Keeble Hawson Branson Bramley	67	11	5	2
404	Every & Phillips with Dunnings	67	10	3	2
405	Warner Cranston	67	9	8	1
406	Neves	67	9	6	4
407	Blocks	67	9	3	2
408	Seifert Sedley Williams	67	8	5	4
409	Withy King & Lee	67	6	6	7
410	J Keith Park & Co	67	3	6	1
411	Sparling Benham & Brough	66	14	2	3
412	Simmonds Church Smiles & Co	66	13	5	3
413	Burley & Geach	66	11	8	0
414	Cooper & Burnett	66	10	2	5
415	Robert Gore and Company	66	7	10	6
416	Owston & Co	66	7	7	4
417	Tarlo Lyons Randall Rose	65	18	6	4
418	Denison Till	65	14	3	3
419	Fitzhugh Gates	65	12	4	2
420	Cartmell Mawson & Main	65	11	6	1
421	Farnfield & Nicholls	65	10	6	1
422	Barlows	65	10	6	4
423	Sharman Sykes	65	8	2	0
424	Kirk Jackson	65	7	6	5
425	Donn & Co	65	6	6	3
426	Rooks Rider	64	11	14	5
427	Nicholson Cadge & Gilbert	64	11	5	1
428	Elgoods	64	9	4	2
429	Attwater & Liell	64	9	2	0
430	Sheridans	63	12	6	5
431	Gregory Rowcliffe & Milners	63	12	3	6
432	Hawley & Rodgers	63	10	5	1
433	Simon Olswang & Co	63	9	13	4
434	Leathes Prior	63	9	7	6
435	Staffurth & Bray	63	9	1	0
436	Varley Hibbs & Co	63	8	6	3
437	Burt Brill & Cardens	63	7	6	1
438	Yaffe Jackson & Ostrin	63	7	1	8
439	Askew & Askew	62	9	4	4
440	Malcolm Wilson & Cobby	62	8	1	0
441	Pitmans	62	6	6	2
442	Thorpe & Co	61	12	1	1
443	Woolsey Morris & Kennedy	61	10	1	0
444	Gartside Harding & Davies	61	9	3	3
445	Peter Peter & Wright	61	9	3	0
446	Mincoff Science & Gold	61	7	3	4
447	Le Brasseur & Monier-Williams	60	16	9	6
448	Janners	60	13	7	6
449	Merrils Ede	60	13	4	7
450	Williamson & Co	60	13	3	2

		Total staff	Partners	Assistant solicitors	Articled clerks
451	Stones Porter	60	12	5	4
452	Rotheras	60	12	4	2
453	Hobson Audley	60	10	12	4
454	Punch Robson Gilchrist Smith	60	10	4	4
455	Wellingtons	60	10	4	2
456	Bremner Sons & Corlett	60	10	3	3
457	Walter Gray & Co	60	10	2	0
458	Nelsons	60	9	11	4
459	Michael Freeman & Co	60	9	7	4
460	Wilsons	60	9	6	3
461	Charsley Harrison	60	9	3	1
462	Stokes	60	9	2	1
463	Nalder & Son	60	9	2	2
464	Rapers	60	9	2	0
465	Hopkins & Wood	60	8	11	2
466	Harrison Clark	60	7	2	1
467	Timms	59	9	1	1
468	Prince Evans	59	8	4	4
469	Enoch Evans	59	7	2	5
470	Pattinson & Brewer	58	15	0	2
471	Brindley Twist Tafft & James	58	11	3	0
472	John Barkers	58	8	0	1
473	Wannop & Falconer	58	7	6	2
474	Actons	58	6	6	3
475	Norton Peskett & Forward	58	6	0	1
476	Patterson Glenton & Stracey	57	10	3	1
477	Aldridge & Brownlee	57	8	4	1
478	Barnard & Co	57	4	4	0
479	Cozens-Hardy & Jewson	56	11	4	3
480	Dibb & Clegg	56	8	1	3
481	Memery Crystal	56	7	11	3
482	Marshalls	56	5	10	8
483	Gorna & Co	55	10	4	4
484	Burton Copeland	55	10	2	0
485	Glovers	55	9	12	3
486	Finn Gledhill & Co	55	9	2	1
487	Herbert Wilkes & Company	55	8	3	1
488	Wiseman Lee	55	7	5	4
489	David Law & Co	55	7	1	2
490	JE Dell & Loader	55	6	1	1
491	Grahame Stowe Bateson & Co	55	5	2	1
492	Sacker & Partners	54	17	7	4
493	The Simkins Partnership	54	13	11	2
494	Goughs	54	12	4	1
495	Rootes & Alliott	54	11	2	2
496	Brooke North and Goodwin	54	10	8	2
497	Pickering Kenyon	54	9	5	3
498	Powell Magrath & Spencer	54	7	6	3
499	Oswald Hickson, Collier & Co	53	14	4	4
500	James Chapman & Co	53	12	8	6

		Total staff	Partners	Assistant solicitors	Articled clerks
501	Thatcher & Hallam	53	5	3	1
502	Vizards	52	14	4	6
503	Trump & Partners	52	11	5	4
504	Rowleys & Blewitts	52	11	2	5
505	Beaumont & Son	52	10	5	4
506	Harris & Cartwright	52	10	2	3
507	Beale and Company	52	9	7	6
508	Tilly, Bailey & Irvine	52	9	4	1
509	Few & Kester	52	8	9	2
510	Glaisyers	52	8	5	4
511	Steggles Palmer	52	8	5	3
512	Green David Conway & Co	52	7	6	5
513	Hooper & Wollen	52	7	3	1
514	Townsend Livingston	52	7	0	1
515	Berry & Berry Cocker Smith & Co	52	6	4	2
516	E Rex Makin & Co	52	5	5	0
517	Adlers	51	11	5	6
518	Lawrence Jones	51	10	9	3
519	Davenport Lyons	51	10	9	3
520	Hyde Mahon Bridges	51	10	3	5
521	Lyon Clark	51	10	3	1
522	Frederic Hall & Co	51	10	2	1
523	Mundays	51	9	2	5
524	Dawbarns	51	9	2	0

See *How The Legal 500 is compiled* for interpretation of these figures. Note that total staff includes partners. Information believed correct at 1 January 1989. Scottish firms are not included. Towards the bottom of the table (ie from firm 400 on) the league table position becomes of limited significance because the size differential between firms decreases.

AFTERWORD

Afterword

Since the last edition of The Legal 500 was published we have received numerous letters from solicitors. Some were supportive; some were critical; some were rude; and some even threatened writs for defamation! In fact, all these letters were gratefully received — after all, our opinions are influenced by those of other people. If we have been unfair to a firm we are extremely anxious to know about it. Incidentally, threatening to issue a writ does not help one get into the editorial: if anything, it is counter-productive (on the basis that any solicitor who argues that non-inclusion in The Legal 500 is libellous clearly does not know much about defamation law!).

In fact, we are privileged to have been made party to a lot of confidential information. We are extremely grateful to the many partners who have sent confidential background information about the nature of their practices — for instance, a breakdown of fees by department, plans for the future, and also their merger proposals. All such information is, of course, received in total confidence and is never disclosed to any third party.

It goes without saying that we are conscious of the responsibilities of being party to so much confidential information. However, we are convinced that it is an integral part of the success of The Legal 500 that solicitors know that they can write in confidence and be sure that what they say will not be disclosed to anyone else. Apart from giving us the largest collection of solicitors' brochures in the country (!), it has also given us a unique insight into how firms are developing, and how they are planning for the future. A few general observations might, therefore, not be amiss.

Conveyancing: A few years ago, many small and medium sized firms made a policy decision to reduce their dependence on domestic conveyancing. Not unnaturally, many targeted company and commercial work as an alternative growth area. In fact, what seems to have happened with many firms is that they have swapped a dependence on domestic conveyancing for a dependence on commercial conveyancing. In other words, they have successfully reduced the proportion of their income that is attributable to domestic conveyancing by acting for commercial property developers (including developers of residential property), at a time when there has been a property boom.

In addition, many of those firms have tended to do lightweight commercial work for their property developer clients. Thus one has the impression that there are a surprising number of firms which have convinced themselves that they have reduced their dependence on conveyancing — whereas the reality is that they have simply changed the type of conveyancing that they are dependent upon. If — or when — there is a downturn in commercial property work, then it is not difficult to see that some of these firms will be in difficulties.

Boom time: The last few years have been a boom time for many lawyers. No doubt legal aid practitioners will disagree, but for any solicitor involved in commercial work (including commercial property) there have been fat profits. This has fuelled an expansion amongst many firms. Indeed, it is quite common for firms to state that their gross fee income is growing by 30 per cent a year. Many of the firms are busy spending this money. Inevitably, a sizeable chunk has to be used to pay the increased wages demanded by sought-after assistant solicitors.

But a large number of firms are using the money to fuel a furious expansion (involving taking on extra premises and staff) in the expectation that these boom days will continue. Perhaps they will – or perhaps they won't. However, one thing is certain: if there is a decline in commercial activity, then many firms of solicitors will find that they have expanded too quickly, and they will face some major problems if forced to retrench.

It should not be thought that this scenario is confined to the smaller and medium sized firms. There are several large firms which are also in danger of being caught napping if there is a downturn. No one is suggesting that we face a **Finley Kumble** situation (**Finley Kumble** grew in a short space of time to become one of the largest firms in the USA – and then crashed in 1988), but we suspect that some firms will face problems. Undoubtedly, when those problems arise, they will be solved by mergers (or, at least, they will be described as mergers – but the reality is that they will be takeovers).

Boutiques: One of the interesting aspects of the research for The Legal 500 has been identifying specialist niche firms – especially those in the provinces. These 'boutique' practices can be located in the most unusual of places (for instance, **Wiggin & Co** of Cheltenham). Generally firms such as this have identified a particular commercial niche, often as a result of the partners having done this type of work whilst training with one of the large City firms. What is interesting is that several of these niche firms seem very well established, and to be running highly successful practices. There is often a conscious decision not to expand beyond a certain size but to retain the position as a 'boutique' player. It is certainly

a different approach from that of those generalists who see growth in merger for merger's sake.

Partnership: The most important by-product of the merger phenomenon has been the consequent breakdown (at least in several London firms) of partnership loyalty. Increasingly it is the individual department that matters to the fee-earner; his loyalty lies to his colleagues in that department and not to the partnership as a whole. This is especially likely to be the case when a merger has resulted in an influx of new faces at partnership level to whom the fee-earner feels no established personal loyalty. Thus the strong sense of personal commitment within the partnership is breaking down in many large firms, to be replaced by a loyalty to the departmental unit. At its most extreme, this can result in the department leaving and joining another firm where it feels its work will be more adequately remunerated (even though this may then result in the collapse of the firm it has left).

Thus partnership loyalty is becoming a thing of the past. This, in turn, is likely to increase job mobility, with solicitors less likely to stay with a particular firm for most of their working lives. Naturally, it also encourages the headhunter (and even the department hunter) to enter the fray.

One profession? It is no longer possible to talk of 'the solicitors profession'. There is no longer one profession: there are several! The reality is that there are several different types of practice which really have no connection with each other. For instance, the increase (or lack of increase) in Crown Court legal aid pay rates is of vital importance to the criminal legal aid practitioner; however, it is a total irrelevancy to most commercial firms. Indeed, it is a myth to think there is any common bond between a legal aid practice and (say) a major City firm: apart from the fact that the partners all call themselves 'solicitors' (and thus share a common professional code of conduct), they have nothing in common.

As another example, consider the position of the sole practitioner; there are those (mainly sole practitioners!) who feel passionately that the rules should not be fixed so as to discriminate against sole practitioners. On the other hand, most solicitors in partnerships have little sympathy for this argument, and are more concerned about the high level of negligence claims against sole practitioners and the resulting increase in solicitors' insurance premiums! Thus we no longer have a single profession – what we do have are various different interest groups operating under the one umbrella of 'solicitor'.

This leads to the next logical question – what should the role of the Law Society be in all of this? Is not the reality that the Law Society is in the impossible position of having to wear several hats at once, to try and satisfy several different interest groups? At the end of the day it is arguable that the interests of those groups are irreconcilable – and indeed, contrary.

Thus one might suggest that solicitors practices should join their respective interest groups (eg city firms; sole practitioners; legal aid firms; major provincial commercial practices; traditional provincial family practices; and so on – whatever category one wishes to think of). After all, the Law Society cannot promote the aims and objectives of each of these groups. Logically, if one accepts that argument, the next step is to say that the Law Society should simply exist as a regulatory and disciplinary professional body, and abandon all its other activities. However, we should emphasise that we are

not necessarily advocating this, but are merely raising a few fundamental questions (that some people might prefer were not asked!).

Lord Mackay's reforms: At the time of going to press the legal profession is agonising over the radical changes proposed by the Lord Chancellor. Whilst this is not the place for a commentary on those reforms (which, in broad terms, we support) we cannot help but think that most lawyers seem to be unable to see the wood for the trees. The big argument seems to be whether the Bar will survive or whether barristers will join firms of solicitors. But we suspect that there is a more fundamental issue that is being ignored – the fact that the proposed changes would allow lawyers to go into partnership with other professionals and would also allow solicitors to operate as companies (ie have shareholders).

How long will it be before the large accountancy firms (which are massive when compared to even the largest firms of solicitors) take over the major commercial law firms? If that happens, then solicitors may find themselves operating under the umbrella of accountancy firms – and the issue of whether barristers should be kept separate from solicitors will be seen to have been of only minor importance. Perhaps the issue is not whether barristers should be subsumed into solicitors' practices, but whether lawyers should be subsumed into accountancy firms!

Obviously, readers may disagree with the points raised above. But, like the rest of the editorial in The Legal 500, the object of the exercise is at least to stimulate discussion.

FIRMS MENTIONED IN THE EDITORIAL

Aaron & Partners *Chester*	0244 315366
Abson Hall & Co *see main A-Z section*	
Actons *see main A-Z section*	
Addleshaw, Sons & Latham *see main A-Z section*	
Adlers *see main A-Z section*	
Ake Moore & Co *Leeds*	0532 448808
Alan Turner & Haddleton *Preston*	0772 562222
Alex Morison & Co WS *see main A-Z section*	
Alexander & Partners *London*	01 965 7121
Alexander Stone & Co *Glasgow*	041 332 8611
Alexander, Tatham & Co *see main A-Z section*	
Allan Janes & Co *High Wycombe*	0494 21301
Allan McDougall & Co *see main A-Z section*	
Allen & Overy *see main A-Z section*	
Allen & Son *London*	01 437 4001
Allington Hughes (& David Hughes) *Wrexham*	0978 291000
Allison & Humphreys *London*	01 377 8715
Alsop Wilkinson *London*	01 242 4499
Alsop Wilkinson *see main A-Z section*	
Amery-Parkes & Co *see main A-Z section*	
Andrew M Jackson & Co *see main A-Z section*	
Andrews McQueen *Bournemouth*	0202 290628
Anstey & Thompson *Exeter*	0392 38011
Archer Parkin & Townsend *Stockton on Tees*	0642 673431
Archibald Campbell & Harley WS *Edinburgh*	031 557 1445
Argles & Court *see main A-Z section*	
Armitage Sykes & Hinchcliffe *Huddersfield*	0484 538121
Ashington Denton & Co *Sheffield*	0742 768987
Ashton Hill Bond *Nottingham*	0602 476651
Ashurst Morris Crisp *see main A-Z section*	
B M Birnberg & Co *London*	01 403 3166
Bailey Morgan & Co *Skegness*	0754 68383
Baileys Shaw & Gillett *see main A-Z section*	
Baker & McKenzie *see main A-Z section*	
Balderston Warren *see main A-Z section*	
Baldocks *Guildford*	0483 573303
Balfour & Manson *see main A-Z section*	
Band Hatton & Co *Coventry*	0203 632121
Bankes Ashton *see main A-Z section*	
Banner Jones & Hawkins *Chesterfield*	0246 209773
Barker Son & Isherwood *Andover*	0264 53411
Barker Travers & Co *Sale*	061 973 4410
Barlow Lyde & Gilbert *see main A-Z section*	
Barlows *see main A-Z section*	
Barr Ellison *Cambridge*	0223 67531
Barry Lewis *Guildford*	0483 64626
Bates Wells & Braithwaite *see main A-Z section*	
Batten & Co *see main A-Z section*	
Beachcroft Stanleys *see main A-Z section*	
Beale and Company *see main A-Z section*	

Becke Phipps *see main A-Z section*	
Bell Russell & Co *Airdrie*	0236 64781
Bells *Kingston upon Thames*	01 546 5611
Beltrami & Co *Glasgow*	041 221 0981
Ben Pearson G J Starling & Co *King's Lynn*	0553 761441
Bendle Dodds & Co *Carlisle*	0228 22215
Bennett & Robertsons WS *Edinburgh*	031 226 2011
Bennett Brooke-Taylor & Wright *Buxton*	0298 2741
Benson Burdekin *Sheffield*	0742 760791
Beresford Lowe & Company *London*	01 930 8222
Berg & Co *Manchester*	061 833 9211
Bermans *see main A-Z section*	
Bernard Chill & Axtell *Southampton*	0703 228821
Berry & Berry *Tunbridge Wells*	0892 26344
Berry & Berry Cocker Smith & Co *see main A-Z section*	
Berry & Walton *King's Lynn*	0553 764398
Berrymans *London*	01 638 2811
Berwin Leighton *see main A-Z section*	
Betesh Fox & Co *Bolton*	0204 382531
Bettinsons *Birmingham*	021 236 8282
Bevan Ashford *see main A-Z section*	
Biggart Baillie & Gifford *see main A-Z section*	
Bindman & Partners *London*	01 278 8131
Binks Stern and Partners *see main A-Z section*	
Bircham & Co *see main A-Z section*	
Bird & Bird *see main A-Z section*	
Bird Semple Fyfe Ireland WS *see main A-Z section*	
Birkbeck Montagu's *see main A-Z section*	
Birketts *see main A-Z section*	
Bischoff & Co *see main A-Z section*	
Bishop Longbotham & Bagnall *see main A-Z section*	
Bishop and Robertson Chalmers *see main A-Z section*	
Blackadder Reid Johnston *see main A-Z section*	
Blackhurst Parker & Yates *see main A-Z section*	
Blair & Bryden *see main A-Z section*	
Blair Allison & Co *Birmingham*	021 233 2904
Blake Lapthorn *see main A-Z section*	
Blakemores *see main A-Z section*	
Blakesley & Rooth *Chesterfield*	0246 72293
Blandy & Blandy *Reading*	0734 587111
Blaser Mills *see main A-Z section*	
Blyth Dutton *see main A-Z section*	
Blythe Liggins *see main A-Z section*	
Bobbetts *Bristol*	0272 299001
Bolitho Way *Portsmouth*	0705 820747
Bond Pearce *see main A-Z section*	
Boodle Hatfield *see main A-Z section*	
Booth & Blackwell *see main A-Z section*	
Booth & Co *see main A-Z section*	
Borneo Martell & Partners *see main A-Z section*	

Boyce Hatton *see main A-Z section*	
Boyes Turner & Burrows *Reading*	0734 597711
Boys & Maughan *see main A-Z section*	
Brabner Holden & Co *see main A-Z section*	
Braby & Waller *see main A-Z section*	
Brachers *see main A-Z section*	
Brafman Morris *London*	01 631 4883
Brain & Brain *see main A-Z section*	
Bray & Bray *see main A-Z section*	
Brecher & Co *see main A-Z section*	
Brechin Robb *Glasgow*	041 248 5921
Breeze and Wyles *see main A-Z section*	
Brendan Fleming & Co *Birmingham*	021 236 5707
Bretherton & Price *Cheltenham*	0242 514688
Brian Thompson & Partners *see main A-Z section*	
Brian Thompson & Partners *Newcastle*	091 261 5341
Brignall White & Orchard *Stevenage*	0483 359311
Brindley Twist Tafft & James *see main A-Z section*	
Bristows, Cooke & Carpmael *see main A-Z section*	
Brodies WS *see main A-Z section*	
Brooke Blain Russell *London*	01 251 5700
Brooke North and Goodwin *see main A-Z section*	
Brown & Corbishley *Newcastle under Lyme*	0782 717888
Brown Beer & Co *Redcar*	0642 490202
Brown Cooper *London*	01 404 0422
Browne Jacobson *see main A-Z section*	
Brutton & Co *see main A-Z section*	
Buckle Mellows *see main A-Z section*	
Buller Jeffries *Birmingham*	021 643 8201
Bullivant & Co *Liverpool*	051 227 5671
Bunker & Co *see main A-Z section*	
Burges Salmon *see main A-Z section*	
Burley & Geach *see main A-Z section*	
Burnetts *see main A-Z section*	
Burr & Company *Farnham*	0252 713242
Burroughs *Maidstone*	0622 676976
Burstows *see main A-Z section*	
Burt Brill & Cardens *see main A-Z section*	
Burton Copeland *see main A-Z section*	
Bury & Walkers *see main A-Z section*	
Buss Murton Partnership *see main A-Z section*	
C A Norris *Ringwood*	04254 78822
Calow Easton *London*	01 404 4701
Cameron Markby *see main A-Z section*	
Campbell Hooper *see main A-Z section*	
Cannons *see main A-Z section*	
Canter Levin & Berg *Liverpool*	051 236 8574
Carrick Carr & Garwood *Hull*	0482 25385
Carter Faber *see main A-Z section*	
Cartmell Mawson & Main *see main A-Z section*	

Cartwright & Lewis Vernon & Shakespeare *see main A-Z section*	
Cartwrights *see main A-Z section*	
Cartwrights *Cardiff*	0222 465959
Chaffe Street *Manchester*	061 236 5800
Challinor & Roberts *see main A-Z section*	
Charles Russell Williams & James *see main A-Z section*	
Chattertons *see main A-Z section*	
Chethams (inc Duke-Cohan & Co) *London*	01 935 7360
Christian Fisher & Co *London*	01 379 6928
Church Adams Tatham & Co *see main A-Z section*	
Clarke Willmott & Clarke *see main A-Z section*	
Clarks *see main A-Z section*	
Clarksons & Steele *Halifax*	0422 58531
Claude Hornby & Cox *London*	01 437 8873
Clifford Chance *see main A-Z section*	
Clintons *see main A-Z section*	
Clutton Moore & Lavington *Bristol*	0272 299447
Clyde & Co *see main A-Z section*	
Cobbett Leak Almond *see main A-Z section*	
Cochran Sayer & Cook *Glasgow*	041 248 5961
Cocks Lloyd & Co *Nuneaton*	0203 348441
Coffin Mew & Clover *see main A-Z section*	
Cole & Company *Norwich*	0603 617018
Cole and Cole *see main A-Z section*	
Colemans *Maidenhead*	0628 31051
Coles *Poole*	0202 673011
Collins Woods & Vaughan Jones *Swansea*	0792 474002
Collyer-Bristow *see main A-Z section*	
Compton Carr *London*	01 831 6981
Constant & Constant *see main A-Z section*	
Cozens-Hardy & Jewson *see main A-Z section*	
Crane & Walton *Leicester*	0530 34466
Cranswick Watson *Leeds*	0532 451541
Crellins *Weybridge*	0932 858833
Cripps & Shone *Marlow*	062 84 2115
Cripps Harries Hall *see main A-Z section*	
Crosse & Crosse *Exeter*	0392 58451
Crotch Brenner & Dunkley *Norwich*	0603 617331
Crutes *Middlesbrough*	0642 248683
Crutes *see main A-Z section*	
Cuff Roberts North Kirk *see main A-Z section*	
Currey & Co *London*	01 828 4091
Curry Littlejohn *Harrow*	01 907 8896
Curtis & Parkinson *Nottingham*	0602 278867
Curtler & Hallmark *Worcester*	0905 726600
Cutts and Shiers *Chesterfield*	0246 37231
D J Freeman & Co *see main A-Z section*	
D J Griffiths and Co *Bromley*	01 460 6668
D M Landsman & Co *London*	01 636 6602
Dale & Newbery *see main A-Z section*	

Dallas Brett *Oxford*	0865 513557
Darby & Son *Oxford*	0865 247294
Darlington & Parkinson *London*	01 992 5054
Davenport Lyons *see main A-Z section*	
David Blank & Co *Manchester*	061 832 9433
David Jones & Harvey *Llanidloes*	05512 2951
David Law & Co *see main A-Z section*	
David Phillips Harris & Whalley *Bootle*	051 922 5525
Davies Arnold Cooper *see main A-Z section*	
Davies Wallis *see main A-Z section*	
Davis Campbell *see main A-Z section*	
Dawbarns *see main A-Z section*	
Dawson Cornwell & Co *London*	01 242 2556
Day & Son *Huntingdon*	0480 64600
Daynes Hill & Perks *see main A-Z section*	
Deacon Goldrein Green *see main A-Z section*	
Debenham & Co *London*	01 581 2471
Denison Till *see main A-Z section*	
Dennis Faulkner & Alsop *Northampton*	0604 20161
Denton Hall Burgin & Warrens *see main A-Z section*	
Dexter Montague & Partners *Reading*	0734 393999
Dibb & Clegg *see main A-Z section*	
Dibb Lupton Broomhead *see main A-Z section*	
Dickinson Dees *see main A-Z section*	
Dickinson Manser & Co *see main A-Z section*	
Dickson Minto WS *Edinburgh*	031 225 4455
Digby Brown & Co *Glasgow*	041 221 9572
Doberman Richardson Broady & Horsman *Middlesbrough*	0642 230130
Dolmans *see main A-Z section*	
Donn & Co *see main A-Z section*	
Donne Mileham & Haddock *see main A-Z section*	
Downs *Dorking*	0306 880110
Drummond & Co *see main A-Z section*	
Dundas & Wilson CS *see main A-Z section*	
Dunderdale Wignall *Manchester*	061 831 7434
Dutton Gregory & Williams *see main A-Z section*	
E L Murphy & Co *London*	01 405 9433
E Rex Makin & Co *see main A-Z section*	
Eaton & Co *Bradford*	0274 728327
Eaton-Evans & Morris *Haverfordwest*	0437 3383
Eddowes Waldron & Cash *Derby*	0332 48484
Edge & Ellison *see main A-Z section*	
Edward Fail Bradshaw & Waterson *London*	01 790 4032
Edward Lewis & Co *Cardiff*	0222 462562
Edwards Geldard *see main A-Z section*	
Edwin Coe *see main A-Z section*	
Eking Manning *Nottingham*	0602 481148
Elborne Mitchell *see main A-Z section*	
Elliot Mather Smith *see main A-Z section*	
Elliott & Co *Birmingham*	021 236 9690
Ellison & Co *see main A-Z section*	
Ellison Westhorp *London*	01 375 1836
Emmet & Tacon *Norwich*	0603 660701
Evans Butler Smith *London*	01 858 8926
Evershed & Tomkinson *see main A-Z section*	
Fairchild Greig & Co *London*	01 992 1164
Farrer & Co *see main A-Z section*	
Fennemores *see main A-Z section*	
Few & Kester *see main A-Z section*	
Field Fisher & Martineau *see main A-Z section*	
Field Seymour Parkes *Reading*	0734 391011
Finers *see main A-Z section*	
Finn Gledhill & Co *see main A-Z section*	
Fishburn Boxer *London*	01 925 2884
Fisher Meredith *London*	01 622 4468
Fitzhugh Gates *see main A-Z section*	
Fladgate Fielder *see main A-Z section*	
Flint Bishop & Barnett *see main A-Z section*	
Flint Hand *Gloucester*	0452 307407
Foinette Quinn *Milton Keynes*	0908 316351
Foot & Bowden *see main A-Z section*	
Ford & Warren *see main A-Z section*	
Ford Simey & Ford *see main A-Z section*	
Forresters *Barrow in Furness*	0229 20297
Forsyte Kerman *see main A-Z section*	
Foster Baxter Cooksey *see main A-Z section*	
Fosters *Norwich*	0603 620508
Fox Brooks Marshall *see main A-Z section*	
Foysters *see main A-Z section*	
Francis Rees & Kelly *Swansea*	0792 470707
Franklins *see main A-Z section*	
Fraser Woodgate & Beall *Wisbech*	0945 582664
Freeboroughs *London*	01 602 3474
Freeth Cartwright & Sketchley *Nottingham*	0602 506861
Frere Cholmeley *see main A-Z section*	
Freshfields *see main A-Z section*	
Furley Page Fielding & Barton *see main A-Z section*	
G D Cann & Hallett *Exeter*	0392 75295
Gadsby Coxon & Copestake *Derby*	0332 372372
Gamlens *see main A-Z section*	
Gamlin Kelly & Beattie *see main A-Z section*	
Gardner & Croft *Canterbury*	0227 456731
Gasters *London*	01 405 3761
Gaynor-Smith Owen & Co *Malvern*	06845 60771
George Green & Co *see main A-Z section*	
George Jonas & Co *Birmingham*	021 643 0660
Gepp & Sons *see main A-Z section*	
German & Soar *Nottingham*	0602 470756
Gershon Young Finer and Green *London*	01 631 4611
Gilfedder & McInnes *Edinburgh*	031 225 1216

Gill Akaster *see main A-Z section*	
Girlings *see main A-Z section*	
Glaisyers *see main A-Z section*	
Glaisyers *see main A-Z section*	
Glanvilles *see main A-Z section*	
Glovers *see main A-Z section*	
Goodger Auden *see main A-Z section*	
Goodman Derrick & Co *see main A-Z section*	
Goodswens *Redcar*	0642 482424
Gordon & Penney *Weston super Mare*	0934 414161
Gordon & Smyth *Glasgow*	041 332 5705
Gordon Dadds *London*	01 493 6151
Gordons and H M Dawson & Co *see main A-Z section*	
Gorna & Co *see main A-Z section*	
Gosschalk Wheldon Chambers Thomas *see main A-Z section*	
Gotelee & Goldsmith *see main A-Z section*	
Gould & Swayne *Glastonbury*	0458 33700
Gouldens *see main A-Z section*	
Graeme John & Partners *Aberdare*	0685 872491
Graham & Rosen *Hull*	0482 23123
Graham Evans & Ptrs *Swansea*	0792 655822
Grahame Stowe Bateson & Co *Leeds*	0532 606191
Granville-West Chivers & Morgan *Pontypool*	04955 3158
Greene & Greene *Bury St Edmunds*	0284 62211
Greenhouse Stirton & Co *London*	01 226 3552
Greenland Houchen *see main A-Z section*	
Greenwoods *see main A-Z section*	
Gregory Rowcliffe & Milners *see main A-Z section*	
Grindeys *see main A-Z section*	
Grossman Hermer & Seligman *Cardiff*	0222 371991
Gwilym Hughes & Partners *Wrexham*	0978 291456
H Montlake and Co *Ilford*	01 553 1311
Hacking Ashton Jervis & Co *Newcastle under Lyme*	0782 634111
Haden Stretton Slater Miller *see main A-Z section*	
Hallinan Blackburn Gittings & Co *Cardiff*	0222 482316
Halliwell Landau *see main A-Z section*	
Hambly Smith Hurley Clements *Monmouth*	0600 4621
Hamilton Burns & Moore *Glasgow*	041 248 6668
Hamlin Slowe *see main A-Z section*	
Hammon & Co *Coventry*	0203 27537
Hammond Suddards *see main A-Z section*	
Hancock & Lawrence *Truro*	0872 72333
Harbottle & Lewis *see main A-Z section*	
Harold Benjamin & Collins *Harrow*	01 422 5678
Harper & Co *Bristol*	0272 739011
Harris Cooper & Co *Solihull*	021 705 2255
Hart Brown & Co *see main A-Z section*	
Hart Fortgang *London*	01 436 3300
Hart Reade & Co *Eastbourne*	0323 27321
Harvey Ingram Stone & Simpson *see main A-Z section*	

Hatcher Rogerson *Wem*	0939 32203
Hatten Wyatt & Co *Gravesend*	0474 351199
Hawkins Russell Jones *see main A-Z section*	
Hawley & Rodgers *see main A-Z section*	
Hay & Kilner *see main A-Z section*	
Hedleys & Co *Sunderland*	091 567 0101
Hegarty & Co *see main A-Z section*	
Hempsons *see main A-Z section*	
Henman Ballard *Oxford*	0865 722181
Henniker-Major *Ipswich*	0473 212681
Hepherd Winstanley & Pugh *see main A-Z section*	
Hepworth & Chadwick *see main A-Z section*	
Herbert & Gowers *Oxford*	0865 249999
Herbert Smith *see main A-Z section*	
Herbert Wilkes & Company *see main A-Z section*	
Hewitt Woollacott & Chown *see main A-Z section*	
Hextall Erskine & Co *see main A-Z section*	
Hicks Arnold *London*	01 242 5250
Hill Bailey *see main A-Z section*	
Hobson Audley *see main A-Z section*	
Hodge Jones & Allen *London*	01 482 1974
Hodson Parsons *Newport*	0633 843122
Hollis Briggs Booth & Ashworth *Derby*	0332 31631
Holman, Fenwick & Willan *see main A-Z section*	
Holmes Mackillop *Glasgow*	041 226 4942
Holt Jones & Collins *Swansea*	0792 409717
Holt Phillips *Bristol*	0272 299555
Hood Vores & Allwood *Dereham*	0362 2424
Hooper & Wollen *see main A-Z section*	
Hopkins & Wood *see main A-Z section*	
Horrocks & Co *London*	01 404 4645
Horwood & James *see main A-Z section*	
Howard Kennedy *see main A-Z section*	
Howes Percival *see main A-Z section*	
Hugh James Jones & Jenkins *see main A-Z section*	
Hughes Dowdall & Co *Glasgow*	041 332 5321
Hughmans *London*	01 636 5693
Humphreys & Co *Bristol*	0272 292662
Hunt & Coombes *Peterborough*	0733 65312
Hunt Dickins *see main A-Z section*	
Hunters *London*	01 242 4931
Hutton's *Cardiff*	0222 378621
Hyde Mahon Bridges *see main A-Z section*	
Iain Adam *London*	01 328 2540
Ince & Co *see main A-Z section*	
Ingham Clegg & Crowther and Laytons *see main A-Z section*	
Ingledew Botterell *see main A-Z section*	
Ingledew Brown Bennison & Garrett *see main A-Z section*	
Ironsides Ray & Vials *see main A-Z section*	
Irvine & Co *Bradford*	0274 737537

Irwin Mitchell *see main A-Z section*	
Isadore Goldman & Son *London*	01 242 3000
J & F Anderson WS *see main A-Z section*	
J & W H Sale & Son *Derby*	0332 362171
J Friel & Co *Glasgow*	041 429 2919
J H Milner & Son *Leeds*	0532 450852
J Keith Park & Co *see main A-Z section*	
J Levi & Co *Leeds*	0532 449931
J P Kennedy & Co *London*	01 724 4707
JW Ward & Son *Bristol*	0272 292811
Jackaman Smith & Mulley *Ipswich*	0473 255591
Jacksons *see main A-Z section*	
Jacobs & Kane *London*	01 937 4444
Jagger Son & Tilley *Birmingham*	021 236 9245
James Chapman & Co *see main A-Z section*	
James and Sarch *London*	01 242 9103
Jaques & Lewis *see main A-Z section*	
Jeffrey Green & Russell *see main A-Z section*	
Joelson Wilson & Co *London*	01 580 5721
John Barkers *see main A-Z section*	
John G Gray & Co *Edinburgh*	031 557 4452
John Howell & Co *Sheffield*	0742 754950
John Lindley & Company *Bristol*	0272 736851
John Pearson *New Malden*	01 942 9191
John Pickering *Oldham*	061 6336667
Joseph Sydney Isaacs Stewart & Dawson *Cardiff*	0222 371131
Joynson-Hicks *see main A-Z section*	
Keeble Hawson Branson Bramley *see main A-Z section*	
Keely Smith & Jobson *Lichfield*	0543 414222
Kennedys *see main A-Z section*	
Kenneth Bush & Co *see main A-Z section*	
Keogh Ritson *see main A-Z section*	
Kershaw Tudor & Co *Sheffield*	0742 27527
Kevills *Chorley*	02572 65711
Kidd & Spoor *see main A-Z section*	
Kidd Rapinet *see main A-Z section*	
Kimbell & Co *Milton Keynes*	0908 668555
King & Co *Cambridge*	0223 65432
King & Franckeiss *Portsmouth*	0705 827555
Kingsford Dorman & Routh Stacey *see main A-Z section*	
Kingsford Flower & Pain *Ashford*	0233 24545
Kingsley Napley *see main A-Z section*	
Kingsley Smith & Co *Gillingham*	0634 577261
Kirwan Nicholas Jones *see main A-Z section*	
Knight & Sons *see main A-Z section*	
Knowles Cave & Co *Luton*	0582 36861
Kuit Steinart Levy & Co *Manchester*	061 832 3434
L Mulcahy Smith & Co *Gateshead*	0632 771412
L Watmore & Co *London*	01 405 1512
Lace Mawer *see main A-Z section*	

Lamb Brooks Wills Chandler *see main A-Z section*	
Lambert Storey & Co *Manchester*	061 832 5696
Lamport Bassitt *see main A-Z section*	
Lane & Partners *London*	01 242 2626
Langleys *see main A-Z section*	
Lanyon Bowdler *see main A-Z section*	
Larcomes *see main A-Z section*	
Latimer Hinks Marsham & Little *Darlington*	0325 467791
Lawford & Co *see main A-Z section*	
Lawrance, Messer & Co *see main A-Z section*	
Lawrence Graham *see main A-Z section*	
Lawrence Jones *see main A-Z section*	
Lawrence Tucketts *see main A-Z section*	
Laytons *see main A-Z section*	
Laytons & Ingham Clegg & Crowther *Bristol*	0272 291626
Le Brasseur & Monier-Williams *see main A-Z section*	
Leathes Prior *see main A-Z section*	
Lee & Pembertons *see main A-Z section*	
Lee & Priestley *see main A-Z section*	
Lee & Thompson *London*	01 935 4665
Lee Bolton & Lee *see main A-Z section*	
Lee Brailsford & Co *Leyland*	0772 421748
Lee Davies and Co *Harlow*	0279 441266
Lees Lloyd Whitley *see main A-Z section*	
Leftley & Co *Harrow*	01 423 1919
Leigh Williams *see main A-Z section*	
Leo Abse & Cohen *see main A-Z section*	
Lester Aldridge *see main A-Z section*	
Levinsons Walker & Lister *Hartlepool*	0429 268151
Levy & McRae *Glasgow*	041 331 2311
Lewis Silkin *see main A-Z section*	
Lindsays WS *see main A-Z section*	
Linklaters & Paines *see main A-Z section*	
Linnells *see main A-Z section*	
Linsley & Mortimer *Newcastle*	091 232 4192
Little & Shepherd *Penrith*	0768 62326
Lonsdales *Blackpool*	0253 45258
Loosemores *see main A-Z section*	
Lovell White Durrant *see main A-Z section*	
Lowless & Lowless *Pembroke*	0646 683222
Lucas & Wyllys *Great Yarmouth*	0493 855555
Lyons Davidson *see main A-Z section*	
MacRoberts *see main A-Z section*	
Mace & Jones *see main A-Z section*	
Macfarlane Guy *Bath*	0225 333800
Macfarlanes *see main A-Z section*	
Machins *Luton*	0582 21181
Mackenzie Patten *London*	01 326 1952
Mackrell Turner Garrett *Woking*	04862 6022
Maclay Murray & Spens *see main A-Z section*	

Malkin Cullis & Sumption *see main A-Z section*	
Manby & Steward *see main A-Z section*	
Manches & Co *see main A-Z section*	
Mander Hadley & Co *Coventry*	0203 631212
March Pearson & Skelton *see main A-Z section*	
Marchant Harries & Co *Aberdare*	0685 872224
Marriott Harrison Bloom & Norris *London*	01 405 7954
Marron Dodds & Waite *Leicester*	0533 28596
Marsh & Ferriman *Worthing*	0903 34911
Marshalls *see main A-Z section*	
Marsland & Barber *Margate*	0843 221466
Martin-Kaye & Partners *Telford Salop*	0952 291757
Martineau Johnson *see main A-Z section*	
Mason Bond *Leeds*	0532 424444
Masons *see main A-Z section*	
Masters & Co *Cambridge*	0223 311141
Maurice Putsman & Co *Birmingham*	021 236 9116
Max Barford & Co *Tunbridge Wells*	0892 48568
Maxwell Batley *see main A-Z section*	
Maxwell Cooke & Co *Birkenhead*	051 647 4491
Maycock Laverack Lewenstein *Kingston upon Hull*	0482 224367
Mayo & Perkins *see main A-Z section*	
McClure Naismith Anderson & Gardiner *see main A-Z section*	
McCormicks *Leeds*	0532 460622
McGrigor Donald *see main A-Z section*	
McKay & Norwell WS *Edinburgh*	031 228 2491
McKeag & Co *Newcastle*	091 284 1112
McKenna & Co *see main A-Z section*	
McKenzie Bell & Sons *Sunderland*	091 5674857
McMillan Bennett *Telford*	0952 291100
Mears Hobbs & Durrant *Lowestoft*	0502 83621
Memery Crystal *see main A-Z section*	
Merritt & Co *Yarm*	0642 785555
Metcalfe, Copeman & Pettefar *see main A-Z section*	
Michael Freeman & Co *see main A-Z section*	
Michelmores *Exeter*	0392 36244
Middleton Potts *see main A-Z section*	
Milburn Kerr (inc Broatch & Son) *Workington*	0900 3531
Miller & Co (with Underwoods) *Cambridge*	0223 66741
Miller Parris *Worthing*	0903 205771
Mills & Reeve Francis *see main A-Z section*	
Mills Kemp & Brown *Barnsley*	0226 281551
Mincoff Science & Gold *see main A-Z section*	
Mishcon de Reya *see main A-Z section*	
Mitchells Robertson *see main A-Z section*	
Montagu J Martin & Haigh *Scunthorpe*	0724 847888
Moore & Blatch *see main A-Z section*	
Moore Brown & Dixon *Tewkesbury*	0684 292341
More & Co *Edinburgh*	031 557 1110
Morgan Bruce & Hardwickes *see main A-Z section*	

Moriarty & Co *Torquay*	0803 214181
Morrish & Co *Leeds*	0532 450733
Morton Fraser & Milligan WS *see main A-Z section*	
Mounseys *see main A-Z section*	
Mullis & Peake *see main A-Z section*	
Murray Beith & Murray WS *see main A-Z section*	
Myer Wolff & Manley *Hull*	0482 223693
Nabarro Nathanson *see main A-Z section*	
Nalder & Son *see main A-Z section*	
Nash & Co *Plymouth*	0752 661202
Needham & James *see main A-Z section*	
Needham and Grant *London*	01 242 5866
Neil F Jones & Co *Birmingham*	021 456 4564
Nelsons *see main A-Z section*	
Neves *see main A-Z section*	
Newbys *Stockton on Tees*	0642 673733
Newsome Vaughan & Co *Coventry*	0203 52261
Nicholas Bennett & Co *Sandwich*	0304 617988
Nicholas Tanner & Co *Cirencester*	0285 659061
Nicholson Cadge & Gilbert *see main A-Z section*	
Nicholson Graham & Jones *see main A-Z section*	
Nightingales *Manchester*	061 832 6722
Norton Peskett & Forward *see main A-Z section*	
Norton Rose *see main A-Z section*	
Norton and Coker *London*	01 885 1404
Nunes & Co *Cambridge*	0223 315806
Offenbach & Co *London*	01 491 1343
Oliver & Co *Lincoln*	0522 28889
Oppenheimers *London*	01 628 9611
Osborne Clarke *see main A-Z section*	
Oswald Hickson, Collier & Co *see main A-Z section*	
Ottaways *St Albans*	0727 63131
Overbury Steward & Eaton *see main A-Z section*	
Owston & Co *see main A-Z section*	
Paisner & Co *see main A-Z section*	
Palmer Wheeldon *Cambridge*	0223 355933
Pannone Blackburn *see main A-Z section*	
Pannone Napier *London*	01 430 1987
Pannone Napier *Manchester*	061 834 6955
Pardoes *see main A-Z section*	
Paris Smith & Randall *see main A-Z section*	
Park Woodfine & Co *see main A-Z section*	
Parker Bullen *see main A-Z section*	
Parker Rhodes Field & Co *Rotherham*	0709 364844
Parkinson Wright *Worcester*	0905 726789
Parrott & Coales *Aylesbury*	0296 82244
Patterson Glenton & Stracey *see main A-Z section*	
Pattinson & Brewer *see main A-Z section*	
Paul Rooney & Co *Liverpool*	051 227 2851
Payne Hicks Beach *see main A-Z section*	

Peake & Co *London*	01 242 8223
Peard Webster Pringle & John *Croydon*	01 680 5262
Penningtons *see main A-Z section*	
Percy Hughes & Roberts *see main A-Z section*	
Peter Carter-Ruck & Partners *London*	01 379 3456
Peter Peter & Wright *see main A-Z section*	
Peter Soar *Cambridge*	0223 242944
Peters & Peters *London*	01 629 7991
Pettman Smith *London*	01 235 1288
Philip Evans & Co *Bournemouth*	0202 26616
Philip Jones Hillyer & Jackson *Chester*	0244 45551
Phillips & Buck *see main A-Z section*	
Phoenix Walters *Cardiff*	0222 482731
Pickering Kenyon *see main A-Z section*	
Pictons *see main A-Z section*	
Pinsent & Co *see main A-Z section*	
Piper Smith & Basham *London*	01 828 8685
Pitmans *see main A-Z section*	
Porter Bartlett & Mayo *see main A-Z section*	
Porter Hope & Knipe *Bolton*	0204 386001
Powell Magrath & Spencer *see main A-Z section*	
Powleys *Lowestoft*	0502 581121
Prettys *see main A-Z section*	
Price & Kelway *Milford Haven*	06462 5311
Price & Son *Haverfordwest*	0437 5331
Pritchard Englefield & Tobin *see main A-Z section*	
Punch Robson Gilchrist Smith *see main A-Z section*	
R C Moorhouse & Co *Leeds*	0532 443121
R G Frisby & Small *Leicester*	0533 555232
R Gwynne & Sons *see main A-Z section*	
R I Lewis & Co *London*	01 404 5641
R M Broudie & Co *Liverpool*	051 227 1429
Radcliffes & Co *see main A-Z section*	
Raeburn Christie & Co *Aberdeen*	0224 640101
Rapers *see main A-Z section*	
Rawlins Davy and Wells *Bournemouth*	0202 28844
Rawlison and Butler *see main A-Z section*	
Raymond C Tetlow *Newport Pagnell*	0908 610330
Rayner De Wolfe *London*	01 405 1212
Read Hind Stewart *see main A-Z section*	
Redfern & Stigant *see main A-Z section*	
Rees Edwards Maddox & Co *Birmingham*	021 643 0111
Restons Linaker & Linaker *Runcorn*	0928 580066
Reynolds Dawson *London*	01 379 4496
Reynolds Porter Chamberlain *see main A-Z section*	
Richard CM Sykes *London*	01 235 2508
Richard White & Michael Sherwin *Croydon*	01 681 2256
Richards Butler *see main A-Z section*	
Richmonds *Newcastle*	091 232 2155
Rickerby Jessop *Cheltenham*	0242 222022

Rigbeys *Birmingham*	021 200 3343
Riley Mumford & Rausa *Cardiff*	0222 44341
Roach Pittis *Newport*	0983 524431
Robbins Olivey *Woking*	0483 755575
Robert Muckle Son & Hall *Newcastle*	091 232 4402
Robert Render & Partners *Cardiff*	0222 371036
Robertsons *Cardiff*	0222 480206
Robin Thompson & Partners *Cardiff*	0222 484136
Robin Thompson & Partners *Birmingham*	021 236 7944
Robin Thompson & Partners *see main A-Z section*	
Robin Thompson & Partners *Nottingham*	0602 584999
Robinson Jarvis & Rolf *see main A-Z section*	
Robinsons *Ilkeston*	0602 324101
Rogers & Norton *Norwich*	0603 666001
Rollit Farrell & Bladon *see main A-Z section*	
Ross Harper & Murphy *see main A-Z section*	
Ross Strachan *Dundee*	0382 201010
Rotheras *see main A-Z section*	
Rowberry Morris & Co *Reading*	0734 585611
Rowe & Maw *see main A-Z section*	
Rowlands *see main A-Z section*	
Rowley Ashworth *London*	01 543 2277
Rowley Ashworth *see main A-Z section*	
Rowleys & Blewitts *see main A-Z section*	
Roy Morgan & Co *Cardiff*	0222 595155
Roythorne & Co *see main A-Z section*	
Rubinstein Callingham Polden Gale *see main A-Z section*	
Rundle McDonald & Rendle's *Plymouth*	0752 224277
Russell & Russell *see main A-Z section*	
Russell Jones & Walker *see main A-Z section*	
Russell Steward and Co *Norwich*	0603 660341
Russell-Cooke Potter & Chapman *see main A-Z section*	
Russells *Glasgow*	041 332 4176
Russells *London*	01 439 8692
Rutherfords *see main A-Z section*	
S J Berwin & Co *see main A-Z section*	
S Rutter & Co *London*	01 623 8641
Sampson Parker *London*	01 870 6378
Samuel Phillips & Co *Newcastle*	091 232 8451
Sansbury Hill *Bristol*	0272 265341
Sargent & Probert *Exeter*	0392 32555
Saunders & Co *London*	01 960 5611
Saunders Sobell Leigh & Dobin *see main A-Z section*	
Schilling & Lom *London*	01 935 1228
Sears Blok *London*	01 703 2324
Seifert Sedley Williams *see main A-Z section*	
Shacklocks *see main A-Z section*	
Shakespeare Duggan Lea & Co *see main A-Z section*	
Sharman & Trethewy *see main A-Z section*	
Sharpe Pritchard & Co *London*	01 405 4600

Shaw & Croft *London*	01 283 6293
Shepherd & Wedderburn WS *see main A-Z section*	
Sheratte Caleb & Co *London*	01 583 5823
Sheridans *see main A-Z section*	
Sherwin Oliver *Portsmouth*	0705 667511
Shoosmiths & Harrison *see main A-Z section*	
Short Richardson & Forth *Newcastle*	091 232 0283
Shulmans *Leeds*	0532 452833
Silverman Livermore & Co *Liverpool*	051 227 1871
Simmonds Church Smiles & Co *see main A-Z section*	
Simmons & Simmons *see main A-Z section*	
Simms & Co *Oxford*	0865 240023
Simon North and Nam *Cardiff*	0222 343993
Simon Olswang & Co *see main A-Z section*	
Simons Muirhead & Burton *London*	01 836 7023
Simpson & Marwick WS *Edinburgh*	031 557 1545
Simpson Curtis *see main A-Z section*	
Sinclair Roche & Temperley *see main A-Z section*	
Sinclair Taylor & Martin *London*	01 969 3667
Sinton & Co *Newcastle*	091 281 5211
Slater Atkinson Cave & Stuart *Blackpool*	0253 293151
Slater Heelis *see main A-Z section*	
Slaughter and May *see main A-Z section*	
Slee Blackwell *see main A-Z section*	
Smeath Mann & Co *Northampton*	0604 32277
Smith & Harrison *see main A-Z section*	
Smith Morton & Long *see main A-Z section*	
Smith Spring & Co *Swansea*	0792 51234
Snape & Co *Coventry*	0203 220707
Snow & Bispham *Basingstoke*	0256 51313
Southwells *Wisbech*	0945 582798
Speechly Bircham *see main A-Z section*	
Spon-Smith & Co *Bromley*	01 464 4311
Stafforth & Bray *see main A-Z section*	
Stamp Jackson & Procter *see main A-Z section*	
Stanley Tee & Co *see main A-Z section*	
Staunton Townsend *Leicester*	0533 470123
Steed & Steed *Sudbury*	0787 73387
Steedman Ramage & Co WS *see main A-Z section*	
Steele & Co *see main A-Z section*	
Steele Raymond *Bournemouth*	0202 294566
Steggles Palmer *see main A-Z section*	
Stephen Rimmer and Co *Eastbourne*	0323 644222
Stephens & Scown *see main A-Z section*	
Stephenson Harwood *see main A-Z section*	
Stephensons *see main A-Z section*	
Stevens & Bolton *see main A-Z section*	
Stevens Drake & Pope *see main A-Z section*	
Stokes *see main A-Z section*	
Stones *see main A-Z section*	

Stones Porter *see main A-Z section*	
Swepstone Walsh & Son *London*	01 353 3115
T G Bannigan & Co *Glasgow*	041 221 1496
T V Edwards & Co *London*	01 791 1050
Talbot Davies & Copner *Andover*	0264 63354
Tallents Godfrey & Co *see main A-Z section*	
Taylor Garrett *see main A-Z section*	
Taylor Simpson & Mosley *Derby*	0332 372311
Taylor Vinters *see main A-Z section*	
Taylor Walker *see main A-Z section*	
Teeman Levine & Co *Leeds*	0532 459344
The Simkins Partnership *see main A-Z section*	
The Smith Partnership *Burton on Trent*	0283 36471
Theodore Goddard *see main A-Z section*	
Thomas Eggar Verrall Bowles *see main A-Z section*	
Thomas Flavell & Sons *Hinckley*	0455 610747
Thomas Mallam *Oxford*	0865 244661
Thomson Snell & Passmore *see main A-Z section*	
Thornton Lynne & Lawson *London*	01 580 6688
Thornton Oliver WS *see main A-Z section*	
Thralls *Truro*	0872 72356
Thrings & Long *see main A-Z section*	
Tilly, Bailey & Irvine *see main A-Z section*	
Tilston MacLaurin *Glasgow*	041 332 5666
Timms *see main A-Z section*	
Tinsdill Hullinshead & Moody *see main A-Z section*	
Titmuss Sainer & Webb *see main A-Z section*	
Tods Murray WS *see main A-Z section*	
Toller Hales & Collcutt *see main A-Z section*	
Townsends *see main A-Z section*	
Tozers *see main A-Z section*	
Travers Smith Braithwaite *see main A-Z section*	
Treasures *Blackwood*	0495 223328
Trethowans *see main A-Z section*	
Trowers & Hamlins *see main A-Z section*	
Truman Close Kendall & Appelby *see main A-Z section*	
Trump & Partners *see main A-Z section*	
Tuck & Mann & Geffen *see main A-Z section*	
Turberville Woodbridge *see main A-Z section*	
Turner & Debenhams *see main A-Z section*	
Turner Kenneth Brown *see main A-Z section*	
Turner Martin & Symes *Ipswich*	0473 211561
Turners *see main A-Z section*	
Ungoed-Thomas & King *Carmarthen*	0267 237441
Urquhart Knight & Broughton *Liverpool*	051 236 3355
Varley Hibbs & Co *see main A-Z section*	
Vaudrey Osborne & Mellor *Manchester*	061 834 6877
Veale Wasbrough *see main A-Z section*	
Victor D Zermansky & Co *Leeds*	0532 459766
Victor Lissack & Roscoe *London*	01 240 2010

517

Vizards *see main A-Z section*	
W & J Burness *see main A-Z section*	
W Anthony Daniel *Plymouth*	0752 662671
Wade Gery Farr *St Neots*	0480 74061
Wake Smith & Co *see main A-Z section*	
Walker Martineau *see main A-Z section*	
Walker Morris Scott Turnbull *see main A-Z section*	
Walker Smith & Way *see main A-Z section*	
Wallace & Partners *London*	01 404 4422
Wallace Robinson & Morgan *Birmingham*	021 236 0251
Waller Needham & Co *Peterborough*	0733 311422
Wallis Prance *Basingstoke*	0256 464311
Waltons *Luton*	0582 31161
Waltons & Morse *see main A-Z section*	
Wannop & Falconer *see main A-Z section*	
Wansbroughs *see main A-Z section*	
Ward, Gethin & Co *see main A-Z section*	
Warner & Co *Edinburgh*	031 662 4747
Warner Cranston *see main A-Z section*	
Warner Goodman & Streat *see main A-Z section*	
Warren & Allen *Nottingham*	0602 507121
Watson Burton *see main A-Z section*	
Watson Sinnott *Bristol*	0272 277011
Watson, Farley & Williams *see main A-Z section*	
Watterson Todman *Cheltenham*	0242 39991
Wayman-Hales *Chester*	0244 321122
Weaver & Co *Caerphilly*	0222 868811
Wedlake Bell *see main A-Z section*	
Wedlake Saint *see main A-Z section*	
Weightman Rutherfords *see main A-Z section*	
Wellingtons *see main A-Z section*	
Wells & Hind *see main A-Z section*	
West Anderson & Co *Glasgow*	041 332 6671
Westhorp Ward & Catchpole *see main A-Z section*	
Whatley Weston & Fox *Worcester*	0905 20361
Wheldon Houlsby & Scott *South Shields*	091 456 8721
Whiskers *Epping*	0378 76131
White Brooks & Gilman *see main A-Z section*	
Whitehead Monckton *see main A-Z section*	
Whittles *Manchester*	061 228 2061
Widdows *Leigh*	0942 673311
Wild Hewitson & Shaw *see main A-Z section*	
Wilde Sapte *see main A-Z section*	
Wilkin & Chapman *Grimsby*	0472 350101
Wilkinson Maughan *see main A-Z section*	
Willey Hargrave *see main A-Z section*	
Willey Hargrave *London*	01 405 0945
William F Hatton & Co *Dudley*	0384 211211
William Prior & Company *Manchester*	061 236 2646
William Prior & Company *see main A-Z section*	

Williamson & Co *see main A-Z section*	
Wilson & Wilson Inc Burgess & Jeffries *Kettering*	0536 513121
Wilsons *see main A-Z section*	
Wiltshire Sons & Tunbridge *Great Yarmouth*	0493 857503
Winckworth & Pemberton *see main A-Z section*	
Winstanley-Burgess *London*	01 278 7911
Winter Wilkinson *see main A-Z section*	
Winter-Taylors *see main A-Z section*	
Wiseman Lee *see main A-Z section*	
Withers Crossman Block *see main A-Z section*	
Withy King & Lee *see main A-Z section*	
Wolferstans *see main A-Z section*	
Wollastons *Chelmsford*	0245 265222
Woodford & Ackroyd *Southampton*	0703 227681
Woodford Robinson Williams & Co *Northampton*	0604 24926
Woodham Smith *see main A-Z section*	
Woolf Seddon Roscoe Phillips *London*	01 486 9681
Woollcombe Watts *see main A-Z section*	
Wragge & Co *see main A-Z section*	
Wright Hassall & Co *Leamington Spa*	0926 27955
Wright Johnson & MacKenzie *see main A-Z section*	
Wright Webb Syrett *London*	01 439 3111
Wynne Baxter Godfree *see main A-Z section*	
Yaffe Jackson & Ostrin *see main A-Z section*	
Young & Co *Stoke on Trent*	0782 599222
Young & Lee *Birmingham*	021 772 5012
Zaiwalla & Co *London*	01 831 7791

How The Legal 500 is compiled

The 500: There is no special significance in the title of this book. Basically reasons of space have dictated that we must restrict the A-Z section to a relatively small number of firms. To us, the right number seems to be about 500 firms. To have included many more firms would have made the book that much larger and relatively unwieldy. After all, we are not attempting to produce a Law List with details of every firm in the country. On the other hand, to have restricted entry to (say) the largest 250 firms would have excluded many of the medium sized provincial practices that are of considerable importance.

Our cut-off for inclusion in the A-Z section is firms with more than 50 total staff. Obviously, there will always be arguments about which firms should be included, and which excluded; once you get down to firm 450, it really is arguable as to which to include, and which to exclude. But we have to draw the line somewhere.

In the editorial section we have no size constraints on which firms to include. We happily name the firms that we think should be mentioned – irrespective of how large or small they are. Indeed, many people wrongly think that it is only large firms (ie those in the top 500) that can be mentioned anywhere in The Legal 500. That is not so: our editorial contains numerous recommendations of smaller firms, but we simply do not have the space to include full details of them all in the A-Z section. This is not meant as a slight to small firms.

Inevitably there will be firms that take offence because they have not been included – whether in the editorial or the A-Z section. Our message to them is simple: please write and tell us about your firm (ie the type of work you do, your areas of expertise, and also your staffing figures).

The editorial section: The editorial section is a mixture of fact and opinion. The factual information (eg staffing figures, number of assistant solicitors) has been supplied by the firms. The opinions, such as recommendations, represent the personal views of the editor. Being a lawyer, the editor wishes to make it quite clear that these opinions are expressed in good faith, but without the assumption of any legal liability or responsibility for mistakes and/or inaccuracies!

In self-defence the editor would point out that his recommendations have been largely influenced by the confidential opinions expressed to him by solicitors throughout the country. Many have sent lengthy letters with constructive comments and criticisms, as well as recommendations.

In addition, thousands of solicitors responded to our survey in which we asked practitioners to recommend other firms for particular categories of work.

Obviously, solicitors were not allowed to recommend their own firms when replying (also our computer was trained to reject votes for associated firms, firms within the same grouping, block voting within an individual firm, and so on). The twelve categories of work covered in the survey were commercial leases; commercial litigation; crime; building and construction; insolvency; family/matrimonial; intellectual property; entertainment; town and country planning; tax; general company law; and personal injury litigation. In addition, we asked which firms 'do you think are likely to go 'from strength to strength' in the next 5-10 years?' Finally, we asked respondents to give their own area of practice or specialisation. This last piece of information enabled us to compare the overall results of our survey with those of a separate poll on the role of specialists.

In the editorial mix of opinion and data it is not always possible to say where the personal opinion ends and the results of the survey begin! All of which means that those who are unhappy with the recommendations and suggestions in the editorial (and, in particular, those who look in vain for references to their own firm!) can happily dismiss the whole exercise as completely unscientific.

A-Z section: The main A-Z section of the book appears after the editorial. It is an alphabetical listing of the largest 500 (or so) firms. In fact, the section contains slightly more than 500 firms. This is partly due to the inclusion of leading Scottish firms. Last year we treated Scotland as a separate section; this year, in response to suggestions made to us, we have included the larger Scottish firms in the A-Z section along with the English and Welsh ones. In part this is a reflection of the growing links between the two jurisdictions.

The size of a standard entry for each firm is a quarter of a page containing basic factual information supplied by the individual firms. All firms can opt to increase the standard quarter page into a full-page description of the firm. It should be noted that we have retained full editorial control and, accordingly, the text of such full-page entries has been written by the publishers of The Legal 500 and not by the firms themselves. Further, it should be appreciated that the firms are in no way holding themselves out as having particular skills or expertise; any such comments or statements are merely the opinion of the publishers.

Address: The standard entry in the A-Z section

gives one address for the firm. Unfortunately there is not room to print more than one address (although we are able to give the number of other offices that a firm has). In deciding which address to give we have generally selected the one that seems to be the administrative headquarters of the firm, or the office where the senior partner is based. The point to appreciate is that the selection of a particular address does not imply that it is the head office (and therefore more important than the other offices): in short, no undue significance should be attached to the fact that a particular address has been selected.

Similarly, when we refer to firms in the editorial section, the name of the firm is generally followed by the name of the town in which the firm is located. Occasionally this can cause problems – especially if a firm has offices in several major towns and is reluctant to nominate only one, since that might be regarded as a snub by the others! Once again, we have overcome this problem by selecting what seems – to us – to be the administrative headquarters (so those in the other offices of such firms should not take offence!).

For similar reasons the A-Z section refers to 'other offices' of firms, rather than 'branches'. The latter term might be misconstrued as implying that one office is the main one (when it might not be). Incidentally, when listing the other offices, we have included only those that are properly part of the firm in question; ' associated offices' have generally been excluded.

Phone/fax/telex/DX: Only one phone number is given for each firm (although, obviously, most firms have several). Virtually all have fax numbers; if a firm does not have a fax, then we say 'none'. Use of telex is not so widespread, but if a firm does have a telex facility then we include the number; if not, we say 'none'.

For non-solicitors it may be necessary to explain what DX stands for. It is an abbreviation of Document Exchange, a private enterprise delivery service that counts many lawyers among its subscribers. In fact, some 95 per cent of the firms in our A-Z section belong to DX (and we specifically say if a firm is not a member). For Scottish firms, there are references to Rutland Exchange, which is the Scottish equivalent of DX. Unfortunately, DX and Rutland Exchange are not linked, and so a member of one exchange cannot send a package direct to a member of the other exchange.

Total staff: The traditional way of gauging the size of a solicitor's firm has been to look at the number of partners. But we have always taken the view that this can be highly misleading. Instead, we prefer to look at the total workforce within a firm – what we refer to as 'total staff'. For our purposes this includes partners, even though legal eagles will point out that it is semantically wrong

to refer to partners as 'staff'. Be that as it may, our figure for total staff includes partners.

Reading too much into the figures: The Legal 500 contains many facts and figures – especially staff numbers. It is vital not to place too much significance on these figures. Generally they are there as an approximate guide so that rough comparisons can be made between firms. In short, whilst the figures are accurate, they should not be given undue importance.

There are several reasons for this. Firstly, figures change from week to week, especially with the larger firms. The second reason why the figures should be treated with caution is that – like all statistics – they can be misleading. For instance, suppose you are looking at the top 50 in London: by partnership size alone you will find that Ashurst Morris Crisp and Beachcroft Stanleys both have 35 partners and are in position 30. On the other hand, if you list the firms by overall total staff then they appear (respectively) in positions 19 and 42. Thus to look at one figure alone (in this case, partnership size) can be totally misleading. What you have to do is get a general picture by looking at all the figures (ie the total number of staff, partners, assistant solicitors, and articled clerks).

League tables, by themselves, are dangerously misleading. Size alone is really an irrelevant criterion when selecting a firm of solicitors. The most important factor is the general reputation and style of a firm: in other words, whether it has a 'good' name. The quality of a firm's name is intangible – it cannot easily be measured by those outside the profession.

Who acts for whom: Many people have asked us to include a table showing which firms of solicitors act for which commercial companies. Because of this it was our intention to include such a list in this edition of The Legal 500. However, we have now changed our mind about the desirability of such a list. We take the view that any such list is likely to be misleading and inaccurate. There are several reasons for this. Firstly, more than one firm will often act for one particular company; for instance, how many firms could have said they acted for Guinness in 1987/88? Secondly, how does one decide what counts as 'acting for' a particular company; for instance, if a firm acts for National Westminster Bank on a mortgage transaction, can it really be said that they are Nat West's solicitors? Thirdly, there is the problem of deciding what companies are worthy of inclusion in such a list (eg does one limit it to PLCs?).

The end result is that we have decided that lists of 'who acts for whom' are of little real importance. Instead the quality of the client list is a factor that we take into account when assessing the expertise of a firm and whether or not it should be recommended.